INTRO STATS
PRELIMINARY EDITION UPDATE

Richard D. DeVeaux
Williams College

Paul F. Velleman
Cornell University

with contributions by
David E. Bock

This packet contains prepublication material of the text. The material will undergo additional revision, accuracy checking, and proofreading prior to final text publication. Page layout is preliminary; additional graphics will be included in the final version.

Addison
Wesley

Boston San Francisco New York
London Toronto Sydney Tokyo Singapore Madrid
Mexico City Munich Paris Cape Town Hong Kong Montreal

Credits

Photographs

Chapter 2, pg 6, Gold Rush General Store in Placerville's El Dorado Museum in California, c Dorling Kindersley

Chapter 1, pg 2, Commuters make their way in New York's Grand Central Terminal, AP/Wide World Photos

Chapter 2, pg 6, Courtesy of Amber Chand, EZIBA

Chapter 2, pg. 9, An early dated telephone, c Dorling Kindersley

Chapter 3, pg. 14, The Titanic leaves from Southampton, England on her maiden voyage, AP/Wide World Photos

Chapter 3, pg. 15, From F. Nightingale, "Notes on Matters Affecting Health, Efficiency and Hospital Administration of the British Army," 1858, Florence Nightingale Museum

Chapter 3, pg 19, Titanic Exhibit, ship's bell, Stephen J. Carrera/Associated Press AP

Chapter 3 pg 23, Great barracuda, Stone/Getty Images

Chapter 3 pg 25, Students on campus, University of California, Berkeley, Spencer Grant/Photo Researchers, Inc.

Chapter 19, pg. 36, Fiji Sea Fan, c Stuart Westmorland/CORBIS

Chapter 19, pg. 39 GARFIELD 'Paws, Inc. Reprinted with permission of UNIVERSAL PRESS SYNDICATE. All rights reserved

Chapter 27, p. 27-9, Nenana Ice Contest; © Nenana Ice Classic

Illustrations

Chapter 4, p. 4-15, Rising Signs. © 2000, Ithaca Times. Reprinted with permission.

Chapter 7, p. 7-21, Presidential Election Results for Florida, by County: Greg D. Adams, Chris Fastnow, A Note on the Voting Irregularities in Palm Beach, FL (2000).

Chapter 14, p. 14-8, What Colors Come in Your Bag?: M&M Mars, M&M's ® Milk Chocolate Candies Color Chart, 2002.

Reproduced by Addison-Wesley from files supplied by the authors.

Printed in the United States of America.

ISBN   0-321-12523-1

1 2 3 4 5 6 7 8 9 10 PHC 05 04 03 02

Dear Student

Here's a chance to read some preliminary chapters from our new statistics text, *Intro Stats*. We're hoping you find this book as exciting as we do!

Exciting?! This book is *different!* In fact, we believe it is so *unique* that we really want to get an idea of whether we've written the right book. So, we've put together this booklet to gather your reactions in preparation for its premiere in the summer of 2003. *Take a look!*

While these pages aren't final, they do give a good idea of how the book will look and read. We'd love to have detailed comments on the writing, graphs, features, and anything else that strikes you. Attached is a questionnaire to help, but feel free to add any thoughts you'd like. We want to hear from you! We promise to pay attention to your comments, because you help improve the experience of students to follow.

Thanks in advance. We hope you find this fun!

Sincerely,

Deirdre Lynch
Senior Acquisitions Editor

Rachel S. Reeve
Project Editor

Dear Student:

This text is loaded with features designed to help you through your statistics course. Here's a brief introduction to them:

Readability

You'll see immediately that this book doesn't read like other statistics texts. T. downside of that is that you actually have to read it to see what it says. (You just look for the sample solutions in the little boxes.) But we've tried to make experience reasonably enjoyable. The chapters are shorter than in most other so you can focus on one topic at a time.

STEP-BY-STEP Think, Show, Tell

Think

Show

Tell

All uses of statistics start with careful thought about what we want to know end with a clear account of what we have learned. We summarize these steps **"Think, Show, and Tell"** and show step-by-step worked examples with runn commentary. *Use your tools.* The Show step, where the calculation occurs, relie calculator or computer program. This book will guide you through using techn but you're still on the hook for the Think and Tell.

What Can Go Wrong?

Most texts don't admit that things go wrong. **But we know that Statistics can misused by accident (or even on purpose).** We try to arm you against these e Each chapter ends with a "What Can Go Wrong?" section that illustrates the n common misuses and misconceptions of statistical thinking.

Connections

The book may be cut up into more than 20 chapters, but they all tell one over story. So each chapter has a Connections section to link key terms and concep with previous discussions, and to point out the continuing themes. The Connections help you see how what you just learned fits with what you alrea understand.

Key Concepts

The critical concepts from the chapter are always collected at the end, to help review and check your understanding.

Skills

There's a list of skills at the end of each chapter. If you know the Key Concept have the Skills, you're ready for the exercises (and the exam).

Exercises

Exercises in a book like this are almost never solved with a single number. To these exercises, you'll need to discuss the problem and justify the method (Thi to show a worked solution or computer output (Show), and to draw a reasone conclusion that responds to the initial motivation for the exercise (Tell). You w that the topics selected reflect topics you are likely to encounter in everyday li that you can see the importance of having a clearly constructed conclusion.

DeVeaux/Velleman, *Intro Stats*
Class Test
STUDENT QUESTIONNAIRE

We greatly appreciate your participation in this class test. The feedback you provide will help us to continue to develop better textbooks. Your comments will be shared with our editorial staff and authors. We look forward to reading your comments!

Your Name: _____   Your School: _____

City/State: _____   Professor Name: _____

E-mail: _____   Your Major: _____

1. Several features are included in this text to make the material more accessible, relevant, and interesting. Using other texts as a basis of comparison, please rate this text by circling the appropriate number: **4 = you found it very useful/helpful, 1 = you found it not at all useful/helpful, N/A = you did not cover it**. Please use the space underneath each item to make any additional comments.

	Not helpful		Very helpful	

a) Examples/Applications (interesting and understandable).................................1 ....2 ....3 4

b) Writing Style ....1 ....2 ....3 4

c) Step-by-Step: Think, Show, & Tell ....1 ....2 ....3 4

d) What Can Go Wrong? ....1 ....2 ....3 4

e) Computer Sections...1 ....2 ....3 ....4 ....N/A

End of Chapter Material

f) Skills...1 ....2 ....3 ....4 ....N/A

g) Key Concepts...1 ....2 ....3 ....4 ....N/A

h) Connections ....1 ....2 ....3 ....4 ....N/A

2. What is the most difficult topic you had to learn in this text (or in these chapters)?

_____

Did the text explain this topic clearly? (circle one) .... Yes.........No

3. Did you find that the exercises at the end of the chapters helped test your understanding of the concepts? Please comment on the quality, applicability, and relevancy of the exercises.

4. What did you like most about this text?

5. What did you like least about this text?

6. Based on your reaction to this text, would you recommend this book to your professor for this course? .... Yes ....No Why or why not?

7. May we quote you in our promotion or in summaries of our findings? .... Yes.........No

Once you have completed this survey, please hand it in to your professor.

Again, thanks for your feedback and participation.

Rachel S. Reeve
Addison-Wesley
Mathematics & Statistics
75 Arlington Street, Suite 300
Boston, MA 02116

Table of Contents

Chapter | 1

Stats Starts Here[1]

"But where shall I begin?"
asked Alice. "Begin at the
beginning," the King said
gravely, "and go on till
you come to the end: then
stop."
—Lewis Carroll Alice's
Adventures in Wonderland

tatistics gets no respect. People say things like "you can prove anything with Statistics." Or "Lies, damn lies, and statistics," as the English Prime Minister Disraeli is reputed to have said. People will write off a claim based on data as "just a statistical trick." And statistics courses don't have the reputation of being students' first choice for a fun elective.

But Statistics *is* fun. That's probably not what you heard on the street, but it's true. Statistics is about how to think clearly with data. A little practice thinking statistically is all it takes to start seeing the world more clearly and accurately.

So, What Is (Are?) Statistics?

Q: What is Statistics?
A: Statistics is a way of reasoning, along with a collection of tools and methods, designed to help us understand the world.
Q: What are statistics?
A: Statistics (plural) are particular calculations made from data.
Q: So what is data?
A: You mean, "what *are* data?" Data is the plural form. The singular is datum.
Q: OK, OK, so what are data?
A: Data are values along with their context.

It seems every time we turn around, someone is collecting data on us, from every purchase we make in the grocery store, to every click of our mouse as we surf the Web. The United Parcel Service (UPS) tracks every package it ships from one place to another around the world and stores these records in a giant database. You can access part of it if you send or receive a UPS package. The database is about 17 terabytes big—about the same size as a database that contained every book in the Library of Congress would be. (But, we suspect, not *quite* as interesting.) What can anyone hope to do with all these data?

Statistics plays a role in making sense of the complex world in which we live today. Statisticians assess the risk of genetically engineered foods or of a new drug being considered by the FDA. They predict the number of new cases of AIDS by regions of the country or the number of customers likely to respond to a sale at the market. And statisticians help scientists and social scientists understand how unemployment is related to environmental controls, whether enriched early edu-

---

[1]This chapter might have been called "Introduction," but nobody reads the introduction, and we wanted you to read this. We feel safe admitting this here, in the footnote, because nobody reads footnotes either.

> The ads say, "Don't drink and drive; you don't want to be a statistic." But you can't be a statistic.
>   We say: "Don't be a datum."

cation affects later performance of school children, and whether vitamin C really prevents illness. Whenever there are data and a need for understanding the world, you need Statistics.

So our objectives in this book are to help you develop the insights to think clearly about the questions, use the tools to show what the data are saying, and acquire the skills to tell clearly what it all means.

Statistics in a Word

> Statistics is about variation.
>   Data vary because we don't see everything and because even what we do see and measure, we measure imperfectly.
>   So, in a very basic way, Statistics is about the real, imperfect world in which we live.

It can be fun, and sometimes useful, to summarize a discipline in only a few words. So,

Economics is about . . . *Money (and why it is good).*
Psychology: *Why we think what we think (we think).*
Biology: *Life.*
Anthropology: *Who?*
History: *What, where, and when?*
Philosophy: *Why?*
Engineering: *How?*
Accounting: *How much?*
In such a caricature, Statistics is about . . . **Variation.**

Data vary. People are different. We can't see everything. And even what we do measure, we measure imperfectly. So the data we wind up looking at and basing our decisions on provide, at best, an imperfect picture of the world. This fact lies at the heart of what Statistics is all about. How to make sense of it is a central challenge of Statistics.

So, How Will This Book Help?

A fair question. Most likely, this book will not turn out to be quite what you expected.
What's different?

> *Close your eyes and open the book to a page at random. Is there an equation on that page? Do that again, say, 10 times. We'll bet you saw only a few pages with equations.*

Equations are a great way of expressing a mathematical idea concisely. But, they're not the main point of statistics. Rather than just listing definitions and equations, this book leads you through the entire process of *thinking* about a problem, finding and *showing* results for the problem, and *telling* others about what you have discovered.

You looked at only a few randomly selected pages to get an impression of the entire book. We'll see soon that doing so was sound statistics practice and reasoning.

> *Next, pick a chapter and read the first two sentences. (Go ahead; we'll wait.)*

We'll bet you didn't see anything about Statistics. Why? Because the best way to understand Statistics is to see it at work. In this book, chapters usually start by presenting a story and posing questions. That's when Statistics really gets down to work.

There are three simple steps to doing Statistics right: *think, show,* and *tell:*

Think first. Know where you're headed and why. It will save you a lot of work.

Show is what most folks think Statistics is about. The *mechanics* of calculating statistics and making displays is important, but not the most important part of Statistics.

Tell what you've learned. Until you've explained your results so that someone else can understand your conclusions, the job is not done.

Each chapter applies new concepts in a worked example called a **Step by Step.** These examples model the way statisticians attack and solve problems. They illustrate how to think about the problem, what to show, and how to tell what it all means. These step-by-step examples will show you how to produce the kind of solutions instructors hope to see.

One of the interesting challenges of Statistics is that, unlike some math and science courses, there can be more than one right answer. This is why two statisticians can testify honestly on opposite sides of a court case. And it's why some people think that you can prove anything with statistics. But that's not true. People make mistakes using statistics, sometimes on purpose in order to mislead others. But most of the unintentional mistakes people make are avoidable. We're not talking about arithmetic. More often the mistakes come from using a method in the wrong situation or misinterpreting the results. Each chapter has a section called **What Can Go Wrong** to help you avoid some of the most common mistakes.

Although we'll show you all the formulas you need to understand the calculations, you'll most often use a calculator or computer to perform the mechanics of a statistics problem. The easiest way to calculate statistics with a computer is with a specialized program called a "statistics package." There are a number of statistics packages available, and they differ widely in the details of how to use them and in how they present their results. But they all work from the same basic information and find the same results. Rather than adopt one package for this book, we'll present generic output and point out common features that you should look for. We'll also give a table of instructions to get you started on any of five commonly used packages. The **. . . And the Computer** section of most chapters holds this information.

From time to time we'll take time out to discuss an interesting or important side issue. We indicate these by setting them apart like this.[3]

We'll also highlight **Key Concepts** as they come up, and collect them at the end of each chapter, together with a summary of important **Skills.** Use these to check your knowledge of the important ideas in the chapter. If you have the skills and

---

Think

Show

Tell

STEP-BY-STEP

"Get your facts first, and then you can distort them as much as you please. (Facts are stubborn, but statistics are more pliable.)"
—Mark Twain

What Can Go Wrong?

You'll find all sorts of stuff in margin notes, such as stories and quotations. For example:

". . . geographers . . . crowd into the edges of their maps parts of the world which they do not know about, adding notes in the margin to the effect that beyond this lies nothing . . ."
—Plutarch (46? C.E.–120 C.E.) A Life of Theseus

---

[3]Or in a footnote.

understand the key concepts you should be well prepared for the exam—and ready to use Statistics!

But, no one can learn Statistics just by reading about it. The only way to learn it is to do it. So, of course, every chapter (except this one) has **Exercises** designed to help you learn the material. At the end of each chapter you'll find exercises so you can use what you've just read about.

At the back of the book, you'll find **"answers"** to the odd numbered exercises, and **"solutions"** to several problems in each chapter. Huh? What's the difference? The answers are just numerical responses. If your calculations match the numerical "answer," you're on the right track, but you're not done. A complete solution explains the context and draws a conclusion.

But in the real world, there's no chapter just before the question. So in addition to the problems at the end of the chapter we've also collected more problems at the end of each section to make it more like the real world. This should help you to see whether you can sort out which methods to use when.

*Optional Sections and Chapters

Some sections and chapters of this book are marked with an asterisk (*). These are optional in the sense that subsequent material does not depend on them directly. We hope you'll read them anyway, as you did this section.

Onward!

It's only fair to warn you: You can't get there by just picking out the highlighted sentences and the summaries. This book is different. It's not about memorizing definitions and learning equations. It's deeper than that. And much more fun. But . . .

You have to read the book![4]

---

[4]So, turn the page.

Chapter 2

Data

Amber Chand (foreground) co-founder of Eziba, with colleagues from Aid to Artisans a non-profit organization

Many years ago, most stores in small towns knew their customers personally. If you walked into the hobby shop, the owner might tell you about a new bridge that had come in for your Lionel train set. The tailor knew your dad's size and the hairdresser knew how your mom liked her hair. There are still some stores like that around today, but we're increasingly likely to shop at large stores, by phone, or on the Internet. Even so, when you phone an 800 number to buy new running shoes, customer service representatives may call you by your first name, or ask about the socks you bought 6 weeks ago. Or the company may send an e-mail in October offering new head warmers for winter running. This company has millions of customers and you called without identifying yourself. How did it know who you are, where you live, and what you had bought?

The answer to all these questions is data. Collecting data on their customers, transactions, and sales enables companies to know where their inventory is and what their customers prefer. These data can help them predict what their customers may buy in the future and how much of each item to stock. The store can use the data and what they learn from the data to improve customer service, mimicking the kind of personal attention a shopper had 50 years ago.

Eziba was founded in 1999 as an exclusively Web-based bazaar by Richard Sabot, a development economist and Amber Chand, a Ugandan-born specialist in sourcing handmade crafts from developing countries. They hoped to forge a link between artisans in developing countries and customers in the West. To meet this challenge, they needed to collect and analyze data to track hundreds of inventory items from around the world, tens of thousands of customers, and marketing initiatives that include direct mail and print advertising. A small company must make smart decisions. How could Eziba compare the success of its print advertisement in the *New York Times* magazine with the effectiveness of its new Web site design?

Eziba designed its Web site to collect data on customer behavior. The company wanted to know how long a visitor to the site spent on each page and how likely she was to make a purchase. The Web site asked customers where they had heard of the company and recorded the number who mentioned the *Times* magazine ads. Analyses of these and other data have enabled Eziba to manage customer relationships and expand sales.

But What *Are* Data?

We bet you thought you knew this instinctively. But think about it for a minute. What exactly do we mean by "data"?

You might say that data are numbers. The amount of your last purchase in dollars is numeric data. But some data record names or other labels. Your name in Eziba's database is data, but not numeric.

Sometimes, just to make things confusing, data can have values that look like numeric values but are just numerals serving as labels. The item stock numbers Eziba uses to track inventory are really just names.

But data values, no matter what kind, are useless without their context. Newspaper journalists know that the lead paragraph of a good story should establish the "Five W's": *Who, What, When, Where,* and (if possible) *Why.* Often, we add *How* to the list as well. Answering these questions can provide the **context** for data values. The answers to the first two questions are essential. If you can't answer those questions, you don't have **data,** and you don't have any useful information.

> **The W's:**
> **WHO**
> **WHAT**
>   and in what units
> **WHEN**
> **WHERE**
> **WHY**
> **HOW**

Data Tables

Here are some customer records from another company's database:

7O28YT	24		305	Boston	18	Kansas	5
Veterans		Orange	Y	CKJ245		413	Y
Garbage	43	Wrigley	Y	Chicago	N		Fenway
610		130		7TY734	368	JKN234	312

Try to guess what they represent. Why is that hard? Because they have no *context*. It's impossible to know what they're about or what they refer to without knowing the W's. We can make the context clear if we organize the values into a **data table** such as this one.

Name	Age (yrs.)	Time Since Last Purchase (days)	Area Code	Nearest Stadium	Internet Purchase?	Catalog Number of Last CD Bought	Artist
Katharine H.		130	312	Wrigley	Y	7TY734	Kansas
Samuel P.	24	18	305	Orange	N	CKJ245	Boston
Chris G.	43	368	610	Veterans	Y	JKN234	Chicago
Monique D.		5	413	Fenway	Y	7O28YT	Garbage

Table 2.1

Now we can see that these are four customer records from an Internet CD store (that advertises at sporting events). The column titles tell *What* has been recorded. The rows tell us *Who*. The other W's might have to come from the company's database administrator.[1]

Who

In general, each row of a data table corresponds to an **individual** about whom (or about which—if they're not people) we record some characteristics. These individuals go by different names, depending on the situation. Individuals who answer a survey are referred to as **respondents.** People on whom we experiment are **subjects** or (in an attempt to acknowledge the importance of their role in the experiment) **participants,** but animals, plants, Web sites, and other inanimate subjects are often just called **experimental units.** In a database, rows are called **records**—in this example, **customer records.** Perhaps the most generic term is **cases.** In the table, the cases are the customers, Katherine, Samuel, Chris, and Monique.

Sometimes people just refer to data values as **observations** without being clear about the *Who*. Be sure you know the *Who* of the data or you may not know what the data say.

What

But it is wise to be careful. The *What* and *Why* of area codes are not as simple as they may first seem. When area codes were first introduced, AT&T was still the source of all telephone equipment and phones had dials. To reduce wear and tear on the dials, the area codes with the lowest digits (for which the dial would have to spin least) were assigned to the most populous regions—those with the most phone numbers and thus the area codes most likely to be dialed. New York City was assigned 212, Chicago 312, and Los Angeles 213, but rural upstate New York was given 607, Joliet was 815, and San Diego 619. For that reason, at one time, the numeric value of an area code could be used to guess something about the population of its region. Since the advent of push-button phones, area codes have finally become just categories.

The characteristics recorded about each individual are called **variables.** These are usually shown as the columns of a data table, and they should have a name that identifies *what* has been measured.

Whether a data value is a number or a name may depend on how we use it. Although area codes are numbers, do we use them that way? Is 610 twice 305? Of course, but is Allentown, PA, (610) equal to two times Key West, FL (305)?

The numbers here are just labels and their values are arbitrary. They represent categories of the variables. We call such variables **categorical.**[2]

The International System of Units links together all systems of weights and measures by international agreement. There are seven base units from which all other physical units are derived:

- Distance   Meter
- Mass   Kilogram
- Time   Second
- Electric current   Ampere
- Temperature   Kelvin
- Amount of substance Mole
- Intensity of light Candela

Variables recorded in numbers that we use as numbers are called **quantitative.** Familiar examples include incomes, heights, weights, ages, and counts.

Quantitative variables have measurement **units.** Units tell how a quantitative value has been measured. Units are such things as yen, cubits, carats, angstroms, nanoseconds, miles per hour, and degrees Celsius. Without units, the values of a quantitative variable have no meaning. It does little good to be promised a salary of 40,000 a year if you don't know whether it will be paid in euros, dollars, yen, or Estonian kroon. Knowing

---

[1] In database management, this kind of information is called "metadata."
[2] You may also see them called *qualitative.*

the attribute may not be sufficient. You might be surprised to see someone whose age is 72 listed in a database on childhood diseases until you find out that age is measured in months. No quantitative variable is complete without its units.

Often, just seeking the units can reveal a variable whose definition is dubious. For example, how should we measure "friendliness," "success," "study effort," or "commitment"? It may not be clear how to measure these concepts, yet people make scientific-sounding claims about such "variables." For example, a claim such as "Performance in school is highly correlated with self-esteem" might sound scientific—until we ask in what units one might measure "school performance" or "self-esteem."

Although we've described categorical and quantitative as if they were properties of variables, really they're properties of how we *use* a variable. For example, if we measure someone's age, we might measure it in years and use it as a quantitative variable. Taking the average age would make sense. But sometimes we treat age as categorical, as, for example, in the categories "child" and "adult." Many variables can be treated either way, depending on the use we want to put them to.

Some variables fall right in between categorical and quantitative. These are variables whose values are not categorical, but not quite quantitative either. For example, think about a survey that asks a question, "What did you think about the pace of the Statistics course you took?" 1 = Way too slow; 2 = A little too slow; 3 = About right; 4 = A little too fast; 5 = Way too fast. Is this variable categorical or quantitative? There is certainly an *order* of perceived speed here. Higher numbers indicate higher perceived speed. A course that averages 4.5 is perceived as going faster than one that averages 2. But we should be careful about treating them as purely quantitative. A course that averages 4.0 is not necessarily *twice* as fast as one that averages 2.0.

These variables are often called **ordinal** variables. Again, depending on what one wants to do with them, they might be treated as numeric (with caution) or categorical, or sometimes even both. For example, the figure numbers in this book can be categorical labels (as in "see Figure 2.1"[3]) or they could be quantitative and count the number of figures in a chapter, although there's little reason to want to know that. The main point is to think about what the values mean and how they are being used. Be careful of automatically treating values as quantitative just because they look like numbers.

What is measured tells us the meaning of the values. In the internet CD database, there are seven variables measuring various characteristics about the customers. The variable names often give a lot of information about the *What* if they are well chosen. For this reason, it's a good idea to avoid names like x_1, TEMP, or even XPECHR8, as tempting as this may be. Use names that clearly show what the variable is about.

One tradition that hangs on in some quarters is to name variables with cryptic abbreviations written in uppercase letters. This can be traced back to the 1960s when the very first statistics computer programs were controlled with instructions punched on cards. The earliest punch card equipment used only uppercase letters, and the earliest statistics programs limited variable names to six or eight characters, so variables were called things like PRSRF3. But modern programs do not have such restrictive limits, so there is no longer an excuse for variable names that you wouldn't use in an ordinary sentence.

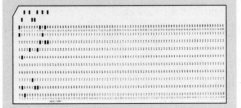

Where, When, How, and Why

We must know *Who* and *What* to analyze data. But the more we know, the more we'll understand.

For example, we'd like to know the **When** and **Where** of data as well. Values recorded in 1803 may mean something different than similar

---

[3]But you won't see the phrase "see Figure xx" in this book. (Except, of course, for the two times you just saw.) So why *are* there figure numbers? Only so the figures can be tracked during production of the book. They are identifiers—a special type of categorical variable.

values recorded last year. Values measured in Tanzania may differ in meaning from similar measurements made in Mexico.

How the data are collected can make the difference between insight and nonsense. As we'll see later, data that come from a voluntary survey on the Internet are almost always worthless. One primary concern of statistics, discussed in Part III, is the design of sound methods for collecting data.

Often the most revealing W is **Why.** Knowing why data were collected can alert us to potential problems in *How* the data were measured or observed or in the decisions made about the *Who* and *What* of the data. For example, knowing that Levi Strauss conducted the survey may make us skeptical when we hear that 90% of students predicted Levi's 501 jeans to be the most popular clothing item on campus.[4]

Throughout this book, whenever we introduce data, we will provide a marginal note listing the W's (and H) of the data. It is a habit we recommend. Whenever you encounter data (or values masquerading as data) ask yourself whether you know the W's. You may be surprised to see how often this vital information is missing. That simple question will protect you from many of the most common misuses of statistics.

An Example

A study compared the lifetimes of actors who had won Academy Awards (Oscars) with those of actors who had been nominated but had not won and with actors who had been in the movies that led to the awards but had not been nominated. The study found that actors who had won tended to live longer than the other actors considered.

What are the W's in this account? Pause for a moment and try to determine them to the extent that we can tell.

The *Who* are actors, and specifically actors who won Oscars, were nominated for Oscars, or acted in films in which others won Oscars. The *What* of concern in this study is the length of the lives of these actors (which suggests that we may need to modify the *Who* to be only dead actors who meet the other criteria). The *When* isn't clear, although the study may well have spanned the several decades of Academy Awards. *Where* is not really an issue here, although most of the actors nominated are American. The *Why* is, as far as we can tell, a scientific concern with whether fame, or winning, affects lifetimes.

Always refer to variables by name. Your conclusions from statistical analyses should be in clear sentences and about the variables. For example, here is a brief description of a study that was analyzed with statistics[5]:

> *Researchers gave 117 people either echinacea or a placebo (sugar pill) for two weeks, then exposed them to cold viruses. Those who took the echinacea were just as likely to develop a cold as those who took a placebo. The researchers concluded that echinacea treatments do not reduce the risk of catching colds.*

---

[4]Learning that these were the only jeans on the list might increase our skepticism.
[5]Reported in the June 2000 issue of *Antimicrobial Agents and Chemotherapy.*

It is easy to tell the *Who* (117 people) and *What* (susceptibility to colds) from this description and to understand the conclusions of the study in terms of the variables (*treatment:* a categorical variable with values of either echinacea or placebo; and *cold:* a categorical variable recording whether the people got colds).

What Can Go Wrong?

- *Just because your variable's values are numbers, don't assume that it's quantitative.* Categories are often given numeric labels. Don't let that fool you into thinking they have quantitative meaning. Look at the context.
- *Always be skeptical.* Even when you are told a context for the data, it may turn out that the truth is a bit (or even a lot) different. The context colors our interpretation of the data, so those who want to influence what you think may slant the context. A survey that seems to be about all students may in fact report just the opinions of those who visited a fan Web site. The question that respondents answered may be slanted.

One reason to analyze data is to discover the truth.

Data and the Computer

Most often we find statistics on a computer using a program, or *package,* designed for that purpose. There are many different statistics packages, but they all do essentially the same things. If you understand what the computer needs to know to do what you want and what it needs to show you in return, you can figure out the specific details of most packages pretty easily.

For example, to get your data into a computer statistics package you need to tell the computer:

- Where to find the data. This usually means directing the computer to a file stored on your computer's disk or to data on a database. Or it might just mean that you have copied the data from a spreadsheet program or Internet site, and it is currently on your computer's clipboard. Usually, the data should be in the form of a data table. Most computer statistics packages prefer the *delimiter* that marks the division between elements of a data table to be a *tab* character and the delimiter that marks the end of a case to be a *return* character.
- Where to put the data. (Usually this is handled automatically.)
- What to call the variables. Some data tables have variable names as the first row of the data, and often statistics packages can take the variable names from the first row automatically.

Key Concepts

Context   The context ideally tells *Who* was measured, *What* was measured, *How* the data were collected, *Where* the data were collected, and *When* and *Why* the study was performed.

Data   Systematically recorded information, whether numbers or labels, together with its context.

Data table	An arrangement of data in which each row represents a case and each column represents a variable.
Case	A case is an individual about whom or which we have data.
Variable	A variable holds information about the same characteristic for many cases.
Categorical variable	A variable that names categories (whether with text or numerals) is called categorical.
Quantitative variable	A variable in which the numbers act as numeric values is called quantitative. Quantitative variables always have units.
Units	A quantity or amount adopted as a standard of measurement; such as dollars, hours, or grams.

Skills

When you complete this lesson you should:

- Be able to identify the *Who, What, Where, When, Why,* and *How* of data, or recognize when some of this information has not been provided.
- Be able to identify the cases and variables in any data set.
- Be able to classify a variable as categorical or quantitative.
- For any quantitative variable be able to identify the units in which the variable has been measured (or note that they have not been provided).

- Be able to describe a variable in terms of its *Who, What, When, Where, How,* and *Why* (and be prepared to remark when that information is not provided).

Exercises

2 Data

Exercises

1. **The News** Find a newspaper or magazine article in which some data are reported. For the data discussed in the article answer the same questions. Include a copy of the article with your report.

2– 21. For each description of data, identify the W's, name the variables, classify each variable as categorical or quantitative and, for any quantitative variable, identify the units in which it was measured (or note that they were not provided.)

2. **Investments** According to an article in *Fortune*, (Dec.28, 1992), 401(k) plans permit employees to shift part of their before-tax salaries into investments such as mutual funds. Employers typically match 50% of the employees' contribution up to about 6% of salary. One company, concerned with what it believed was a low employee participation rate in its 401(k) plan, sampled 30 other companies with similar plans and asked for their 401(k) participation rates.

3. **Oil Spills** Owing to several major ocean oil spills by tank vessels, Congress passed the 1990 Oil Pollution Act, which requires all tankers to be designed with thicker hulls. Further improvements in the structural design of a tank vessel have been proposed since then, each with the objective of reducing the likelihood of an oil spill and decreasing the amount of outflow in the event of a hull puncture. To aid in this development, *Marine Technology* (Jan. 1995) reported on the spillage amount and cause of puncture for 50 recent major oil spills from tankers and carriers.

4. **Oscars** *Ages of Oscar-Winning Best Actors and Actresses* by Richard Brown and Gretchen Davis gives the ages of actors and actresses at the time they won Oscars. We might use these data to see whether actors and actresses are likely to win Oscars at about the same age or not.

5. **Weighing Bears** Because of the difficulty of weighing a bear in the woods, researchers caught and measured 54 bears, recording their weight, neck size, length, and sex. They hoped to find a way to estimate weight from the other, more easily determined quantities.

6. **Molten Iron** The Cleveland Casting Plant is a large, highly automated producer of gray and nodular iron automotive castings for Ford Motor Company. According to an article in *Quality Engineering*, (Vol. 7, 1995), Cleveland Casting is interested in keeping the pouring temperature of the molten iron (in degrees Fahrenheit)

DRAFT: Do not distribute or copy

page 13B follows

/3

close to the specified value of 2,550 degrees. Cleveland Casting measured the pouring temperature for a random sample of ten crankshafts.

7. **Arby's Menu** A listing posted by the Arby's restaurant chain gives, for each of the sandwiches they sell, the type of meat in the sandwich, the number of calories, and the serving size in ounces. Th data might be used to assess the nutritional value of the different sandwiches.

8. **Firefighters** A study was conducted to compare the abilities of men and women to perform the strenuous tasks required of a shipboard firefighter (*Human Factors*, Vol. 24, 1982). The study reports the pulling force (in newtons) that a firefighter was able to exert in pulling the starter cord of a P-250 water pump. The study also give the weight and, of course, the gender of the firefighters.

9. **Babies** Medical researchers at a large city hospital investigating the impact of prenatal care on newborn health collected data from 882 births during 1998 – 2000. They kept track of the mother's age, the number of weeks the pregnancy lasted, the type of birth (caesarean, induced, natural), the level of prenatal care the mother had (none, minimal, adequate), the birth weight and gender of the baby, and whether the baby exhibited health problems (none, minor, major).

10. **Flowers** In a study appearing in the journal *Science* a research team reports that plants in southern England are flowering earlier in the spring. Records of the first flowering dates for 385 species over a period of 47 years indicate that flowering has advanced an average 15 days per decade, an indication of climate warming according to the authors.

11. **Fitness** Are physically fit people less likely to die of cancer? An article in the May 2002 issue of *Medicine and Science in Sport and Exercise* reported results of a study that followed 25892 men aged 3 to 87 for 10 years. The most physically fit men had a 55% lower risk of death from cancer than the least fit group.

12. **Schools** The State Education Department requires local school districts to keep these records on all students: age, race or ethnicity, days absent, current grade level, standardized test scores in reading and mathematics, and any disabilities or special educational needs the student may have.

13. **Herbal Medicine** Scientists at a major pharmaceutical firm conducted an experiment to study the effectiveness of an herbal compound to treat the common cold. They exposed each patient to cold virus, then gave them either the herbal compound or a sugar

page 13c follo

solution known to have no effect on colds. Several days later they assessed each patient's condition using a cold severity scale ranging 0 - 5. They found no evidence of the benefits of the compound.

14. **Tracking Sales** A start up company is building a data base of their customers and sales information. For each customer they record their name, ID number, region of the country (1=East, 2=South, 3= Midwest, 4= West), date of last purchase, amount of purchase and item purchased.

15. **Cars** A survey of autos parked in student and staff lots at a large university recorded the make, country of origin, type of vehicle (car, van, SUV, etc), and age.

16. **Wineries** Business analysts hoping to provide information helpful to producers of American wines compiled these data about vineyards: size (acres), number of years in existence, state, varieties of grapes grown, average case price, gross sales, and percent profit.

17. **Streams** As research for an Ecology class, students at an upstate NY college collect data on streams each year. They record a number of biological, chemical, and physical variables, including the stream name, the substrate of the stream (Limestone, Shale, or Mixed), the acidity of the water (pH), the temperature (°C), and BCI (a numerical measure of biological diversity).

18. **Age and Party** The Gallup Poll conducted a representative telephone survey of 1180 American voters during the first quarter of 1999. Among their reported results were the voter's region (Northeast, South, etc), age, party affiliation, and whether or not the person had voted in the 1998 midterm Congressional election.

19. **Air Travel** The FAA monitors airlines for safety and customer service. For each flight the carrier must report the type of aircraft, number of passengers, whether or not the flights departed and arrived on schedule, and any mechanical problems.

20. **Fuel Economy** The Environmental Protection Agency tracks fuel economy of automobiles. Among the data they collect are the manufacturer (Ford, Toyota, etc.), vehicle type (car, SUV, etc.), weight, horsepower, and gas mileage (mpg) for city and highway driving.

21. **Refrigerators** In 2002 *Consumer Reports* published an article evaluating refrigerators. They listed 41 models, giving the brand, cost, size (cu. ft.), type (top-freezer, etc), estimated annual energy

page 13D follows

cost, an overall rating (good, excellent, etc), and the repair history fo
that brand (percent requiring repairs over the past 5 years).

page 14 follows

Chapter 3

Displaying Categorical Data

WHO	People on the *Titanic*
WHAT	Survival status, age, sex, ticket class
WHEN	April 14, 1912
WHERE	North Atlantic
HOW	A variety of sources and Internet sites
WHY	Historical interest (or maybe just morbid curiosity)

What happened on the *Titanic* at 11:40 on the night of April 14, 1912, is well known. Frederick Fleet's cry of "Iceberg, right ahead" and the three accompanying pulls of the crow's nest bell signaled the beginning of a nightmare that has become legend. By 2:15 a.m. the *Titanic*, thought by many to be unsinkable, had sunk, leaving over 1500 passengers and crewmembers on board to meet their icy fate.

Here are some data about the passengers and crew aboard the *Titanic*. Each record of the data table (each row) shows the data for one person on board the ship. The variables are whether or not the person *Survived* (Dead or Alive), the person's *Age* (Adult or Child), *Sex* (Male or Female), and ticket *Class* (First, Second, Third, or Crew).

The problem with a data table like this—and in fact with all data tables—is that you can't *see* what's going on. And seeing is just what we want to do. We need ways to show the data so that we can see patterns, relationships, trends, and even exceptions.

Survived	Age	Sex	Class
Dead	Adult	Male	Third
Dead	Adult	Male	Crew
Dead	Adult	Male	Third
Dead	Adult	Male	Crew
Dead	Adult	Male	Crew
Dead	Adult	Male	Crew
Alive	Adult	Female	First
Dead	Adult	Male	Third
Dead	Adult	Male	Crew

Part of a data table showing four variables for nine passengers aboard the *Titanic*. **Table 3.1**

The Three Rules of Data Analysis

So, what should we do with data like these? There are three things you should always do first with data:

1. **Make a picture.** A display of your data will reveal things you are not likely to see in a table of numbers and will help you to *think* clearly about the patterns and relationships that may be hiding in your data.

2. **Make a picture.** A well-designed display will *show* the important features and patterns in your data. And a picture will show you the things you did not expect to see: the extraordinary (possibly wrong) data values or unexpected patterns.

3. **Make a picture.** The best way to *tell* others about your data is with a well-chosen picture.

These are the three rules of data analysis. There are pictures of data throughout the book, and new kinds keep showing up. These days, technology makes drawing pictures of data easy, so there is no excuse for not following the three rules.

A Picture To Tell a Story

Florence Nightingale, a founder of modern nursing, was also well versed in statistics. To argue forcefully for better hospital conditions for soldiers, she invented this display, which showed that in the Crimean War, far more soldiers died of illness and infection than died of battle wounds. Her campaign succeeded in improving hospital conditions and nursing for soldiers.   **Figure 3.1**

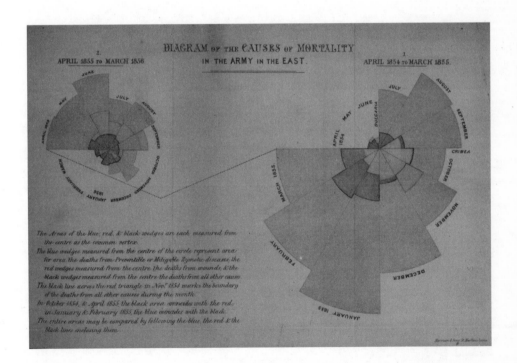

What to Do First: Make Piles

But in order to make a picture, the first thing we have to do with data is to make piles. Believe it or not, making piles is the start of all science and the beginning of all understanding about data. We pile together things that seem to go together. Later we'll ask how they go together, why they go together, and how the piles relate and compare with one another. But first, we pile.

Frequency Tables

Class	Count
First	325
Second	285
Third	706
Crew	885

A frequency table of the
Titantic passengers.
Table 3.2

Class	%
First	14.766
Second	12.949
Third	32.076
Crew	40.209

The same data as
relative frequency table.
Table 3.3

One way to put all 2201 people on the Titanic into piles is by ticket *Class*, counting up how many had each kind of ticket. We can organize these **counts** into a **frequency table,** which records the totals and the category names.

The variable ticket *Class* has only a few categories, so a frequency table is easy to read even though we have thousands of cases. A frequency table with dozens or hundreds of categories would be much harder to read. We use the names of the categories to label each row in the frequency table. For ticket *Class*, these are: "First," "Second," "Third," and "Crew."

A **relative frequency table** is similar but gives the *percentages*, rather than the counts, of the values in each category. Both types of tables describe the **distribution** of a categorical variable because they name the possible categories and tell how frequently each occurs.

The Area Principle

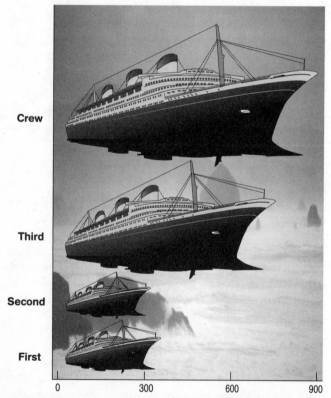

Crew

Third

Second

First

0	300	600	900

How many people were in each class on the *Titanic?* From this display it looks as though the service must have been great, since most aboard were crew members. Although the *length* of each ship here corresponds to the correct number, the impression is all wrong. In fact, only 40 percent were crew. **Figure 3.2**

Now that we have the frequency table, we're ready to follow the three rules of data analysis and make a picture of the data. But a bad picture can distort our understanding rather than help it. Here's a graph of the *Titanic* data. What impression do you get about who was aboard the ship?

It sure looks like most of the people on the *Titanic* were crew members, with a few passengers along for the ride. That doesn't seem right. What's wrong? The lengths of the ships *do* match the totals in the table. (You can check the scale at the bottom.) But experience and psychological tests show that our eyes tend to be more impressed by the *area* than by other aspects of each ship image. So, even though the *length* of each ship matches up with one of the totals, it's the associated *area* in the image that we notice. Since there were about 3 times as many crew as second-class passengers, the ship depicting the number of crew is about 3 times longer than the ship depicting second-class passengers. But it occupies about 9 times the area. As you can see from the frequency table, (Table 3.2) that just isn't a correct impression.

The best data displays observe a fundamental principle of graphing data called the **area principle.** The area principle says that the area occupied by a part of the graph should correspond to the magnitude of the value it represents. Violations of the area principle are a common way to lie (or, since most mistakes are unintentional, we should say err) with statistics.

Bar Charts

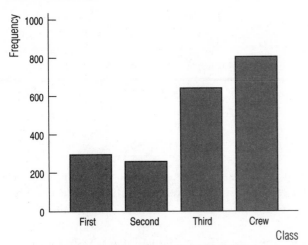

People On The *Titanic* By Ticket Class

With the area principle satisfied, we can see the true distribution more clearly. **Figure 3.3**

For some reason, some computer programs give the name "bar chart" to any graph that uses bars. And others use different names according to whether the bars are horizontal or vertical. Don't be misled. "Bar chart" is the term for a *display of counts of a categorical variable* with bars.

Here's a chart that obeys the area principle. It's not as visually entertaining as the ships, but, it does give an *accurate* visual impression of the distribution. The height of each bar shows the count for its category. Because the bars are the same width, their heights determine their areas. And the areas are proportional to the counts in each class. Now it's easy to see that the majority of people on board were *not* crew, as the ships picture led us to believe. And it's now clear that there were about 3 times as many crew as second-class passengers. It's also easy to see that there were more than twice as many third-class passengers than either first- or second-class passengers, something you may have missed in the frequency table. Bar charts make these kinds of comparisons easy and natural.

A **bar chart** displays the distribution of a categorical variable, showing the counts for each category next to each other for easy comparison. Bar charts have small spaces between the bars to indicate that these are free-standing bars that could be rearranged into any order. The bars are lined up along a common base.

Usually they stick up like this 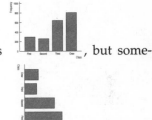 , but sometimes they run sideways like this 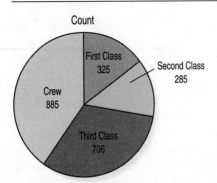 .

Pie Charts

Count

The number of *Titanic* passengers in each class. **Figure 3.4**

If we want to draw attention to the relative *proportion* of passengers falling into each of these classes, we could replace the counts with percentages in a bar chart. But a better choice might be a pie chart. **Pie charts** show the whole group of cases as a circle and slice the circle into pieces whose size represents the fraction of the whole in each category.

Here again it's easy to see that the crew was the largest segment of those aboard. Pie charts give a quick impression of how a whole group is partitioned into smaller groups. Because we're used to cutting up pies into 2, 4, or 8 pieces, pie charts are OK for seeing if the relative frequency of a category is near 1/2, 1/4, or 1/8. For example, you may be able to tell that the green slice, representing the second-class passengers, is very close to 1/8 of the total. But it's a bit harder to see that there were about twice as many third-class as first-class passengers. And were there more crew or more third-class passengers? Comparisons such as these are easier in a bar chart.

Children and First-Class Ticket Holders First?

We know how many tickets of each class were sold on the *Titanic*. And we know that only 32% of all those aboard the *Titanic* survived. Was there a relationship between the kind of ticket you held and your chances of making it into the lifeboat? To answer this question, we need to look at the two categorical variables *Class* and *Survival* together.

Contingency Tables

When we look at two categorical variables together, we often arrange the counts in a two-way table. Because the table shows how the individuals are distributed along each variable, contingent on the value of the other variable, such a table is called a **contingency table.**

Here is a contingency table of those aboard the *Titanic* classified according to class of ticket and whether they survived or didn't:

		Class				
		First	Second	Third	Crew	Total
Survival	Alive	202	118	178	212	710
	Dead	123	167	528	673	1491
	Total	325	285	706	885	2201

Contingency table of ticket *Class* and *Survival*. The bottom line of "Totals" is the same as the previous frequency table.   **Table 3.4**

The margins of the table, both on the right and at the bottom, give totals. The bottom line of the table is just the frequency distribution of ticket *Class*. A distribution like this of one of the variables in a contingency table is called its **marginal distribution.**

The **cells** of the table give the counts or frequencies for every combination of values for the two variables. If you look down the column for second-class passengers to the first cell, you can see that 118 second-class passengers survived. Looking at the third-class passengers, we see that more third-class passengers (178) were that lucky. Those 118 surviving second-class passengers were nearly half of the 285 total in second class. But the 178 third-class survivors were a much smaller fraction of the total of 706 third-class passengers.

It might be more useful to have percentages, but to do that we have to make choices. We know that 118 second-class passengers survived. We could display this number as a percentage, but as a percentage of what? The total number of passengers (118 is 5.4% of the total, 2201)? The number of second-class passengers (118 is 41.4% of the 285 second-class passengers)? The number of survivors (118 is 16.6% of the 710 survivors)? All of these are possibilities, and all are potentially useful or interesting. You'll probably wind up calculating (or letting your technology

A bell-shaped artifact from the *Titanic*.

calculate) lots of percentages. Most statistics programs offer a choice of total percent, row percent, or column percent for contingency tables. Here are the counts and all three percentages displayed as they might be by a computer package:

			Class				
			First	Second	Third	Crew	Totals
Survival	Alive	Count	202	118	178	212	710
		% of Row	28.5%	16.6%	25.1%	29.9%	100%
		% of Column	62.2%	41.4%	25.2%	24.0%	32.3%
		% of Table	9.18%	5.36%	8.09%	9.63%	32.3%
	Dead	Count	123	167	528	673	1491
		% of Row	8.25%	11.2%	35.4%	45.1%	100%
		% of Column	37.8%	58.6%	74.8%	76.0%	67.7%
		% of Table	5.59%	7.59%	24.0%	30.6%	67.7%
	Totals	Count	325	285	706	885	2201
		% of Row	14.8%	12.9%	32.1%	40.2%	100%
		% of Column	100%	100%	100%	100%	100%
		% of Table	14.8%	12.9%	32.1%	40.2%	100%

Another contingency table of ticket *Class*. This time we see not only the counts for each combination of *Class* and *Survival* (in bold) but the percentages these counts represent. For each count, there are three choices for the percentage: by row, by column, and by table total. There's probably too much information here for this table to be useful.   **Table 3.5**

Each cell of this table gives the count, row percent, column percent, and table percent in that order. This is an example of why contingency tables can look so confusing. There's too much information to sort through at one glance. While it's fine to consider all these choices, it's probably better to look at them one at a time. In this table each column shows what percentage of passengers in that class survived.

			Class				
			First	Second	Third	Crew	Total
Survival	Alive	Count	202	118	178	212	710
		% of Column	62.2%	41.4%	25.2%	24.0%	32.3%
	Dead	Count	123	167	528	673	1491
		% of Column	37.8%	58.6%	74.8%	76.0%	67.7%
	Total	Count	325	285	706	885	2201

A contingency table of *Class* by *Survival* with only counts and column percentages. Notice how much easier this table is to read than the previous one. Of course, two other similar tables could be made for row percentages and table percentages.   **Table 3.6**

Marginal and Conditional Distributions

So, did the chance of surviving the *Titanic* sinking depend on ticket class? Does the distribution of survivors' ticket class look the same as that distribution for nonsurvivors? Let's look at the table. Among first-class ticket holders, 62.2% survived compared with only 25.2% in third class. That looks like a difference.

To answer the question, we first restricted our attention only to the survivors. This is like redefining the *Who* of the study. Now, the *Who* is only the survivors. Their numbers are in the first row of the contingency table. A distribution, of one variable for only those individuals satisfying some condition on another variable is called a **conditional distribution.**

| | Class | | | | |
	First	Second	Third	Crew	Total
Alive	202	118	178	212	710
	62.2%	41.4%	25.2%	24.0%	32.3%

The *conditional distribution* of ticket *Class*, conditional on having survived.   **Table 3.7**

What if we do the same thing for the nonsurvivors? The numbers for the nonsurvivors are found in the following row:

| | Class | | | | |
	First	Second	Third	Crew	Total
Dead	123	167	528	673	1491
	37.8%	58.6%	74.8%	76.0%	67.7%

The *conditional distribution* of ticket *Class*, conditional on having perished.   **Table 3.8**

Pie charts of the distribution of *Class* for the survivors and nonsurvivors separately. Do the distributions appear to be the same? We're primarily concerned with percentages here, so pie charts are a good choice.   **Figure 3.5**

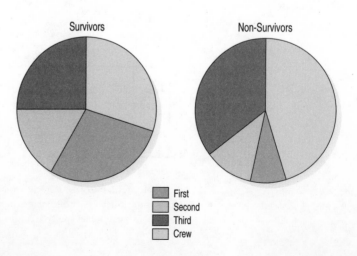

The nonsurvivors are mostly crew and third-class passengers. The survivors, on the other hand, are fairly evenly split up across all four classes. If the percentages of ticket class had been about the same across the two survival groups, we would have said that survival was independent of class. But it's not. The differences we see between the two conditional distributions suggest that survival may have depended on class.

It is interesting to know that *Class* and *Survival* are associated. That's an important part of the *Titanic* story. And we know they're associated because we can see how the distribution of *Survival* differs from ticket class to ticket class.

Variables can be associated in many ways and to different degrees. So the best way to tell whether two variables are associated is to ask whether they are *not*.[1] In a contingency table, when the distribution of *one* variable is the same for all categories of another, we say that the variables are **independent.** We'll see a way to check for independence formally later in the book. For now, we'll just compare the distributions.

Segmented Bar Charts

We could display the same information by dividing up bars rather than circles. The resulting **segmented bar chart** treats each bar as the "whole" and divides it proportionally into segments corresponding to the percentage in each group.

A segmented bar chart for
Class* by *Survival

Notice that although the totals for survivors and nonsurvivors are quite different, the bars are the same heights because we have converted the numbers to *percentages.* Compare this to the side-by-side pie charts of the same data.

Figure 3.6

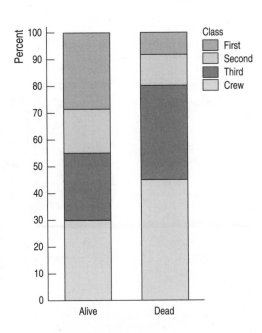

---

[1] This kind of "backwards" reasoning shows up surprisingly often in science—and in Statistics. We'll see it again.

Examining Contingency Tables   STEP-BY-STEP

Medical researchers followed 6272 Swedish men for 30 years to see if there was any association between the amount of fish in their diet and prostate cancer. ("Fatty fish consumption and risk of prostate cancer," *Lancet*, June 2001). Their results are summarized in this table.

We asked for a picture of a "man eating fish." This is what we got.

	Prostate Cancer	
Fish consumption	**No**	**Yes**
Never/seldom	110	14
Small part of diet	2420	201
Moderate part	2769	209
Large part	507	42

Table 3.9

Is there an association between fish consumption and prostate cancer?

Think

Variable Identify the variables and report the W's. Be certain that the data are counts and that the categories do not overlap so that no individual is counted twice.

The individuals are 6272 Swedish men followed by medical researchers for 30 years. The variables record their fish consumption and whether or not they were diagnosed with prostate cancer. The data are reported as counts. The categories of diet do not overlap and the diagnoses do not overlap.

Show

Mechanics Make an appropriate display to see whether there is a difference in the relative proportions. Bar charts might have worked equally well.

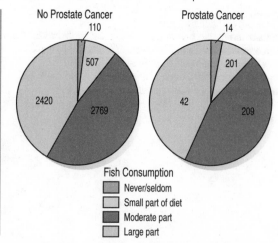

Tell

Interpretation Discuss the patterns in the table and displays.

If you can, discuss possible real-world consequences.

There appears to be little difference between the two groups in terms of their fish consumption. Fish consumption appears to be independent of the incidence of prostate cancer.

We see no reason for men to change their diets in an attempt to reduce their risk of prostate cancer based on this study.

What Can Go Wrong?

- ***Don't violate the area principle.*** This is probably the most common mistake in a graphical display. It is often made in the cause of artistic presentation. Here, for example, is a display of the pie chart of the *Titanic* passengers by class:

Looks pretty, doesn't it? But showing the pie on a slant violates the area principle and makes it much more difficult to compare fractions of the whole made up of each class—the principal feature that a pie chart ought to show.

- ***Keep it honest.*** Here's a pie chart that displays data on the percentage of high school students who engage in specified dangerous behaviors as reported by the Centers for Disease Control. What's wrong with this plot?

Try adding up the percentages. Or look at the 50% slice. Does it look right? Then think: What are these percentages of? Is there a "whole" that has been sliced up? In a pie chart, the proportions shown by each slice of the pie must add up to 100% and each individual must fall into only one category. Of course, showing the pie on a slant makes it even harder to detect the error.

Here's another. This bar chart shows the number of airline passengers searched by security screening.

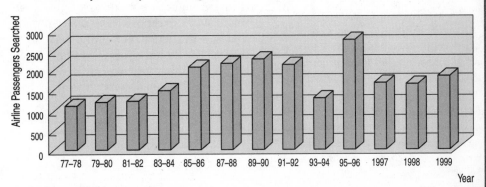

Looks like things didn't change much in the final years of the 20th century—until you read the bar labels and see that the last three bars represent single years, while all the others are for *pairs* of years. Of course, the false depth makes it harder to see the problem.

- ***Don't confuse similar-sounding percentages.*** These percentages sound similar but are different:
    - The percentage of those who were both in first class and survived: This would be 202/2100, or 9.18%.

		Class				
		First	Second	Third	Crew	Total
Survival	Alive	202	118	178	212	**710**
	Dead	123	167	528	673	**1491**
	Total	**325**	**285**	**706**	**885**	**2201**

Contingency table of ticket *Class* and *Survival*. The bottom line of "Totals" is the same as the previous frequency table.

Entering Centerville

Established	1793
Population	7943
Elevation	710
Average	3,482

One famous example of Simpson's paradox arose during an investigation of admission rates for men and women at the University of California at Berkeley's graduate schools. As reported in an article in *Science*, about 45% of male applicants were admitted, but only about 30% of female applicants got in. It looked like a clear case of discrimination. But when the data were broken down by school (Engineering, Law, Medicine, etc.) it turned out that within each school, the women were admitted at nearly the same or, in some cases, much *higher* rates than the men. How could this be? Women applied in large numbers to schools with very low admission rates (Law and Medicine, for example, admitted fewer than 10%). But men tended to apply to Engineering and Science. Those schools have admission rates above 50%. So, when the *average* was taken, the women had a much lower *overall* rate, but the average didn't really make sense.

- The percentage of those who survived among those who were in first class: This is 202/325, or 62.5%.
- The percentage of those who were in first class among those who survived: This is 202/710, or 28.5%.

In each instance, pay attention to the *Who* implicitly defined by the phrase. Often there is a restriction to a smaller group (all aboard the *Titanic*, those in first class, and those who survived, respectively) before a percentage is found. Your discussion of results must make these differences clear.

- **Be sure to use enough individuals.** When you consider percentages, take care that they are based on a large enough number of individuals. Take care not to make a report such as this one:
  - *We found that 66.67% of the rats improved their performance with training. The other rat died.*

- **Don't overstate your case.** Independence is an important concept, but it is rare for two variables to be *entirely* independent. We don't know, for example, that fish consumption has no effect whatever on prostate cancer. All we know is that no effect was observed in that study. Other studies of other groups under other circumstances could find different results.

Simpson's Paradox

- **Don't use unfair or silly averages.** Sometimes averages can be misleading. And sometimes they just don't make sense at all. Be careful when averaging different variables that the quantities you're averaging are comparable. The Centerville sign says it all.

  When using averages of proportions across several different groups, it's important to make sure that the groups really are comparable.

It's easy to make up an example showing that averaging across very different values or groups can give absurd results. Here's how that might work. Suppose there are two pilots, Moe and Jill. Moe argues that he's the better pilot of the two, since he managed to land 83% of his last 120 flights on time compared with Jill's 78%. But let's look at the data a little more closely. Here are the results for each of their last 120 flights, broken down by the time of day they flew:

		Time of Day		
		Day	Night	Overall
Pilot	Moe	90 out of 100	10 out of 20	100 out of 120
		90%	50%	83%
	Jill	19 out of 20	75 out of 100	94 out of 120
		95%	75%	78%

On-time flights by Time of Day and Pilot. Look at the percentages within each Time of Day category. Who has a better on-time record during the day? At night? Who is better overall?   **Table 3.10**

Look at the day and nighttime flights separately. For day flights, Jill had a 95% on-time rate, and Moe only a 90% rate. At night, Jill was on time 75% of the time, and Moe only 50%. So Moe is better "overall," but Jill is better both during the day and at night. How can this be?

What's going on here is a problem known as **Simpson's paradox,** named for the statistician who discovered it in the 1960s. It comes up rarely in real life, but there have been several well-publicized cases of it. As we can see from the pilot example, the problem is *unfair averaging* over different groups. Jill has mostly night flights, which are more difficult, so her *overall average* is heavily influenced by her nighttime average. Moe, on the other hand, benefits from flying mostly during the day, with its higher on-time percentage. With their very different patterns of flying conditions, taking an overall average is misleading. It's not a fair comparison.

The moral of Simpson's paradox is to be careful when you average across different levels of a second variable. It's always better to compare percentages or other averages *within* each level of the other variable. The overall average may be misleading.

Displaying Categorical Data with a Computer

Although every package makes a slightly different bar chart, they all have similar features:

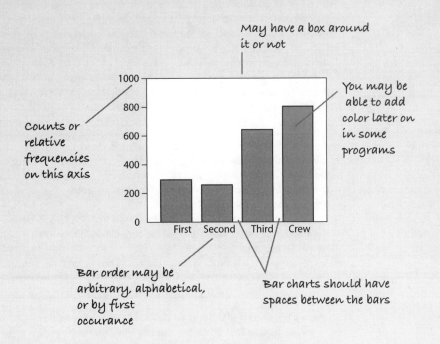

Sometimes the count or a percentage is printed above or on top of each bar to give some additional information. You may find that your statistics package sorts category names in annoying orders by default. For example, many packages sort categories alphabetically or by the order the categories are seen in the data set. Often, neither of these is the best choice.

The commands to make displays of categorical data are not always found in obvious places on common statistics technology. Here are some clues and comments to get you started.

Package	Commands and Location	Comments

Data Desk	To make a bar chart or pie chart,
	    select the variable.
	 In the **Plot** menu choose **Bar Chart** or **Pie Chart**.
	 To make a frequency table,
	    in the **Calc** menu choose **Frequency Table**.
		These commands treat the data as categorical even if they are numerals. If you select a quantitative variable by mistake, you'll see an error message warning of too many categories.

Excel	First make a pivot table (Excel's name for a frequency table).
	    From the **Data** menu choose **Pivot Table** and **Pivot Chart Report**.
	    When you reach the Layout window, drag your variable to the row area and drag your variable again to the data area. This tells Excel to count the occurrences of each category.
	 Once you have an Excel pivot table, you can construct bar charts and pie charts.
	    Click inside the Pivot Table.
	    Click the Pivot Table Chart Wizard button. Excel creates a bar chart.
	 A longer path leads to a pie chart; see your Excel documentation.
		Excel uses the pivot table to specify the category names and find counts within each category. If you already have that information, you can proceed directly to the Chart Wizard.

JMP	JMP makes a bar chart and frequency table together. From the **Analyze** menu, choose **Distribution**. In the Distribution dialog, drag the name of the variable into the empty variable window beside the label "Y, Columns"; click **OK**. To make a pie chart in JMP choose **Chart** from the **Graph** menu. In the Chart dialog, select the variable name from the Columns list, click on the button labeled "Statistics," and select "N" from the drop-down menu. Click the "X, Level" button to assign the same variable name to the X-axis. Under Options, click on the top button—labeled "Vertical"—and select "Pie" from the drop-down menu. Click **OK**.	
Minitab	To make a bar chart choose **Chart** from the **Graph** menu. In the Chart dialog, enter the name of the variable that you wish to graph in the first row of the "Graph variables" table under the column marked X. In the "Data display" table, make sure that the first row reads "Display: Bar" and "For each: Graph", click **OK**. To make a pie chart in MINITAB choose **Pie Chart** from the **Graph** menu. In the Pie Chart dialog, make sure that the button next to the words "Chart data in:" is selected. Enter the name of the variable to plot in the empty box to the right. And click **OK**.	
SPSS	To make a bar chart in SPSS choose **Bar** from the **Graphs** menu. From the Bar Charts Dialog, choose **Simple** and indicate the nature of the data. In the Define Simple Bar dialog, select the variable name from the source list and click on the **Category Axis** arrow. Click the **OK** button to create the display. A similar path makes a pie chart by choosing **Pie** rather than Bar from the **Graphs** menu.	
TI-83	The TI-83 won't do displays for categorical variables.	

Connections

All of the methods of this chapter work with *categorical variables.* You must know the *Who* of the data to know who is counted in each bar and the *What* of the variable to know where the categories come from.

Key Concepts

Frequency table	A frequency table lists the categories in a categorical variable and gives the counts or percentage of observations of each category.
Distribution	The distribution of a variable gives • the possible values of the variable and • the relative frequency of each value.
Area principle	In a statistical display, each data value should be represented by the same amount of area.
Bar chart	Bar charts show a bar representing the count of each category in a categorical variable.
Pie chart	Pie charts show how a "whole" divides into categories by showing a wedge of a circle whose area corresponds to the proportion in each category.
Contingency table	A contingency table displays counts and, sometimes, percentages of individuals falling into named categories on two or more variables. The table categorizes the individuals on all variables at once, to reveal possible patterns in one variable that may be contingent on the category of the other.
Marginal Distribution	In a contingency table, the distribution of either variable alone is called the marginal distribution. The counts or percentages are the totals found in the margins (last row or column) of the table.
Conditional distribution	The distribution of a variable restricting the *Who* to consider only a smaller group of individuals is called a conditional distribution.
Independence	Variables are said to be independent if the conditional distribution of one variable is the same for each category of the other. We'll show how to check for independence in a later chapter.
Simpson's paradox	When averages are taken across different groups, they can appear to be contradictory. This is known as Simpson's paradox.

Skills

When you complete this lesson you should:

• Be able to identify that a variable is categorical and choose an appropriate display for it.

• Understand how to examine the association between categorical variables by comparing conditional and marginal percentages.

- Summarize the distribution of a categorical variable with a frequency table.
- Display the distribution of a categorical variable with a bar chart or pie chart.
- Know how to make and examine a contingency table.
- Know how to make and examine displays of the conditional distributions of one variable for two or more groups.

Tell

- Describe the distribution of a categorical variable in terms of its possible values and relative frequencies.
- Describe any anomalies or extraordinary features revealed by the display of a variable.
- Be able to describe and discuss patterns found in a contingency table and associated displays of conditional distributions.

Exercises

3 Describing Categorical Data

Exercises

Comments in [ ] refer to exercise numbers in the preview sample chapters

1. **Graphs in the News** Find a bar graph of categorical data from a newspaper or magazine.
   a) Is the graph clearly labeled?
   b) Does it violate the area principle?
   c) Does the accompanying article tell the W's of the variable?
   d) Do you think the article correctly interprets the data? Explain

2. **Graphs in the News II** Find a pie chart of categorical data from a newspaper or magazine.
   a) Is the graph clearly labeled?
   b) Does it violate the area principle?
   c) Does the accompanying article tell the W's of the variable?
   d) Do you think the article correctly interprets the data? Explain.

3. **Tables in the News** Find a frequency table of categorical data from a newspaper or magazine.
   a) Is it clearly labeled?
   b) Does it display percentages or counts?
   c) Does the accompanying article tell the W's of the variable?
   d) Do you think the article correctly interprets the data? Explain.

4. **Tables in the News II** Find a contingency table of categorical data from a newspaper or magazine.
   a) Is it clearly labeled?
   b) Does it display percentages or counts?
   c) Does the accompanying article tell the W's of the variables?
   d) Do you think the article correctly interprets the data? Explain.

5. **Causes of Death** The Center for Disease Control lists causes of death in the US during 1999.

   [table from 3.]

Cause of Death	Percent
Heart disease	30.3
Cancer	23.0
Circulatory diseases & stroke	8.4
Respiratory diseases	7.9
Accidents	4.1

   a) Is it reasonable to conclude that heart or respiratory diseases were the cause of approximately 38% of US deaths in 1999?
   b) What percent of deaths were from causes not listed here?

page 34B follows

c) Create an appropriate display for these data.

6. **Education** In a December 2000 report the US Census Bureau listed the levels of educational attainment for Americans over 65. Create an appropriate display for these data, and write a sentence or two that might appear in a newspaper article about the report.

[table from 2.]

Education Level	Count (thousands)
No high school diploma	9,945
HS graduate, but no college	11,701
Some college, no degree	4,481
2-year degree	1,390
4-year degree	3,133
Master's degree	1,213
PhD or Professional degree	757

7. **Ghosts** A May 2001 Gallup poll found that many Americans believe in ghosts and other supernatural phenomena. The poll was based on telephone responses from 1012 randomly selected adults. The table shows the percentages of people who expressed belief in various phenomena.

[table from 4.]

Phenomenon	% expressing belief
Psychic healing	54
ESP	50
Ghosts	38
Astrology	28
Channeling	15

a) Is it reasonable to conclude that 66% of those polled expressed belief in either ghosts or astrology?
b) Can you tell what percent of the people did not believe in any of these phenomena? Explain.
c) Create an appropriate display for these data.

8. **Illegal Guns** A study by the U.S. Bureau of Alcohol, Tobacco, and Firearms (BATF) (*USA Today*, 22 June 2000) surveyed 1,530 investigations by the U.S. BATF into illegal gun trafficking from July 1996 through December 1998. The study reports the portion of cases that were the result of each of five gun trafficking violations:
   o 46% Straw purchase (legal gun buyer acting on behalf of an illegal buyer)
   o 21% Unlicensed sellers
   o 14% Gun shows and flea markets
   o 14% Stolen from federally licensed dealers
   o 10% Stolen from residences

a) State the "W's" for this study to the extent the story gives them.
b) What do you notice about the percentages listed? What does that probably mean?
c) Make a bar chart to display these results, and label it correctly.
d) Write a brief report on what they say about illegal gun trafficking. Note any possible problems with the data.

DRAFT: Do not distribute or copy

(page 34C follows

e) The study also noted that although corrupt licensed dealers accounted for 133 of the 1,530 investigations, they were linked to 40,365 of the 84,128 firearms involved in those investigations. How does this new information about the "who" of the study affect your conclusions.

9. **Oil Spills** To improve the structural design of oil tankers with the objective of reducing the likelihood of an oil spill and decreasing the amount of outflow in the event of a hull puncture, a study (*Marine Technology*, Jan. 1995) reported the spillage amount and cause of puncture for 50 recent major oil spills from tankers and carriers. Here are displays. Write a brief report interpreting what the displays show. Is a pie chart an appropriate display for these data? Why or why not?

[from 7.]

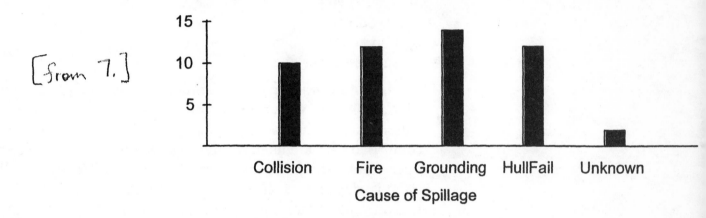

[from 7.]

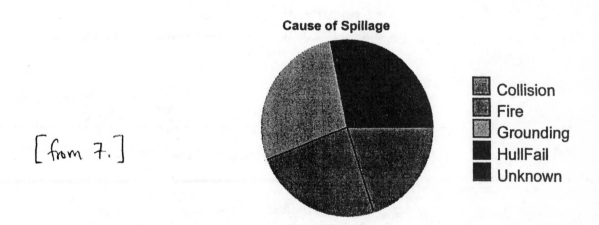

10. **Winter Olympics 2002** 25 countries won medals in the 2002 Winter Olympic games. The table lists them, along with the total number of medals each won:

Country	Medals	Country	Medals
Germany	35	Croatia	4
USA	34	Korea	4
Norway	24	Bulgaria	3
Canada	17	Estonia	3
Austria	16	Great Britain	3
Russia	16	Australia	2
Italy	12	Czech Republic	2
France	11	Japan	2
Switzerland	11	Poland	2
China	8	Spain	2
Netherlands	8	Belarus	1
Finland	7	Slovenia	1
Sweden	6		

[table from 8.]

a) Try to make a display of these data. What problems do you encounter?

b) Can you find a way to organize the data so that the graph is mor successful?

11. **Teens and Technology** "The Gallup Organization, in conjunction w CNN, USA Today, and the National Science Foundation, conducted national survey of 744 children in grades 7 through 12 -- mostly comprised of students in the "teenage" years of 13 to 17. Telephone interviews were conducted from March 20-27, 1997 from Gallup interviewing centers throughout the country. The focus of the surve was on students' familiarity with and use of modern technology, wit special attention given to use of computers and the Internet."[1] The teenagers were asked if they used each of the following technologie a daily basis and if the technology were critically important to own. each question, the percent of those responding yes is given. Gallup dubbed the difference between the two percentages the "Importance Gap". Here are the results:

[table from 9.]

Technology	Use Daily	Critically Important to Own	Importanc Gap
Computer	44%	77%	33
Telephone Answering Machine	46%	62%	16
VCR	39%	51%	12
Calculator	67%	71%	4
Stereo/CDs/Audio	85%	69%	-16
Video games	46%	18%	-28

Consider the following graphical display showing the percentages teens that use each of the technologies on a daily basis.

---

[1] http://www.nsf.gov/od/lpa/nstw/teenov.htm

[art
from 10.]

a) How much more often do teens use a calculator than an answering machine?
b) Is that the impression given by the display? Explain.
c) How would you improve this display?
d) Make an appropriate display for the Importance Gap. (Hint: make the *y*-axis of your chart span the range from –30 to +35).
e) Write a few sentences describing what you have learned about teens' attitudes toward technology.

12. **Teens and Technology II** Here's a display of the percentages of students who use the various technologies daily. List the errors in this display.

[from 11.]

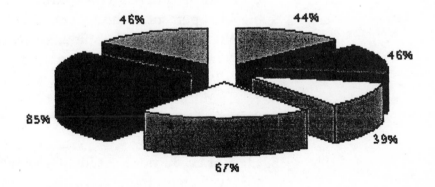

13. **Auditing Reform** In the wake of the Enron Corporation scandal, the Gallup Organization asked 1001 American adults what kind of changes,

34 F

if any, are needed in the way major corporations are audited. Here i
display of the results. [http://www.gallup.com/poll/releases/pr020226.asp

[from 12.]

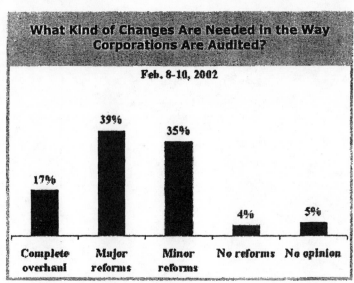

a) Make a pie chart of the same data.
b) Which chart works better to summarize the data? Why?
c) Summarize the findings of the poll in a few sentences that might
   appear in a newspaper article.

14. **Cars** A survey of autos parked in student and staff lots at a large
    university classified the brands by country of origin, as seen in the t

	Driver	
Origin	Student	Staff
American	107	105
European	33	12
Asian	55	47

a) What percent of all the cars surveyed were foreign?
b) What percent of the American cars were owned by students?
c) What percent of the students owned American cars?
d) What is the marginal distribution of Origin?
e) What are the conditional distributions of Origin by Driver
   classification?
f) Do you think that Origin of the car is independent of the type of
   Driver? Explain.

15. **Class of 2000** Prior to graduation a high school class of 2000 was
    surveyed about their plans. The table below displays the results for
    White and Minority students. (The "Minority" group included Afric
    American, Asian, Hispanic, and Native American students.)

[table from 14]

Plans	White	Minority
4-year college	198	44

page 34(

2-year college	36	6
Military	4	1
Employment	14	3
Other	16	3

a) What percent of the graduates are White?

b) What percent of the graduates are planning to attend a 2-year college?

c) What percent of the graduates are White and planning to attend a 2-year college?

d) What percent of the White graduates are planning to attend a 2-year college?

e) What percent of the graduates planning to attend a 2-year college are White?

f) Create a graph comparing the plans of White and Minority students.

g) Do you see any important differences in the post graduation plans of White and Minority students? Write a brief summary of what these data show, including comparisons of conditional distributions.

16. **After High School** The table below compares what Ithaca High School students did after graduation in 1959, 1970, and 1980.

[table from 13.]

What graduates did	1959	1970	1980
Continuing education	197	388	320
Employed	103	137	98
In the military	20	18	18
Other	13	58	45

a) What percent of all these graduates joined the military?

b) What percent of these students graduated in 1970?

c) What percent of the 1970 graduates joined the military?

d) Of the students in these surveys who joined the military, what percent graduated in 1970?

e) What is the marginal distribution of post-graduation activities?

f) What is the conditional distribution of post graduation activities among the class of 1959?

g) Does this study present any evidence that post-graduation plans have changed over this 21-year period? Write a brief description of these data. Include an appropriate graph.

17. **Canadian languages:** Statistics Canada provides, on its web site, the following data on the Canadian population (in thousands) (Zeros indicate counts below 500.)

Province	English only	French Only	Both	Neither	Total

page 34 H follows

Newfoundland	525	0	21	1	**547**
Prince Edward Island	118	0	15	0	**133**
Nova Scotia	813	1	84	1	**900**
New Brunswick	418	73	238	0	**730**
Quebec	359	3952	2661	74	**7045**
Ontario	9116	47	1235	245	**10643**
Manitoba	984	1	103	12	**1100**
Saskatchewan	921	0	51	5	**977**
Alberta	2455	2	179	34	**2669**
British Columbia	3342	2	249	97	**3690**
Yukon Territory	27	0	3	0	**31**
Northwest Territories	36	0	3	1	**39**
Nunavut	20	0	1	4	**25**
Total	**19134**	**4078**	**4843**	**474**	**28529**

[table from 15.]

a) What percent of Canadian citizens speak only English?
b) What percent of Canadian citizens speak French?
c) What percent of Quebec residents speak French?
d) What percent of French-speaking Canadians live in Quebec?
e) Do you think that language knowledge and Province of residence a independent for Canadians? Explain.

18. **Tattoos** A study by the University of Texas Southwestern Medical Center examined 626 people to see if there was an increased risk of contracting hepatitis C associated with having a tattoo. If the subject ha a tattoo, researchers asked whether it had been done in a commercial tattoo parlor or elsewhere. Write a brief description of the association between tattooing and hepatitis C, including an appropriate graphical display.

[table from 17.]

	Tattoo done in commercial parlor	Tattoo done elsewhere	No tattoo
Has Hep - C	17	8	18
No Hep - C	35	53	495

19. **Weather Forecasts** Just how accurate are the weather forecasts we hear every day? **The table below compares the daily forecast with a city's** actual weather for a year.

[table from 16.]

	Actual Weather	
Forecast	Rain	No rain
Rain	27	63
No rain	7	268

a) On what percent of days did it actually rain?
b) On what percent of days was rain predicted?
c) What percent of the time was the forecast correct?

page 34/I

d) Do you see evidence of an association between the type of weather and the ability of forecasters to make an accurate prediction? Write a brief explanation, including an appropriate graph.

20. **Federal prisons** The table below shows the number of federal prison inmates serving sentences for various types of offenses in 1990 and 1998. Counts given are in thousands of prisoners.

[table from 19.]

Type of Offense	1990	1998
Violent (murder, robbery, etc.)	10	13
Property (burglary, fraud, etc.)	8	9
Drugs	30	63
Public Order (immigration, weapons, etc.)	9	22
Other	1	2

a) Write a brief description of these data, in the proper context, highlighting any important changes you see in the prison population.

b) Does this data indicate that there was an increase in drug use in the U.S. during the 1990's? Explain.

21. **Working parents** In July 1991 and again in April 2001 the Gallup poll asked random samples of 1015 adults about their opinions on working parents. The table summarizes responses to this question:

"*Considering the needs of both parents and children, which of the following do you see as the ideal family in today's society?*"

Based upon these results, do you think there was a change in people's attitudes during the ten years between these polls? Explain.

[table from 18.]

Response	1991	2001
Both work fulltime	142	131
One works fulltime, other parttime	274	244
One works, other works at home	152	173
One works, other stays home for kids	396	416
No opinion	51	51

22. **Twins** In 2000 JAMA published a study that examined pregnancies that resulted in the birth of twins. Births were classified as preterm with intervention (induced labor or caesarean), preterm without procedures, or term/postterm. Researchers also classified the pregnancies by the level of prenatal medical care the mother received (inadequate, adequate, or intensive). The data, from the years 1995 – 97, are summarized in the table below. Figures are in thousands of births. [JAMA. 2000;284:335-341]

Twin Births 1995-97 (in thousands)				
Level of Prenatal Care	Preterm (Induced or Caesarean)	Preterm (without procedures)	Term or Postterm	Total
Intensive	18	15	28	61
Adequate	46	43	65	154
Inadequate	12	13	38	63
Total	76	71	131	278

page 34() follows 3-9

a) What percentage of these mothers did not receive adequate medical care during their pregnancies?
b) What percentage of all twin births were preterm?
c) Among the mothers who did not receive adequate medical care, what percentage of the twin births were preterm?
d) Create an appropriate graph comparing the outcomes of these pregnancies by the level of medical care the mother received.
e) Write a few sentences describing the association between these two variables.

23. **Blood Pressure** A company held a blood pressure screening clinic for employees. The results are summarized in the table below by age group and blood pressure level.

[table from 20.]

Blood pressure	under 30	30 - 49	over 50
low	27	37	31
normal	48	91	93
high	23	51	73

a) Find the marginal distribution of blood pressure level.
b) Find the conditional distribution of blood pressure level within each age group.
c) Compare these distributions with a segmented bar graph.
d) Write a brief description of the association between age and blood pressure among these employees.
e) Does this prove that people's blood pressure increases as they age? Explain.

24. **Obesity and Exercise** In the year 2000, the Centers for Disease Control (CDC) estimated that 19.8% of Americans over 15 years old were obese. The CDC conducts a survey on obesity and various behaviors. Here is table on self reported exercise classified by body mass index (BMI):

Body Mass Index

[table from 23.]

Physical Activity	Normal (%)	Overweight (%)	Obese (%)
Inactive	23.8	26.0	35.6
Irregularly active	27.8	28.7	28.1
Regular, not intense	31.6	31.1	27.2
Regular, intense	16.8	14.2	9.1

a) Are these percentages column percentages, row percentages or table percentages?
b) Use graphical displays to show different percentages of physical activities for the three BMI groups.
c) Do these data prove that lack of exercise causes obesity? Explain.

page 34K follow

25. **Family Planning** Before the introduction of birth control pills many young women experienced unplanned pregnancies. A 1954 study of 1438 pregnant women examined the association with the woman's education level, producing these data:

Education level	<3 yrs HS	3+ years HS	some college
Number of pregnancies	591	608	239
% unplanned	66.2%	55.4%	42.7%

Does this indicate that more schooling taught young women better family planning? What other explanations for these data can you think of? [*Fertility Planning and Fertility Rates by Socio-Economic Status*, Social and Psychological Factors Affecting Fertility, 1954]

26. **Pet Ownership** The U.S. Census Bureau reports the number of households owning various types of pets. Specifically they keep track of dogs, cats, birds and horses.
    a) Do you think the income distributions of the households who own these different animals would be roughly the same? Why or why not?
    b) Here are the percentages of income levels for each type of animal owned. Are these row percentages, column percentages, or table percentages?

[table from 22.]

INCOME DISTRIBUTION OF HOUSEHOLDS OWNING PETS (percent)

INCOME	Dog	Cat	Bird	Horse
Under $12,500	14	15	16	9
$12,500 to $24,999	20	20	21	21
$25,000 to $39,999	24	23	24	25
$40,000 to $59,999	22	22	21	22
$60,000 and over	20	20	18	23

    c) Do the data support your initial guess? Explain.

27. **Worldwide Toy Sales** Around the world, toys are sold through different channels. For example, in some parts of the world toys are sold primarily through large toy store chains, while in other countries, department stores sell more toys. The table below shows the percentages by region of the distribution of toys sold for various channels in 1999.

page 34 L follows

Exploring and Understanding Data

REGIONAL TOY SALES
BY CHANNEL OF DISTRIBUTION 1999

[table from 24.]

millions $	Toy Chains	General Merchandise (including Hypers & Discounters)	Toy, Hobby & Game Retailers	Department Stores	Food, Drug and Misc. Outlets	Catalog Sales	E-Tail
World	17773.75	24883.25	7109.50	5687.60	12088.15	2843.80	710
North America	6571.11	12516.40	1251.64	938.73	7822.75	1877.46	312
Europe*	5105.40	5105.40	2552.70	2042.16	1701.80	510.54	0
Asia	4294.75	4122.96	4981.91	2233.27	1546.11	0.00	0
Latin & South America	440.80	1129.55	523.45	440.80	220.40	0.00	0
Oceania	218.55	728.50	291.40	87.42	101.99	29.14	0

a) What percent of all toys sold through department stores are sold in Europe?

b) What percent of all toys worldwide are sold through catalogs?

c) Compare the distribution of channels for Europe to North America

d) Summarize the distribution of toy sales by channel in a few sentences.

28. **Drivers' Licenses** The following table shows the number of licensed U Drivers by age and by gender.

[table from 21.]

AGE	MALE DRIVERS NUMBER	FEMALE DRIVERS NUMBER
19 and under	5,029,498	4,714,021
20-24	8,158,599	7,807,078
25-29	8,988,142	8,597,716
30-34	9,767,476	9,387,297
35-39	10,621,910	10,437,549
40-44	10,576,976	10,516,251
45-49	9,578,268	9,575,363
50-54	8,448,424	8,419,527
55-59	6,394,207	6,366,285
60-64	4,970,258	4,944,370
65-69	4,182,933	4,202,950
70-74	3,644,990	3,822,570
75-79	2,820,136	3,091,013
80-84	1,656,789	1,854,278
85 and over	957,463	1,092,687

a) What percentage of total drivers are under 20?

page 34 M foll

b) What percentage of total drivers are male?

c) Write a few sentences comparing the number of male and female licensed drivers in each age group.

d) Do a driver's age and gender appear to be independent? Explain?

29. **Hospitals** Most patients who undergo surgery make routine recoveries and are discharged as planned. Others suffer excessive bleeding, infection, or other post-surgical complications and have their discharges from the hospital delayed. Suppose your city has a large hospital and a small hospital, each performing major and minor surgeries. You collect data to see how many surgical patients have their discharges delayed by post-surgical complications, and find the results shown in the following table.

Procedure	Discharge delayed	
	Large Hospital	Small Hospital
Major surgery	120 of 800	10 of 50
Minor surgery	10 of 200	20 of 250

[table from 26.]

a) Overall, for what percentage of patients was discharge delayed?

b) Were the percentages different for major and minor surgery?

c) Overall, what were the discharge delay rates at each hospital?

d) What were the delay rates at each hospital for each kind of surgery?

e) The small hospital advertises that they have a lower rate of post-surgical complications. Do you agree?

f) Explain, in your own words, why this confusion occurs.

30. **Delivery Service** A company must decide which of two delivery services they will contract with. During a recent trial period they shipped numerous packages with each service, and have kept track of how often deliveries did not arrive on time. Here are the data:

Delivery Service	Type of Service	Number of deliveries	Number of late packages
Pack Rats	Regular	400	12
	Overnight	100	16
Boxes R Us	Regular	100	2
	Overnight	400	28

a) Compare the two services overall percentage of late deliveries.

b) Based on the results in a the company has decided to hire Pack Rats. Do you agree they deliver on time more often? Why or why not? Be specific.

c) The results here are an instance of what phenomenon?

31. **Graduate Admissions** A 1975 article in the magazine *Science* examined the graduate admissions process at Berkeley for evidence of gender bias. The table below shows the number of applicants accepted to each of six graduate programs.

Program	Males Accepted (of applicants)	Females Accepted (of applicants)
1	511 of 825	89 of 108

& [next page]

page 34N follows

Program	(of applicants)	(of applicants)
1	511 of 825	89 of 108
2	352 of 560	17 of 25
3	137 of 407	132 of 375
4	22 of 373	24 of 341
Total	1022 of 2165	262 of 849

a) What percent of total applicants were admitted?
b) Overall were a higher percentage of males or females admitted?
c) Compare the percentage of males and females admitted in each program.
d) Which of the comparisons you made do you consider to be the mos valid? Why?

4 Displaying Quantitative Data

ENRON CORPORATION WAS ONCE ONE OF THE WORLD'S biggest corporations. From its humble beginnings as an interstate natural gas supply company in 1985, it grew steadily throughout the 1990's, diversifying into nearly every form of energy transaction and eventually dominating the energy trading business.

Its stock price followed this spectacular growth. In 1985 Enron stock sold for about $5 a share, but at the end of 2000, Enron stock closed at a 52 week high of $89.75 and the company's stock was worth more than $6 billion. Less than a year later it hit a low of $0.25 a share, having lost more than 99% of its value. Many employees who had taken advantage of generous stock plans lost retirement packages worth hundreds of thousands of dollars. Just how volatile was Enron stock? And were there hints of trouble that might have been seen?

Rather than look at the stock prices themselves, let's look at how much they changed from month to month. For example, on February 3 (the first trading day of the month) of 1997 Enron stock sold for $.75 less than it had on January 2 (the first trading day of that month.) Table 4.1 gives the monthly changes in stock price (in dollars) for the 5 years leading up to the company's failure.

ho: Months
hat: Changes in Enron's
ock price in dollars
w: Difference of closing
ice on first day of each
nth minus the first day of
evious month.
hen: 1997 to 2002
here: New York Stock
change

Monthly stock price change in dollars of Enron stock for the period January 1997 to December 2001. Table 4.1

	Jan	Feb	Mar	Apr	May	Jun	Jul	Aug	Sep	Oct	Nov	Dec
1997	-$1.44	-0.75	-0.69	-0.88	0.12	0.75	0.81	-1.75	0.69	-0.22	-0.16	0.34
1998	0.78	0.62	2.44	-0.28	2.22	-0.50	2.06	-0.88	-4.50	4.12	1.16	-0.50
1999	3.28	3.34	-1.22	0.47	5.62	-1.59	4.31	1.47	-0.72	-0.38	-3.25	0.03
2000	5.72	21.06	4.50	4.56	-1.25	-1.19	-3.12	8.00	9.31	1.12	-3.19	-17.75
2001	14.38	-1.08	-10.11	-12.11	5.84	-9.37	-4.74	-2.69	-10.61	-5.85	-17.16	-11.59

It's hard to tell very much from the data. Don't try too hard. Tables with lots of numbers are hard to understand by just reading them. You might get a rough idea of how much the stock changed from month to month, but even that would be very approximate. "Looks like usually less than 10 dollars in either direction," you might say.

Instead, let's follow the first rule of data analysis and make a picture. What kind of picture should we make? It can't be a bar chart or a pie chart. Those are for categorical variables and the values here are in dollars. Price change is a *quantitative* variable, not a categorical one.

The Distribution of Price Changes

How can we display a quantitative variable? With a categorical variable life was easy. There were just a few values, and we could make one pile for each. But usually we can't list all the individual values in a quantitative variable; there are just too many of them. So instead, we slice up the entire span of values covered by the quantitative variable into equal-width piles called **bins**. (For the Enron price changes we might try bins from –$15 to -$10, -$10 to -$5, -$5 to $0, and so on.) Then we count the number of values that fall into each bin. The bins and the counts in each bin give the **distribution** of the quantitative variable.

We can display the bin counts in a display called a histogram. Like a bar chart, a **histogram** plots the bin counts as the heights of bars. For the Enron data, the cases are months, so the height of each bar is proportional to the number of months that have price changes falling into that bin. (We usually put values that fall exactly on a bin boundary in the bin to the right.)

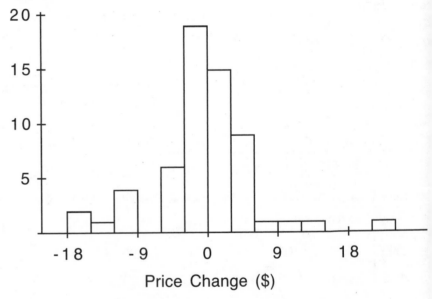

Monthly price changes of Enron stock. Fig 4.1

Some computer programs make a display they call a "histogram" with bars that have spaces between them. Because the bars represent bins that slice up the range of values so that every value is in a bin, spaces between them are not appropriate; they suggest that some values might "slip through the cracks". If you see an empty space in a histogram it is a real "gap" where there are no data values.

Does the distribution of price change look as you expected? It's often a good idea to *imagine* what the distribution might look like before you ask a computer or calculator to make a picture for you. That way you'll be ready if the picture shows something unexpected, and less likely to let bad data or wrong data fool you.

The first bar, which counts changes from -$20 to -$15, has only two months in it. We can see that although they vary, most of the

4-2   **DRAFT: Do not distribute or copy**

monthly price changes are less than $5 in either direction. Only in a very few months were the changes larger than $10 in either direction. There appear to be about as many positive as negative price changes.

A bar chart has spaces between the bars because the categories could appear in any order. But in a histogram, there are no gaps because the bins slice up *all the values* of a quantitative variable. Both kinds of display satisfy the area principle because the area covered by each bar corresponds to the count of the cases falling in the range covered by that bar. A **relative frequency histogram** is faithful to the area principle by displaying the *percentage* of cases in each bin instead of the count.

Stem-and-Leaf Displays

Stem-and-leaf displays show the distribution as well, but also give the individual values. They are easy to make by hand for data sets that aren't too large so let's look at the first 3 years of price change data. Here are a histogram and stem-and-leaf display of those 36 values.

The Stem-and-Leaf display is due to John W. Tukey, one of the greatest statisticians of the 20th century. It is called a "Stemplot" in some texts and computer programs, but we prefer Tukey's original name for it. After all, he invented it, and an inventor has the right to name his own invention.

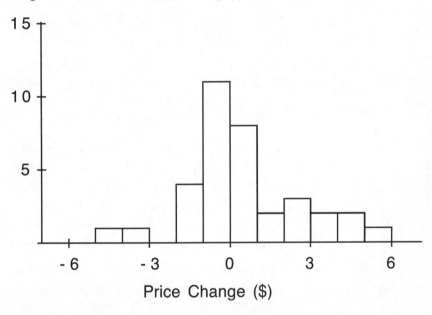

The first 36 months of Enron monthly stock price changes. Fig 4.2

-4|5

```
-3 |2
-2 |
-1 |7642
-0 |99777554322
 0 |13567888
 1 |25
 2 |124
 3 |33
 4 |13
 5 |6
```

> Stem-and-Leaf displays are best made by hand, so we are most likely to use them for small datasets. This much data is a typical number of data values for a Stem-and-Leaf display. For much larger data sets, use a histogram. Fig 4.3

Turn the stem-and-leaf on its side (or turn your head to the right) and squint at it. It should look roughly like the histogram of the same data. Does it? Good. It is easy to see, for example, that the distribution has two separate groups of values.

But, what does the line that says **2 | 124** near the bottom of the display mean? It stands for the three numbers $2.1, $2.2 and $2.4. The histogram shows these same values as a bar of height 3 between $2 and $3. The stem-and-leaf uses the actual digits of the number to form the "bar". In the next group, we can easily see that the largest price change is $5.6—something we couldn't tell precisely from the histogram.

To make a stem-and-leaf display, we cut each data value into leading digits (which become the "stem") and trailing digits (the "leaves"). We use the stems to label the *bins*. For the Enron stock prices, the best choice of stem is the first digit (the $1 units). So $5.6 has a stem of 5 and a leaf of 6. We use only *one* digit for the leaf, so we round the data values to one decimal place after the stem before splitting them into stem and leaves.[1]

Does a stem-and-leaf display satisfy the area principle? It does as long as each digit takes up the same amount of space. When doing this by hand, be careful to write a "1" and a "3" to take up the *same amount* of horizontal space. That way, each bar's length will be proportional to the number of observations that fall into its bin.

There are both positive and negative values in the price changes. Values of $0.3 and $0.5 are displayed as leaves of "**3**" and "**5**" on the "**0**" stem. But values of -$0.3 and -$0.5 must be plotted *below* zero. So the stem-and-leaf has a "**-0**" stem to hold them – again with leaves of "**3**" and "**5**". It may seem strange to see two zero stems, one labeled "-0", but if you

---

[1] It is equally good, and perhaps a bit easier, to truncate, just using the next digit regardless of the third digit. The shape of the stem-and-leaf display will not change and you will still be able to identify any individual data value easily.

DRAFT: Do not distribute or copy

think about it, you'll see that it is the sensible way to deal with negative values.

Stem-and-leaf displays contain all the information found in a histogram, and when carefully drawn, satisfy the area principle and show the distribution. In addition, stem-and-leaf displays preserve the individual data values. Few data displays can do this as effectively.

Unlike most other displays discussed in this book, stem-and-leaf displays are great pencil-and-paper constructions. They are well-suited to moderate amounts of data -- say, between 10 and a few hundred values. For larger data sets, histograms do a better job.

Dotplots

A **dotplot** is a simple display. It just places a dot for each case in the data. Dotplots are a great way to display a small data set (especially if you've forgotten how to write the digits from 0 to 9.) Here's a dotplot of the time (in seconds) that the winning horse took to win the Kentucky Derby in each race between the first Derby in 1875 and 2001.

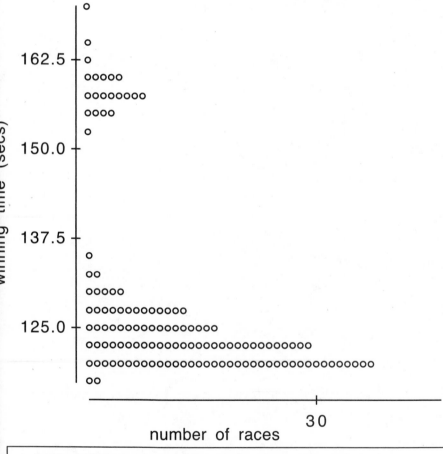

number of races

Dotplots show basic facts about the distribution. We can easily see the slowest and quickest races. It is also clear that there are two clusters of points, one at about 160 seconds and the other at about 126 seconds. Something strange happened to the Derby times. Once we know to look for it, we can find out that in 1896 the distance of the Derby race was changed from 1.5 miles to the current 1.25 miles. That explains the two clusters of winning times.

Some dotplots stretch out side-to-side. Others, such as the one shown here, run up-and-down. Some dotplots place points next to each other when they would otherwise overlap. Others just place them on top of one-another. Newspapers sometimes offer dotplots with the dots made up of little

A dotplot of Kentucky Derby winning times shows the bimodal distribution but plots each race as its own dot.   Fig 4.4

pictures.

Shape, Center, and Spread

Step back from a histogram or stem and leaf display. What can you say about the distribution? When you describe a distribution, you should always tell about three things: its **shape, center,** and **spread.**

What is the Shape of the Distribution?

The mode is sometimes defined as the single value that appears most often. That definition is fine for categorical variables because we need only to count the number of cases for each category. For quantitative variables, the mode is more ambiguous. What's the mode of the Enron data? No price change occurred more than twice, but two months had drops of $0.50 Should that be the mode? Probably not. It makes more sense to use the word "mode" in the more general sense of peak in a histogram – rather than as a single summary value.

1. *Does the histogram have a single, central hump, or several separated bumps?* These humps are called **modes**[2]. The Enron stock price changes have a single mode at just about $0. A histogram with one main peak, such as the price changes, is dubbed **unimodal**; histograms with two peaks are **bimodal**, and those with three or more are called **multimodal.** For example, here is a bimodal histogram.

A bimodal histogram has two apparent peaks.

Fig 4.5

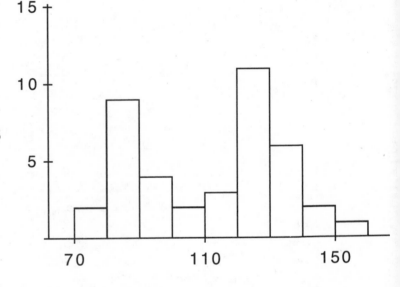

You've heard of pie à la mode. Is there a connection between pie and the mode of a distribution? Actually, there is! The mode of a distribution is a *popular* value near which a lot of the data values gather. And a la mode means "in style" – *not* with ice cream. That just happened to be a *popular* way to have pie in Paris around 1900.

A histogram that doesn't appear to have any mode and in which all the bars are approximately the same height is called **uniform.**

---

[2] Well, technically, it's the value on the horizontal axis of the histogram that is the mode, but anyone asked to point to the mode would point to the hump.

DRAFT: Do not distribute or copy

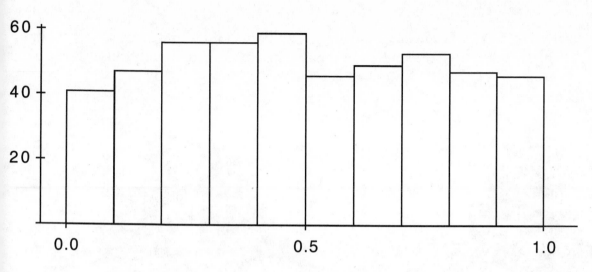

In a uniform histogram, the bars are all about the same
height. The histogram doesn't appear to have a mode. Fig
4.6

2. *Is the histogram **symmetric**?* Can you could fold it along a vertical line through the middle and have the edges match pretty closely, or are more of the values on one side?

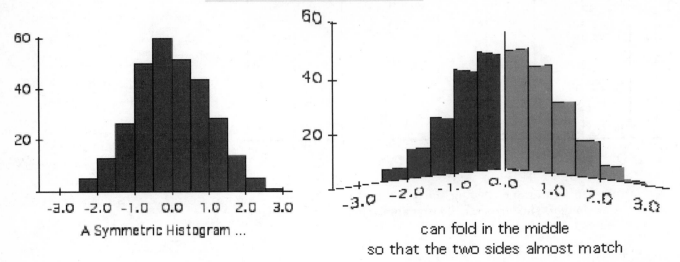

A Symmetric Histogram ...

can fold in the middle
so that the two sides almost match

[fig 4.7]

The (usually) thinner ends of a distribution are called the **tails**. If one tail stretches out farther than the other, the histogram is said to be **skewed** to the side of the longer tail.

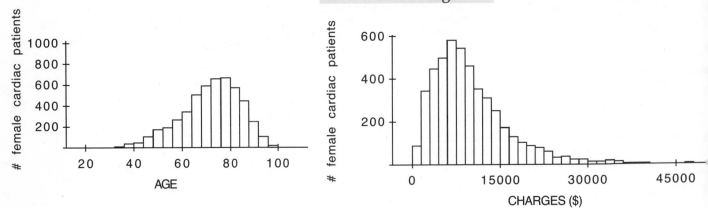

Two skewed histograms showing data for all female heart attack patients in New York state in one year. The [blue one] is skewed to the left. The[purple one] is skewed to the right. Fig 4.8

3. *Do any unusual features stick out?* Often such features tell us something interesting or exciting about the data. You should always mention any stragglers or **outliers** that stand off away from the body of the distribution. If you're collecting data on nose lengths and Pinocchio is in the group, you'd probably notice him, and you'd certainly want to mention it.

DRAFT: Do not distribute or copy

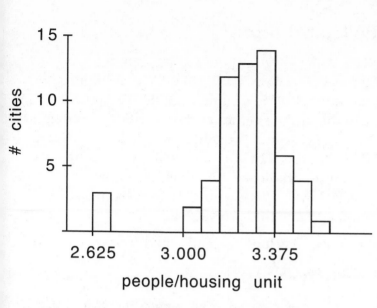

A histogram with outliers. There are three cities in the leftmost bar. Fig 4.9

Outliers can affect almost every method we discuss in this course. So we'll always be on the lookout for them. An outlier can be the most informative part of your data. (Or it might just be an error.) But don't just throw it away without comment. Treat it specially and discuss it when you tell about your data. (Or find the error and fix it if you can.)

Are there any **gaps** in the distribution? The Kentucky Derby data that we saw in the dotplot on page xx, has a large gap between two groups, one near 2 minutes, one near 2:40. Gaps warn us that the data may not be homogeneous. They may come from different sources, or contain more than one group.

How you characterize a distribution is often a judgment call. Some may see outliers where others just see a long tail on one side. Generally, we look at the main body of the data. If it seems roughly symmetric, then stragglers are best regarded as outliers. But if the main part of the data is skewed, then the long tail that continues that skewness is part of the overall pattern and probably not full of outliers. Be sure to look for outliers. Always. We'll discuss a good rule of thumb for deciding when a point might be considered an outlier in the next chapter.

Where is the Center of the Distribution?

If you had to pick a single number to describe all the data, what would you pick? The center is an easy description of a typical value and a concise summary of the whole batch of numbers. When a histogram is unimodal and symmetric, it's easy to find its center. It's right in the middle. (Where else would you look?) The center of the Enron price changes is about $0. That tells us that over the period we've examined, the stock when down about as often as it went up.

But for distributions with other shapes, the situation isn't as clear. If the histogram is skewed, defining the center is more of a challenge. And, if the histogram has more than one mode, the center might not even be a useful concept. You might have two different groups thrown together, so it's probably a good idea to find out why you don't have a single mode.

The next chapter discusses some ways to locate centers numerically, but for now, we'll just eyeball a picture of the distribution and give a rough idea of where the center seems to be.

How Spread out is the Distribution?

Why do banks favor a single line that feeds several teller windows rather than separate lines for each teller? The average waiting time is the same. But the time you can expect to wait is less variable when there is a single line, and people prefer consistency.

The center gives a typical value, but not everyone is typical. Variation matters. Statistics is about variation. But how can we see it? We can look to see whether all the values of the distribution are tightly clustered around the center or spread out. Because distributions that vary a lot around the center are harder to predict or model, we often prefer distributions with less variability. Would you rather invest in a stock whose price gyrates wildly, or one that grows steadily?

You are not done describing a distribution until you discuss its spread.

Displaying Quantitative Data Step-by-Step

Who: CEO's
What: Annual base salary in Dollars
How: Survey from *Forbes* magazine.
When: 1994
Where: U.S.
Why: Inspiration?

With the current state of the economy[3], there has been more attention paid to the compensation of Chief Executive Officers of major companies. Let's look at the CEO salaries of the 800 largest corporations in 1994.

Think

Variable: Identify the *variable* and how you wish to display it.

To identify a variable, report the W's

Select an appropriate display based on the nature of the data and what you want to know about it.

We examine the base salaries of the Chief Executive Officers (CEO's) of the 800 largest Corporations in 1994, reported (in dollars) by *Forbes* magazine.

The data are quantitative and we are interested in how they are distributed, so we will make a histogram.

---

[3] In fact, we don't know what state the economy is in as you read this, but it really doesn't matter. People still want to know how much CEO's make and will use the economy as an excuse.

DRAFT: Do not distribute or copy

Show

Mechanics: We almost always make histograms with a computer or graphing calculator.

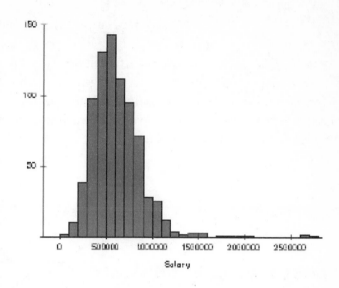

✓ Reality Check

It is always a good idea to think about what we expected to see and to check whether the histogram is close to what we expected. Could CEO's really earn this much? Yes, six to seven figure salaries are about what we might expect.

Tell

Interpretation:

Describe the shape, center, and spread of the distribution. Be sure to report on the symmetry, number of modes, and any gaps or outliers.

The main body of the distribution is unimodal and nearly symmetric[4] around $500,000 with slightly more than half of CEO's earning salaries higher than that. But there are some high outliers. The outliers are CEO's whose salaries are higher than what is typical for most CEO's of large corporations. Even though the vast majority of CEO's have salaries below $1,000,000 a year, there are a few with salaries between $2,500,000 and $3,000,000 a year.

Comparing Distributions

Up to now, we've looked at one distribution at a time. But this route can take us only so far. While it may be interesting to know the distribution of CEO salaries, it might be more interesting to know how salaries in high tech industries compare to those in manufacturing. The fact is that most interesting results about data involve making comparisons or modeling relationships.

Many common diseases show different patterns in women and men. In the past couple of decades, researchers have been more careful to collect

---

[4] Do you think it is skewed? Well, maybe. Here, if we cut off the tail, what's left behind is pretty symmetric. There is often more than one right answer. Just be prepared to defend your choice.

Copyright © 2001, Dick De Veaux and Paul Velleman

data on women. What kinds of questions might we ask about these data? Here's one: do men and women tend to get heart attacks at different ages? That's the kind of question that's well-suited to investigating with a graph. Here are two histograms of the ages of every heart attack patient hospitalized during 1993 in New York State, one for women and one for men.

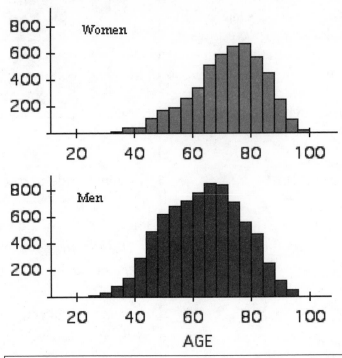

The distributions of ages for female and male heart attack patients differ in interesting ways.   fig 4.10

What can we tell from these histograms? We'll start, as usual, by looking at Shape, Center, and Spread, but here we'll reverse the order.

Notice first that the age distribution for men is more spread out than that for women. This is especially apparent if you look at the left sides of the histograms. The ages at which men tend to have heart attacks is less predictable than it is for women because their distribution is more spread out. It's relatively easy to see this because the two histograms have been put on the *same scale*.

We can also see that the distributions have different centers. The men's histogram is centered to the left of the women's. Men tend to have heart attacks at younger ages.

What of the shapes of the distributions? The age distribution for women is unimodal and skewed to the low end. There is a broad peak just below 80 years old. For men, the picture is a little different. The histogram is more nearly symmetric, with a narrower peak near 70 years. Looking at the tails of the histograms, it's clear that some men have heart attacks before they're 30 years old. And the percentage of men who've had heart attacks by the age of 50 is substantially higher than that of women. At the high end, there are clearly more women over the age of 90 who have heart attacks than men, but that may reflect the fact that there simply are more women than men alive in that age bracket to have heart attacks in the first place!

Order, Please!

The Enron price changes were collected over time; the changes are for *consecutive* months from January 1997 to December 2001. When data are collected in a specific order like that, you should check to see if they have a pattern when plotted in that order. We can array the dots of a dotplot across the page in the data's order. Often, connecting successive points with a line helps to show the pattern.

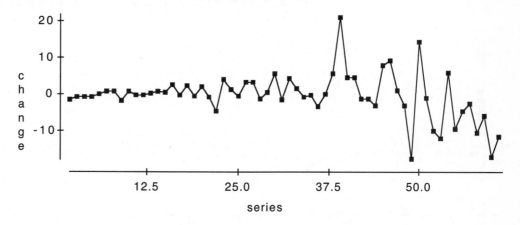

Monthly Enron stock price changes stretched out over time in a line plot. **The increased volatility in price that began in mid 1999 is easy to see. Fig 4.11**

The Enron price changes show relatively stable stock prices until the middle of 1999. Then the stock price starts to oscillate wildly. (Remember that these are the *changes* in price, not the prices themselves.) Curiously, few stock analysts seem to have been concerned about this behavior at the time. Perhaps they weren't looking at a **time plot** such as this one.

*Re-expressing Skewed Data to Improve Symmetry[5]

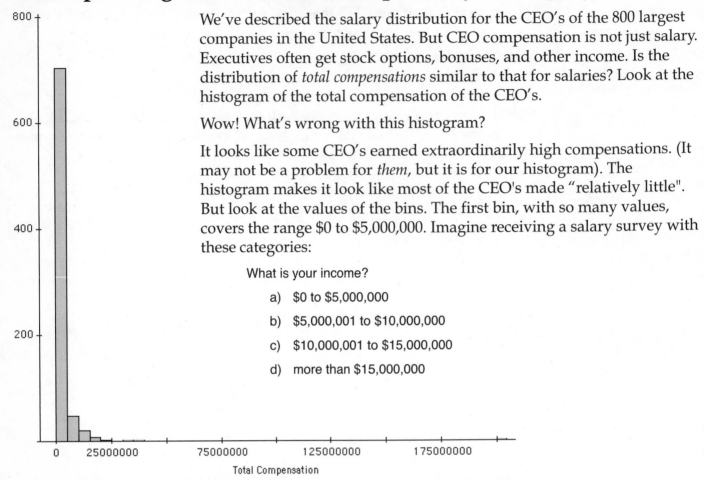

We've described the salary distribution for the CEO's of the 800 largest companies in the United States. But CEO compensation is not just salary. Executives often get stock options, bonuses, and other income. Is the distribution of *total compensations* similar to that for salaries? Look at the histogram of the total compensation of the CEO's.

Wow! What's wrong with this histogram?

It looks like some CEO's earned extraordinarily high compensations. (It may not be a problem for *them*, but it is for our histogram). The histogram makes it look like most of the CEO's made "relatively little". But look at the values of the bins. The first bin, with so many values, covers the range $0 to $5,000,000. Imagine receiving a salary survey with these categories:

What is your income?

    a) $0 to $5,000,000

    b) $5,000,001 to $10,000,000

    c) $10,000,001 to $15,000,000

    d)   more than $15,000,000

The total compensation for CEO's of 800 largest companies is extremely skewed and includes some extraordinarily large values..   **Fig 4.12**

As ridiculous as that first category appears, more than 10% of the CEO's had compensation too large to fit in that bin. In fact there are 16 of them who received more than $15,000,000. The reason that the histogram seems to leave so much of the area blank is these observations are spread all along the range from about $15,000,000 to $200,000,000. But after $20,000,000 there are so few for each bin that it's very hard to see the tiny bars. What we *can* see from this histogram is that this distribution is *very* skewed to the right.

Total compensation for CEO's consists of their base salaries, bonuses, and extra compensation, usually in the form of stock or stock options. Data that add together several variables, such as the compensation data,

---

[5] This section is optional. It is not required for other parts of the book. But we do recommend that you at least look at these ideas.

DRAFT: Do not distribute or copy

can easily have skewed distributions. It is often a good idea to separate the component variables and examine them individually to understand the data.

Skewed distributions are hard to summarize. It is hard to know what we mean by the "center" of a skewed distribution, so it is hard to pick a typical value to summarize the distribution. What would you say was a typical CEO total compensation?

Dealing with Logarithms

You have probably learned about logs in math courses and seen them in psychology or science classes. In this book, we use them only for making data behave better. Base 10 logs are the easiest to understand. You can think of them as roughly one less than the number of digits you need to write the number. So 100, which is the smallest number to require 3 digits, has a $\log_{10}$ of 2. And 1000 has a $\log_{10}$ of 3. The $\log_{10}$ of 500 has to be between 2 and 3, but you'd need a calculator to find that it's about 2.7. A salary of "six figures" has a $\log_{10}$ between 5 and 6. Logs are incredibly useful for making skewed data more symmetric. But, don't worry. Nobody does logs without technology and neither should you. Often, remaking a histogram or other display using the logs of the data is as easy as pushing another button.

One way to make a skewed distribution more symmetric is to **re-express** or **transform** the data by applying a simple function. For example, we could take the square root or logarithm of each data value. Variables that have a distribution that is skewed to the right often benefit from a re-expression by logarithms or square roots. Those skewed to the left may benefit from squaring the data values.

The histogram of the logs of the total CEO compensations is much more nearly symmetric, so we can see that a typical *log compensation* is about 6.0, which corresponds to $1,000,000. Notice that nearly all the values are between 5.0 and 7.0, in other words, between six and eight figures. That's $100,000 to $10,000,000 a year, but who's counting? Because computers and calculators are available to do the calculating, you should consider re-expression as a helpful tool whenever you have skewed data.

Taking logs makes the histogram of CEO total compensation nearly symmetric. The center of the distribution is around 6. How much money is that? It's 6+1 = "seven figures"– or $1,000,000.   Fig 4.13

What Can Go Wrong?

A data display should tell a story about the data. To do that it must speak in a clear language, making clear what variable is displayed, what any axis shows, and what the values of the data are. And it must be consistent in those decisions.

A display of quantitative data can go wrong in many ways. The most common failures arise from only a few basic errors:

- *Don't make a histogram of a categorical variable.* Just because the variables contains numbers doesn't mean it is quantitative. Here's a histogram of the insurance policy numbers of some workers. It's not very informative because the policy numbers are categorical. A histogram or stem-and-leaf display of a categorical variable makes no sense. Use a bar chart or pie chart instead.

- *Choose a scale appropriate to the data.* Computer programs usually do a pretty good job of choosing histogram bin widths. Often, there is an easy way to adjust the width, sometimes interactively. Here is the Enron price change histogram with two other choices for the bin size.

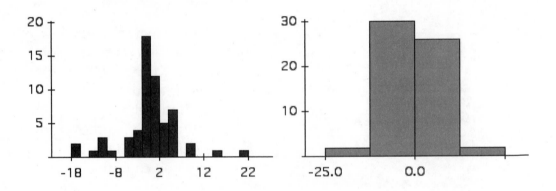

Changing the bin width changes how the histogram looks. The Enron stock price changes look different with these two choices. Fig 4.14

- *Avoid Inconsistent Scales.* Parts of displays should be mutually consistent – no fair changing scales in the middle or plotting two variables on different scales but on the same display. When comparing two groups be sure to compare them on the same scale.

- *Label Clearly.* Variables should be identified clearly and axes labeled so a reader knows what the plot displays.

Here's a remarkable example of a plot gone wrong. It illustrated a news story about rising college costs. It uses time plots, but it gives a very misleading impression. First think about the story you are being told by this display. Then try to figure out what has gone wrong.

DRAFT: Do not distribute or copy

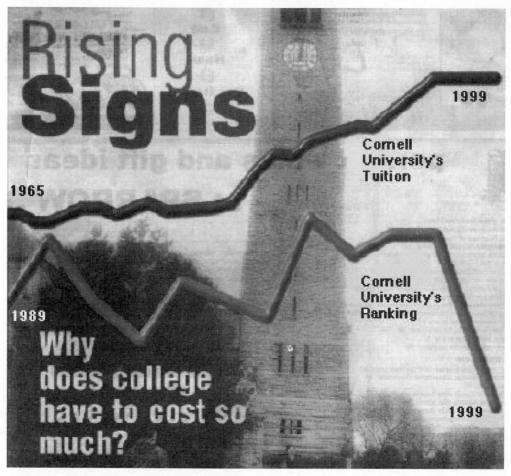

What's wrong? Just about everything.

o   The horizontal scales are inconsistent. Both lines show trends over time, but exactly what years? The tuition sequence starts in 1965, but rankings are graphed from 1989. Plotting them on the same (invisible) scale makes it seem that they are for the same years.

o   The vertical axis is not labeled. That hides the fact that it is inconsistent. Does it graph dollars (of tuition) or ranking (of Cornell University)?

So this display violates three of the rules. But it is still worse than that. It violates a rule that we didn't even bother to mention. The two inconsistent scales for the vertical axis don't point in the same direction! The line for Cornell's rank shows that it has "plummeted" from 15th place to 6th place in academic rank. Most of us think that's an *improvement*, but that's not the message of this graph.

Displaying Quantitative Data on a Computer

Almost any program that displays data can make a histogram, but some will do a better job of determining where the bars should start and how they should partition the range of the data.

The vertical scale may be counts or proportions. Sometimes it isn't clear which. But the shape of the histogram is the same either way

most packages choose the number of bars for you automatically. Often you can adjust that choice.

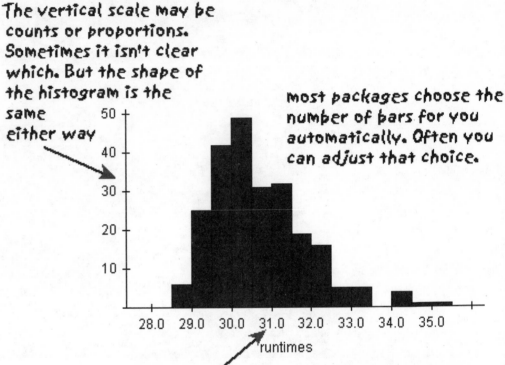

runtimes

The axis should be clearly labeled so you can tell what "pile" each bar represents. You should be able to tell the lower and upper bounds of each bar.

Package	Commands & Location	Comments
Data Desk	To make a histogram in Data Desk, o Select the variable to display. o In the **Plot** menu choose **Histogram**.	
Excel	Excel cannot make histograms or dotplots without a third-party add-in.	Excel's Data Analysis add-in does offer something called a histogram, but it just makes a crude frequency table, and the Chart Wizard cannot then create a statistically appropriate histogram.
JMP	To make a histogram in JMP o Choose **Distribution** from the **Analyze** menu. o In the **Distribution dialog**, drag the name of the variable that you wish to analyze into the empty window beside the label "**Y, Columns**" o Click **OK**.	
Minitab	To make a histogram in Minitab o Choose **Histogram** from the **Graph** menu.	

DRAFT: Do not distribute or copy

		In the **Plot dialog**, assign the name of a quantitative variable to the first row of the box labeled "X" ○ Click **OK**.	
SPSS		To make a histogram in SPSS ○ Choose **Interactive** from the **Graphs** menu. ○ From the **Interactive Graphs** submenu, choose **Histogram**. ○ In the **Create Histogram dialog**, drag a variable from the source list, into the target. SPSS creates a variable called Counts and places it in the vertical axis target automatically to indicate making a frequency histogram. You can specify a relative frequency histogram with the "Percentage" variable name instead. ○ Click **OK**.	

Key Concepts

Distribution	The distribution of a variable gives • the possible values of the variable and • the frequency or relative frequency of each value.
Histogram (Relative Frequency Histogram)	A histogram shows the distribution of values in a quantitative variable with adjacent bars. Each bar represents the frequency (relative frequency) of values falling in an interval of values.
Stem-and-Leaf Display	A Stem-and-Leaf display shows quantitative data values in a way that sketches the distribution of the data. It is best described in detail by example.
Dotplot	A dotplot graphs a dot for each case against a single axis.
Time Plot	A time plot displays data that changes over time. Often successive values are connected with lines to show trends more clearly.
Shape	To describe the shape of a distribution, look for • single vs multiple modes • symmetry *vs* skewness • outliers, clusters, or gaps.
Uniform	A distribution that is roughly flat is said to be uniform.
Mode	A hump or local high point in the shape of the distribution of a variable is called a mode. The apparent location of modes can change as the scale of a histogram is changed.
Unimodal	Having one mode. This is a useful term for describing the shape of a histogram when it is generally mound-shaped. If

	distributions with more than one mode are called **bimodal**, if they have two, and **multimodal** if they have more than two. Statisticians don't like to count very high.
Symmetric	A distribution is symmetric if the two halves on either side of the center look approximately the same.
Skewed	A distribution is skewed if it is not symmetric and one tail stretches out farther than the other.
Tails	The tails of a distribution are the parts that typically trail off on either side. Distributions can be characterized as having long tails (if they straggle off for some distance) or short tails (if they don't.)
Outliers	Outliers are extreme values that don't appear to belong with the rest of the data. They may be unusual values that deserve further investigation, or just mistakes; there is no obvious way to tell. Outliers can affect many statistical analyses, so you should always be alert for them.

Connections

Distributions of quantitative variables, like those for categorical variables, show the possible values and the relative frequencies. A histogram shows the distribution of values in a quantitative variable with adjacent bars. Don't confuse them with bar charts, which display categorical variables. For categorical data, the mode is the category with the biggest count. But for quantitative data, modes are peaks in the histogram.

The shape of the distribution of a quantitative variable is an important concept in most of the subsequent chapters. We will be especially interested in distributions that are unimodal and symmetric. And we will continue to check for outliers because we will need to deal with them specially.

Skills:

After completing this lesson you should be able to:

Think
• Be able to identify an appropriate display for any quantitative variable.
• Be able to guess the shape of the distribution of a variable by knowing something about the data.
Show
• Display the distribution of a quantitative variable with a stem-and-leaf display (by hand for smaller data sets), a dotplot, or a

DRAFT: Do not distribute or copy

histogram (made by computer for larger data sets).

- Make a time plot of data that may vary over time.

Tell

- Describe the distribution of a quantitative variable in terms of its shape, center, and spread.

- Describe any anomalies or extraordinary features revealed by the display of a variable.

- Know how to compare the distributions of two or more groups by comparing their shapes, centers, and spreads.

- Describe patterns over time shown in a time plot.

- Discuss any outliers in the data, noting how they deviate from the overall pattern of the data.

Exercises

1   **Statistics in Print** Find a histogram that shows the distribution of a variable in a newspaper or magazine article.
   a) Does the article identify the W's?
   b) Discuss whether the display is appropriate for the data.
   c) Discuss what the display reveals about the variable and its distribution.
   d) Does the article accurately describe and interpret the data? Explain.

2   **Not a Histogram** Find a graph other than a histogram that shows the distribution of a quantitative variable in a newspaper or magazine article.
   a) Does the article identify the W's?
   b) Discuss whether the display is appropriate for the data.
   c) Discuss what the display reveals about the variable and its distribution.
   d) Does the article accurately describe and interpret the data? Explain.

3   **Thinking about Shape** Would you expect distributions of these variables to be uniform, unimodal, or bimodal? Symmetric or skewed? Explain why.
   a) The number of speeding tickets each student in the senior class of a college has ever had.
   b) Players' scores (number of strokes) at the U.S. Open golf tournament in a given year.
   c) Weights of female babies born in a particular hospital over the course of a year.

Copyright © 2001, Dick De Veaux and Paul Velleman

    d) The length of the average hair on the heads of students in a large class.

4 **More Shapes** Would you expect distributions of these variables to be uniform, unimodal, or bimodal? Symmetric or skewed? Explain why.
    a) Ages of people at a Little League game.
    b) Number of siblings of people in your class.
    c) Pulse rates of college-age males.
    d) Number of times each face of a die shows in 100 tosses.

5 **Heart Attack Stays** Here are the lengths of hospital stays (in days) for all the female patients admitted to hospitals in New York in 1993 with a primary diagnosis of acute miocardial infarction (heart attack). Write a few sentences describing this distribution (shape, center, spread, unusual features).

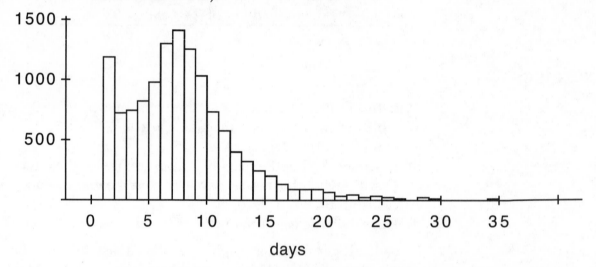

days

6 **Emails** A university teacher saved every e-mail received from students in a large introductory statistics class during an entire term. He then counted, for each student who had sent him at least one e-mail, how many e-mails each student had sent. Based on the histogram below, describe the distribution of e-mails.

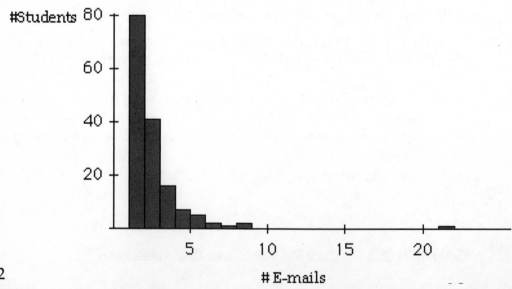

E-mails

7   **Sugar in Cereals** The histogram displays the sugar content (as a percent of weight) of 49 brands of breakfast cereals.

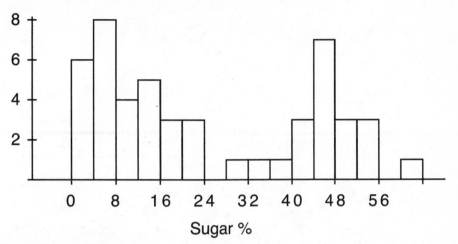

a) Describe this distribution.
b) What do you think might account for this shape?

8   **Singers** The display shows the heights of some of the singers in a chorus, collected so that they could be positioned on stage with shorter singers in front and taller ones in back.

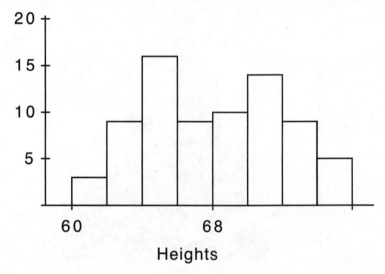

a) Describe the distribution.

b) Can you account for the features you see here?

9 **Wineries** The histogram shows the sizes (in acres) of 36 wineries in the Finger Lakes region of New York.

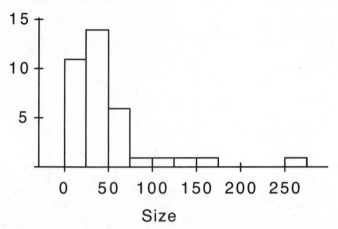

a) Approximately what percentage of these wineries are under 50 acres?
b) Write a brief description of this distribution (shape, center, spread, unusual features).

10 **Runtimes** One of the authors collected the times (in minutes) it took him to run 4 miles on various courses during the period 1986 to 1997. Here is a histogram of the times.

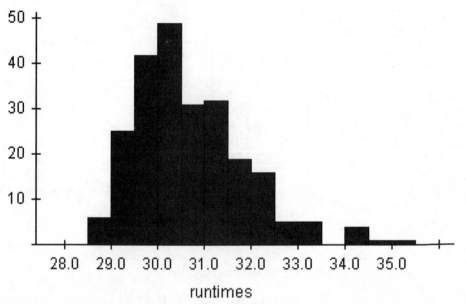

Describe the distribution and summarize the important features. What about running might account for the shape that you see?

DRAFT: Do not distribute or copy

11 **Home Runs** The stem-and-leaf display shows the number of homeruns hit by Mark McGwire during the 1982 - 2001 seasons. Describe the distribution, mentioning its shape and any unusual features.

```
7|0
6|5
5|28
4|29
3|22399
2|2
1|
0|399
```

12 **Bird Species** The Laboratory of Ornithology holds an annual Christmas Bird Count, in which birdwatchers at various locations around the country see how many different species of birds they can spot. Here are some of the counts reported from sites in Texas during the 1999 event.

228	178	186	162	206	166	163
183	181	206	177	175	167	162
160	160	157	156	153	153	152

a) Create a stem and leaf display of these data.
b) Write a brief description of the distribution. Be sure to discuss the overall shape as well as any unusual features.

13 **Horsepower** Create a stem-and-leaf plot displaying the horsepower of autos reviewed by *Consumer Reports* one year, and describe the distribution.

155	103	130	80	65
142	125	129	71	69
125	115	138	68	78
150	133	135	90	97
68	105	88	115	110
95	85	109	115	71
97	110	65	90	
75	120	80	70	

14 **Population Growth** Here is a "back-to-back" stem-and-leaf display that shows two data sets at once – one going to the left, one to the right. It compares the percent change in population for two regions of the United States (based on census figures for 1990 and 2000). The fastest growing states were Nevada at 66% and Arizona at 40%.

NE/MW States		S/W States
	6	6
	6	
	5	
	5	
	4	
	4	0
	3	
	3	001
	2	6
	2	001134
	1	578
0012	1	001134444
55667889999	0	6999
1344	0	1

Population Growth Rate (%)
(US Census Bureau)

15 **Hurricanes** The data below give the number of hurricanes that happened each year from 1944 through 2000 as reported by *Science* magazine.

3, 2, 1, 2, 4, 3, 7, 2, 3, 3, 2, 5, 2, 2, 4, 2, 2, 6, 0, 2, 5, 1, 3, 1, 0, 3, 2, 1, 0, 1, 2, 3, 2, 1, 2, 2, 2, 3, 1, 1, 1, 3, 0, 1, 3, 2, 1, 2, 1, 1, 0, 5, 6, 1, 3, 5, 3

a) Create a dotplot of these data.
b) Describe the distribution.

DRAFT: Do not distribute or copy

16 **Hurricanes, Again** A bimodal distribution usually indicates that there are actually two different behaviors present in the data, and investigating those two behaviors separately can produce important insights. Here are the data again, broken into two groups showing the number of hurricanes recorded annually before and after 1970. Create an appropriate visual display and write a few sentences comparing the two distributions.

1944 - 1969	1970 - 2000
3, 2, 1, 2, 4, 3, 7, 2, 3, 3, 2, 5, 2,	2, 1, 0, 1, 2, 3, 2, 1, 2, 2, 2, 3, 1, 1, 1, 3,
2, 4, 2, 2, 6, 0, 2, 5, 1, 3, 1, 0, 3	0, 1, 3, 2, 1, 2, 1, 1, 0, 5, 6, 1, 3, 5, 3

17 **Acid Rain** Two researchers measured the pH (a scale on which a value of 7 is neutral and values below 7 are acidic) of water collected from rain and snowfall over a six-month period in Allegheny County, Pennsylvania. Describe their data with a graph and a few sentences.

4.57	5.62	4.12	5.29	4.64	4.31	4.30	4.39	4.45	5.67	4.39	4.52	4.26
4.26	4.40	5.78	4.73	4.56	5.08	4.41	4.12	5.51	4.82	4.63	4.29	4.60

18 **Marijuana** In 1995 the Council of Europe published a report on entitled The *European School Survey Project on Alcohol and Other Drugs*. Among other issues, the survey investigated the percentages of 9th graders who had used marijuana. Here are the results for twenty Western European countries. Create an appropriate graph of these data, and describe the distribution.

Austria	10%	Belgium	19%
Denmark	17%	England	40%
Finland	5%	France	12%
Germany	21%	Greece	2%
Iceland	10%	Ireland	37%
Italy	19%	Luxembourg	6%
Netherlands	31%	No. Ireland	23%
Norway	6%	Portugal	7%
Scotland	53%	Spain	15%
Sweden	6%	Switzerland	27%

19 **Hospital Stays** The U.S. National Center for Health Statistics compiles data on the length of stay by patients in short-term hospitals and publishes its finding in Vital and Health Statistics. Data from a sample of 39 male patients and 35 female patients on length of stay (in days) as displayed in these histograms.

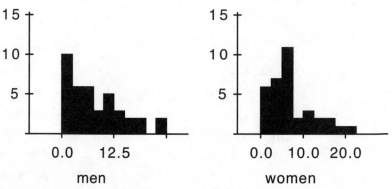

men   women

a)   What would you suggest be changed about these histograms to make it easier to compare them?

b)   Describe these distributions by writing a few sentences comparing the duration of hospitalization for men and women.

c)   Can you suggest a reason for the peak in women's length of stay?

20 **Deaths** A National Vital Statistics Report indicated that nearly 300,000 Black Americans died in 1999, compared with just over 2 million white Americans. Here are calculator histograms displaying the distributions of their ages at death.

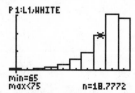
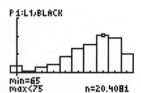

Most of the bars in these histograms display ten-year age groups. For example, the first histogram shows that for White Americans about 19% of the deaths were of people between 65 and 74 years old. The leftmost bars represent the percentage of total deaths that were children aged 0 through 4 years and the rightmost bars people over 85.
Write a brief comparison of the distributions.

21 **Final Grades** A professor (of something other than statistics!) distributed the following histogram to show the distribution of grades on his 200-point final exam. Comment on the display.

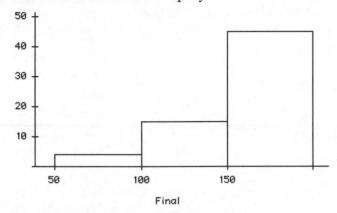

Final

22 **Final Grades Revisited** After receiving many complaints about his final grade histogram from students currently taking a statistics course, the professor distributed the following revised histogram.

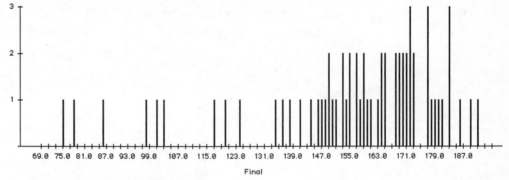

Final

a) Comment on this display.
b) Describe the distribution of grades.

23 **Zipcodes** Holes R Us, an Internet company that sells piercing jewelry keeps transaction records on their sales. At a recent sales meeting, one of the staff presented a histogram of the zipcodes of their last 500 customers to understand where their sales are coming from. Comment on the usefulness and appropriateness of the display.

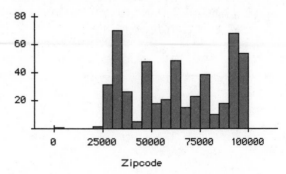

Zipcode

Copyright © 2001, Dick De Veaux and Paul Velleman

24 **CEO data revisited** For each CEO, a code is listed that corresponds to the industry of the CEO's company. Here are a few of the codes and the industries to which they correspond.

Industry	Industry.code
Financial services	1
Fooddrinktobacco	2
Health	3
Insurance	4
Retailing	6
Forest products	9
Aerospacedefense	11
Energy	12
Capital goods	14
Computerscommunications	16
Entertainmentinformation	17
Consumer nondurables	18
Electric utilities	19

A recently hired investment analyst has been assigned to examine the industries and the compensations of the CEO's. To start the analysis, he produces the following histogram of industry codes.

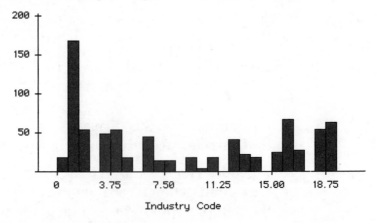

a) What might account for the gaps seen in the histogram?
b) Is the histogram unimodal?
c) What advice might you give the analyst about the appropriateness of this display?

25 **Productivity Study** The National Center for Productivity releases information on the efficiency of workers. In a recent report they included the following graph showing a rapid rise in productivity. What questions do you have about this display?

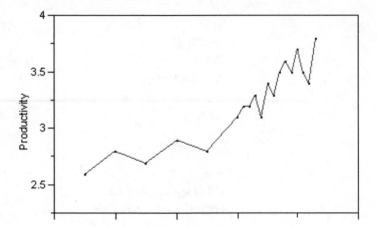

26 **Productivity Revisited** A second report by the National Center for Productivity analyzed the relationship between productivity and wages. Comment on the graph they used.

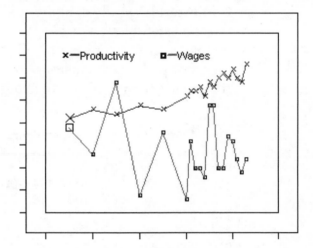

27 **Law Enforcement** Some federal employees have the authority to carry firearms and make arrests. There is obviously some danger associated with these jobs, but how much? The table below summarizes the rates of assault and injury (or death) for these employees for five years, 1995-1999.

Agency	Assaults (per 1000)	Killed-Injured (per 1000)
BATF	31.1	2.2
Capitol Police	5.0	3.6
Customs Service	9.7	5.1
DEA	17.9	1.1
FBI	3.9	1.2
INS	14.1	2.5
IRS	1.7	0.2
US Marshall Service	9.7	3.0
National Park Service	38.7	15.0
Postal Service	5.7	2.9
Secret Service	9.7	3.0

a) Create a visual display of these data.
b) Describe these data (shape, center, spread, unusual features).
c) Which agencies are outliers?

28 **Cholesterol** A study examining the health risks of smoking measured the cholesterol levels of people who had smoked for at least 25 years and people of similar ages who had smoked for no more than 5 years and then stopped. Create histograms for both groups and write a brief report comparing their cholesterol levels.

Smokers				Ex-smokers		
225	211	209	284	250	134	300
258	216	196	288	249	213	310
250	200	209	280	175	174	328
225	256	243	200	160	188	321
213	246	225	237	213	257	292
232	267	232	216	200	271	227
216	243	200	155	238	163	263
216	271	230	309	192	242	249
183	280	217	305	242	267	243
287	217	246	351	217	267	218
200	280	209		217	183	228

DRAFT: Do not distribute or copy

29 **MPG** A consumer organization compared gas mileage figures for several models of cars made in the US to autos manufactured in other countries. The data are shown in the table.
a) Create a back-to-back stemplot for these data.
b) Write a few sentences comparing the distributions.

US Models	Others
16.9	16.2
15.5	20.3
19.2	31.5
18.5	30.5
30.0	21.5
30.9	31.9
20.6	37.3
20.8	27.5
18.6	27.2
18.1	34.1
17.0	35.1
17.6	29.5
16.5	31.8
18.2	22.0
26.5	17.0
21.9	21.6
27.4	
28.4	
28.8	
26.8	
33.5	
34.2	

30 **Baseball** American League baseball teams play their games with the designated hitter rule, meaning that pitchers do not bat. The League believes that replacing the pitcher, traditionally a weak hitter, with a another player in the bating order produces more runs and generates more interest among fans. Below are the average number of runs scored in American League and National League stadiums for the first half of the 2001 season.

American				National			
11.1	10.8	10.8	10.3	14.0	11.6	10.4	10.3
10.3	10.1	10.0	9.5	10.2	9.5	9.5	9.5
9.4	9.3	9.2	9.2	9.5	9.1	8.8	8.4
	9.0	8.3		8.3	8.2	8.1	7.9

a) Create back-to-back stemplots of these data.
b) Write a few sentences comparing the average number of runs scored per game in the two leagues. (Remember: shape, center, spread, unusual features!)
c) Coors Field, in Denver, stands a mile above sea level, an altitude far greater than any other major league ballpark. Some believe that the thinner air makes it harder for pitchers to throw curve balls and easier for batters to hit the ball a long way. Do you see any evidence that the 14 runs scored per game there is unusually high? Explain.

31 **Nuclear Power** For a while in the 20th Century many nuclear-powered electrical generating plants were built, but then growing environmental concerns and construction costs led to increasing reliance on other forms of energy. The table shows the dates of completion (in months after January 1967) and costs (in thousands of dollars per megawatt) of 12 nuclear generators.

a) Create a stemplot of the costs.
b) Describe the distribution.
c) Create a timeplot of the costs.
d) What information about the construction of nuclear plants can you see from the timeplot that does is not obvious in the stemplot?

Time of Completion (months after Jan 1, 1967)	Construction Cost ($1000 / mW
2	35
3	28
10	32
12	60
17	56
19	63
21	62
26	81
30	84
32	79
41	88
47	80

32 **Drunk Driving** Accidents involving drunk drivers account for about 40% of all deaths on the nation's highways. The table tracks the number of alcohol-related fatalities for 20 years. [www.madd.org/stats]

a) Create a stemplot of these data.
b) Create a timeplot.
c) Using features apparent in the stemplot and the timeplot, write a few sentences about deaths caused by drunk driving.

Year	Deaths (thousands)
1982	25.2
1983	23.6
1984	23.8
1985	22.7
1986	24.0
1987	23.6
1988	23.6
1989	22.4
1990	22.0
1991	19.9
1992	17.9
1993	17.5
1994	16.6
1995	17.2
1996	17.2
1997	16.5
1998	16.0
1999	16.0
2000	16.7
2001	16.7

33 **Assets** Here is a histogram of the assets (in millions of dollars) of 79 companies chosen from the *Forbes* list of the nation's top corporations.

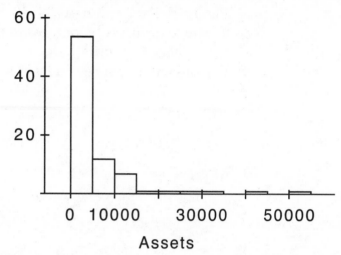

a) What aspect of this distribution makes it difficult to summarize, or to discuss center and spread?

b) Here are the same data after reexpressions as the square root of assets and the logarithm of assets. Which reexpression do you prefer? Why?

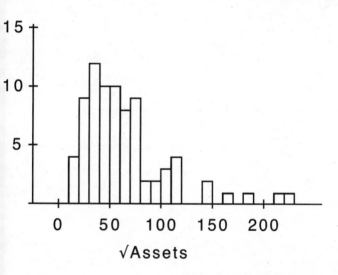

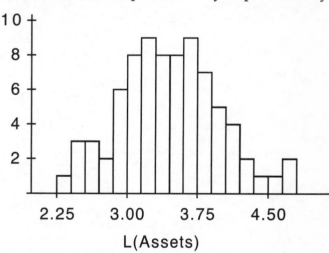

c) In the square root reexpression, what does the value 50 actually indicate about the company's assets?

d) In the logarithm reexpression, what does the value 3 actually indicate about the company's assets?

34 **Rainmakers** The table lists the amount of rainfall (in acre-feet) from 26 clouds seeded with silver iodide.
  a) Why is "acre-feet" a good way to measure the amount of precipitation produced by cloud-seeding?
  b) Plot these data, and describe the distribution.
  c) Create a reexpression of these data that produces a more advantageous distribution.
  d) Explain what your reexpressed scale means.

2745	200
1697	198
1656	129
978	119
703	118
489	115
430	92
334	40
302	32
274	31
274	17
255	7
242	4

DRAFT: Do not distribute or copy

5 Describing Distributions Numerically

THE WORLD HEALTH ORGANIZATION (WHO) collects health data worldwide on every member country of the United Nations. One traditional measure of the overall health of a country has been the life expectancy of its citizens—the number of years that a newborn can expect to live. Starting in 1999, WHO scientists introduced a revised measure to take account of the fact that illness and injuries can affect the quality of life. The Disability Adjusted Life Expectancy (DALE) adjusts for years of ill-health to give a measure of years of healthy life.

Here is a histogram of the DALE's for all 191 United Nations countries:

Who: 191 countries (not WHO!)
What: DALE (Disability Adjusted Life Expectancy)
Unit: Years
When: Data are for babies born in 1999
Where: Earth
Why: Annual report by World Health Organization

When distributions are mixed together the result is often a multimodal and/or skewed distribution. These data are combined from countries of different economic and social conditions, so a skewed distribution is no surprise.

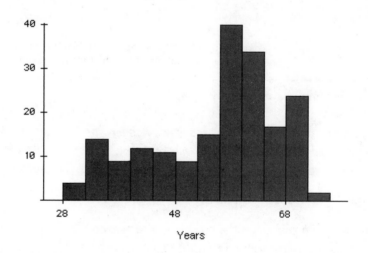

DALE's for the 191 United Nations countries In 1999, Japan had the top DALE of 73.8 years while Sierra Leone had the lowest at 29.5 years. Fig 5.1

The distribution may be multimodal and is clearly skewed to the left.

Center: Finding the Median

What is a typical life expectancy? Try to put your finger on the histogram at the value you think is typical. (Read the value from the horizontal axis and remember it.) When we think of a typical value, we usually look for the **center** of the distribution. Where do you think the center of this distribution is? For a unimodal, symmetric distribution, it's easy. We'd all agree on the center of symmetry, where we would fold the histogram to match the two sides. But, when the distribution is skewed as this one is, it's not immediately clear what we even mean by the center.

You might think of taking the average of the maximum and minimum values as a way of finding the center. This is called the **midrange**, but it's too sensitive to the outlying values to be safe for summarizing the whole distribution. A more reasonable choice of typical value is the value that is literally in the middle, with half the values below it and half above it.

Notation Alert:
We always use n to indicate the number of values. Some people even say "how big is the n?" when they mean the number of data values.

> **Using the midrange**
> There actually is *one* everyday use of the midrange. Whenever you make a plot of data, you're likely to center the plot at the midrange, exactly half way between the two extremes of the data.

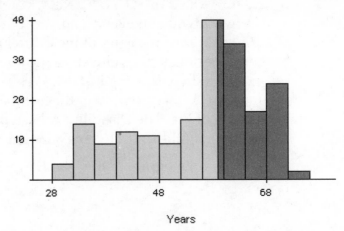

The median splits the histogram into two halves of equal area. Notice that the halves of this histogram have very different shapes. Fig 5.2

Finding the median by Hand

Finding the median of a batch of *n* numbers is easy as long as you remember to *order* the values first. If *n* is odd, the median is the middle value. Counting in from the ends, we find this value in the $\frac{n+1}{2}$ st position. When *n* is even, there are two middle values. So, in this case, the median is the average of the two values in positions *n/2* and *(n+1)/2* . Here are two examples.

Suppose the batch has values: 14.1,3.2,25.3,2.8,-17.5, 13.9 and 45.8. First we order the values: -17.5, 2.8,3.2,13.9,14.1,25.3,45.8. Since there are 7 values, the median is the (7+1)/2 = 4th value counting from the top or bottom: 13.9.

Suppose we had the same batch with another value at 35.7. Then the ordered values are: -17.5, 2.8,3.2,13.9,14.1,25.3,35.7,45.8. The median is the average of the 8/2 or 4th and the (8/2)+1 or 5th values. So the median is (13.9+14.1)/2 = 14.0.

Histograms follow the area principle, and each half of the data has about 95 countries, so each colored region has the same area in the display. The middle value that divides the histogram into two equal areas is called the **median**.

The median has the same units as the data. Be sure to include the units whenever you discuss the median.

For the DALE data, there are 191 countries so the median is found at the (191 + 1)/2 = 96th place in the sorted data. This median DALE is 58.5 years.

The median is one way to find the center of the data. But there are many others. We'll look at an even more important measure later in this chapter.

Knowing the median, we could say that a typical life expectancy, worldwide, was about 58.5 years. But how much does that really say? How well does the median describe the data? After all, not all countries have DALEs near 58.5 years. Whenever we find the center of data, the next step is always to ask how well it actually summarizes the data.

Spread: Home on the Range

Statistics pays close attention to what we *don't* know as well as what we do know. Understanding how spread out the data are is a first step in understanding what a summary *cannot* tell us about the data. It's the beginning of telling us what we don't know.

If every country had a DALE of 58.5, knowing the median would tell us everything about the distribution of life expectancy worldwide. But the more the data vary, the less the median alone can tell us. So we need to measure how much the data values vary around the center. In other words, how spread out are they? When we describe a distribution numerically, we always report a measure of its **spread** along with its center.

How should we measure the spread? We could simply look at the extent of the data. How far apart are the two extremes? The **range** of the data is defined as the *difference* between the maximum and minimum values,

$$Range = Max - Min$$

Notice that the range is a *single number, not* an interval of values, as you might think from its use in common speech. The maximum DALE is 73.8 years and the minimum is 29.5 years, so the *range* is 73.8 – 29.5 = 44.3 years.

The range (like the midrange) has the disadvantage that a single extreme value can make it very large, giving a value that doesn't really represent the data overall. For example, in the CEO compensations from chapter 4, the range is $202,991,184 - $28,816 = $202,962,368! But most of the compensations were between 0 and $5,000,000, so the range doesn't give a very accurate impression of the spread.

The Interquartile Range

A better way to describe the spread of a variable might be to ignore the extremes and concentrate on the middle of the data. We could, for example, find the range of just the middle half of the data. So, where's the middle half? First, split the sorted data at the median and then find the medians of each half. (When *n* is odd, so that one of the data values is the median, include the median with each of the halves.) These values are the **quartiles**,[1] and they border the middle half of the data.

---

[1] Textbooks, computer packages, and even statisticians do not always agree on the exact definition of the quartiles. We have seen six different definitions of the quartile, but the one we give here is a common one – and all of the definitions agree pretty closely anyway unless there are very few data values (in which case there's no need to summarize them.)

Finding quartiles by Hand

A simple way to find the quartiles is to split the batch into two halves at the median. (When *n* is odd, include the median in both halves.)The lower quartile, *Q1*, is the median of the lower half, and *Q3*, the upper quartile is the median of the upper half.

Here are our two examples again.
The ordered values of the first batch were :

   -17.5, 2.8,3.2,13.9,14.1,25.3,45.8 with a median of 13.9. Since 7 is odd, we include the median in both halves to get:
-17.5, 2.8,3.2,13.9   and   13.9,14.1,25.3,45.8.
Each half has 4 values, so the median of each is the average of its 2nd and 3rd values. So *Q1* is (2.8+3.2)/2= 3.0 and *Q3* is (14.1+25.3)/2 = 19.7.

The second batch had ordered values:
   -17.5, 2.8,3.2,13.9,14.1,25.3,35.7,45.8.
Here n is even, so the two halves of 4 are:
-17.5, 2.8,3.2,13.9,   and   14.1,25.3,35.7,45.8.
So, *Q1* is (2.8+3.2)/2 = 3.0 and *Q3* is (25.3+35.7)/2 = 30.5

The difference between the quartiles is the **interquartile range**, commonly abbreviated IQR (and pronounced "eye-cue-are" – not ikker):

$$IQR= Upper\ quartile - Lower\ quartile$$

For the DALE data, there are 95 values below and 95 values above the median. Including the median with each half of the data gives 96 values in each half. So in each half, we'd average the 48th and 49th values. For the DALE's, the lower quartile is 46.9 years and the upper quartile is 63.6 years. The *difference* between the quartiles gives the IQR:

$$IQR = 63.6 – 46.9\ years = 16.7\ years.$$

Now we know that the middle half of the countries (in terms of DALE) extend for a (interquartile) range of 16.7 years. This seems like a reasonable summary of the spread of the distribution as we can see from the histogram:

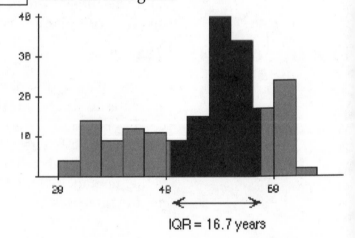

The IQR contains the middle 50% of the values of the distribution. It also gives a visual indication of the spread of the data. Here we see that the IQR is 16.7 years. Fig 5.3

The IQR is often a reasonable summary of the spread of a distribution. For the CEO compensations, the median is $1,304,470 and the quartiles are at $787,304 and $2,518,628, so the IQR is $2,518,628 -$787,304 = $1,731,324. The IQR gives a different impression of how spread out CEOs' salaries are than we might get from the range of $202,962,368.

The lower and upper quartiles are also known as the 25th and 75th **percentiles** of the data, respectively, since the lower quartile falls above 25% of the data and the upper quartile of the data falls above 75% of the data. Counting this way, the median is the 50th percentile. We could, of

DRAFT: Do not distribute or copy

course, define and calculate any percentile that we want. For example, the 10th percentile would be the number that falls above 10% of the data values.

Five Number Summary

Notation Alert
We will always use Q1 to label the low (25%) quartile and Q3 to label the high (75%) quartile. The skipped number is because the median would, by this system, naturally be labeled Q2 – but we don't usually do that.

The **five-number summary** of a distribution reports its median, quartiles, and extremes (maximum and minimum). The 5-number summary for the DALE data looks like this.

Max	73.8 years
Q3	63.6
Median	58.5
Q1	46.9
Min	29.5

It's a good idea to report the number of data values and the identity of the cases (the "who"). Here there are 191 countries.

Rock Concert Deaths: Making Boxplots

Who: Rock concert goers who died from being crushed
What: Age at death
Units: Years
Where: Internationally
When: The period 1999-2000.
Why: To think twice about going to concerts?

Whenever we have a 5-number summary of a (quantitative) variable, we can put the information together in one graphical display called a **boxplot**. Here's another example. During the two years 1999 and 2000 there were 66 deaths recorded internationally at rock concerts attributed to "crowd crush". How old were these crowd crush victims? Here's a five-number summary of their ages.

Max	47 years
Q3	22
Median	19
Q1	17
Min	13

To make a boxplot of the rock concert victims' ages, follow these steps:

Draw a single vertical axis spanning the range of the data[2]. Draw short horizontal lines at the lower and upper quartiles and at the median. Then connect them with vertical lines to form a box. The box can have any width that looks OK.

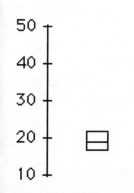

---

[2] The axis could also run horizontally.

Copyright © 2001, Dick De Veaux and Paul Velleman

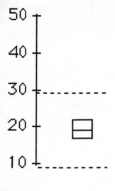

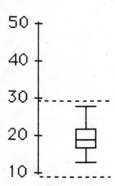

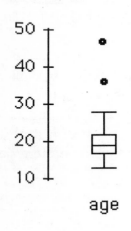

age

To help us construct the boxplot, we erect "fences" around the main part of the data. We place the upper fence 1.5 IQR's above the upper quartile and the lower fence 1.5 IQR's below the lower quartile. For the rock concert data, we compute

Upper fence= Q3 + 1.5IQR = 22 + 1.5 * 5 = 29.5 years

and

Lower fence = Q1 – 1.5IQR = 17 – 1.5 * 5 = 9.5 years

The fences are just for construction and are not part of the display. We show them here with dotted lines for illustration. You should never include them in your boxplot.

We use the fences to grow "whiskers". Draw lines from the ends of the box up and down to *the most extreme data values found within the fences*. If a data value falls outside one of the fences, we do *not* connect it with a whisker.

Finally, we add the outliers by displaying any data values beyond the fences with a special symbol. (Some programs even use a different symbol for "far outliers" – data values farther than 3 IQR's from the quartiles.)

Now that we've drawn the boxplot, let's summarize what it shows. The center of a boxplot is (remarkably enough) a box that shows the middle half of the data, between the quartiles. The height of the box is equal to the IQR. If the median is roughly centered between the quartiles, then the middle half of the data is roughly symmetric. If it is not centered, the distribution is skewed. The whiskers show skewness as well if they are not roughly the same length. Any outliers are displayed individually both to keep them out of the way for judging skewness and to encourage you to give them special attention. They may be mistakes, but they may be the most interesting cases in your data.

From the boxplot, we see that half of the rock concert victims fans were between 17 and 22 years old. The distribution of ages is roughly symmetric with most of the victims between about 13 and 28 years old. But there were also two victims who were substantially older. In a careful analysis of these data we'd want to learn more about them.

The prominent statistician, John W. Tukey, the originator of the boxplot, was asked (by one of the authors) why the outlier nomination rule cut at 1.5 IQR beyond each quartile. He answered that the reason was that 1 IQR would be too small and 2 IQR's would be too large. In the next chapter we'll see some reasons more why 1.5 works well for nominating outliers.

Boxplots complement histograms by providing more specific information about the center, the quartiles and outliers. When looking at one variable it's a good idea to look at the boxplot and histogram together. But when *comparing* groups, boxplots really start to shine.

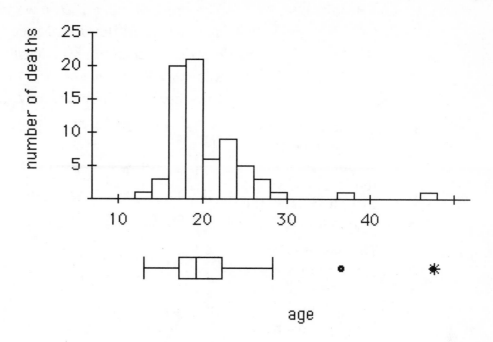

By turning a boxplot and putting it on the same scale, we can compare the boxplot and histogram of the rock concert deaths and see how each represents the distribution. Fig 5.4

Comparing Groups with Boxplots

Histograms show a lot about the shape of the distribution, but get a little unwieldy when we want to look at more than one group at a time. Boxplots work well for comparing groups because they let the fundamental story show through. When we place them side by side we can easily see which group has the higher median, which has the greater IQR, where the central 50% of the data are located, and which has the greater overall range. And we can get a general idea of symmetry from whether the medians are centered within their boxes and whether the whiskers extend roughly the same distance on either side of the boxes. Equally important, we can see past any outliers in making these comparisons because they've been separated from the rest of the data.

Comparing Groups Step-by-Step

A student designed an experiment to test the efficiency of various coffee containers by placing hot (180° F) liquid in each of four different container types 8 different times. After 30 minutes she measured the temperature again and recorded the difference in temperature. Because these are temperature *differences*, smaller differences mean that the liquid stayed hot – what we probably want in a coffee mug.

What can we say about the effectiveness of these four mugs? Let's see what story the data tell us.

Think

Variable: Identify the *variable* and report the W's.

The student place 180 °F water in each of 4 mugs and measured the difference in temperature (in °F) of the water after 30 minutes to see which mug was more effective at maintaining temperature. She repeated the procedure eight times.

Show

Mechanics: Report the 5-number summaries of the four groups. Including the IQR is a good idea as well.

	Min	Q1	Median	Q3	Max	IQR
CUPPS	6	6	8.25	14.25	18.5	8.25
Nissan	0	1	2	4.5	7	3.50
SIGG	9	11.5	14.25	21.75	24.5	10.25
Starbucks	6	6.50	8.50	14.25	17.5	7.75

Display: Because we want to compare the distributions for four groups, boxplots are an obvious choice.

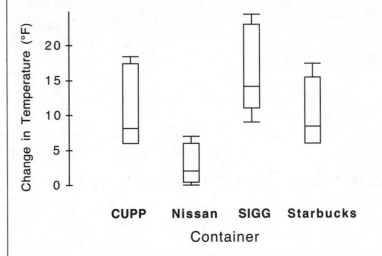

Tell

Interpretation: Describe what the boxplots and summaries say about these mugs' ability to maintain heat. Compare the shapes, centers, and spreads, and note any outliers.

The individual distributions are all slightly skewed to the high end. The Nissan cup does the best job of keeping liquids hot with a median loss of only 2°F and the SIGG cup does the worst, typically losing 14°F. The difference is large enough to be important; a coffee drinker would be likely to notice a 14° drop in temperature. And the mugs are clearly different; 75% of the Nissan tests showed less heat loss than any of the other mugs in the study. The IQR of results for the Nissan cup is also the smallest of these tests cups indicating that it is a consistent performer.

DRAFT: Do not distribute or copy

Summarizing Symmetric Distributions

Medians do a good job of locating the center of a distribution when the shape is skewed. But when we have symmetric data, there's another alternative. You probably already know how to average values. In fact, to find the median when n is even, we said for you to average the two middle values, and you didn't even flinch. In general, to average values, add them up and divide by n, the number of values.

In everyday language, sometimes "average" *does* mean what we want it to mean. We don't talk about your Grade point mean or a baseball player's batting mean, or the Dow Jones Industrial mean. So, we'll continue to say "average" when that seems most natural. When we do, though, you may assume that what we mean is the mean.

Averaging is a common thing to do with data. But once we've averaged some data, what do you think the result is called? The *average*? No, that would be too easy. Informally, we talk about the "average person" or the "average family" but we don't actually add up families and divide by n. So to be more precise we call this summary the mean.

Who: 52 adults
What: Resting heart rates
 Units: Beats per minute

Pulse rates are useful for monitoring medical conditions. But, resting heart rates depend on age. For children over 10 and adults 60-100 beats per minute is considered normal. Here are a histogram and summaries for the pulse rates of 52 adults.

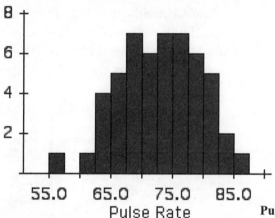

Mean	72.7 beats/min
Min	57
Q1	68
Median	73
Q3	78
Max	86
IQR	10

Pulse rates of 52 adults. Fig 5.5

The histogram shows a generally symmetric distribution, and the mean and median agree quite closely. That's what we expect for symmetric data. So when the shape of the distribution is symmetric, there is no numerical reason to prefer the median or the mean. But, as we'll see, it turns out that there is more we can do and say with the mean than with the median. Remember that the mean is only appropriate when the shape is symmetric and there are no outliers. (How do you check? Plot the data!)

The Formula for Averaging (Say it in Greek)

You already know how to average values. But this is a good opportunity to introduce some notation that will make it easier to describe calculations later on. Here's the formula:

Notation Alert:

In Algebra you used letters to represent values in a problem, but it didn't matter what letter you picked. You could call the width of a rectangle *X* or you could call it *w* (or Fred for that matter). But in Statistics, the notation is part of the vocabulary. For example, in Statistics *n* is always the number of data values. Always.

We will point out such special notation conventions. Think of them as part of the terminology you need to learn in this course.

Here's the second one:

Whenever we put a bar over a symbol it means "find the mean".

$$\bar{y} = \frac{Total}{n} = \frac{\sum y}{n}.$$

The *y* with a line over it is pronounced "y-bar". In general, a bar over any symbol or variable name in statistics denotes finding its mean. The symbol $\sum$ is the Greek letter capital sigma – equivalent to an "S" as in "Sum" – and means just that; add up all the observations. So the formula says that to find the **mean**, add up all the numbers and divide by *n*—but you knew that.

Mean or Median?

The median splits a histogram so that the *areas* of the bars on either side of the median are equal — regardless of how far they are from the center. The mean balances the histogram, taking into account both the size of the bars and their distance from the center, but as a result it may not have equal numbers of data values on either side.

Does it make a difference whether we choose a mean or a median? Well, sometimes it does. The median of the DALE's is 58.5 years. But the mean is only 55.5 years. Why are they different? The answer lies in the shape of the distribution. The **mean** is the point at which the histogram would balance:

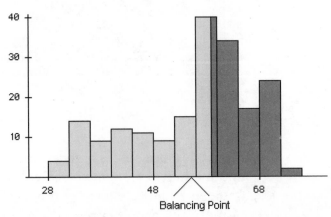

The mean is located at the *balancing point* of the histogram. Since this distribution is skewed to the left, the mean is *lower* than the median. The points at the left have pulled the mean toward them, away from the median. Fig. 5.6

Just like a child who moves away from the center of a see-saw, a bar of the histogram far from the center has more leverage, pulling the mean in its direction. If the skewness is strong or if there are straggling outliers, the mean can be pulled quite far from the median. The skewness on the

DRAFT: Do not distribute or copy

left pulls the mean somewhat to the left of the median here. For the CEO compensation data from chapter 4, the skewness was to the right. The median compensation is $1,304,470, but the mean is $2,818,743 -- more than *twice* the median. It's hard to argue that a value pulled in this way is what we meant by the center of the data. For skewed data, it's better to report the median than the mean as a measure of center.

What about Spread? The Standard Deviation

The IQR is always a reasonable summary of spread, but because it uses only the two quartiles of the data, it ignores much of the information about how individual values vary. A more powerful approach uses the standard deviation, which takes into account how far *each* value is from the mean. But like the mean, the standard deviation is only appropriate for symmetric data.

One way to think about spread is to examine how far each data value is from the mean. This difference is called a *deviation*. We could just average the deviations, but the positive and negative differences always cancel each other out. So the average deviation is always zero, not very helpful.

Instead, we *square* each deviation. Squaring always gives a positive value, so the sum won't be zero. That's great. Squaring also emphasizes larger differences—a feature that turns out to be both good and bad.

When we add up these squared deviations and find their average (almost), we call the result the **variance**:

otation Alert:
'e always write s^2 for
ιe variance.

$$s^2 = \frac{\sum (y - \bar{y})^2}{n-1}.$$

otation Alert:
ιlways denotes the
ιandard deviation.

Why almost? It would be a mean if we divided the sum by n. But instead we divide by $n-1$. Why? The simplest explanation is "to drive you crazy." But there are good technical reasons, some of which we'll see later.

How to say "square root". [near the formula for s]
We usually write a square root with the $\sqrt{}$ symbol. But, especially on computers, you may see it as a special function, usually called SQRT(y).
You might recall from algebra that we can also write the square root as the 1/2 power. On the computer, powers are indicated with an up arrow or carat: y^.5. That may not look like a square root at first, but it is, and you should recognize it if you happen to see it written like this.

The variance will play an important role later in this book, but it has a problem as a measure of spread. Whatever the units of the original data are, the variance is in *squared* units. We want measures of spread to have the same units as the data. And we probably don't want to talk about squared dollars, or mpg^2. So, to get back to the original units, we take the square root of s^2. The result, s, is the **standard deviation**.

Putting it all together, the standard deviation of the data is found by the formula:

$$s = \sqrt{\frac{\sum (y - \bar{y})^2}{n - 1}}$$

You will almost always rely on a calculator or computer to do the calculating.

Finding the Standard Deviation by Hand
[roughly here, but try to avoid interrupting the page and making this look important – it is a minor aside.]

To find the standard deviation, you start with the mean, $\bar{y}$. Then you find the *deviations* by taking $\bar{y}$ from each value: $(y - \bar{y})$. Square each deviation:

$(y - \bar{y})^2$. Now you're nearly home. Just add these all up, and divide by n-1. That gives you the variance, s^2. To find the standard deviation, s, take the square root. Here we go:

Suppose the batch of values contains 4,3,10,12,8,9 and 3.

The mean, $\bar{y} = 7$. So the deviations are found by subtracting 7 from each value:

Original values	Deviations	Squared deviations
4	4-7 = -3	(-3)2 = 9
3	3-7 = -4	(-4)2= 16
10	10-7 = 3	9
12	12-7 = 5	25
8	8-7 = 1	1
9	9-7=2	4
3	3-7=-4	16

Add these all up: 9+16+9+25+1+4+16=80

Now, divide by n-1: 80/7 = 11.43

Finally take the square root:
$s = \sqrt{11.43} = 3.38$

Thinking about Variation

Statistics is about variation, so spread is an important fundamental concept in Statistics. Measures of spread help us to be precise about what we *don't* know. If many data values are scattered far from the center, the IQR and the standard deviation will be large. If the data values are close to the center, then these measures of spread will be small. If all our data values were exactly the same, we'd have no question about summarizing the center, and all measures of spread would be zero – and we wouldn't need Statistics. You might think this would be a big plus, but it would be a boring world. Fortunately (at least for Statistics), data do vary.

Measures of spread tell how well other summaries describe the data. That's why we always (always!) report a spread along with any summary of the center.

Shape, Center, and Spread

What should you tell about a quantitative variable? Report the shape of its distribution, and include a center and a spread. But which measure of center and which measure of spread? The rules are pretty easy:

- If the shape is skewed report the median and IQR. You may want to include the mean and standard deviation, but you should point out why the mean and median differ. The fact that the mean and median do not agree is a sign that the distribution may be skewed. A histogram will help you make that point.

- If the shape is symmetric, report the mean and standard deviation and possibly the median and IQR as well.

- If there are any clear outliers and you are reporting the mean and standard deviation, report them with the outliers present *and* with the outliers removed. The differences may be revealing. (Of course, the median and IQR are not likely to be affected by the outliers.)

We always pair the median with the IQR and the mean with the standard deviation. It's not useful to report one without the other. Reporting a center without a spread is dangerous. You may think you know more than you do about the distribution. Reporting only the spread leaves us wondering where we are.

Summarizing a Distribution, Step-by-Step

One of the authors owned a 1989 Nissan Maxima for 8 years. Being a statistician, he recorded the car's fuel efficiency (in *mpg*) each time he filled the tank.[3] He wanted to know what fuel efficiency to expect as "ordinary" for his car. (Hey, he's a statistician, what would you expect?) Knowing this, he'll be able to predict when he'll need to fill the tank again, and to notice if the fuel efficiency suddenly gets worse, which could be a sign of trouble. What do the data say?

Think

Variable: Identify the variable and report the W's.	The data are the fuel efficiency values in miles per gallon for 100 fill ups of a 1989 Nissan Maxima between 1989 and 1997.

---

[3] He also recorded the time of day, temperature, price of the gas, and the phase of the moon, but we won't go there.

Show

Mechanics: Make a histogram. Based on its shape, choose appropriate numerical summaries.

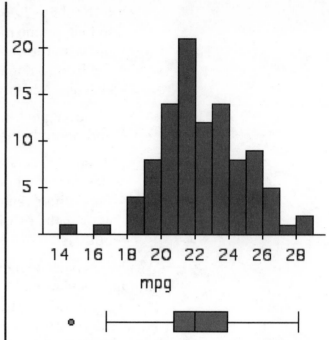

A histogram of the data shows a fairly symmetric distribution with a low outlier.

Count	100
Mean	22.4 mpg
StdDev	2.45
Median	22.0
IQR	3.2
Q1	20.8
Q3	24.0

Reality Check

22 mpg seems reasonable for such a car. The spread seems reasonable, although the range may be a bit large.

The mean and median are close, so the outlier doesn't seem to be a problem. We can use the mean and standard deviation.

Tell

Interpretation: Summarize and interpret your findings.

The distribution of mileage is unimodal and symmetric with a mean of 22.4 mpg. There is a low outlier that should be investigated, but it does not influence the mean very much. The standard deviation is 2.4 mpg. The boxplot shows that half of the time, the car had a fuel efficiency between about 21 and 24 mpg.

DRAFT: Do not distribute or copy

What Can Go Wrong?

The task of summarizing a quantitative variable is relatively simple, and there is a simple path to follow. However, you need to watch out for certain features of the data that make summarizing them with a number dangerous. Here's some advice:

- *Do a reality check.* Don't let the computer (or calculator) do your thinking for you. Make sure the calculated summaries make sense. For example, does the mean look like it is in the center of the histogram? Think about the spread: an IQR of 50 mpg would clearly be wrong for a family car. And no measure of spread can be negative. The standard deviation can take the value 0, but only in the very unusual case that all the data values equal the same number. If you see the IQR or standard deviation equal to 0, it's probably a sign that something's wrong with the data

- *Don't forget to sort the values before finding the median or percentiles.* It seems obvious, but when you work by hand, it's easy to forget to sort the data first before counting in to find medians, quartiles or other percentiles. Don't report that the median of the five values: 194, 5,1,17, 893 is 1 just because 1 is the middle value!

- *Don't compute numerical summaries of a categorical variable.* The mean zip code or the standard deviation of social security numbers is not meaningful. If the variable is categorical, you should instead report summaries such as percentages. It is easy to make this mistake when using technology to do the summaries for you. After all, the computer doesn't care what the numbers mean.

- *Watch out for multiple modes.* If the distribution, as seen in a histogram for example, has multiple modes, consider separating the data into different groups. If you cannot separate the data in a meaningful way, you should not summarize the center and spread of the variable.

- *Be aware of slightly different methods.* Finding the 10th percentile in a data set sounds easy enough. But it turns out that the practical definition of a percentile is not exactly clear. There are at least 6 reasonable definitions of quartiles alone[4]. If you compare different statistics packages or calculators, you may find that they give slightly different

---

[4] The method we give works well and is easy to do by hand. A similar method that omits the median before finding medians of each half of the data works a bit less well, but at the second step you always have an odd number of values in each half, which makes finding the median a bit easier and makes each quartile one of the data values. If you are willing to do a bit more calculating, there are several other methods of counting in that includes interpolating between adjacent values.

answers for the same data. But these differences are unlikely to be important in interpreting the data, the quartiles, or the IQR. So don't let them worry you.

- *Beware of outliers.* If the data have outliers but are otherwise unimodal, consider holding the outliers out of the further calculations and reporting them individually. If you can find a simple reason for the outlier (for instance a data transcription error) you should remove or correct it. If you cannot do either of these, then choose the median and IQR to summarize the center and spread.

- *Make a picture (make a picture, make a picture).* The sensitivity of the mean and standard deviation to outliers is one reason why you should *always* make a picture of the data. Summarizing a variable with its mean and standard deviation when you have not looked at a histogram or dotplot to check for outliers invites disaster. You may find yourself drawing absurd or dangerously wrong conclusions about the data. And, of course, you should demand no less of others. Don't accept a mean and standard deviation blindly without some evidence that the variable they summarize has no outliers or severe skewness.

Be careful when comparing groups that have very different spreads. For example, look at this boxplot. Researchers measured the concentration (nanograms per milliliter) of cotinine in the blood of three groups of people: nonsmokers who have not been exposed to smoke, nonsmokers who have been Exposed To Smoke (ETS), and smokers. Cotinine is left in the blood when the body metabolizes nicotine, so this measure gives a direct measurement of the effect of passive smoke exposure. The boxplots of the cotinine levels of the three groups tell us that the smokers have higher cotinine levels, but if we want to compare the levels of the passive smokers to the nonsmokers, we're in trouble, because on this scale, the cotinine levels for both nonsmoking groups are too low to be seen.

Who: Smokers, nonsmokers, and passive smokers.
What: Blood Cotinine levels
 Units: nanograms per milliliter (ng/ml)

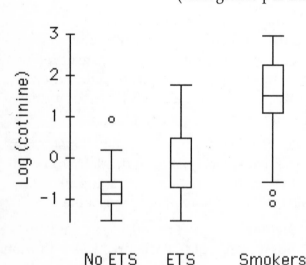

Cotinine levels (nanograms per milliliter) for three groups with different exposures to tobacco smoke. Can you compare the ETS and No ETS groups? Fig 5.7

DRAFT: Do not distribute or copy

Re-expressing to Equalize the Spread of Groups

We can often alleviate the problem of comparing groups that have very different spreads by re-expressing the data values. For measurements like the cotinine data, whose values can't be negative and whose distributions are skewed to the high end, a good first guess at a re-expression is the logarithm.

Blood cotinine levels after taking logs. What a difference a log makes! Fig 5.8

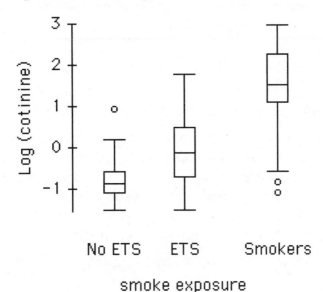

After taking logs we can compare the groups and see that the nonsmokers exposed to environmental smoke (the ETS group) do show increased levels of (log) cotinine, although not the high levels found in the blood of smokers. Notice that the same re-expression has also improved the symmetry of the cotinine distribution for smokers and pulled in most of the apparent outliers in all of the groups. It is not unusual for a re-expression that improves one aspect of data to improve others as well. We'll talk about other ways to re-express data as the need arises throughout the book.

Numerical Summaries and the Computer

Many statistics packages offer a pre-packaged collection of summary measures. The result of such a command might look like this:

```
Variable: Weight
N = 234
Mean = 143.3          Median = 139
St. Dev = 11.1        IQR = 14
```

Alternatively, a package might make a table for several variables and summary measures.

Variable	N	mean	median	stdev	IQR
Weight	234	143.3	139	11.1	14
Height	234	68.3	68.1	4.3	5
Score	234	86	88	9	5

It is usually easy to read the results and identify each computed summary. You should be able to read the summary statistics produced by any computer package.

Packages often provide many more summary statistics than you need. Of course, some of these may not be appropriate when the data are skewed or have outliers. It is your responsibility to check a histogram or stem-and-leaf display and decide which summary statistics to use.

It is common for packages to report summary statistics to many decimal places of "accuracy". Of course, it is rare data that have such accuracy in the original measurements. The ability to calculate to six or seven digits beyond the decimal point doesn't mean that those digits have any meaning. Generally, it is a good idea to round these values allowing perhaps one more digit of precision than was given in the original data.

Summary statistics are easy to find in most packages.

Package	Commands & Location	Comments
Data Desk	To find summary statistics in Data Desk, select the variable(s) to summarize. In the **Calc** menu open the **Summaries** submenu. **Options** offer separate tables, a single unified table, and other formats.	
Excel	To compute the mean of a column of data in Excel Click on an empty cell. Enter an equals sign and choose "**Average**" from the popup list of functions that appears to the left of the text editing box. Enter the data range in the box that says "**Number 1**" Click the **OK** button. To compute the standard deviation of a column of data directly, use the **STDEV** from the popup list of functions in the same way.	Excel's STDEV function should not be used for data values larger in magnitude than 100,000 or for lists of more than a few thousand values. It is programmed with an unstable formula that can generate rounding errors when these limits are exceeded.
JMP	To find summary statistics in JMP choose **Distribution** from the **Analyze** menu. In the **Distribution dialog**, drag the name of the variable that you wish to analyze into the empty window beside the label "Y, Columns" Click **OK**. JMP computes standard summary statistics along with displays of the variable.	
Minitab	To compute summary statistics in MINITAB choose **Basic Statistics** from the **Stat** menu. From the **Basic Statistics submenu**, choose **Display Descriptive Statistics**. Assign variables from the variable list box to the Variables box. MINITAB makes a Descriptive Statistics table	
SPSS	To compute summary statistics in SPSS choose **Descriptive Statistics** from the **Analyze** menu and then choose **Explore....** In the **Explore dialog**, assign one or more	

DRAFT: Do not distribute or copy

	variables from the source list to the Dependent List and click the **OK** button. SPSS will generate several plots and tables.	

Key Concepts

Center	We summarize the center of a distribution with the mean, or median.
Median	The median is the middle value with half data above and half below it.
Quartile	The lower quartile (Q1) is the value with a quarter of the data below it. The upper quartile (Q3) has a quarter of the data above it. The median and quartiles divide data into four equal parts.
Spread	We summarize the spread of a distribution with the standard deviation, interquartile range, and range.
Range	The difference between the lowest and highest values in a data set. Range = Max − Min.
Interquartile range (IQR)	The IQR is the difference between the first and third quartiles. IQR = Q3 − Q1.
Five-number Summary	A five-number summary for a variable consists of: • The minimum and maximum • The quartiles: *Q1* and *Q3* • The median
Percentile	The ith percentile is the number that falls above i% of the data.
Boxplot	A boxplot displays the five-number summary as a central box with whiskers that extend to the non-outlying data values. Boxplots are particularly effective for comparing groups.
Mean	The mean is found by summing all the data values and dividing by the count.
Variance	The variance is the sum of squared deviations from the mean, divided by the count minus one.
Standard deviation	The standard deviation is the square root of the variance.

Comparing Distributions	When comparing the distribution of several groups consider their • Shape • Center • Spread
Comparing Boxplots	When comparing groups with boxplots: • Compare the medians; which group has the higher center? • Compare the IQR's; which group is more spread out? • Compare the difference between the medians to the IQR's. • On the scale of the IQR's are the medians very different? • Check for possible outliers. Identify them if you can.

Connections

We discussed the value of summarizing a distribution with Shape, Center, and Spread in Chapter 4. Now we have numerical summaries for Center and Spread to go with our general observations. The shape of the distribution helps us to decide which numerical summaries are most appropriate.

We compared distributions in Chapter 4 by just looking at histograms. Working with numerical summaries and boxplots adds depth to our comparisons.

Skills

When you complete this lesson you should:

Think

• Be able to select a suitable measure of center and a suitable measure of spread for a variable based on information about its distribution.

• Know the basic properties of the median: the median divides the data into the half values that are below the median and the half that are above the median.

• Know the basic properties of the mean: the mean is the point on which the histogram balances and the value that minimizes the sum of squared deviations.

• Know that the standard deviation summarizes how far all the data are from the mean.

DRAFT: Do not distribute or copy

Show

- Know how to compute the mean and median of a set of data.

- Know how to compute the standard deviation and IQR of a set of data.

- Be able to create a five-number-summary of a variable.

- Be able to construct a boxplot by hand from a five-number summary.

- Know how to compare the distributions of two or more groups by comparing their shapes, centers, and spreads.

- Understand that the median and IQR resist the effects of outliers, while the mean and standard deviation do not.

- Understand that in a skewed distribution, the mean is pulled in the direction of the skewness (toward the longer tail) relative to the median.

Tell

- Know how to describe summary measures in a sentence. In particular, know that the common measures of center and spread have the same units as the variable that they summarize, and should be described in those units.

- Be able to describe the distribution of a quantitative variable with a description of the shape of the distribution, a numerical measure of center, and a numerical measure of spread.

- Be able to compare two or more groups by comparing their boxplots.

- Use the 1.5 IQR rule to identify possible outliers. Interpret outliers found in boxplots made on a computer.

Exercises

1. **In the News** Find an article in a newspaper or a magazine that discusses an "average".
   a) Does the article discuss the W's for the data?
   b) What are the units for the variable?
   c) Is the average used the median or the mean? How can you tell?
   d) Is the choice of median or mean appropriate for the situation? Explain.

2. **In the News II** Find an article in a newspaper or a magazine that discusses a measure of spread.
   a) Does the article discuss the W's for the data?
   b) What are the units for the variable?
   c) Does the article use the range, IQR, or standard deviation?

    d) Is the choice of measure of spread appropriate for the situation? Explain.

3. **Summaries** Here are costs of 10 electric smoothtop ranges rated very good or excellent by *Consumer Reports* in August 2002.

    850   900   1400   1200   1050   1000   750   1250   1050   565

    Find these statistics *by hand* (no calculator!):
    a) mean
    b) median and quartiles
    c) range and IQR

4. **More summaries** Here are the annual numbers of deaths from tornadoes in the US from 1990 through 2000. [www.spc.noaa.gov]

    53   39   39   33   69   30   25   67   130   94   40

    Find these statistics *by hand* (no calculator!):
    a) mean
    b) median and quartiles
    c) range and IQR

5. **Mistake** A clerk entering salary data into a company spreadsheet accidentally put an extra "0" in the boss's salary, listing it as $2,000,000 instead of $200,000. Explain how this error will affect these summary statistics for the company payroll:
    a) measures of center: median and mean.
    b) measures of spread: range, IQR, and standard deviation.

6. **Sick days** During contract negotiations a company seeks to change the number of sick days employees may take, saying that the annual "average" is 7 days off work per employee. The union negotiators counter that the "average" employee misses only 3 days of work each year. Explain how both sides might be correct, identifying the measure of center you think each side is using and why the stated difference might exist.

7. **Payroll** A small warehouse employs a supervisor at $1200 a week, an inventory manager at $700 a week, six stock boys at $400 a week, and four drivers at $500 a week.
    a) Find the mean and median wage.
    b) How many employees earn more than the mean wage?
    c) Which measure of center best describes a typical wage at this company, the mean or the median?

d) Which measure of spread would best describe the payroll, the range the IQR, or the standard deviation? Why?

8. **Singers** The frequency table shows the heights (in inches) of 130 members of a choir.
   a) Find the 5-number summary for these data.
   b) Display these data with a boxplot.
   c) Find the mean and standard deviation.
   d) Display these data with a histogram.
   e) Write a few sentences describing the distribution of heights.

Height	Count
60	2
61	6
62	9
63	7
64	5
65	20
66	18
67	7
68	12
69	5
70	11
71	8
72	9
73	4
74	2
75	4
76	1

9. **Standard Deviation** Examine the two given sets of numbers. Without doing any calculations, decide which set has the larger standard deviation and explain why. Then check by finding the standard deviations *by hand*.

	Set 1	Set 2
a)	3, 5, 6, 7, 9	2, 4, 6, 8, 10
b)	10, 14, 15, 16, 20	10, 11, 15, 19, 20
c)	2, 6, 6, 9, 11, 14	82, 86, 86, 89, 91, 94

10. **Standard Deviation** Examine the two given sets of numbers. Without doing any calculations, decide which set has the larger standard deviation and explain why. Then check by finding the standard deviations *by hand*.

	Set 1	Set 2
a)	4, 7, 7, 7, 10	4, 6, 7, 8, 10
b)	100, 140, 150, 160, 200	10, 50, 60, 70, 110
c)	10, 16, 18, 20, 22, 28	48, 56, 58, 60, 62, 70

11. **Home Runs** In 1961 Roger Maris made baseball headlines by hitting 61 home runs, breaking a famous record held by Babe Ruth. Here are Maris's home run totals for his ten seasons in the American League. Would you consider his record-setting year to be an outlier? Explain.

8, 13, 14, 16, 23, 26, 28, 33, 39, 61

12. **Campsites** Shown below are the histogram and summary statistics for the number of campsites at public parks in Vermont.
    a) Which statistics would you use to identify the center and spread of this distribution? Why?
    b) How many parks would you classify as outliers? Explain.
    c) Create a boxplot for these data.
    d) Write a few sentences describing the distribution.

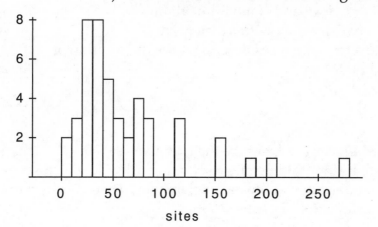

Summary of	sites
Count	46
Mean	62.78 sites
Median	43.50
StdDev	56.196
Min	0
Max	275
Lower Q	28
Upper Q	78

13. **Marriage Age** Do men and women marry at the same age? Here are boxplots of the age at first marriage for a sample of U.S. citizens. Write a brief report discussing what these data show.

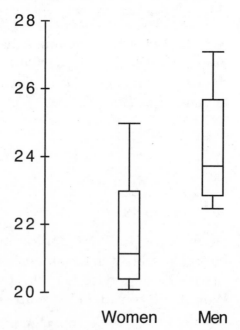

DRAFT: Do not distribute or copy

14. **Fuel Economy** Describe what these boxplots tell you about the relationship between the number of cylinders a car's engine has and the car's fuel economy (miles per gallon).

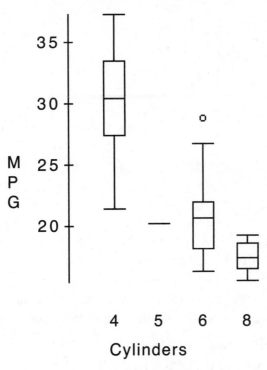

15. **Wines** The boxplots display case prices (in dollars) of wines produced by wineries along three of the Finger Lakes.

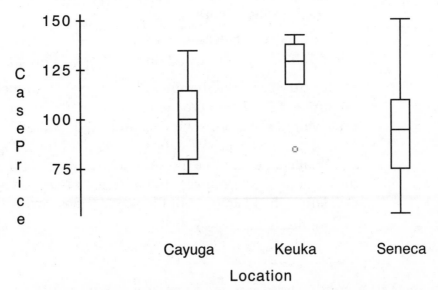

a) Which lake region produces the most expensive wine?
b) Which lake region produces the cheapest wine?
c) In which region are the wines generally more expensive?
d) Write a few sentences describing these wine prices.

16. **Ozone** Ozone levels were recorded at sites in New Jersey monthly between 1926 and 1971. Here are boxplots of the data for each month (over the 46 years) lined up in order.

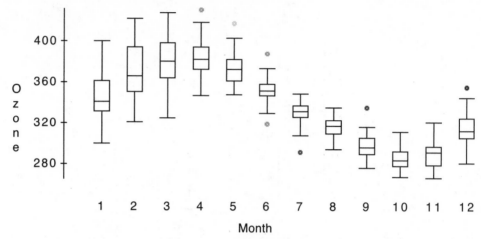

a) In what month was the highest ozone level ever recorded?
b) Which month has the largest IQR?
c) Which month has the smallest range?
d) Write a brief comparison of the ozone levels in January and June.
e) Write a report on the annual patterns you see in the ozone levels.

17. **Unemployment** In May of 2001, the U.S. Bureau of Labor Statistics issued a news release that said, in part:

> *"In April, 223 metropolitan areas recorded unemployment rates below the U.S. average of 4.2 percent (not seasonally adjusted), while 99 areas registered higher rates."*

Sketch what the distribution of unemployment rates for the 322 metropolitan areas reported on by BLS probably looks like.

18. **Wild card Summer Olympics** Seventy one swimmers finished the qualifying first day of the men's 100 m swim in Sydney. The average time was 52.65 seconds with a standard deviation of 7.66 seconds. The median time was 51.34 seconds and the IQR was 2.58 seconds.
a) What shape would expect the distributions of times to have?
b) What might account for the difference between these statistics?
c) Here is the histogram of the actual times. Write a couple of sentences summarizing what you see[5].

---

[5] IOC president Juan Antonio Samaranch initiated a special program in the 2000 Olympics. As a way of spreading sport around the world a handful of athletes were allowed to compete even though they didn't meet qualifying standards. Moussambani, who trains in a 20m pool with no lane markers in his African homeland, became an international celebrity after completing his swim in more than twice the time of the next slowest competitor. He carried the national flag in the opening ceremony, leading an 11-person team that also includes a female swimmer. He actually won his heat of 3 swimmers when the other two failed to qualify.

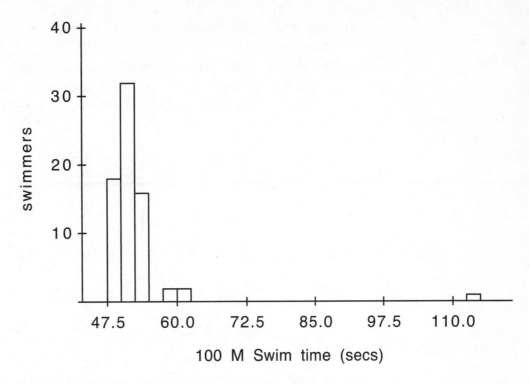

19. **Test scores** Three Statistics classes all took the same test. Histograms of the scores for each class are shown below.

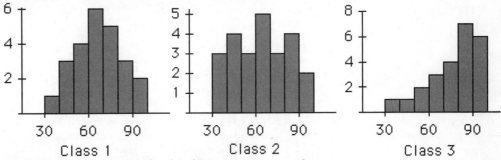

a) Which class had the highest mean score?
b) Which class had the highest median score?
c) For which class are the mean and median most different? Which is higher? Why?
d) Which class had the smallest standard deviation?
e) Which class had the smallest IQR?

20. **Test scores** Look again at the histograms of test scores for the three
Statistics classes.
a) Overall, which class do you think performed better on the test? Why?
b) How would you describe the shape of each distribution?
c) Match each distribution with the corresponding boxplot.

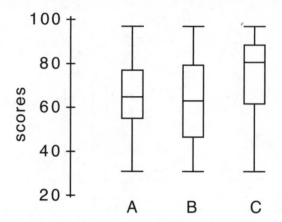

21. **Still Rockin'** In the chapter you read about the 66 deaths attributed to
"crowd crush" at rock concerts during the years 1999 and 2000. Here are
the histogram and boxplot of the victims' ages we saw earlier:

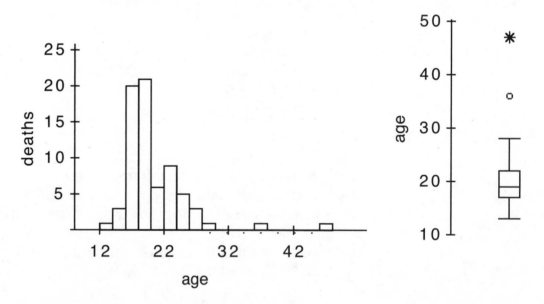

a) What features of the distribution can you see in both the histogram
and the boxplot?
b) What features of the distribution can you see in the histogram that
you could not see in the boxplot?
c) What summary statistic would you choose to summarize the center
of this distribution? Why?
d) What summary statistics would you choose to summarize the spread
of this distribution? Why?

DRAFT: Do not distribute or copy

22. **Golf Courses** One measure of the difficulty of a golf course is its length: the total distance (in yards) from tee to hole for all 18 holes. Below are the histogram and summary statistics for the lengths of all the golf courses in Vermont.

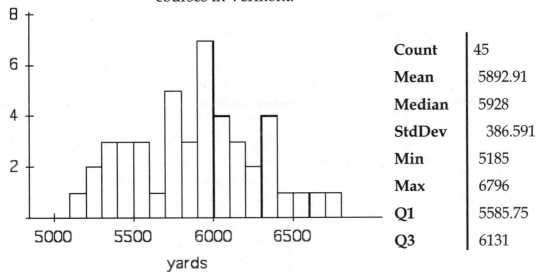

Count	45
Mean	5892.91
Median	5928
StdDev	386.591
Min	5185
Max	6796
Q1	5585.75
Q3	6131

a) What is the range of these lengths?
b) Between what lengths do the central 50% of these courses lie?
c) What summary statistics would you use to describe these data?
d) Write a brief description of these data (shape, center, and spread).

23. **Graduation?** A survey of major universities asked what percent of incoming freshmen usually graduate in 4 years. Use the summary statistics given to answer these questions.

	% on time
Count	48
Mean	68.35
Median	69.90
StdDev	10.196
Min	43.20
Max	87.40
Range	44.20
25th %tile	59.15
75th %tile	74.75

a) Would you describe this distribution as symmetric or skewed? Explain.
b) Are there any outliers? Explain.
c) Create a boxplot of these data.
d) Write a few sentences about the universities.

24. **Wineries** Here are summary statistics for the sizes (in acres) of Finger Lakes wineries.

Summary of	Size
Count	36
Mean	46.5000
Median	33.5000
StdDev	47.7556
Range	244
25th %tile	18.5000
75th %tile	55
Min	6

    a) Would you describe this distribution as symmetric or skewed? Explain.
    b) Are there any outliers? Explain.
    c) Create a boxplot of these data.
    d) Write a few sentences about the wineries.

25. **Caffeine** Should you have a cup of coffee to make you more alert when studying for a big test? A student study of the effects of caffeine asked volunteers to take a memory test two hours after drinking soda. Some drank caffeine free cola, some drank regular cola (with caffeine), and others drank a mixture of the two (getting a half-dose of caffeine). Here are the 5-number summaries for each group's scores (number of items recalled correctly) on the memory test:

Drink	n	Min	Q1	Median	Q3	Max
No caffeine	15	16	20	21	24	26
Low caffeine	15	16	18	21	24	27
High caffeine	15	12	17	19	22	24

    a) Describe the W's for these data: who, what, where, why, when, how.
    b) Name the variables and classify each as categorical or quantitative.
    c) Create parallel boxplots to display these results.
    d) Write a few sentences comparing the performances of the three groups.

26. **Rainmakers?** In an experiment to determine whether seeding clouds with silver iodide increases rainfall, 52 clouds were randomly assigned to be seeded or not. The amount of rain they generated was then measured(in acre-feet).

Variable	Count	Mean	Median	StdDev	IQR	Q1	Q3
Unseeded	26	164.59	44.20	278.43	138.60	24.40	163
Seeded	26	441.98	221.60	650.79	337.60	92.40	430

    a) Which of the summary statistics are most appropriate for describing these distributions. Why?
    b) Do you see any evidence that seeding clouds may be effective? Explain.

DRAFT: Do not distribute or copy

27. **States** The stem-and-leaf display shows populations of the 50 states and Washington, D.C., in millions of people, according to the 2000 census.

```
3 | 4
2 |
2 | 1
1 | 6 9
1 | 0 1 2 2
0 | 5 5 5 5 6 6 6 6 6 7 8 8 8
0 | 1 1 1 1 1 1 1 1 1 1 1 1 1 2 2 2 2 2 3 3 3 3 3 3 3 4 4 4 4 4
```
State Populations (1|2 means 12 million)

a) What measures of center and spread are most appropriate?
b) Without doing any calculations, which must be larger - the median or the mean? Explain how you know.
c) From the stem-and-leaf display, find the median and the interquartile range.
d) Write a few sentences describing this distribution.

28. **Population Growth** The back-to back stem-and-leaf display compares the percent change in population of northeastern and midwestern states against the changes in southern and western states between the 1990 and 2000 census. The fastest growing states were Nevada at 66% and Arizona at 40%. Use the data displayed in the stem-and-leaf display to construct comparative boxplots.

```
              6 | 6
              6 |
              5 |
              5 |
              4 |
              4 | 0
              3 |
              3 | 001
              2 | 6
              2 | 001134
              1 | 578
       0012   1 | 001134444
55667889999   0 | 6999
       1344   0 | 1
```

NE/MW States | **S/W States**
Population Growth Rate (%) (*US Census Bureau*)

29. **Derby Speeds** How fast do horses run? Kentucky Derby winners top 30 miles per hour, as shown in the graph below. In fact, this graph shows the percentage of Derby winners that have run *slower* than a given speed. Note that few have won running less than 33 miles per hour, but about 95% of the winning horses have run less than 37 miles per hour. (A cumulative frequency graph like this is called an "ogive".)

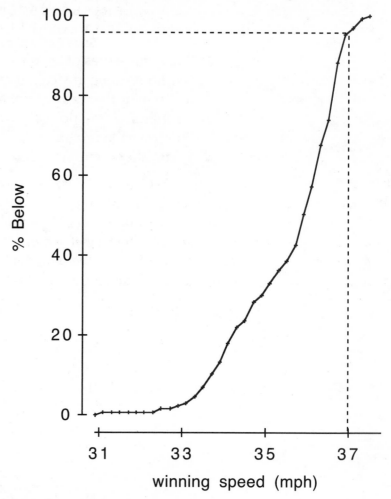

a) Estimate the median winning speed.
b) Estimate the quartiles.
c) Estimate the range and the IQR.
d) Create a boxplot of these speeds.
e) Write a few sentences about the Kentucky Derby winners.

DRAFT: Do not distribute or copy

30. **Cholesterol** The Framingham Heart Study recorded the cholesterol levels of over 1400 men. Here is an ogive of the distribution of these cholesterol measures. (Recall that an ogive shows the percentage of cases at or below a certain value.) Construct a boxplot for these data and write a few sentences describing the distribution.

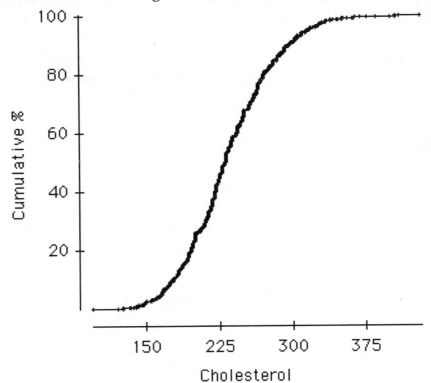

31. **Reading scores** A class of fourth graders takes a diagnostic reading test, and the scores are reported by reading grade level. The five number summaries for the 14 boys and 11 girls are shown:

    Boys: 2.0 - 3.9 - 4.3 - 4.9 - 6.0
    Girls: 2.8 - 3.8 - 4.5 - 5.2 - 5.9
    a) Which group had the highest score?
    b) Which group had the greatest range?
    c) Which group had the greatest interquartile range?
    d) Which group's scores appear to be more skewed? Explain.
    e) Which group generally did better on the test? Explain.
    f) If the mean reading level for boys was 4.2 and for girls was 4.6, what is the overall mean for the class?

32. **SAT Scores** Here are the summary statistics for Verbal SAT scores for a high school graduating class.

	Count	Mean	Median	StdDev	Min	Max	Q1	Q3
Male	80	590	600	97.2	310	800	515	650
Female	82	602	625	102.0	360	770	530	680

a) Create parallel boxplots comparing the scores of boys and girls.

b) Write a brief report on these results. Be sure to discuss shape, center, and spread of the scores.

33. **Phone calls** In an advertisement in USA Today (July 9, 2001), the company Net2Phone listed its long distance rates to 24 of the 250 countries to which it offers service.

Country	Cost per minute (cents)
Belgium	7.9
Chile	17
Canada	3.9
Colombia	9.9
Dominican Rep	15
Finland	9.9
France	7.9
Germany	7.9
Hong Kong	7.9
India	49
Ireland	7.9
Israel	8.9
Italy	9.9
Japan	7.9
Mexico	16
Pakistan	49
Philippines	21
Puerto Rico	6.9
Singapore	11
South Korea	9.9
Taiwan	9.9
United Kingdom	7.9
United States	3.9
Venezuela	22

a) Make a display of these rates.

b) Find the mean and the median. Which is a more appropriate measure of center?

c) Find the IQR and the standard deviation. Which is the more appropriate measure of spread?

d) Would you consider any of these to be outliers? Carefully explain how you reached your decision.

e) Write a brief description of these rates. Don't forget to mention shape, center, and spread as well as any unusual features of the distribution.

f) What can you conclude about Net2Phone's rates to the 250 countries the ad says they service?

DRAFT: Do not distribute or copy

34. **Job Growth** In 1996 the firm Standard and Poor's DRI predicted that the cities listed below would experience the fastest growing job markets in the US over the next three years and predicted their growth rates, given here.

City	Growth(%)
Las Vegas, NV-AZ	3.72
Raleigh-Durham-Chapel Hill, NC	2.69
Austin-San Marcos, TX	2.64
Riverside-San Bernardino, CA	2.62
Boise, ID	2.61
Orlando, FL	2.51
Phoenix-Mesa, AZ	2.44
West Palm Beach-Boca Raton, FL	2.37
Sacramento, CA	2.26
Atlanta, GA	2.25
Sarasota-Bradenton, FL	2.22
Portland-Vancouver, OR-WA	2.16
Fort Lauderdale, FL	2.13
Charlotte-Gastonia-Rock Hill, NC-SC	2.07
Tucson, AZ	2.07
Vallejo-Fairfield-Napa, CA	2.02
Omaha, NE-IA	1.93
Salt Lake City-Ogden, UT	1.90
Albuquerque, NM	1.87
Fort Worth-Arlington, TX	1.86

a) Make a suitable display of the growth rates.
b) Summarize the central growth rate with a median and mean. Why do they differ?
c) Given what you know about the distribution, which of these measures does the better job of summarizing the growth rates? Why?
d) Summarize the spread of the growth rate distribution with a standard deviation and with an IQR.
e) Given what you know about the distribution, which of these measures does the better job of summarizing the growth rates? Why?
f) Suppose we subtract from each of these growth rates, the predicted U.S. average growth rate of 1.20% so that we could look at how much these growth rates exceed the U.S. rate. How would this change the values of the summary statistics you calculated above? (Hint: you need not recompute any of the summary statistics from scratch.)
g) If we were to omit Las Vegas from the data, how would you expect the mean, median, standard deviation, and IQR to change? Explain your expectations for each.
h) Write a brief report about these growth rates.

35. **Math Scores** The National Center for Education Statistics reported 1999 average mathematics achievement scores for eighth graders in 38 nations. Singapore led the group, with an average score of 604, while South Africa had the lowest average of 275. The US scored 502. The average score for each nation are given below.

604	587	585	582	579	558	540	534	532	531
530	526	525	520	520	519	511	505	502	496
491	482	479	476	472	469	467	466	448	447
429	428	422	403	392	345	337	275		

a) Find the five number summary, the IQR, the mean and the standard deviation of these national averages.

b) Write a brief summary of the performance of eighth graders worldwide. Be sure to comment on the performance of the United States.

36. **Prisons** A report from the U.S. Department of Justice gave the following percent increases in federal prison populations in 20 northeastern and midwestern states during 1999.

5.9, 1.3, 3.0, 5.9, 4.5, 5.6, 2.1, 6.3, 4.8, 6.9, 4.5, 3.5, 7.2, 6.4, 5.5, 5.3, 8.0, 4.4, 7.2, 3.2

a) Graph these data.
b) Calculate appropriate summary statistics.
c) Write a few sentences about these data. (Remember: shape, center, spread, unusual features.)

37. **Gasoline Usage** The U.S. Department of Transportation collects data on the amount of gasoline sold in each state. The following data show the per capita (gallons used per person) consumption in the year 2000. Using appropriate graphical displays and summary statistics, write a report on the gasoline use by state in the year 2000.

Alabama	544.71	Hawaii	327.27	Mass	438.1	NM	474.28	SD	555.06
Alaska	433.08	Idaho	500.34	Michigan	502.77	New York	551.18	TN	586.58
Arizona	452.82	Illinois	406.66	MN	528.06	NC	296.66	Texas	515.17
Arkansas	532.96	Indiana	518.7	MS	559.29	ND	513.3	Utah	498.66
CA	422.65	Iowa	534.7	Missouri	563.56	Ohio	574.83	Vermont	456.27
Colorado	461.90	Kansas	511.34	Montana	548.5	OK	457.63	Virginia	584.03
CT	431.04	Kentucky	510.9	Nebraska	508.28	Oregon	520.42	WA	506.92
Delaware	481.45	LA	522.12	Nevada	446.17	PA	441.44	WV	450.4
Florida	542.36	Maine	542.36	NH	542.86	RI	410.31	WI	462
Georgia	452.82	Maryland	452.82	NJ	474.28	SC	381.86	Wyoming	462.67

38. **Industrial experiment** Engineers at a computer production plant tested two methods for accuracy in drilling holes into a PC board. They tested how fast they could set the drilling machine by running 10 boards at each of two different speeds. To assess the results, they measured the distance (in inches) from the center of a target on the board to the center of the hole. The data and summary statistics are shown in the table:

	Fast	Slow
	0.000101	0.000098
	0.000102	0.000096
	0.000100	0.000097
	0.000102	0.000095
	0.000101	0.000094
	0.000103	0.000098
	0.000104	0.000096
	0.000102	0.975600
	0.000102	0.000097
	0.000100	0.000096
Mean	0.000102	0.097647
Std Dev	0.000001	0.308481

Write a report summarizing the findings of the experiment. Include appropriate visual and verbal displays of the distributions, and make a recommendation to the engineers if they are most interested in the accuracy of the method.

39. **Customer Data Base** A philanthropic organization has a database of millions of donors that thy contact by mail to raise money for charities. One of the variables in the database, *Title*, contains the title of the person or persons printed on the address label. The most common are Mr., Ms., Miss and Mrs., but there are also Ambassador and Mrs., Your Imperial Majesty, and Cardinal to name a few others. In all there are over 100 different titles, each with a corresponding numeric code. Here are a few of them:

Code	Title
000	MR.
001	MRS.
002	MR. and MRS.
003	MISS
004	DR.
005	MADAME
006	SERGEANT
009	RABBI
010	PROFESSOR
126	PRINCE
127	PRINCESS
128	CHIEF
129	BARON
130	SHEIK
131	PRINCE AND PRINCESS

132	YOUR IMPERIAL MAJESTY
1035	M. ET MME.
1210	PROF.

Mean	54.41
Std Dev	957.5
Median	1
IQR	2
n	94649

An intern who was asked to analyze the organization's fundraising efforts presented these summary statistics for the variable *Title*:

a) What does the mean of 54.41 mean?

b) What are the typical reasons that cause measures of center and spread to be as different as those in this table?

c) Is that why these are so different?

40. **Zipcodes Revisited** Here are some summary statistics to go with the histogram of the zipcodes of 500 customers from the Holes R Us Internet Jewelry Salon that we saw in Exercise 23 of Chapter 4.

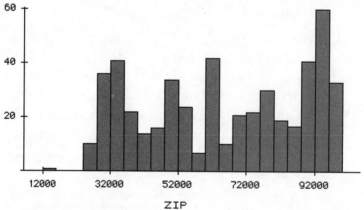

Count	500
Mean	64970.0
Median	64871
StdDev	23523.0
IQR	44183
Q1	46050
Q3	90233

a) Is the mean or median a "better" summary of the center of the zipcode distribution?

b) Is the standard deviation or the IQR a better summary of the spread?

c) What can these statistics tell you about the company's sales?

41. **Eye and Hair Color** A survey of 1021 school age children was conducted by randomly selecting children from several large urban elementary schools. Two of the questions concerned eye and hair color. In the survey, the following codes were used:

Hair color:	Eye color:
• 1 = Blond	1 = Blue
• 2 = Brown	2 = Green
• 3 = Black	3 = Brown
• 4 = Red	4 = Grey
• 5 = Other	5 = Other

The statistics students analyzing the data were asked to study the relationship between eye and hair color. They produced this plot:

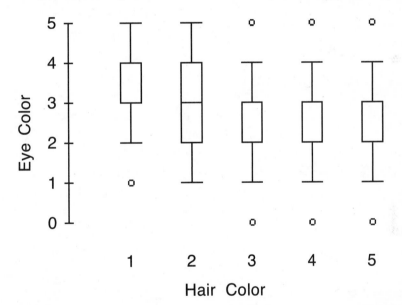

Is their graph appropriate? If so, summarize the findings. If not, explain why not.

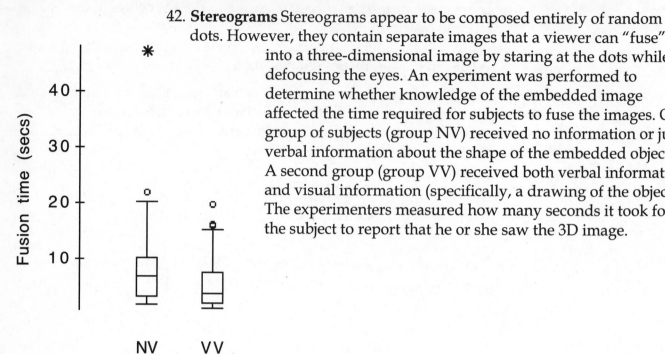

42. **Stereograms** Stereograms appear to be composed entirely of random dots. However, they contain separate images that a viewer can "fuse" into a three-dimensional image by staring at the dots while defocusing the eyes. An experiment was performed to determine whether knowledge of the embedded image affected the time required for subjects to fuse the images. One group of subjects (group NV) received no information or just verbal information about the shape of the embedded object. A second group (group VV) received both verbal information and visual information (specifically, a drawing of the object). The experimenters measured how many seconds it took for the subject to report that he or she saw the 3D image.

a) What two variables are discussed in this description?

b) For each variable, is it quantitative or categorical; if quantitative, what are the units?

c) Here are boxplots comparing the fusion times for the two treatment groups. Write a few sentences comparing these distributions. What does the experiment show?

43. **Stereograms, revisited** Because of the skewness of the distributions of fusion times, we might consider a re-expression. Here are the boxplots of the *log* of fusion times. Is it better to analyze the original fusion times or the log fusion times? Explain.

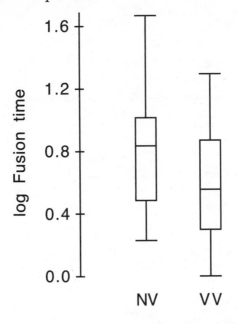

44. **Stereograms, yet again** Here are the boxplots of the *reciprocal* of fusion times. Is it better to analyze the original fusion times, the log fusion times, or the reciprocal? Explain.

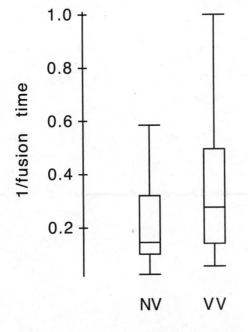

6 The Standard Deviation as a Ruler and the Normal Model

THE WOMEN'S HEPTATHLON in the Olympics consists of seven track and field events: the 200m and 800m runs, 100m high hurdles, shot put, javelin, high jump, and long jump. Somehow, the performances in all seven events have to be combined into one score. How can performances in such different events be compared? They don't even have the same units; the races are recorded in seconds and the throwing and jumping events in meters. The best 800m time, run by Getrud Bacher of Italy was 8 seconds faster than the mean. The winning long jump by the Russian Yelena Prokhorova was 60 centimeters longer than the mean. Which performance deserves more points?

You might think at first that this is a silly question, but it is exactly the kind of question that has to be answered to compute heptathlon scores. And comparisons of values with different units show up in many places.

The Standard Deviation as a Ruler

The trick in comparing very different looking values is to use the standard deviations as our rulers. The standard deviation is the most common measure of variation. So it should come as no surprise that the standard deviation plays a crucial role in how we look at data. Over and over during this course we will ask questions such as "how far is this value from the mean?" or "how different are these two statistics?" The answer in every case will be to measure the distance or difference in standard deviations.

The concept of the standard deviation as a ruler is not special to this course. You'll find statistical distances measured in standard deviations throughout Statistics, up to the most advanced levels. So this approach is one of the basic tools of statistical thinking.

Bacher's winning 800m time of 129 seconds was 8 seconds faster than the mean of 137 seconds. The standard deviation of all 27 qualifying times was 5.0 seconds. How many *standard deviations* better than the mean is that? Her time was $(129-137)/5 = -8/5 = -1.6$ *standard deviations* below the mean. Prokhorova's winning long jump was 60 centimeters *longer* than the average 6 meter jump. The standard deviation was 30 centimeters, so the winning jump was $(60/30) = 2.0$ standard deviations better than the mean. The long jump

Grading on a curve

A similar issue arises in grading a class. If you score 79% on an exam, what grade should you get? One teaching philosophy looks only at the raw percentage, 79 and bases the grade on that alone. Another looks at your *relative* performance, and bases the grade on how you did compared to the rest of the class. Teachers and students still debate which method is better.

performance was a greater improvement over its mean than was the winning 800m time since it was further away in *standard deviations*.

Standardizing

We compared the heptathlon results by asking how many standard deviations they were from the event means. We can write this as

$$z = \frac{(y - \bar{y})}{s}$$

We call the resulting values **standardized values,** and denote them with the letter z. Usually we just call them **z-scores**.

Standardized values have no units. (The numerator has the same units as the data, but so does the denominator. Dividing one by the other "cancels out" the units.) That makes all z-scores comparable regardless of the original units of the data.

Notation Alert
There goes another letter. We always use the letter *z* to denote values that have been standardized with the mean and standard deviation.

In place of real-world units, z-scores measure the distance of each data value from the mean in standard deviations. A z-score of 2.0 indicates that a data value is 2 standard deviations above the mean. Data values below the mean have negative z-scores, so a z-score of -1.6 means that the data value was one and six tenths standard deviations *below* the mean. We are using the standard deviation as a ruler to measure statistical distance from the mean.

Benefits of Standardizing

Standardizing data brings several benefits. Standardized values have been converted from their original units to the standard statistical unit of *standard deviations from the mean*. This makes it possible to compare values that are measured on different scales, with different units, or for different populations. And, as we'll soon see, it offers a useful rule of thumb about distributions.

We have already seen a comparison of values on two quite different variables. To determine the winner of the heptathlon, the judges must combine performances on the seven events. Although they use pre-determined tables, they could have combined scores by standardizing each and then adding the z-scores together to reach a total score.

As an example, let's compare Bacher and Prokhorova in *both* the long jump and the 800m. As we've seen, Bacher ran the 800 in 129 seconds, 1.6 standard deviations better than the mean. But her long jump of 5.84m fell below the mean with a z-score of -.44. So, we'd give her a total of 1.6 - .44 = 0.94 for the two events. Prokhorova ran the 800m in 130.32 seconds, 1.34 standard deviations better than the mean and her long jump was 2.0 standard deviations better than the mean. So her total is 1.34 +2.0 = 3.34 for the two events. Not coincidentally, Prokhorova went on to win the Silver medal while Bacher finished 14th.

DRAFT: Do not distribute or copy

When we standardize data to get a z-score, we do two things. First, we *shift* the data by subtracting the mean. Then, we *rescale* the values by dividing by their standard deviation. Shifting and rescaling data is done all the time. What happens to the grade distribution if *everyone* gets a 5-point bonus? If we switch from feet to meters, what happens to the distribution of heights of students in your class? Before we can talk more about using z-scores, we need to see exactly how shifting and scaling work.

Shifting Data

The Trinidad and Tobago Stock Exchange Ltd. was formally opened on the 26th October, 1981. By the end of the year 2000 it listed the stocks of 28 companies. During that year, the average dividend paid by the stocks was 4.58% with a standard deviation of 3.77%. However, inflation averaged about 4% during this period. So, the *real* return of these stocks from their dividends is the dividend paid minus 4%. If we subtract 4% from the dividends of the 28 stocks, what will this do to the center and spread of the distribution?

When we shift data values by subtracting or adding the same number to all the data values, does the distribution change? How about its numerical summaries?

Here are the histograms of the dividends of the 28 stocks, and the same values with 4% subtracted from them.

Who: The 28 companies listed on the stock exchange f Trinidad and Tobago
What: Dividends paid in the ear 2000
    Unit: Percent
When: Calendar year 2000
Where: Trinidad and Tobago
Why: Annual report of stock xchange

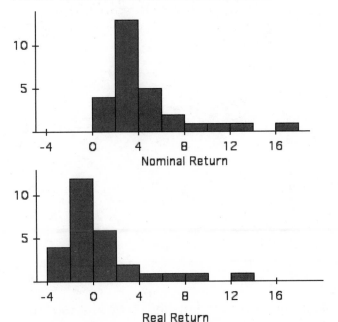

The nominal return on the 28 stocks, and the real return (with 4% subtracted) show the same distribution shape. Fig 6.1

What is the mean now that we've subtracted 4% from each? If you said the mean minus 4% you've got it right. Adding (or subtracting) a *constant* amount to each value just adds (or subtracts) the same constant

Doctors' height and weight charts sometimes give ideal weights for various heights with 2 inch heels. If the mean height of adult women is 66 inches with 2 inch heels on, what is the mean height of women without shoes? Each woman is shorter by 2 inches when barefoot, so the mean is decreased by 2 inches to 64 inches.

to the mean. The same is true for the median. And the quartiles. (Did we mention maximum and minimum?) In fact, we'd probably be pretty unhappy with any measure of position that did not decrease by exactly 4 when we subtract 4 from all the data values.

> Adding a constant to every data value adds the same constant to measures of position, but leaves measures of spread unchanged

What about the spread? What does adding a constant value do to the spread of the distribution? Look at the two histograms again. Because adding a constant increases all the data values equally, the distribution just shifts. Its shape doesn't change and neither does the spread. None of the measures of spread we've discussed, not the range, not the IQR, nor the standard deviation changes.

Rescaling Data

But suppose we *rescale* the data by multiplying or dividing all the values by the same number. Such an operation changes the measurement units. It's exactly how we would convert between fortnights and seconds or between meters and yards. The average price of the 28 stocks on December 31, 2000 was TT $9.12. (TT$ is a Trinidad and Tobago Dollar.) If we want to convert the prices from TT$ to US$, we have to divide by 6.24, the exchange rate on December 31, 2000.

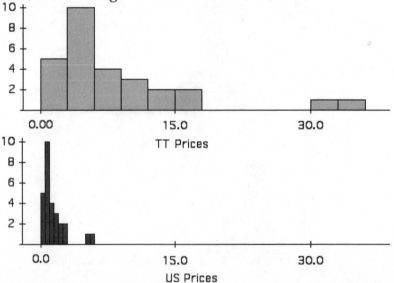

Stock prices in both TT and US dollars. How do the distribution and the numerical summaries change? Fig 6.2

What happens to the mean price? Not too surprisingly, it gets divided by 6.24 as well. The mean price of TT$9.21 became TT $9.21/6.24 = US$1.48. The median is also divided by 6.24. (The quartiles too.)

What happens to the spread? Take a look at the histograms. Clearly the spread is smaller. Consider the range, for example. Since we divided

DRAFT: Do not distribute or copy

each value by 6.24, we divided the maximum and minimum values by 6.24.

$$\frac{max}{6.24} - \frac{min}{6.24} = \frac{max - min}{6.24} = \frac{range}{6.24}$$

And so, their difference, the range, is divided by 6.24.

What about the other measures of spread? The same thing happened to them and for much the same reasons.

> When we divide or multiply all the data values by any constant value, the range, the IQR, and the standard deviation change in the same way by that *same value.*

Back to z-scores

Standardizing data into z-scores is just shifting them by the mean and rescaling them by the standard deviation. So now we can see how standardizing affects the distribution. When we subtract the mean of the data from every data value, we shift the mean to zero. And, as we have seen, such a shift doesn't change the standard deviation.

But when we *divide* each of these shifted values by *s*, the standard deviation gets divided by *s* as well, and so the new standard deviation becomes 1.

z- scores have mean 0 and standard deviation 1.

So how does standardizing affect the distribution of a variable? Let's consider the three aspects of a distribution: the shape, center, and spread.

> - Standardizing does not change the *shape* of the distribution of a variable.
> - Standardizing changes the *center* by making the mean 0.
> - Standardizing changes the *spread* by making the standard deviation 1.

When is a z-score BIG?

A z-score gives us an indication of how unusual a value is because it tells us how far it is from the mean. A standardized value of 0 tells us that the data value is right at the mean. A standardized value of +1 tells us that the value is one standard deviation above the mean. How far from 0 does a z-score have to be to be interesting, or unusual? There is no universal standard, but there is a model that shows up over and over in Statistics. You may have heard of "bell shaped curves". Statisticians call them Normal distributions.

Is Normal normal?

Don't be misled. The name "Normal" doesn't mean that these are the usual shapes for histograms. The name follows a tradition of positive thinking in mathematics and statistics in which functions, equations, and relationships that are easy to work with or have other nice properties are called "normal," "common," "regular," "natural" or similar terms. It's as if by calling them ordinary we could make them actually occur more often and simplify our lives.

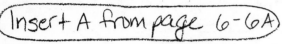

Notation Alert

$N(\mu, \sigma)$ always denotes a Normal model.
μ, pronounced "mew", is the Greek letter for "m" and always represents the mean in a model.
σ, is the lower case Greek letter sigma, and always represents the standard deviation in a model.

Is the Standard Normal a standard?

Well, yes. We call it the "standard Normal" because it models standardized values. But it is also a "standard" because this is the particular Normal model that we almost always use.

Normal models are appropriate for distributions whose shapes are unimodal and roughly symmetric. For these distributions, they provide a measure of how extreme a z-score is. Fortunately, there is a normal distribution for every possible combination of mean and standard deviation. We write $N(\mu, \sigma)$ to represent a Normal model with a mean of μ and a standard deviation of σ. Why the Greek? Well, *this* mean and standard deviation are not numerical summaries of data. They are part of the model. ~~We don't want to confuse them with $\bar{y}$ and s from the data, so we use special symbols.~~

If ~~When~~ we model data with a Normal model and standardize them using the corresponding μ and σ, we still call the standardized value a **z-score**, and write

$$z = \frac{y - \mu}{\sigma}.$$

Usually it's easier to standardize data first (using its mean and standard deviation). Then we need only the model $N(0, 1)$. The Normal model with mean 0 and standard deviation 1 is called the **standard Normal model (or the standard Normal distribution)**.

But be careful. You shouldn't use a normal model for just any data set. Remember that standardizing won't change the shape of the distribution. If the distribution is not unimodal and symmetric to begin with, standardizing won't make it Normal.

The 68-95-99.7 Rule

This margin note goes with figure 6.3)

Normal models give us an idea of how extreme a value is by telling us how likely it is to find one that far from the mean. We'll soon show how to find these numbers precisely. But there's a simple rule that's usually all we need.

These magic 68, 95, 99.7 values come from the Normal model. As a model, it can give us corresponding values for any z-score. For example, it tells us that fewer than 1 out of a million values have z-scores smaller than -5.0 or larger than 5.0. So if someone tells you you're "one in a million" they must really admire your z-score.

It turns out that about 68% of the data fall within one standard deviation of the mean, about 95% of the values fall within two standard deviations of the mean, and about 99.7% -- almost all – of the values fall within

DRAFT: Do not distribute or copy

Here's a trick for writing the symbol σ. Start from the inside top and go clockwise, making sure the top is flat and parallel to the line your writing on. If you start at the far right end and go backward counterclockwise, your σ will look like a 6. Try it!

Insert B—Within Text

They don't come from the data, but rather they are numbers that we choose to help specify the model. Such numbers are called **parameters** of the model. ¶

We don't want to confuse the parameters with summaries of the data such as $\bar{y}$ and s, so we use special symbols. In Statistics, we almost always use Greek letters for parameters. Summaries of data are called **statistics** and are usually written with Latin letters. ¶

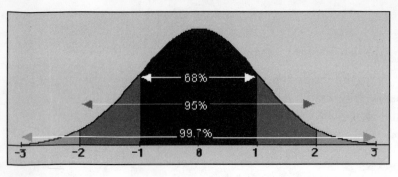

three standard deviations of the mean. These facts are summarized in a rule that we call (uh, let's see…) **The 68-95-99.7 Rule.**[1]

> Reaching out one, two, and three standard deviations on a Normal model gives the 68-95-99.7 rule.
> Fig 6.3

The First Three Rules for Working with Normal Models

Make a picture.

Make a picture.

Make a picture.

We are thinking about models, not histograms of data, but the three rules don't change. To help you think clearly, a simple hand-drawn sketch is all you need. Even experienced statisticians sketch pictures to help them think about Normal models. You should too.

Working with the 68-95-99.7 Rule, Step-by-Step

SAT scores have a shape that is roughly unimodal and symmetric, and are designed to have an overall mean of 500 and a standard deviation of 100. In any one year, the mean and standard deviation may differ from these target values by a very small amount, but they are a good overall approximation.

Suppose you earned a 600 on an SAT test. From that information and the 68-95-99.7 Rule, where you stand among all students who took the SAT?

ink

| **Variable:** Identify the variable, report the W's, | The variable is SAT scores. They are quantitative, but have no meaningful units. |

---

[1] This rule is called the "Empirical Rule" in older texts, because it first came from observation.. The rule was first published by Abraham De Moivre in 1733, 75 years before the Normal model was discovered. So maybe it should be called "De Moivre's Rule". But that wouldn't help us remember the important numbers, 68, 95, and 99.7.

Plan: Check that a Normal model is appropriate in order to use the 68-95-99.7 Rule.

We have no data, so we cannot make a histogram, but we are told that SAT scores are roughly unimodal and symmetric.

Specify μ and σ.

We will model *SAT score* with a N(500, 100) model.

Show

Mechanics: Make a picture of this Normal model. (A simple sketch is all you need.)

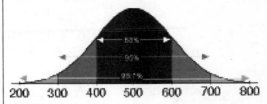

A score of 600 is one standard deviation above the mean. That corresponds to one of the points in the 68-95-99.7% Rule.

Locate your score

Tell

Interpretation: State your conclusion

About 32% (100% - 68%) of those who took the test were more than one standard deviation from the mean, and only half of those were on the high side. So about 16% (half of 32%) of the test scores were better than 600.

The bounds of SAT scoring at 200 and 800 can also be explained by the 68-95-99.7 Rule. Since 200 and 800 are three standard deviations from 500, it hardly pays to extend the scoring on either side any farther. We'd get more information only on 100-99.7 = 0.3% of students.

Finding Normal Percentiles by Hand

An SAT score of 600 is easy to assess, because we can think of it as one standard deviation above the mean. But if your score was 680, where do you stand among the rest of the people tested? Your *z*-score is 1.80, so you are somewhere between 1 and 2 standard deviations above the mean. We figured out that no more than 16% of people score better than 600. By the same logic, no more than 2.5% of people score better than 700. Can we be more specific than "between 16% and 2.5%"?

DRAFT: Do not distribute or copy

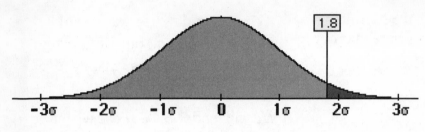

When the value doesn't fall exactly 1, 2 or 3 standard deviations from the mean, we can look it up in a table of Normal percentiles[2]. Nobody wants to lug around a bunch of tables, so we always use the *standard Normal*. That means we have to convert our data to z-scores before using the table. Your score of 680 has a z-score of (680-500)/100 = 1.8. In the piece of the table shown, we find your *z*-score by looking down the left column for the first two digits, 1.8, and across the top row for the third digit 0. The table gives the percentile as .9641. That means that 96.4% of the z-scores are less than 1.8. So only 3.6% of people scored better than 680 on the SAT.

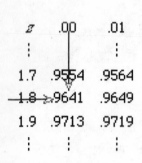

z	.00	.01
⋮	⋮	⋮
1.7	.9554	.9564
1.8	.9641	.9649
1.9	.9713	.9719
⋮	⋮	⋮

A table of Normal percentiles lets us find the percentage of individuals in a Standard Normal distribution falling below any specified z-score value.
Fig 6.4

Finding Normal Percentiles Using Technology

These days, finding percentiles from a Normal probability table is a "desert island" method—something we might do if we desperately needed a Normal percentile and were stranded miles from the mainland with only a Normal probability table. (Of course, you might feel just that way during a Statistics exam, so it's a good idea to know how to do it.) But, fortunately, most of the time, we can just use a calculator or computer. Graphing calculators, such as the TI-83, find normal percentiles and offer to draw the picture as well. And most statistics programs have functions to find normal percentiles.

The *ActivStats* Multimedia Assistant provided on the CD-ROM that accompanies this book offer two methods. The "Normal Model Tool" introduced along with the Normal model makes it easy to see how areas under parts of the normal model correspond to particular cut points. The tool is especially useful for problems in which you want to find the area *between* two z-scores.

---

[2] Many calculators and statistics computer packages do this too.

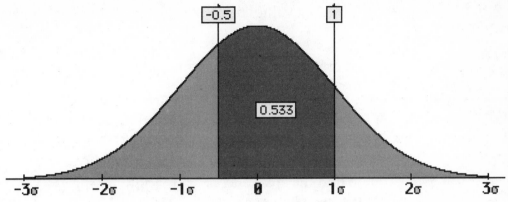

The ActivStats Normal model tool makes it easy to see how areas under parts of the normal model correspond to particular cut points.
Fig 6.5

The tool also allows you to work in the original units if you wish without converting everything to z-scores. This can be particularly helpful for understanding statements about relative frequencies.

ActivStats also offers a Normal table in which the picture of the normal model is interactive[3]. Grab the z-score cut point with your mouse and drag it to the value you are interested in. The table will adjust accordingly.

Working with normal Percentiles Step by Step I

What proportion of scores fall between 450 and 600?

Think

Variable:

We are told that SAT scores are nearly Normal.

Plan: Specify which Normal model to use.

We'll model SAT scores with a N(500, 100) model, using the mean and standard deviation specified for them.

Show

Mechanics: Make a Picture of this Normal model.

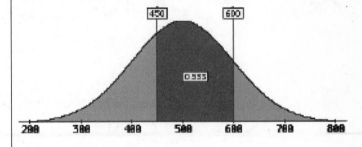

Locate the desired values. The easiest way is to use a technology that allows you to input the

We can see directly from this picture that about 53.3% of scores fall between 450 and 600 under the Normal model.

---

[3] Now it's time to open the CD that accompanies the book if you haven't done so already. The instructions for using the tools are on the CD as well. You can get to the tools directly in the Appendix of the *ActivStats* Lesson Book.

DRAFT: Do not distribute or copy

raw data values directly.

Alternatively, you'll have to convert 450 and 600 to z-scores before using technology or a table to find the two areas. Then you need to subtract them to find the area *between* the two values.	Standarizing the SAT scores, we can see that an SAT score of 600 corresponds to a z-score of z=(600-500)/100 = 1.0 and a score of 450 corresponds to a z-score of z= (450-500)/100 = -.50. From Table Z, we find that Area (Z< 1.0) = .8413 and Area (Z< -0.5) = .3085, so the proportion of z-scores *between* them is .8413-.3085= .5328 or 53.28%

Tell

Interpretation:

State your conclusion

Just a bit more than half the scores fall in the range from 450 to 600.

Finding areas from *z*-scores is the simplest way to work with the Normal model. But sometimes we start with areas and are asked to find the corresponding z-score or even the original data value. Here's an example that's goes the other way around starting with the percentile and working backward.

Working with Normal Percentiles Step-by-Step II

Suppose a college says they admit only people with SAT scores among the top 10%. What SAT score does this correspond to?

(With some technology - like the one on the CD - you can get this answer directly. But we'll show how to do it by looking up the values in a table here.)

Think

Variable:

We have no data, so we cannot make a histogram, but we are told that SAT scores are roughly unimodal and symmetric.

Plan: Specify which Normal model to use.

We'll model SAT scores with a N(500, 100) model.

Show

Mechanics: Make a Picture of this Normal model. Locate the desired percentile approximately. What value leaves about 10% of the area to the right?

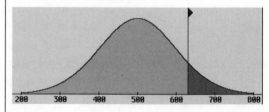

The college takes the top 10%, so their cutoff score is the 90th percentile. Using a Normal table locate the .90 (or as close to it as you can) in the interior of the table and find the corresponding z-score. Here the 1.2 is in the left margin and the .08 is in the margin above the entry. Putting them together gives 1.28.

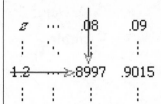

We can't find .90 exactly, but we found .8997. The corresponding z-score is 1.28.

Convert the z-score back to the original units.

A z-score of 1.28 is 1.28 standard deviations above the mean. Since the sd is 100, that's 128. So the cutoff is 128 points above the mean of 500, or 628.

Tell

Interpretation:

State your conclusion

Because the school wants SAT scores in the top 10%, the cutoff is 628. (Actually since SAT scores are reported only in multiples of 10, you'd have to score at least a 630.)

More Working with Normal Percentiles Step-By-Step

Working with normal percentiles can be a little tricky, depending on how the problem is stated. Here are a few more worked examples of the kind you are likely to see.

A cereal manufacturer has a machine that fills the boxes. Boxes are labeled "16 Ounces" so the company wants to have that much cereal in each box, but observations vary so there will be minor variations. If they set the machine at exactly 16 ounces and the normal model applies (or at least the distribution is roughly symmetric), then about 50% of the boxes will be underweight, making consumers unhappy and exposing the company to bad publicity and possible lawsuits. So they have to set the mean a little higher than 16.0 ounces.

Based on their experience with the packaging machine, they believe that the amount of cereal in the boxes fits a Normal Model with standard deviation 0.2 ounces. They decide to set the machine to put an average of 16.3 ounces in each box. Let's use that model to answer a series of questions about these cereal boxes.

DRAFT: Do not distribute or copy

Question 1: What fraction of the boxes will be underweight?

Think

Variable

We have no data, so we cannot make a histogram, but we are told that the distribution of weights from the machine is unimodal and roughly symmetric.

Plan: Specify which Normal model to use.

We use a N(16.3, 0.2) model.

Show

Mechanics: Make a picture of this Normal model. Locate the value you're interested in on the picture, label it and shade the appropriate region. Estimate from the picture the percentage that are underweight. (This will be useful later to check that your answer makes sense.)

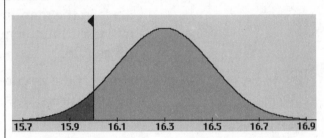

Reality check

It looks like a low percentage. Less than 20% for sure.

Convert your value of interest into a z-score and look up the value in the Normal table.

We want to know what fraction of the boxes will be less than 16. Since the mean is 16.3 ounces, and the standard deviation is 0.2 ounces,

$$z = \frac{16 - 16.3}{0.2} = -1.50$$

From a table, $Area(z < -1.50) = 0.0668$

Tell

Interpretation: State your conclusion. (Check that it is consistent with your earlier guess.)

We estimate that approximately 6.7% of the boxes will contain less than 16 ounces of cereal.

Question 2: The company's lawyers say that 6.7% is too high. They insist that no more than 4% of the boxes can be underweight. So, the company needs to set the machine to put more cereal in each box. What mean setting do they need?

Think

Variable: Check that a Normal model is appropriate

We have no data, so we cannot make a histogram, but we are told that the distribution of weights from the machine is unimodal and roughly symmetric.

Copyright © 2001, Dick DeVeaux, and Paul Velleman

Plan: Specify which Normal model to use. This time you are not given a value for the mean!

Reality check

We found out earlier that setting the machine to μ = 16.3 ounces made 6.7% of the boxes too light. We'll need to raise the mean a bit to reduce this fraction.

We don't know μ, the mean amount of cereal. We have been told that the standard deviation for this machine is 0.2 oz. So the model is N(μ, 0.2). We are also told that only 4% of the boxes can be below 16 oz.

Show

Mechanics: Make a picture of this Normal model. Center it at μ (since you don't know the mean) and shade the region below 16 ounces.

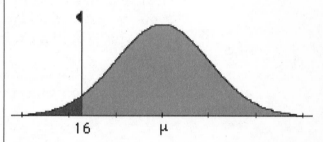

We want to find the z-score that has only 0.04 area to the left of it. The table shows this is z = -1.75.

In the standard Normal table, we can find the z-score that cuts off the lowest 4%.

Use this information to find μ. It's located 1.75 standard deviations to the right of 16.

Since σ is 0.2, that's 1.75*0.2 or 0.35 ounces more than 16.

Since 16 is 1.75 standard deviations below the mean, we need to set the mean at 16 + 1.75*0.2 = 16.35.

Tell

Interpretation: State your conclusion.

(This makes sense; we knew it would have to be just a bit higher than 16.3.)

The company must set the machine to average 16.35 ounces of cereal per box.

Question 3: The company president vetoes that plan, saying the company should give away less free cereal, not more. Her goal is to set the machine no higher than 16.2 ounces and still have only 4% underweight boxes. The only way to accomplish this is to reduce the standard deviation. What standard deviation must the company achieve, and what does that mean about the machine?

Think

Variable: Check that a Normal model is appropriate

We (still!) have no data, so we cannot make a histogram, but we are told that the distribution of weights from the machine is unimodal and roughly

DRAFT: Do not distribute or copy

symmetric.

Plan: Specify which Normal model to use. This time you don't know σ.

Reality check

We know the new standard deviation must be less that 0.2

We do know the mean, but we don't know the standard deviation. So, the model is N(16.2, σ)

Show

Mechanics: Make a picture of this Normal model. Center it at 16.2, and shade the area you're interested in. We want 4% of the area to the left of 16 ounces.

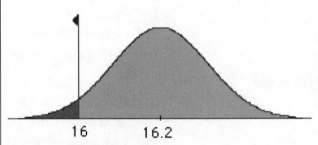

Find the z-score that cuts off the lowest 4% from a table.

We already know that the z-score with 4% below it is –1.75.

Solve for the σ.

We need 16 to be 1.75 σ's below 16.2. So 0.2 must be 1.75 σ's. In other words

$$1.75\sigma = 0.2$$

so $\sigma = 0.114$.

Tell

Interpretation: State your conclusion.

As we expected, the standard deviation is lower than before. Actually, quite a bit lower.

The company must get the machine to box cereal with a standard deviation of only 0.114 ounces. This means the machine must be more consistent (by nearly a factor of 2) in filling the boxes.

Are You Normal? How can I tell?

In the examples we've just worked through, we've assumed that the underlying data distribution was roughly unimodal and symmetric so that using a Normal model makes sense. When you actually have your own data you must *check* to see whether a Normal model is reasonable. Drawing a histogram of the data and looking at the shape is a good idea, but there's a more specialized graphical display that can help you to decide whether the Normal model is appropriate: the **normal probability plot.** If the distribution of the data is roughly Normal, the plot approximates a diagonal straight line.[4] Deviations from a straight line indicate that the distribution is not Normal. This plot is usually able to show deviations from Normality better than the corresponding histogram, but it is usually easier to understand how a distribution fails to be Normal by looking at its histogram.

The Nissan car gas mileage data provides an example of data that are nearly Normal.

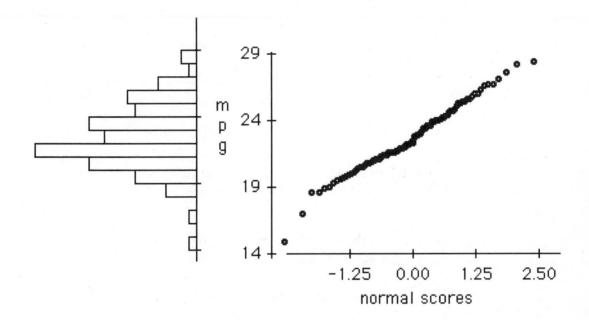

Histogram and Normal probability plot for the Nissan gas mileage data we saw in Chapter 5. The vertical axes are the same so each dot in the probability plot would fall into the bar of the histogram immediately to its left.   Fig 6.6

Most of the plot is straight. The two trailing low values correspond to the values in the histogram that trail off the low end. They're not quite in line with the rest of the data set. The Normal probability plot shows us that they're a bit lower than we'd expect of the lowest two values in a Normal model.

---

[4] In a normal probability plot, the data are shown on one axis and the values we would expect if the distribution were exactly Normal are shown on the other axis.

DRAFT: Do not distribute or copy

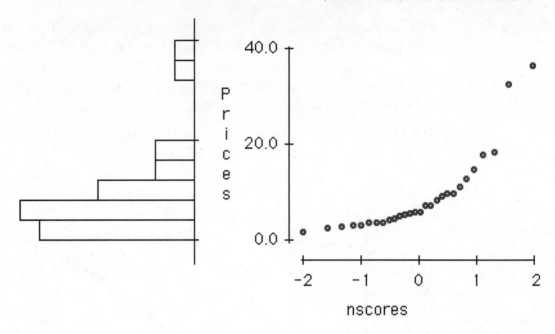

Histogram and probability plot for the Trinidad stock prices. Note how a skewed distribution corresponds to a bent probability plot.   **Fig 6.7**

By contrast, this line is far from straight. The Trinidad stock prices are skewed to the high end and the normal probability plot line is curved. We'd conclude from these pictures that approximations using the 68-95-99.7% rule for the stock data would not be very accurate.

How does a Normal Probability Plot Work?

Why does the normal probability plot work like that? We have 100 fuel efficiency measures for the Nissan car. The smallest of these has a z-score of –3.16. The Normal model can tell us what value to expect for the smallest number in a batch of 100. That turns out to be –2.48. So our first data value is smaller than we would expect from the Normal.

We can continue this and ask a similar question for each value. For example, the 14th smallest fuel efficiency has a z-score of almost exactly –1, and that's just what we should expect (well, -1.1 to be exact). A Normal Probability plot just makes all of these comparisons and plots them so it is easy to see how they come out.

When the values match up well the line is straight. If one or two points are surprising from the Normal's point of view they appear as not lining up. When the entire distribution is skewed or different from the Normal in some other way, the values won't match up very well at all and the plot will appear to bend.

It turns out to be tricky to find the values we expect. They are called "normal scores," but you can't just look them up in the tables. That's why probability plots are always made with technology and not by hand.

The best advice on using Normal probability plots is to see whether they are straight. If so, then your data look like data from a Normal model. If not, make a histogram to understand how they differ from the model.

What Can Go Wrong

- *Don't use Normal models when the distribution is not unimodal and symmetric.* Normal models are so easy and useful that it is tempting to use them even when they don't describe the data very well. That can lead to wrong conclusions. Don't use a Normal model without first looking at a picture of the data to check that it is unimodal and symmetric. A histogram, or better yet a normal probability plot, can help us tell whether a Normal model is appropriate.

  The CEO's had a mean total compensation of $2,818,743.10 and a standard deviation of $8,320,052.70. So, using the normal model rule, we should expect about 68% of the CEO's to have compensations between -$5, 501,309.5 and $11,138,795.80. In fact, fewer than 5% of the CEO's total compensations fall outside this range. What went wrong? The distribution is *clearly* not symmetric. Using the 68-95-99.7% rule on data like this will lead to silly results.

- *Don't use the mean and standard deviation when outliers are present.* Means and standard deviations can both be distorted by outliers, and no model based on distorted values will do a good job. So it's a good idea to always check for outliers. How? Make a picture.

Connections

(Insert A from Page 6-18A)

The only part of the data's context changed by standardizing is the *units*. All other aspects of the context do not depend on the choice or modification of measurement units. This fact points out an important distinction between the numbers the data provide for calculation and the meaning of the variables and the relationships among them. Standardizing can make the numbers easier to work with, but it does not alter the meaning.

Another way to look at this is to note that standardizing may change the center and spread values, but it does not affect the *shape* of a distribution. A *histogram* or *boxplot* of standardized values looks just the same as the histogram or boxplot of the original values except, perhaps, for the numbers on the axes.

When we summarized *shape, center,* and *spread* for *histograms,* we compared them to *unimodal, symmetric* shapes. You couldn't ask for a nicer example than the Normal model. And if the shape *is* like a Normal, we'll use the the mean and standard deviation to standardize the values.

DRAFT: Do not distribute or copy

Changing the center and spread of a variable is equivalent to changing its *units*. Indeed,

Key Concepts

Changing the center	Adding a constant to each data value adds the same constant to the mean, the median, and the quartiles, but does not change the standard deviation or IQR.
Changing the scale	Multiplying each data value by a constant multiplies both the measures of position (mean, median, and quartiles) and the measures of spread (standard deviation and IQR) by that constant.
Standardizing	We standardize to eliminate units. Standardized value can be compared and combined even if the original variables had different units and magnitudes.
Standardized value	A value found by subtracting the mean and dividing by the standard deviation.
Normal model	A useful family of models for unimodal, symmetric distributions.
Standard Normal model	A normal model with ~~mean~~ $\mu = 0$ and ~~standard deviation~~ $\sigma = 1$. $, \underline{N}(\mu, \sigma),$
z-score	A z-score tells how many standard deviations a value is from the mean ~~in a Normal model~~. Z-scores have a mean of zero and a standard deviation of one.
68-95-99.7 Rule	In a Normal model, 68% of values fall within one standard deviation of the mean, 95% fall within two standard deviations of the mean, and 99.7% fall within three standard deviations of the mean.
Normal Percentile	The Normal percentile corresponding to a z-score gives the percentage of values in a standard normal distribution found at that z-score or below.
Normal probability plot	A display to help assess whether a distribution of data is approximately Normal. If the plot is nearly straight, a Normal model is appropriate.
Changing center and spread	Changing the center and spread of a variable is equivalent to changing its *units*.

sert A
om
page 6-19A

Parameter   A numerically valued attribute of a model. For example, the values of μ and σ in a $N(\mu, \sigma)$ model are parameters.

Statistic   A value calculated from data to summarize aspects of the data. For example, the mean, $\bar{y}$, and standard deviation, s, are statistics.

Please note that the exercises in Chapter 6 need to be renumbered.

Skills

When you complete this lesson you should:

> *Think*
>
> - Understand how adding a constant and multiplying by a constant change the center or spread of a variable.
> - Recognize when standardization can be used to compare values.
> - Understand that standardizing uses the standard deviation as a ruler.
> - Recognize when a Normal model is appropriate.
>
> *Show*
>
> - Know how to calculate the z-score of an observation.
> - Know how to compare values from two different distributions using their z-scores.
> - Be able to use Normal models and the 68-95-99.7 rule to estimate the percentage of observations falling within one, two, or three standard deviations of the mean.
> - Know how to find the percentage of observations falling below any value in a Normal model using a Normal table or appropriate technology.
>
> *Tell*
>
> - Know what z-scores mean.
> - Be able to explain how extraordinary a standardized value may be using a Normal model.

Exercises

2. **Payroll** Here are the summary statistics for the weekly payroll of a small company: lowest salary = $300, mean salary = $700, median = $500, range = $1200, IQR = $600, first quartile = $350, standard deviation = $400.
   a) Do you think the distribution of salaries is symmetric, skewed to the left, or skewed to the right? Explain why.
   b) Between what two values are the middle 50% of the salaries found?
   c) Suppose business has been good and the company gives every employee a $50 raise. Tell the new value of each of the summary statistics.
   d) Instead, suppose the company gives each employee a 10% raise. Tell the new value of each of the summary statistics.

DRAFT: Do not distribute or copy

3. **Hams** A specialty foods company mails out "gourmet hams" to customers willing to pay a gourmet price. The hams vary in size from 4.15 to 7.45 pounds, with a mean weight of 6 pounds and standard deviation 0.65 pounds. The quartiles and median weights are 5.6, 6.2, and 6.55 pounds.
   a) Find the range and the IQR of the weights.
   b) Do you think the distribution of the weights is symmetric or skewed? If skewed, which way? Why?
   c) If these weights were expressed in ounces (1 pound = 16 ounces) what would the mean, standard deviation, quartiles, median, IQR, and range be?
   d) When the company ships these hams the box and packing materials add 30 ounces. What are the mean, standard deviation, quartiles, median, IQR, and range of weights of boxes shipped (in ounces)?
   e) One customer made a special order of a 10-pound ham. Which of these summary statistics might not change if that data value is added to the distribution?

4. **SAT or ACT?** Each year thousands of high school students take either the SAT or the ACT, standardized tests used in the college admissions process. Combined SAT scores can go as high as 1600, while the maximum ACT composite score is 36. Since the two exams use very different scales, comparisons of performance are difficult. A convenient rule of thumb is $SAT = 40 * ACT + 150$; that is, multiply an ACT score by 40 and add 150 points to estimate the equivalent SAT score.

   An admissions officer reports the following statistics about the ACT scores of 2355 students who applied to her college. Find the summaries of equivalent SAT scores.

Lowest score = 19	Mean = 27	Standard deviation = 3
Top 25% above 30	Median = 28	IQR = 6

5. **Cold U?** A high school senior uses the internet to get information on February temperatures in the town where he'll be going to college. He finds a website with some statistics, but they are given in degrees Celsius. The conversion formula is $F = \frac{9}{5}C + 32$. Determine the Fahrenheit equivalents for the summary information below.

Maximum temperature = 11°	Range = 33°	Mean = 1°
Standard deviation = 7°	Median = 2°	IQR = 16°

6. **Temperatures** A town's January high temperatures average 36° with a standard deviation of 10°, while in July the mean high temperature is 74° and standard deviation 8°. In which month is it more unusual to have a day with a high temperature of 55°? Explain.

Copyright © 2001, Dick DeVeaux, and Paul Velleman

7. **Placement Exams** An incoming freshman took her college's placement exams in French and mathematics. In French, she scored 82, and in math 86. The overall results on the French exam had a mean of 72 and standard deviation 8, while the mean math score was 68 with standard deviation 12. On which exam did she do better compared to the other freshmen?

8. **Final exams** Anna, a language major, took final exams in both French and Spanish and scored 83 on both. Her roommate Megan, also taking both courses, scored 77 on the French exam and 95 on the Spanish exam. Overall, student scores on the French exam had a mean of 81 and standard deviation 5, and the Spanish scores had mean 74 and standard deviation 15.
   a) In order to qualify for language honors, a major must maintain at least an 85 average for all language courses taken. So far, which student qualifies?
   b) Which student's overall performance was better?

9. **MP3s** Two companies market new batteries targeted at owners of personal music players. DuraTunes claim a mean battery life of 11 hours, while RockReady advertises 12 hours.
   a) Explain why you would also like to know the standard deviations of the battery lifespans before deciding which brand to buy.
   b) Suppose those standard deviations are 2 hours for DuraTunes and 1.5 hours for RockReady. You are headed for 8 hours at the beach. Which battery is most likely to last all day? Explain.
   c) If your beach trip is all weekend, and you probably will have the music on for 16 hours, which battery is most likely to last? Explain.

10. **Professors** A friend tells you about a recent study dealing with the number of years of teaching experience among current college professors. He remembers the mean, but can't recall whether the standard deviation was 6 months, 6 years, or 16 years. Tell him which one it must have been, and why.

11. **Rock Concerts** A popular band on tour played a series of concerts in large venues. They always drew a large crowd, averaging 21,359 fans. While they did not announce (and probably never calculated) the standard deviation, which of these values do you think is most likely to be correct: 20, 200, 2000, or 20000? Explain your choice.

DRAFT: Do not distribute or copy

12. **Guzzlers?** EPA fuel economy estimates for automobile models tested recently predicted a mean of 24.8 mpg and standard deviation of 6.2 mpg for highway driving. Assume that a Normal model can be applied.
    a) Draw the model for auto fuel economy. Clearly label it showing what the 68-95-99.7 Rule predicts about miles per gallon.
    b) In what interval would you expect the central 68% of autos to be found?
    c) About what percent of autos should get more than 31 mpg?
    d) About what percent of cars should get between 31 and 37 mpg?
    e) Describe the gas mileage of the worst 2.5% of all cars.

13. **IQ** Some IQ tests are standardized to a normal model with mean 100 and standard deviation 16.
    a) Draw the model for these IQ scores. Clearly label it showing what the 68-95-99.7 Rule predicts about the scores.
    b) In what interval would you expect the central 95% of IQ scores to be found?
    c) About what percent of people should have IQ scores above 116?
    d) About what percent of people should have IQ scores between 68 and 84?
    e) About what percent of people should have IQ scores above 132?

14. **Winter Olympics 2002 Downhill** Fifty-three men qualified for the men's alpine downhill race in Salt Lake City. The gold medal winner finished in 1 minute 39.13 seconds. All competitors' times (in seconds) are found in the following table:

99.13	99.35	99.41	99.78	99.96
100.00	100.30	100.31	100.37	100.39
100.58	100.74	100.74	100.76	100.81
100.84	100.85	101.05	101.24	101.25
101.27	101.56	101.66	101.69	101.70
101.76	101.84	101.85	101.86	101.86
101.88	102.15	102.31	102.52	102.54
103.04	103.19	103.20	103.33	103.63
103.73	103.75	104.35	105.25	105.34
105.49	106.36	107.63	107.65	108.37
108.84	109.75	114.42		

    a) The mean time was 102.71 seconds with a standard deviation of 3.01 seconds. If the normal model is appropriate, what percentage of times will be less than 99.7 seconds?
    b) What is the actual percentage of times less than 99.7 seconds?
    c) Why do you think the two percentages don't agree?

    d) Create a histogram of these times. What do you see?

15. **Rivets** A company that manufactures rivets believes the shear strength (in pounds) is modeled by N(800, 50).
    a) Draw and label the Normal model.
    b) Would it be safe to use these rivets in a situation requiring a shear strength of 750 pounds? Explain.
    c) About what percent of these rivets would you expect to fail below 900 pounds?
    d) Rivets are used in a variety of applications with varying shear strength requirements. Up to what shear strength requirement would you feel comfortable approving the use of this company's rivets? Explain your reasoning.

16. **Trees** A forester measured 27 of the trees in a large woods that is up for sale. He found a mean diameter of 10.4 inches and a standard deviation of 4.7 inches. Suppose these trees provide an accurate description of the whole forest, and that a Normal model applies.
    a) Draw the Normal model for tree diameters.
    b) What size would you expect the central 95% of all trees to be?
    c) About what percent of the trees should be less than an inch in diameter?
    d) About what percent of trees should be between 5.7 and 10.4 inches in diameter?
    e) About what percent of the trees should be over 15 inches in diameter?

17. **Trees, Part II** Later on the forester shows you a histogram of the tree diameters he used in analyzing the woods that were for sale. Do you think he was justified in using a Normal model? Explain, citing some specific concerns.

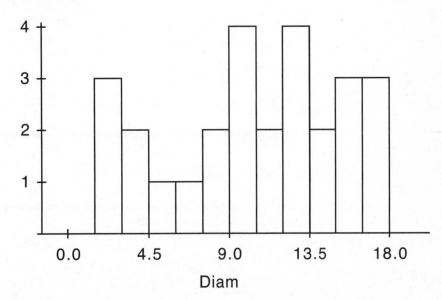

           DRAFT: Do not distribute or copy

18. **TV watching** A survey of 200 college students conducted during the week of March 15 1999 showed the following distribution of the number of hours of TV watched per week:

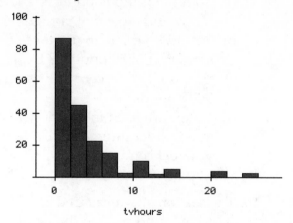

The mean is 3.66 hours with a standard deviation of 4.93 hours.
a) According to the normal model, what percentage of students will watch fewer than 1 standard deviation below the mean number of hours?
b) For these data, what does that mean? Explain.
c) Explain the problem in using the normal model for these data.

19. **Customer Data Base** A large philanthropic organization keeps records on the people who have contributed to their cause. In addition to keeping records of past giving, they buy demographic data on neighborhoods from the U.S. Census Bureau. Eighteen of these variables concern the ethnicity of the neighborhood of the donor. Here is a histogram and summary statistics for the percentage of whites in the neighborhoods of 500 donors:

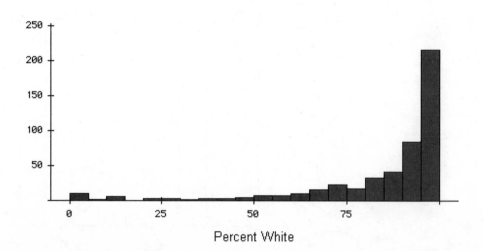

a) Which is a better summary of the percentage of white residents in the neighborhoods, the mean or the median? Explain.
b) Which is a better summary of the spread, the IQR or the standard deviation? Explain.
c) From a Normal model, about what percentage of neighborhoods should have percent white within one standard deviation of the mean?
d) What percentage of neighborhoods actually have percent white within one standard deviation of the mean?
e) Explain the discrepancy between c) and d).

Summary of No Selector	ETH1
Count	500
Mean	83.59
Median	93
StdDev	22.2562
Min	0
Max	99
IntQRange	17

20. **Normal Models** What percent of a standard Normal model is found in each region? Be sure to draw a picture first.
    a) $z > 1.5$
    b) $z < 2.25$
    c) $-1 < z < 1.15$
    d) $|z| > 0.5$

21. **Normal Models, Again** What percent of a standard Normal model is found in each region? Draw a picture first.
    a) $z > -2.05$
    b) $z < -0.33$
    c) $1.2 < z < 1.8$
    d) $|z| < 1.28$

22. **More Normal Models** In a standard Normal model what value(s) of z cuts off the region described? Don't forget to draw a picture.
    a) the highest 20%
    b) the highest 75%
    c) the lowest 3%
    d) the middle 90%

23. **Yet another Normal Model** In a standard Normal model what value(s) of z cuts off the region described? Remember to draw a picture first.
    a) the lowest 12%
    b) the highest 30%
    c) the highest 7%
    d) the middle 50%

24. **Parameters** Every Normal model is defined by its parameters, the mean and the standard deviation. For each model described below, find the missing parameter. As always, start by drawing a picture.
    a) $\mu = 20$, 45% above 30; $\sigma = ?$
    b) $\mu = 88$, 2% below 50; $\sigma = ?$
    c) $\sigma = 5$, 80% below 100; $\mu = ?$
    d) $\sigma = 15.6$, 10% above 17.2; $\mu = ?$

DRAFT: Do not distribute or copy

25. **Parameters II** Every Normal model is defined by its parameters, the mean and the standard deviation. For each model described below, find the missing parameter. Don't forget to draw a picture.
    a) $\mu = 1250$, 35% below 1200; $\sigma = ?$
    b) $\mu = 0.64$, 12% above 0.70; $\sigma = ?$
    c) $\sigma = 0.5$, 90% above 10.0; $\mu = ?$
    d) $\sigma = 220$, 3% below 202; $\mu = ?$

26. **Cholesterol** Assume the cholesterol levels of adult American women can be described by a Normal model with mean 188 and standard deviation 24.
    a) Draw and label the Normal model.
    b) What percent of adult women do you expect to have cholesterol levels over 200?
    c) What percent of adult women do you expect to have cholesterol levels between 150 and 170?
    d) Estimate the interquartile range of the cholesterol levels.
    e) Above what value are the highest 15% of women's cholesterol levels?

27. **Tires** A tire manufacturer believes that the tread life of their snow tires can be described by a Normal model with a mean of 32000 miles and standard deviation 2500 miles.
    a) If you buy a set of these tires, would it be reasonable for you hope they'll last 40000 miles? Explain.
    b) Approximately what fraction of these tires can be expected to last less than 30000 miles?
    c) Approximately what fraction of these tires can be expected to last between 30000 and 35000 miles?
    d) Estimate the IQR of the treadlifes.
    e) In planning a marketing strategy, a local tire dealer wants to offer a refund to any customer whose tires fail to last a certain number of miles. However, the dealer does not want to take too big a risk. If the dealer is willing to give refunds to no more than 1 of every 25 customers, what mileage can he guarantee these tires to last?

28. **Kindergarten** Companies who design furniture for elementary school classrooms produce a variety of sizes for kids of different ages. Suppose the heights of kindergarten children can be described by a Normal model with mean 38.2 inches and standard deviation 1.8 inches.
    a) What fraction of kindergarten kids should the company expect to be less than three feet tall?
    b) In what height interval should the company expect to find the middle 80% of kindergartners?
    c) At least how tall are the biggest 10% of kindergartners?

29. **Body Temperatures** Most people think that "normal" adult body temperature is 98.6°. That figure, based on a 19th century study, has recently been challenged. In a 1992 article in the *Journal of the American Medical Association*, researchers reported that a more accurate figure may be 98.2°. Furthermore, the standard deviation appeared to be around 0.7°. Assume that a Normal model is appropriate.
    a) In what interval would you expect most people's body temperatures to be? Explain.
    b) What fraction of people would be expected to have body temperatures above 98.6°?
    c) Below what body temperature are the coolest 20% of all people?

30. *First Steps** While only 5% of babies have learned to walk by the age of 10 months, 75% are walking by 13 months of age. If the age at which babies develop the ability to walk can be described by a Normal model, find the parameters (mean and standard deviation).

31. *Trout** Wildlife biologists believe that the weights of adult trout can be described by a Normal model. They collect data from fishermen, finding that 22% of the trout caught were thrown back because they were below the 2-pound minimum, and only 6% weighed over 5 pounds. What mean and standard deviation should define the model?

32. **Eggs** Hens usually begin laying eggs when they are about six months old. Young hens tend to lay smaller eggs, often weighing less than the desired minimum weight of 54 grams
    a) The average weight of the eggs produced by the young hens is 50.9 grams, and only 28% of their eggs exceed the desired minimum weight. If a Normal model is appropriate, what would the standard deviation of the egg weights be?
    b) By the time these hens have reached the age of one year, the eggs they produce average 67.1 grams, and 98% of them are above the minimum weight. What is the standard deviation for the appropriate Normal model for these older hens?
    c) Are egg sizes more consistent for the younger hens or the older ones? Explain.
    d) *A certain poultry farmer finds that 8% of his eggs are underweight, and that 12% weigh over 70 grams. Estimate the mean and standard deviation of his eggs.

33. **Tomatoes** Ag scientists are working on developing an improved variety of Roma tomatoes. Marketing research indicates that customers are likely to bypass Romas that weigh less than 70 grams. The current variety of Roma plants produce fruit that average 74 grams, but 11% of the tomatoes are too small. It is reasonable to assume a Normal model applies.
    a) What is the standard deviation of the weights of Romas now being grown?

DRAFT: Do not distribute or copy

b) Scientists hope to reduce the frequency of undersize tomatoes to no more than 4%. One way to accomplish this is to raise the average size of the fruit. If the standard deviation remains the same, what target mean should they have as a goal?

c) The researchers produce a new variety with a mean weight of 75 grams that meets the 4% goal. What is the standard deviation of the weights of these new Romas?

d) Based on their standard deviations, compare the tomatoes produced by the two varieties.

Part I Review

Describing Data – Quick Review

It's time to put it all together. Real data don't come tagged with instructions for use. So let's step back and look at how the key concepts and skills we've seen work together. This brief list and the review exercises that follow should help you check your understanding of Statistics so far.

➤ Data come in two flavors: categorical and quantitative.

➤ To describe categorical data:
  - Make a picture. Bar graphs work well for comparing counts in categories.
  - Summarize the distribution with a table of counts or relative frequencies (percents) in each category.
  - Pie charts and segmented bar charts display divisions of a whole.
  - Compare distributions with plots side-by-side.
  - Look for associations between variables by comparing marginal and conditional distributions.

➤ To describe quantitative data:
  - Make a picture. Use histograms, boxplots, stem-and-leaf displays or dotplots. Stem-and-leaf's are great by hand and good for small data sets. Histograms are a good way to see the distribution. Boxplots are best for comparing several distributions.
  - Describe distributions in terms of their shape, center, spread, and note any unusual features such as gaps or outliers.
  - The shape of most distributions you'll see will likely be uniform, unimodal or bimodal. It may be multimodal. If it is unimodal, then it may be symmetric or skewed.
  - A 5-number summary makes a good numerical description of a distribution: min, Q1, median, Q3, and max.
  - If the distribution is skewed, be sure to include the median and interquartile range (IQR) when you describe its center and spread.
  - A distribution that is severely skewed may benefit from re-expressing the data. If it is skewed to the high end, taking logs often works well.
  - If the distribution is mound-shaped and symmetric, describe its center and spread with the mean and standard deviation.
  - Use the standard deviation as a ruler to tell how unusual an observed value may be, or to compare or combine measurements made on different scales.

DRAFT: Do not distribute or copy

- Changing scales by adding or subtracting a constant affects measures of position but not measures of spread. Multiplying or dividing by a constant affects both.
- When a distribution is roughly mound-shaped and symmetric it may approximate a Normal model. For Normal models the 68-95-99.7% Rule is a good rule of thumb.
- If the Normal model fits well (check a Normal probability plot), then Normal percentile tables or functions found in most statistics technology can provide more detailed values.

Need more help with some of this? It never hurts to re-read sections of the chapters! And in the following pages we offer you more opportunities[1] to review these concepts and skills.

The exercises below use the concepts and skills you've learned in the first six chapters. But, to be more realistic and more useful for your review, they don't tell you which of the concepts or methods you need. But neither will the exam.

> 'You damn sadist,' said mr cummings,
>
> 'you try to make people think'.
>
> Ezra Pound (1885-1972)

Exercises

1. **Bananas** Here are the prices (in cents per pound) of bananas reported from 15 markets surveyed by the US Department of Agriculture.

51	52	45
48	53	52
50	49	52
48	43	46
45	42	50

   a) Display these data with an appropriate graph.
   b) Report appropriate summary statistics.
   c) Write a few sentences about this distribution.

2. **Prenatal Care** Results of a 1996 American Medical Association report about the infant mortality rate for twins carried for the full term of a normal pregnancy are shown below, broken down by the level of prenatal care the mother had received.

Full-Term Pregnancies Level of Prenatal Care	Infant Mortality Rate among Twins (Deaths per thousand live births)
Intensive	5.4
Adequate	3.9
Inadequate	6.1
Overall	5.1

   a) Is the overall rate the average of the other three rates? Should it be? Explain.
   b) Do these results indicate that adequate prenatal care is important for pregnant women? Explain.
   c) Do these results suggest that a woman pregnant with twins should be wary of seeking too much medical care? Explain.

---

[1] If you doubted that we are teachers, this should convince you. Only a teacher would call additional homework exercises an "opportunity".

3. **Singers** The boxplots shown display the heights (in inches) of 130 members of a choir. Write a few sentences describing what you see.

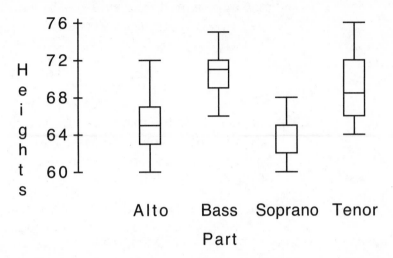

4. **Dialysis** In a study of dialysis researchers found that "of the three patients who were currently on dialysis, 67% had developed blindness and 33% had their toes amputated". What kind of display might be appropriate for these data? Explain.

5. **Beanstalks** Beanstalk Clubs are social clubs for very tall people. To join a man must be over 6'2" tall, and a woman over 5'10". The National Health Survey suggests that heights of adults may be normally distributed with means heights of 63.6" for men and 60.9" for women. The respective standard deviations are 2.5" and 2.8".
   a) You are probably not surprised to learn that men are generally taller than women, but what does the greater standard deviation for women's heights indicate?
   b) Who is more likely to qualify for Beanstalk membership, men or women?

6. **Bread** Clarksburg Bakery is trying to predict how many loaves to bake. In the last 100 days, they have sold between 95 and 140 loaves per day. Here is a histogram of the number of loaves they sold for the last 100 days.
   a) Describe the distribution.
   b) Which should be larger, the mean number of sales, or the median? Explain.

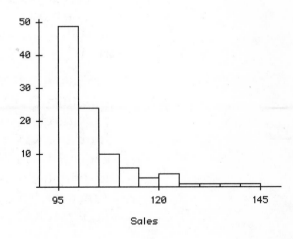

c) Here are the summary statistics for Clarksburg Bakery's bread sales. Use these statistics and the histogram above to create a boxplot. You may approximate the values of any outliers.

Summary of Sales

Median	100
Min	95
Max	140
25th %tile	97
25th %tile	105.5

d) For these data the mean was 103 loaves sold per day, with a standard deviation of 9 loaves. Do these statistics suggest that Clarksburg Bakery should expect to sell between 94 and 112 loaves on about 68% of the days? Explain.

7. **Watsamatta University** Public relations staff at Watsamatta U. collected data on people's opinions of various colleges and universities in their state. They phoned 850 local residents. After identifying themselves, the callers asked the survey participants their ages, whether they had attended college, and whether they had a favorable opinion of the university. The official report to the university's directors claimed that, in general, people had very favorable opinions about Watsamatta U.
   a) Identify the W's of these data.
   b) Identify the variables, classify each as categorical or quantitative, and specify units if relevant.
   c) Are you confident about the report's conclusion? Explain.

8. **Acid Rain** Based on long-term investigation researchers have suggested that the acidity (pH) of rainfall in the Shenandoah Mountains can be described by the Normal model N(4.9, 0.6).
   a) Draw and carefully label the model.
   b) What percent of storms produce rain with pH over 6?
   c) What percent of storms produce rainfall with pH under 4?
   d) The lower the pH, the more acidic the rain. What is the pH level for the most acidic 20% of all storms?
   e) What is the pH level for the least acidic 5% of all storms?
   f) What is the IQR for the pH of rainfall?

9. **Fraud detection** A credit card bank is investigating the incidence of fraudulent card use. They suspect that the type of product bought may provide clues to the fraud. To examine it, they look at the Standard Industrial Code (SIC) of the business related to the transaction. This is a code that was used by the U.S. Census Bureau and Statistics Canada to identify the type of business of every registered business in North America[2]. For example, 1011 designates Meat and Meat Products (except Poultry), 1012 is Poultry Products,1021 is Fish Products, 1031 is Canned

---

[2] Since 1997 the SIC has been replaced by the NASIC, a code of 6 letters.

DRAFT: Do not distribute or copy

and Preserved Fruits and Vegetables, and 1032 is Frozen Fruits and Vegetables.

A company intern produces the following histogram of the SIC codes for 1536 transactions:

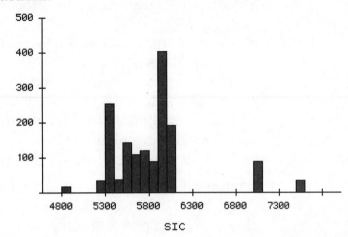

He also reports that the mean SIC is 5823.13 with a standard deviation of 488.17.

a) Comment on any problems you see with the use of the mean and standard deviation as summary statistics.

b) How well do you think the normal model will work on these data? Explain.

10. **Streams** As part of the coursework, a class at an upstate NY college collects data on streams each year. Students record a number of biological, chemical, and physical variables, including the stream name, the substrate of the stream (Limestone, Shale, or Mixed), the pH, the temperature (°C), and BCI, a measure of biological diversity.

a) Name each variable, indicating whether it is categorical or quantitative, and giving the units if available.

b) These streams have been classified according to their substrate – the composition of soil and rock over which they flow – as summarized in the table. What kind of graph might be used to display these data?

Group	Count	%
Limestone	77	44.8
Mixed	26	15.1
Shale	69	40.1

11. **Cramming** One Thursday researchers gave students enrolled in a section of basic Spanish a set of 50 new vocabulary words to memorize. On Friday the students took a vocabulary test. When they returned to class the following Monday they were retested – without advance warning. Both sets of test scores for the 28 students are shown.
    a) Create a graphical display to compare the two distributions of scores.
    b) Write a few sentences about the scores reported on Friday and Monday.
    c) Create a graphical display showing the distribution of the *changes* in student scores.
    d) Describe the distribution of changes.

FRI	MON
42	36
44	44
45	46
48	38
44	40
43	38
41	37
35	31
43	32
48	37
43	41
45	32
47	44
50	47
34	34
38	31
43	40
39	41
46	32
37	36
40	31
41	32
48	39
37	31
36	41

12. **Computers and Internet** A U.S. Census Bureau report (August 2000, Current Population Survey) found that 51.0% of homes had a personal computer and 41.5% had access to the Internet. A newspaper concluded that 92.5% of homes had either a computer or access to the Internet. Do you agree? Explain.

13. **Let's Play Cards** You pick a card from a deck and record its denomination (7, say) and its suit (maybe spades).
    a) Is the variable Suit categorical or quantitative?
    b) Name a game you might be playing for which you would consider the variable Denomination to be categorical. Explain.
    c) Name a game you might be playing for which you would consider the variable Denomination to be quantitative. Explain.

14. **Accidents** In 2001 Progressive Insurance asked customers who had been involved in auto accidents how far they were from home when the accident happened. The data are summarized in the table.
    [www.chase.com/cm/cs?pagename=Chase/Href&urlname=chase/pf/insurance/june02caraccidents]
    a) Create an appropriate graph of these data.
    b) Do these data indicate that it driving near home is particularly dangerous? Explain.

Miles from Home	% of Accidents
less than 1	23
1 to 5	29
6 to 10	17
11 to 15	8
16 to 20	6
over 20	17

15. **Hard Water** In an investigation of environmental causes of disease, data were collected on the annual mortality rate (deaths per 100,000) for males in 61 large towns in England and Wales. In addition, the water hardness was recorded as the calcium concentration (parts per million, ppm) in the drinking water.
    a) What are the variables in this study? For each, indicate whether it is quantitative or categorical and what the units are.
    b) Here are histograms of calcium concentration and mortality. Describe the distributions of the two variables.

DRAFT: Do not distribute or copy

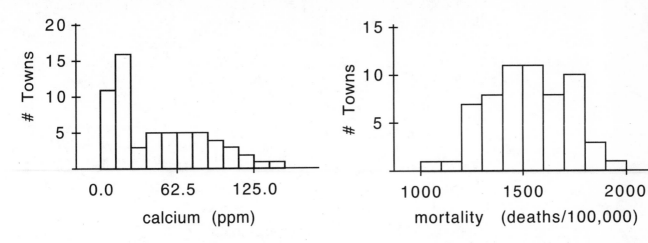

16. **Hard Water II** The dataset from England and Wales also notes for each town whether it was south or north of Derby. Here are some summary statistics and a comparative boxplot for the two regions.

Summary of   mortality

Group	Count	Mean	Median	StdDev
North	34	1631.59	1631	138.470
South	27	1388.85	1369	151.114

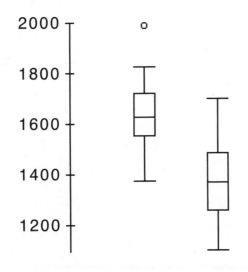

a) What is the overall mean mortality rate for the two regions?
b) Do you see evidence of a difference in mortality rates? Explain.

17. **Seasons** Average daily temperatures in January and July for 60 large US cities are graphed in the histograms below.

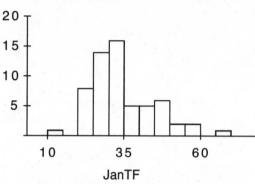

JanTF

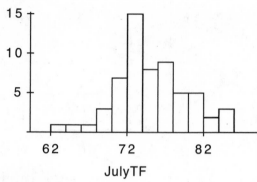

JulyTF

a) What aspect of these histograms makes it difficult to compare the distributions?

b) What differences do you see between the distributions of January and July average temperatures?

c) Differences in temperatures (July – Jan) for each of the cities are displayed in the boxplot at the right. Write a few sentences describing what you see.

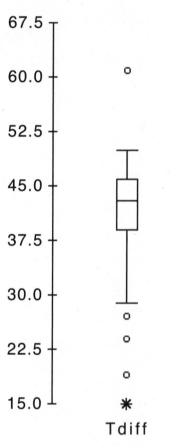

Tdiff

18. **Old Faithful** It is a common belief that Yellowstone's most famous geyser erupts once an hour at very predictable intervals. The histogram below shows the time gaps (in minutes) between 222 successive eruptions. Describe this distribution.

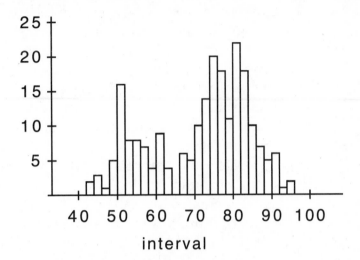

interval

19. **Old Faithful?** Does the duration of an eruption have an effect on the length of time that elapses before the next eruption?
    a) The histogram below shows the duration (in minutes) of those 222 eruptions. Describe this distribution.

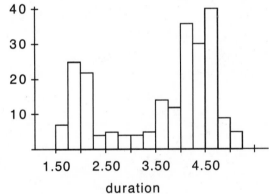

duration

    b) Explain why it is not appropriate to find summary statistics for this distribution.
    c) Let's classify the eruptions as "long" or "short", depending upon whether or not they last at least 3 minutes. Describe what you see in the comparative boxplots.

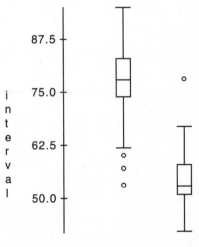

Long   Short

20. **Teen Drivers** In its *Traffic Safety Facts 2000*, the US Department of Transportation reported that 6.8% of licensed drivers are between the ages of 15 and 20, yet this age group is behind the wheel in 14% of all fatal crashes. Use these statistics to explain the concept of independence.

21. **Liberty's Nose** Is the Statue of Liberty's nose too long? Her nose measures 4' 6", but she is a large statue after all. Her arm is 42 feet long. That means her arm is 42/4.5 = 9.3 times as long as her nose. Is that a reasonable ratio? Shown in the table are arm and nose lengths of 18 girls in a statistics class, and the ratio of arm to nose length for each.

    a) Make an appropriate plot and describe the distribution of the ratios.
    b) Summarize the ratios numerically, choosing appropriate measures of center and spread.
    c) Is the ratio of 9.3 for the Statue of Liberty unrealistically low? Explain.

Arm (cm)	Nose (cm)	arm/nose ratio
73.8	5	14.8
74	4.5	16.4
69.5	4.5	15.4
62.5	4.7	13.3
68.6	4.4	15.6
64.5	4.8	13.4
68.2	4.8	14.2
63.5	4.4	14.4
63.5	5.4	11.8
67	4.6	14.6
67.4	4.4	15.3
70.7	4.3	16.4
69.4	4.1	16.9
71.7	4.5	15.9
69	4.4	15.7
69.8	4.5	15.5
71	4.8	14.8
71.3	4.7	15.2

22. **Winter Olympics 2002 Speed Skating** The top 25 men's and 25 women's 500 meter speed skating times are listed in the table below:

Casey FitzRandolph	USA	69.23
Hiroyasu Shimizu	Japan	69.26
Kip Carpenter	USA	69.47
Gerard van Velde	Netherlands	69.49
Lee Kyu-Hyuk	South Korea	69.59
Joey Cheek	USA	69.6
Mike Ireland	Canada	69.6
Toyoki Takeda	Japan	69.81
Jan Bos	Netherlands	69.86
Erben Wennemars	Netherlands	69.89
Dmitry Lobkov	Russia	70.1
Kuniomi Haneishi	Japan	70.11
Sergey Klevchenya	Russia	70.28
Manabu Horii	Japan	70.32
Janne Hanninen	Finland	70.33
Pawel Abratkiewicz	Poland	70.44
Choi Jae-Bong	South Korea	70.57
Dmitry Dorofeyev	Russia	70.75
Michael Kuenzel	Germany	70.84
Patrick Bouchard	Canada	70.88

DRAFT: Do not distribute or copy

Li Yu	China	70.97
Tomasz Swist	Poland	71.27
Davide Carta	Italy	71.39
Eric Brisson	Canada	71.54
Park Jae-Man	South Korea	71.96
Catriona LeMay Doan	Canada	74.75
Monique Garbrecht-Enfeldt	Germany	74.94
Sabine Voelker	Germany	75.19
Andrea Nuyt	Netherlands	75.37
Anzhelika Kotyuga	Belarus	75.39
Tomomi Okazaki	Japan	75.64
Svetlana Zhurova	Russia	75.64
Marianne Timmer	Netherlands	76.17
Yukari Watanabe	Japan	76.2
Svetlana Kaykan	Russia	76.31
Eriko Sannmiya	Japan	76.37
Sayuri Osuga	Japan	76.42
Wang Manli	China	76.62
Chris Witty	USA	76.73
Jenny Wolf	Germany	76.73
Chiara Simionato	Italy	76.92
Marieke Wijsman	Netherlands	77.1
Choi Seung-Yong	South Korea	77.14
Marion Wohlrab	Germany	77.37
Becky Sundstrom	USA	77.6
Susan Auch	Canada	77.6
Eli Ochowicz	USA	77.71
Jin Hua	China	78.26
Yang Chunyuan	China	78.63
Cho Seon-Yeon	South Korea	78.78

a) The mean finishing time was 73.46 seconds with a standard deviation of 3.33 seconds. If the normal model is appropriate, what percent of the times should be within 1.67 seconds of 73.46?

b) What percent of the times actually fall within this range?

c) Explain.

23. **Sample** A study in South Africa focusing on the impact of health insurance identified 1590 children at birth and then sought to conduct follow-up health studies 5 years later. Only 416 of the original group participated in the 5-year follow-up study. This made researchers concerned that the follow-up group might not accurately resemble the total group in terms of health insurance. The table below summarizes the two groups by race and by presence of medical insurance when the child was born. Carefully explain how this study demonstrates

Simpson's paradox. [*Birth to Ten Study,* Medical Research Council, South Africa]

Number (%) insured	Group	
	Follow-up	Not Traced
Black	36 of 404 (8.9%)	91 of 1048 (8.7%)
White	10 of 12 (83.3%)	104 of 126 (82.5%)
Overall	46 of 416 (11.1%)	195 of 1174 (16.6%)

24. **Sluggers** Roger Maris's 1961 home run record stood until Mark McGwire hit 70 in 2000. Listed below are the home run totals for each season McGwire played. Also listed are Babe Ruth's home run totals.

    McGwire 3*, 49, 32, 33, 39, 22, 42, 9*, 9*, 39, 52, 58, 70, 65, 32*
    Ruth 54, 59, 35, 41, 46, 25, 47, 60, 54, 46, 49, 46, 41, 34, 22

    a) Find the 5-number summary for McGwire's career.
    b) Do any of his seasons appear to be outliers? Explain.
    c) McGwire played in only 18 games at the end of his first big league season, and missed major portions of some other seasons because of injuries to his back and knees. Those seasons might not be representative of his abilities. They are marked with asterisks in the list above. Omit these values and make parallel boxplots comparing McGwire's career to Babe Ruth's.
    d) Write a few sentences comparing the two sluggers.
    e) Create a side-by-side stem-and-leaf display comparing the careers of the two players.
    f) What aspects of the distributions are apparent in the stem-and-leaf displays that did not clearly show in the boxplots?

25. **Be Quick!** Avoiding an accident when driving can depend on your reaction time. That time, measured from the moment the driver first sees the danger until he gets his foot on the brake pedal, is thought to follow a Normal model with mean 1.5 seconds and standard deviation 0.18 seconds.
    a) Use the 68-95-99.7 Rule to draw the Normal model.
    b) Write a few sentences describing driver reaction times.
    c) What percent of drivers have a reaction time less than 1.25 seconds?
    d) What percent of drivers have reaction times between 1.6 and 1.8 seconds?
    e) What is the interquartile range of reaction times?
    f) Describe the reaction times of the slowest 1/3 of all drivers.

26. **Music and Memory** Is it a good idea to listen to music when studying for a big test? In a study conducted by some statistics students, 62 people were randomly assigned to listen to rap music, Mozart, or no music while attempting to memorize objects pictured on a page. They were

then asked to list all the objects they could remember. Here are the 5-number summaries for each group:

Music	n	Min	Q1	Median	Q3	Max
Rap	29	5	8	10	12	25
Mozart	20	4	7	10	12	27
None	13	8	9.5	13	17	24

a) Describe the W's for these data: who, what, where, why, when, how.
b) Name the variables and classify each as categorical or quantitative.
c) Create parallel boxplots to display these results.
d) Write a few sentences comparing the performances of the three groups.

27. **Wines** Here are the case prices for 36 wines produced in the Finger Lakes region.
a) Plot these data.
b) Find appropriate summary statistics.
c) Write a brief description of these wine prices.
d) What percent of the prices actually lie within one standard deviation of the mean? Comment.

123	70	90
80	78	72
52	103	138
112	92	93
118	118	106
95	131	59
151	115	97
100	128	130
66	135	76
143	100	88
110	75	60
115	105	85

28. **Pay** According to the *1999 National Occupational Employment and Wage Estimates* for Management Occupations, the mean hourly wage for Chief Executives was $48.67 and the median hourly wage was $52.08. By contrast, for General and Operations Managers, the mean hourly wage was $31.69 and the median was $27.23. Are these wage distributions likely to be symmetric, skewed left, or skewed right? Explain.

[Bureau of Labor Statistics (http://www.bls.gov/oes/1999/oes_nat.htm)].

29. **Engines** One measure of the size of an automobile engine is its "displacement", the total volume (in liters or cubic inches) of its cylinders. Summary statistics for several models of new cars are shown. These displacements were measured in cubic inches.

Summary of Displacement	
Count	38
Mean	177.289
Median	148.500
StdDev	88.8767
Range	275
25th %tile	105
75th %tile	231

a) How many cars were measured?
b) Why might the mean be so much larger than the median?
c) Describe the center and spread of this distribution with appropriate statistics.
d) Your neighbor is bragging about the 227 cubic inch engine he bought in his new car. Is that engine unusually large? Explain.
e) Are there any engines in this data set that you would consider to be outliers? Explain.

f) Is it reasonable to expect that about 68% of car engines measure between 88 and 266 cubic inches? (That's 177.289 ± 88.8767.) Explain.

g) We can convert all the data from cubic inches to cubic centimetes by multiplying by 16.4. For example, a 200 cubic inch engine has a displacement of 3280 cc. How would such a conversion affect each of the summary statistics?

30. **Engines, Again** Horsepower is another measure commonly used to describe auto engines. Here are the summary statistics and histogram displaying horsepowers of the same group of 38 cars.

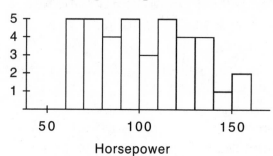

Summary of	**Horsepower**
Count	38
Mean	101.737
Median	100
StdDev	26.4449
Range	90
25th %tile	78
75th %tile	125

a) Describe the shape, center, and spread of this distribution.

b) What is the interquartile range?

c) Are any of these engines outliers in terms of horsepower? Explain.

d) Do you think the 68-95-99.7 Rule applies to the horsepower of auto engines? Explain.

e) From the histogram make a rough estimate of the percentage of these engines whose horsepower is within one standard deviation of the mean.

f) A fuel additive boasts in its advertising that it can "add 10 horsepower to any car". Assuming that is true, what would happen to each of these summary statistics if this additive were used in all the cars?

31. **Age and Party** The Gallup Poll conducted a representative telephone survey during the first quarter of 1999. Among their reported results was the following table concerning the preferred political party affiliation of respondents and their ages (found at www.gallup.com):

Age	Republican	Democratic	Independent	Total
18-29	241	351	409	1001
30-49	299	330	370	999
50-64	282	341	375	998
65+	279	382	343	1004
Total	**1101**	**1404**	**1497**	**4002**

a) What percentage of the people surveyed were Republicans?

b) Do you think this might be a reasonable estimate of the percentage of all voters who are Republicans? Expalin.

c) What percentage of the people surveyed were under 30 or over 65?

d) What percentage of the people were Independents under the age of 30?

DRAFT: Do not distribute or copy

e) What percentage of the Independents were under 30?

f) What percentage of the people under 30 were Independents?

32. **Age and Party II** Consider again the Gallup Poll results on age and political party.

a) What is the marginal distribution of party affiliation?

b) Create segmented bar graphs displaying the conditional distribution of party affiliation for each age group.

c) Summarize these poll results in a few sentences that might appear in a newspaper article about party affiliation in the US.

d) Do you think party affiliation is independent of the voter's age? Explain.

33. **Herbal Medicine** Researchers for the Herbal Medicine Council collected information on people's experiences with a new herbal remedy for colds. They went to a store selling natural health products. There they asked 100 customers whether they had taken the cold remedy and, if so, to rate, its effectiveness (on a scale from 1 to 10) in curing their symptoms. The Council concluded that this product was highly effective in treating the common cold.

a) Identify the W's of these data.

b) Identify the variables, classify each as categorical or quantitative, and specify units if relevant.

c) Are you confident about the Council's conclusion? Explain.

34. **Public Opinion** For many years Martha Stewart was a popular expert in home decorating, an arbiter of good taste, and very successful businesswoman. In June 2002 she came under attack amidst rumors of insider stock trading. A series of Gallup polls each contacted over 1000 people to ask about their overall opinion of her. Those polled could answer favorable, unfavorable, or that they did not know who she was. Results are summarized in the table.

	Oct 1999	June 2002	July 2002
Favorable	49%	46%	30%
Unfavorable	16%	27%	39%
Don't know	32%	23%	27%

a) Each poll should total 100%. Can you think of a reason why these do not?

b) How could the number of people who do not know who Martha Stewart is *increase* from June to July? Did people forget her? Or perhaps the poll is flawed? Explain how these results could be valid.

c) Display these results in a bar graph.

d) Display these results with pie charts.

e) Display these results with a timeplot.

f) Which display do you think best depicts these data? Why?

g) Write a few sentences describing Martha Stewart's public image.

35. **Bike Safety** The Massachusetts Governor's Highway Safety Bureau's report on bicycle injuries for the years 1991-2000 included the counts shown in the table.
a) What are the W's for these data?
b) Display the data in a stem-and-leaf display.
c) Display the data in a timeplot.
d) What is apparent in the stem-and-leaf display that is hard to see in the timeplot?
e) What is apparent in the timeplot that is hard to see in the stem-and-leaf display?
f) Write a few sentences about bicycle injuries in Massachusetts.

Year	Bicycle Injuries Reported
1991	1763
1992	1522
1993	1452
1994	1370
1995	1380
1996	1343
1997	1312
1998	1275
1999	1030
2000	1118

36. **Profits** Here is a stem-and-leaf display showing profits as a percent of sales for 29 of the *Forbes* 500 largest US corporations. The stems are split; each stem represents a span of 5%, from a loss of 9% to a profit of 25%.
a) Find the 5-number summary.
b) Draw a boxplot for these data.
c) Find the mean and standard deviation.
d) Describe the distribution of profits for these corporations.

```
-0 | 9 9
-0 | 1 2 3 4
 0 | 1 1 1 1 2 3 4 4 4
 0 | 5 5 5 5 6 7 9
 1 | 0 0 1 1 3
 1 |
 2 | 2
 2 | 5
```
Profits (% of sales)
(-0l3 means a loss of 3%)

37. **Some Assembly Required** A company that markets build-it-yourself furniture sells a computer desk that they advertise with the claim "Less than an hour to assemble." However, through post-purchase surveys they have learned that only 25% of their customers succeeded in building the desk in under an hour; 5% said it took them over 2 hours. The company assumes that consumer assembly time follows a Normal model.
a) Find the mean and standard deviation of the assembly time model.
b) One way the company could solve this problem would be to change their advertising claim. What assembly time should they quote in order that 60% of customers succeed in finishing the desk by then?
c) Wishing to maintain the "less than an hour" claim, the company hopes that revising the instructions and labeling the parts more clearly can improve the one-hour success rate to 60%. If the standard deviation stays the same, what new lower mean time do they need to achieve?
d) Months later, another post-purchase survey shows the new instructions and part-labeling did lower the mean assembly time, but only to 50 minutes. Nonetheless, the company did achieve the 60%-in-an-hour goal, too. How was that possible?

DRAFT: Do not distribute or copy

38. **Crime and Punishment** Because of the development of statistics and the methods of analysis you are learning about in this book, the 20th Century has been called "The First Measured Century" in a series of documentaries on PBS. Here are two of their graphs. [http://www.pbs.org/fmc/book]

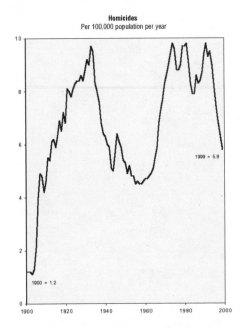

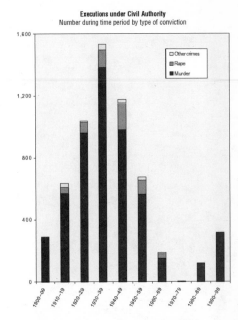

a) Write a few sentences describing the homicide rate in the US.
b) Write a few sentences describing the use of capital punishment in the US.
c) There is a long-running debate concerning the effectiveness of capital punishment as a deterrent. Do you think these graphs provide any information? Explain.

II Exploring Relationships Between Variables

7 Scatterplots, Association, and Correlation

REGULARLY, SINCE 1937, THE GALLUP POLL HAS asked likely U.S. voters whether they would vote for a qualified woman for President if their preferred political party nominated one. Are people more likely to say yes to this question now than they were 70 years ago? If so, has the increase been consistent, or do you think there might have been periods when it didn't increase at all, or even decreased? Here is a plot of the percentage saying they would vote for a woman, plotted against the year in which the survey took place:

Who: U.S. voters
What: Percentage saying they would vote for a woman for president
When: 1937-1999
Where: U.S.
How: Gallup Polls

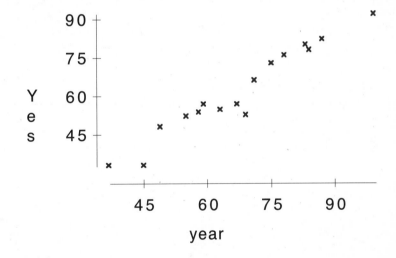

A scatterplot of percentage saying yes they would vote for a women plotted against the year of the survey. Has the increase in willingness to vote for a woman been constant over the entire time period? What features in the trend do you see? Fig 7.1

Clearly attitudes have changed. The plot shows fairly steady growth since 1937, reaching a level of 90% of voters saying yes by the year 1999. But we can also see that there was a period of no growth in the 1960's and early 1970's.

This time plot is an example of a more general kind of display called a **scatterplot.** Scatterplots may be the most common and most effective display for data. By just looking at them, you can see patterns, trends,

DRAFT: Do not distribute or copy

relationships, and even the occasional extraordinary value sitting apart from the others. As the great philosopher Yogi Berra once said "You can observe a lot by watching"[1]. Scatterplots are the best way to start observing the relationship between two *quantitative* variables.

And relationships between variables are often at the heart of what we'd like to learn from data:

- Are grades actually higher now than they used to be?

- Do people tend to reach puberty at a younger age than in previous generations?

- Does applying strong magnets to parts of the body relieve pain? Are stronger magnets more effective?

- Do students learn better with the use of computer technology?

Questions such as these relate two quantitative variables and ask whether there is an **association** between them. Scatterplots are the ideal way to *picture* such associations.

Looking at Scatterplots

The Texas Transportation Institute studies the mobility provided by the nation's transportation system. They issue an annual report on traffic congestion and its costs. Here's a scatterplot of the annual cost per person of traffic delays (in dollars) in 70 cities in the United States against the peak period freeway speed (mph).

Who: 70 U.S. cities
What: Cost/person of traffic delays and peak period freeway speed
   Units: $ per person per year and miles per hour
When: 2000
Why: Annual report from the Texas Transportation institute

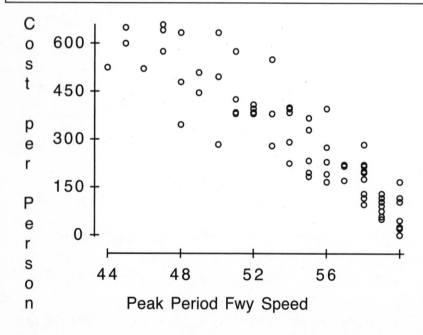

Everyone looks at scatterplots. But, if asked what to look for in a scatterplot, most people would find it hard to say. What do *you* see? Try to describe the scatterplot congestion cost against freeway speed.

Probably, you would say that the **direction** of the relationship is important. As the peak freeway speed goes up, the cost of congestion

Cost per person ($ per year) of traffic delays *vs* Peak Period freeway speed (mph) for 70 U.S. cities. **Fig 7.2**

---

[1] But then he also said "I really didn't say everything I said." So we can't really be sure.

Look for: Direction

goes down. A pattern that runs from the upper left to the lower right is said to have a **negative** direction. A trend running the other way has a **positive** direction.

The second thing to look for in a scatterplot is its **form**. If there is a straight line relationship, it will appear as a cloud, or swarm of points stretched out in a generally consistent, straight, form. For example, the scatterplot of traffic congestion has such an underlying **linear** form with some points that stray away from it.

Look for: Form (especially Straightness)

If the relationship isn't straight, but curves gently, while still increasing or decreasing steadily, we can often find ways to make it more nearly straight. But if it curves sharply—up and then down, for example, , -- there is much less we can say about it with the methods of this book.

Look for: Scatter

The third thing to look for in a scatterplot is how much **scatter** it has. At one extreme, do the points appear to follow a single stream (whether straight, curved, or bending all over the place)? Or, at the other extreme, does the swarm of points seem to form a vague cloud through which we can barely discern any trend or pattern? We are especially interested in the scatter when the underlying form is straight. We'll develop tools for *quantifying* the amount of scatter soon, but for now, we just want to be aware of whether there seems to be large or small amount of scatter. The traffic congestion plot shows little scatter, so we conclude that there is a strong relationship between cost and speed.

Finally, you should always look for the unexpected. Often the most interesting thing to see in a scatterplot is the thing you never thought to look for. One example of such a surprise is an outlier standing away from the overall pattern of the scatterplot. Such a point is almost always interesting and always deserves special attention. Clusters or subgroups that stand away from the rest of the plot or show a trend in a different direction than the rest of the plot should raise questions about why they are different. They may be a clue that you should split the data into subgroups rather than looking at it all together.

Scatterplot Details

Scatterplots were among the first modern mathematical displays. The idea of using two axes at right angles to define a field on which to display values can be traced back to René Descartes (1596-1650), and the playing field he defined in this way is formally called a *Cartesian plane* in his honor.

The two axes Descartes specified characterize the scatterplot. The axis that runs up and down is, by convention, called the *y*-axis and the one that runs from side to side is called the *x*-axis. You can count on these names. If someone refers to the *y*-axis, you may be sure they mean the vertical, up-and-down axis, and similarly with the *x*-axis.[2]

Descartes was a philosopher, famous for his statement *cogito ergo sum; I think, therefore I am.*

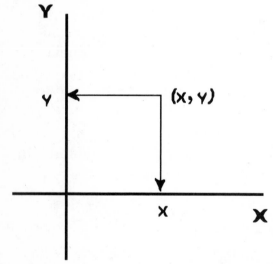

To make a scatterplot of two quantitative variables, assign one to the *y*-axis and the other to the *x*-axis. Be sure to label the axes clearly and indicate the scale of the axes with numbers. Scatterplots display quantitative variables. Each variable has units, which should appear with the display to define what it is showing.

Each point is placed on a scatterplot at a position that corresponds to values on these two variables. Its horizontal location is specified by its value on the *x*-axis variable and its vertical location is specified by its value on the *y*-axis variable. Together, these are known as its *coordinates* and written (*x, y*).

Scatterplots made by computer programs (such as the two we've seen in this chapter) often do not -- and usually should not -- show the *origin*: the point at $x = 0, y = 0$

---

[2] The axes are also called the "ordinate" and the "abscissa" – often by people who want to impress you. We can't remember which is which, so we won't expect you to remember it either. In statistics (and in all statistics computer programs), the axes are always called "*y*" and "*x*".

DRAFT: Do not distribute or copy

where the axes meet. If both variables have values that are near, or both sides of zero, then the origin will be part of the display. But if the values are far from zero, there is no reason to include the origin. In fact, it's far better to focus on the part of the Cartesian plane that contains the data. (We're not interested in the likely cost of delays if the freeways had a peak period speed of 0 mph.) Often, programs indicate this choice by drawing the axes so that they don't quite meet.

Roles for Variables

Which variable should go on the x-axis and which on the y-axis? What we want to know about the relationship can tell us how to make the plot. We often have questions such as:

- Are people who smoke more heavily more likely to get lung cancer?

- Is birth order an important factor in predicting future income?

- Can we estimate a person's body fat more simply by just measuring their girth or wrist size?

In each of these examples, the two variables play different roles. One plays the role of the **explanatory** or **predictor** variable, while the other takes on the role of the **response** variable. When the roles are clear, we always place the explanatory variable on the x-axis, and the response variable on the y-axis. When you make a scatterplot, you can assume that those who view it will think this way, so take care in choosing which variables to assign to which axes.

The roles that we choose for variables are more about how we *think* about them than about the variables themselves. Just placing a variable on the x-axis doesn't necessarily mean that it explains or predicts *anything*. And the variable on the y-axis may not respond to it in any way. We plotted cost per person against peak freeway speed, thinking that the slower you go, the more it costs in delays. But maybe spending $500 per person in freeway improvement would increase speed. If we were examining that option, we might choose to plot cost per person as the explanatory variable and speed as the response.

Older textbooks, and disciplines other than statistics sometimes refer to the x and y variables as the *independent* and *dependent* variables, respectively. The idea was that the y-variable depended on the x-variable and the x-variable acted independently to make y respond. But these names conflict with other uses of the same terms in Statistics. We'll use with the terms explanatory and response when we are thinking about a relationship in those terms, but we'll often just say *x-variable* and *y-variable*.

Notation Alert
So x and y are reserved letters as well, but not just for labeling the axes of a scatterplot. In Statistics, the assignment of variables to the x and y axes (and choice of notation for them in formulas) often conveys information about their roles as predictor or response.

Correlation

Who: Students
What Height (inches)
  Weight (lbs)
Where: Ithaca NY
Why: Data for class
How: Survey

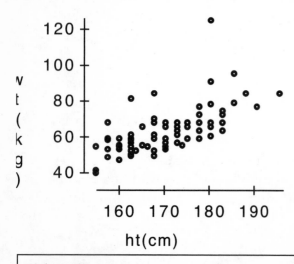

Data collected from students in statistics classes included their height (in inches) and weight (in pounds). It's no great surprise to discover that there is a positive association between the two. As you might suspect, taller students tend to weigh more. (If we had reversed the roles and chosen height as the explanatory variable, we might say that heavier students tend to be taller). And the form of the scatterplot is fairly linear as well, although there seems to be a high outlier.

There is clearly a positive association, but how strong is it? If you had to put a number (say, between 0 and 1) on the strength, what would it be? Clearly, whatever measure we use shouldn't depend on the units of the variables. After all, if we had measured heights and weights in different units, it wouldn't change the direction, form, or scatter, so it shouldn't change the strength.

Weight *vs* Height of statistics students. Fig 7.3

We could have measured the weight in stones -- a stone is a measure in the now outdated UK system of measures equal to 14 pounds.
And we could measure your height in hands -- hands are still commonly used to measure the heights of horses. A hand is 4 inches.
But, no matter what *units* we use to measure the two variables, the *correlation* stays the same.

Since the units don't matter, why not just remove them altogether? If we standardizing both variables, we'll turn the coordinates of each point into a pair of z-scores. Now the center of the scatterplot is at the origin and the axes are in standard deviation units.

Is this the only difference between these plots? Well, no. The underlying linear pattern seems steeper in the standardized plot. That's because we made the scales of the axes the same. Now the length of one standard deviation is the same vertically and horizontally. When we worked in the original units, we were free to

make the plot as tall and thin 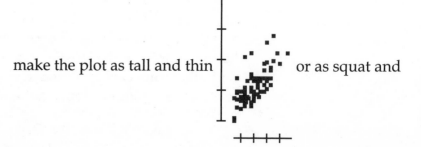 or as squat and

Plotting Weight *vs* Height in different units doesn't change the shape of the pattern.   Fig 7.4

wide as we wanted to. But equal scaling gives a neutral way of drawing the scatterplot and a fairer impression of the strength of the association.[3]

Now we are plotting standardized values, so we should label them as z-scores. Since we have z-scores for each variable, we can distinguish them by calling them z_x and z_y. So we can write the coordinates of a point as (z_x, z_y).

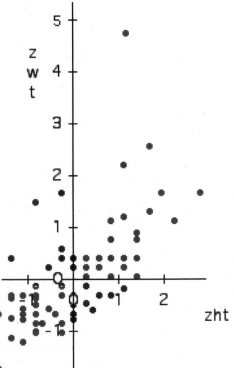

A scatterplot of standardized heights and weights with points colored by how they affect the association: [first color] for positive, [second color] for negative and [third color] for neutral. **Fig 7.5**

Which points in the scatterplot of the z-scores give the impression of a positive association? The points colored [first color] strengthen the impression of a pattern from lower left to upper right. For points in these quadrants z_x and z_y have the same sign. So if we multiplied them together, every point would have a positive product. Points far from the origin (which make the association look more positive) have a bigger product.

The [second color] points in the upper left and lower right quadrants tend to weaken the positive association. For these points, z_x and z_y have opposite signs. So the product, $z_x z_y$ for these points is always negative. Now points far from the origin (which make the association look more negative) have a more negative product.

Points with z-scores of zero on either variable don't vote either way, and $z_x z_y = 0$. We've colored them [third color].

We can turn these products into a measure of the strength of the association. We just add up all the $z_x z_y$ for every point in the scatterplot.

$$\sum z_x z_y.$$

This gives summarizes the direction *and* strength of the association for all the points. If most of the points are in the [first color] quadrants, the sum will tend to be positive. If most are in the [second color] quadrants, it will tend to be negative.

---

[3] When we are free to choose how to draw a scatterplot, what often looks best is to make the range of the x-axis slightly larger than the range of the y-axis. This is an aesthetic choice and is probably related to the Golden Ratio of the Greeks.

> ## Finding the Correlation Coefficient by Hand
>
> To find the correlation coefficient by hand, start with the summary statistics for both variables: $\bar{x}$, $\bar{y}$, s_x, and s_y. Then find the deviations as we did for the standard deviation, but now in *both* x and y: $(x-\bar{x})$ and $(y-\bar{y})$. For each data pair, multiply these deviations together: $(x-\bar{x})(y-\bar{y})$. Add the products up for all data pairs. Finally, divide the sum by the product of $(n-1) \times s_x \times s_y$ to get the correlation coefficient.
>
> Here we go:
>
> Suppose the data pairs are:
>
> | x | y |
> |----|----|
> | 6 | 5 |
> | 10 | 3 |
> | 14 | 7 |
> | 19 | 8 |
> | 21 | 12 |
>
> Then $\bar{x} = 14$, $\bar{y} = 7$, $s_x = 6.2$ and $s_y = 3.4$
>
> | Deviations in x | Deviations in y | Product |
> |-----------------|-----------------|---------|
> | 6 – 14 = -8 | 5 – 7 = -2 | -8 × -2 =16 |
> | 10 – 14 = -4 | 3 – 7 = -4 | 16 |
> | 14 – 14 = 0 | 7 – 7 = 0 | 0 |
> | 19 – 14 = 5 | 8 – 7 = 1 | 5 |
> | 21 – 14 = 7 | 12 – 7 = 5 | 35 |
>
> Add these all up: 16+16+0+5+35 = 72
>
> Finally, we divide by $(n-1) \times s_x \times s_y = (5-1) \times 6.2 \times 3.4 = 84.32$
>
> The ratio is the correlation coefficient:
>
> $r = 72/84.32 = .854$

But the *size* of this sum gets bigger the more data we have. To adjust for this we divide the sum by $n-1$.[4] The ratio is the famous **correlation coefficient**:

$$r = \frac{\sum z_x z_y}{n-1}.$$

For the students' heights and weights, the correlation comes out to 0.644. There are a number of alternative formulas for the correlation coefficient using x and y in their original units. You may find them written elsewhere.[5] They can be more convenient when you want to compute correlation by hand. But this form is best for understanding what it means.

Correlation Conditions

Correlation measures the strength of the *linear* association between two *quantitative* variables. Before you use correlation, you must check several *Conditions*:

- **Quantitative Variables Condition** Correlation applies only to quantitative variables. Don't apply correlation to categorical data masquerading as quantitative. Check that you know the variables' units and what they measure.

- **Linearity Condition** Sure, you can *calculate* a correlation coefficient for any pair of variables. But correlation measures only the strength of the *linear* association, and will be misleading if the relationship is not linear.

- **Outlier Condition** Outliers can distort the correlation dramatically. An outlier can make an otherwise small correlation look big or hide a

---

[4] Yes, the same $n-1$ we saw for the standard deviation. And we offer the same promise to explain it later.

[5] Like here, for example: $r = \dfrac{\sum(x-\bar{x})(y-\bar{y})}{\sqrt{\sum(x-\bar{x})^2 \sum(y-\bar{y})^2}} = \dfrac{\sum(x-\bar{x})(y-\bar{y})}{(n-1)\sqrt{s_x^2 s_y^2}}$

large correlation. It can even give an otherwise positive association a negative correlation coefficient (and vice versa).

Each of these conditions is easy to check with a scatterplot. Many correlations are reported without supporting data or plots. You should still think about the conditions. And you should be cautious in interpreting (or accepting others' interpretations of) the correlation when you can't check the conditions for yourself.

Looking at Association, Step by Step

When your blood pressure is measured, it is reported as two values, systolic blood pressure and diastolic blood pressure. How are these variables related to each other? Do they tend to both be high or low? Let's examine their relationship with a scatterplot.

Think

Variables: Identify two quantitative variables whose relationship we wish to examine. Report the W's and be sure both variables are recorded for the same individuals.

The variables are systolic and diastolic blood pressure (SBP and DBP) recorded (in mm of mercury) for each of 1406 participants in a famous health study in Framingham, MA.

Plan:

Check the conditions:

Make the scatterplot. Use a computer program or graphing calculator if you can.

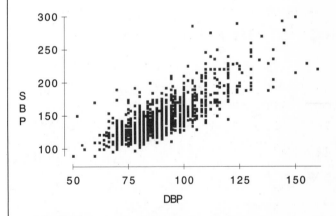

✓ **Quantitative Variables Condition**: Both SBP and DBP are quantitative and measured in mm of mercury.

✓ **Linearity Condition**: The scatterplot looks straight.

Reality check

Looks like a strong positive linear association. We shouldn't be surprised if the correlation

✓ **Outlier Condition**: There are a few straggling points, but none far enough from the body of the data to be called

coefficient is positive and fairly large.

from the body of the data to be called outliers.

We have two quantitative variables that satisfy our conditions, so a correlation would be a suitable measure of association.

Show

Mechanics: We usually calculate correlations with technology. Here we have 1406 cases, so we'd never try it by hand.

The correlation coefficient is 0.792.

Tell

Interpretation: Describe the direction, form, and scatter you see in the plot, along with any unusual points or features

The scatterplot shows a positive direction with higher SBP going with higher DBP. The plot is generally straight with a moderate amount of scatter. The correlation of 0.792 indicates a strong linear association. A few cases stand out with unusually high SBP compared to their DBP. It seems far less common for the DBP to be high by itself.

Correlation Properties

Here's a useful list of facts about the correlation coefficient:

- The sign of a correlation coefficient gives the direction of the association.

- Correlation is always between –1 and +1. Correlation *can* be exactly equal to –1.0 or +1.0, but these values are unusual in real data because they mean that all the data points fall *exactly* on a single straight line.

  A correlation of near zero corresponds to a weak linear association.

- Correlation treats x and y symmetrically. The correlation of x with y is the same as the correlation of y with x.

- Correlation has no units. This fact can be especially appropriate when the data's units were somewhat vague to begin with (IQ score, Personality index, socialization…). Correlation is sometimes given as a percentage, but we discourage that because it suggests a percentage of *something* – and correlation, lacking units, has no "something" of which to be a percentage.

- Correlation is not affected by changes in the center or scale of either variable. Changing the units or baseline of either variable no effect on the correlation coefficient.

DRAFT: Do not distribute or copy

- Correlation measures the strength of the linear association between the two variables. Variables can have a strong association but still have a small correlation if the association isn't linear.

- Correlation is sensitive to outliers. A single outlying value can either make a small correlation large or a large one small.

Correlation Tables

It is common in some fields to compute the correlations between each pair of variables in a collection of variables and arrange these correlations in a table. The rows and columns of the table name the variables and the cells hold the correlations.

Correlation tables are compact, and give a lot of summary information at a glance. They can be an efficient way to start to look at a large dataset, but a dangerous one. By presenting all of these correlations without any checks for linearity and outliers, the correlation table risks showing truly small correlations that have been inflated by outliers, truly large correlations that are hidden by outliers, and correlations of any size that may be meaningless because the underlying form is not linear.

	Assets	Sales	Market Value	Profits	Cash Flow	Employees
Assets	1.000					
Sales	0.746	1.000				
Market Value	0.682	0.879	1.000			
Profits	0.602	0.814	0.968	1.000		
Cash Flow	0.641	0.855	0.970	0.989	1.000	
Employees	0.594	0.924	0.818	0.762	0.787	1.000

A correlation table of data reported by *Forbes* magazine for large companies. From this table, can you be sure that the variables are linearly associated and free from outliers?
Table 7.1

The diagonal cells of a correlation table always hold correlations of exactly 1.0 (can you see why?) Correlation tables are commonly offered by statistics packages on computers. These same packages often offer simple ways to make all the scatterplots you need to look at.[6]

*Straightening Scatterplots

Straight line relationships are the ones that we can measure with correlation. When a scatterplot shows a bent form that consistently increases or decreases, we can often straighten the form of the plot by re-expressing one or both variables.

---

[6] A table of scatterplots arranged just like a correlation table is sometimes called a *scatterplot matrix*, sometimes abbreviated to *SPLOM*. You might see these terms in a statistics package.

Exploring Relationships Between Variables

Some camera lenses have an adjustable aperture, the hole that lets the light through. The size of the aperture is expressed in a mysterious number called the f-stop. Each increase of one f-stop number corresponds to a halving of the light that is allowed to come through. The f-stops of a one 35mm camera are:

2.8	4	5.6	8	11	16	22	32

When you increase the f-stop one notch, you cut down the light, so you have to increase the time the shutter is open. We could experiment to find the best shutter speed for each f-stop value. A table of shutter speeds and f-stops for a camera lists the relationship like this:

2.8	4	5.6	8	11	16	22	32
1/1000	1/500	1/250	1/125	1/60	1/30	1/15	1/8

The correlation of these f-stops and shutter speeds is 0.979. That sounds pretty high. You might assume that there must be a strong linear relationship. But when we check the scatterplot (we *always* check the scatterplot) it shows that something is not quite right:

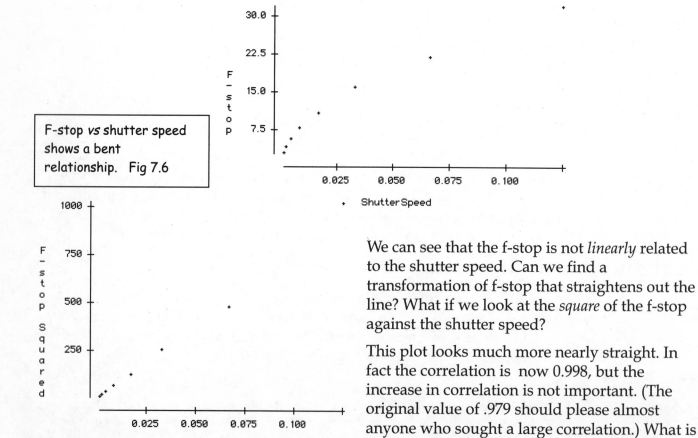

F-stop *vs* shutter speed shows a bent relationship.   Fig 7.6

We can see that the f-stop is not *linearly* related to the shutter speed. Can we find a transformation of f-stop that straightens out the line? What if we look at the *square* of the f-stop against the shutter speed?

This plot looks much more nearly straight. In fact the correlation is now 0.998, but the increase in correlation is not important. (The original value of .979 should please almost anyone who sought a large correlation.) What is important is that the *form* of the plot is now

Re-expressing Shutter speed by squaring straightens the plot.   Fig 7.7

DRAFT: Do not distribute or copy

straight, so the correlation is now an appropriate measure of association.[7]

We can often find transformations that straighten out lines. Here, we found the square. Chapter 10 discusses simple ways to find a good re-expression.

What Can go Wrong?

How often have you heard the word correlation? Chances are pretty good that when you have heard the term, it's been misused. When people want to sound scientific, they often say "correlation" when talking about the relationship between two variables. It is one of the most widely misused statistics terms, and given the competition, that's saying a lot. One of the problems is that many people use the specific term *correlation* when they really mean the more general term *association*. Association is a deliberately vague term describing the relationship between two variables.

Don't fall into the trap of misusing the term *correlation* yourself[8]. And watch out for these other common problems:

Check the Conditions

Did you know that there's a strong correlation between playing an instrument and drinking coffee? No? One reason might be that the statement doesn't make sense. Correlation is valid only for *quantitative* variables.

- *Don't correlate categorical variables.* People who misuse "correlation" to mean "association" often fail to notice whether the variables they discuss are quantitative.

- *Be sure the association is linear.* A student project evaluating the quality of brownies baked at different temperatures reports a correlation of –0.05 between judges' scores and baking temperature. That seems low until we look at the scatterplot:

---

[7] Sometimes we can do a "reality check" on our choice of re-expression. In this case, a bit of research reveals that f-stops are related to the diameter of the open shutter. Since the amount of light that enters is determined by the *area* of the open shutter, which is related to the diameter by squaring, the square re-expression seems reasonable. Not all re-expressions have such nice explanations, but it is a good idea to think about them.
[8] Or if you insist on misusing it, please don't admit that you took this course.

Copyright © 2002, Dick De Veaux and Paul Velleman

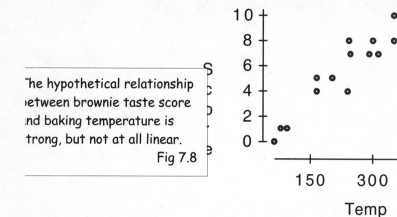

The hypothetical relationship between brownie taste score and baking temperature is strong, but not at all linear.
Fig 7.8

There is a strong association, but the relationship is not linear.

- *Beware of Outliers* You can't interpret a correlation coefficient safely without a background check for outliers. Here's a silly example:

The relationship between IQ and shoe size among comedians shows a surprising strong positive correlation of .50. To check assumptions, we look at the scatterplot:

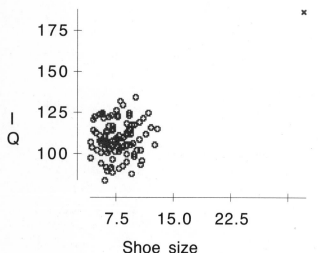

The outlier is Bozo the Clown, known for his large shoes, and widely acknowledged to be a comic genius.

Even a single outlier can dominate the correlation value.

A scatterplot of IQ scores versus shoe size. From this "study", what is the relationship between the two? The correlation is 0.50. Who *does* that point in the upper right hand corner belong to? Fig 7.9

Don't confuse correlation with causation

Once we have a strong correlation, it's tempting to try to explain it by imagining that the predictor variable has *caused* the response to change. Humans are like that; we tend to see causes and effects in everything.

Sometimes we can play with this tendency. Here's a scatterplot shows the population (*y*) of Oldenburg Germany in the beginning of the 1930's plotted against the number of storks nesting in the town (*x*)

DRAFT: Do not distribute or copy

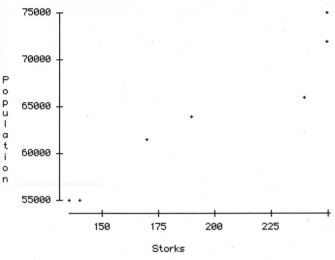

A scatterplot of the number of storks in Oldenburg, Germany plotted against the population of the town for 6 years in the 1930's. The association is clear. How about the causation? (*Ornithologishe Monatsberichte*, 44,2) **Fig 7.10**

Anyone who has seen the beginning of the movie *Dumbo*, remembers Mrs. Jumbo anxiously awaiting the arrival of the stork to bring her new baby. Even though you know it is silly, you can't help but think for a minute that this plot shows that storks are clearly the culprits. The two variables are obviously related to each other (The correlation is 0.97!), but that doesn't prove that storks bring babies.

It turns out that storks nest on house chimneys. More people means more houses, more nesting sites, and so, more storks. The causation is actually in the *opposite* direction, but you can't tell from the scatterplot or correlation. You need additional information—not just the data–to determine the real mechanism.

Does Cancer Cause Smoking?

Even if the correlation of two variables is due to a causal relationship, the correlation itself cannot tell us what causes what.

Sir Ronald Aylmer Fisher (1890-1962) was one of the greatest statisticians of the 20th century. Fisher testified in court (paid by the Tobacco companies) that there might be a causal relationship underlying the correlation of smoking and cancer:

> "Is it possible, then, that lung cancer...is one of the causes of smoking cigarettes? I don't think it can be excluded...the pre-cancerous condition is one involving a certain amount of slight chronic inflammation...
>
> A slight cause of irritation...is commonly accompanied by pulling out a cigarette, and getting a little compensation for life's minor ills in that way. And...is not unlikely to be associated with smoking more frequently.

Ironically, the proof that smoking indeed is the cause of many cancers came from experiments conducted following the principles of experiment design and analysis that Fisher himself developed, and that we'll see in chapter 13.

Scatterplots and correlation coefficients *never* prove causation. This is, for example, one part of the story of why it took so long for the U.S. Surgeon General to get warning labels on cigarettes. Although there was plenty of evidence that increased smoking was *associated* with increased levels of lung cancer, it took years to provide evidence that smoking actually *causes* lung cancer. (And the tobacco companies used this to great advantage.)

Watch out for Lurking Variables

A scatterplot of the damage (in dollars) caused to a house by fire would show a strong correlation with the number of firefighters at the scene. Surely the damage doesn't cause fire fighters. And firefighters do seem to cause damage, spraying water all around and chopping holes. Does that mean we shouldn't call the fire department? Of course not. There is an underlying variable that leads to both damage and fire fighters – the size of the blaze.

A hidden variable that stands behind a relationship and determines it by simultaneously affecting both variables is called a *lurking variable.* You can often debunk claims made about data by finding the lurking variable behind the scenes.

Connections

Scatterplots are the basic tool for examining the relationship between two quantitative variables. Just as we start with a picture when we want to understand the distribution of a single variable, we always make a scatterplot to begin to understand the relationship between two quantitative variables.

We used z-scores as a way to measure the statistical distance of data values from their means. Now we've seen the z-scores of x and y working together to build the correlation coefficient. Correlation is a summary statistic like the mean and standard deviation; only it summarizes the strength of a linear relationship. And we interpret it as we did z-scores, using the standard deviations as our rulers in both x and y.

Scatterplots and Correlation on the Computer

Statistics packages generally make it easy to look at a scatterplot to check whether the correlation is appropriate. Some packages make this easier than others.

Many packages allow you to modify or enhance a scatterplot, altering the axis labels, the axis numbering, the plot symbols, or the colors used. Some options, such as color and symbol choice, can be used to display additional information on the scatterplot.

Package	Commands & Location	Comments
Data Desk	To make a scatterplot of two variables, select one variable as Y and the other as X and choose **Scatterplot** from the **Plot** menu. Then find the correlation by choosing **Correlation** from the scatterplot's HyperView menu Alternatively, select the two variables and choose **Pearson Product-Moment** from the **Correlations** submenu of the **Calc** menu.	We prefer that you look at the scatterplot first and then find the correlation. But if you've found the correlation first, click on the correlation value to drop down a menu that offers to make the scatterplot.
Excel	To make a Scatterplot with the Excel Chart Wizard: • Click on the **Chart Wizard** Button in the menu bar. Excel opens the Chart Wizard's Chart Type Dialog window. • Make sure the **Standard Types** tab is selected, and • select **XY (Scatter)** from the choices offered. • Specify the **scatterplot without lines** from the choices offered in the Chart sub-type selections. The **Next** button takes you to the Chart Source Data dialog. • If it is not already frontmost, click on the **Data Range tab,** and	Excel's scatterplot capability is not really suitable for statistics, as you can see from the number of steps required.

DRAFT: Do not distribute or copy

	enter the data range in the space provided. • By convention, we always represent variables in columns. The Chart Wizard refers to variables as Series. Be sure the **Column** option is selected. • Excel places the leftmost column of those you select on the x-axis of the scatterplot. If the column you wish to see on the x-axis is not the leftmost column in your spreadsheet, • click on the **Series** tab and edit the specification of the individual axis series. • Click the **Next** button. The Chart Options dialog appears. • Select the **Titles** tab. Here you specify the title of the chart and names of the variables displayed on each axis. • Type the chart title in the **Chart title:** edit box. • Type the x-axis variable name in the **Value (X) Axis:** edit box. Note that you must name the columns correctly here. Naming another variable will not alter the plot, only mislabel it. • Type the y-axis variable name in the **Value (Y) Axis:** edit box. • Click the **Next** button to open the chart location dialog. • Select the **As new sheet:** option button. • Click the **Finish** button. Often, the resulting scatterplot will not be useful. By default, Excel includes the origin in the plot even when the data are far from zero. You can adjust the axis scales. To change the scale of a plot axis in Excel: • Double-click on the axis. The **Format Axis Dialog** appears. • If the **scale tab** is not the frontmost, select it. • Enter new minimum or new maximum values in the spaces provided. You can drag the dialog box over the scatterplot as a straightedge to help you read the maximum and minimum values on the axes. • Click the **OK** button to view the rescaled scatterplot. • Follow the same steps for the x-axis scale. Compute a correlation in Excel with the **CORREL** function from the drop-down menu of functions. If CORREL is not on the menu, choose **More Functions** and find it among the statistical functions in the browser. In the dialog that pops up, enter the range of cells holding one of the variables in the space provided. Enter the range of cells for the other variable in the space provided.	
JMP	To make a scatterplot and compute correlation in JMP choose **Fit Y by X** from the **Analyze** menu. In the Fit Y by X dialog, drag the Y variable into the "**Y, Response**" box, and drag the X variable "**X, Factor**" box. Click the **OK** button Once JMP has made the scatterplot, click on the red triangle next to the plot title to reveal a menu of options. Select **Density Ellipse** and select .95. JMP draws an ellipse around the data and reveals the **Correlation tab**. Click the blue triangle next to Correlation to reveal a table containing the correlation coefficient.	
Minitab	To make a scatterplot in MINITAB choose **Plot** from the **Graph** menu. In the Plot dialog, click on the **Y cell** for Graph 1 in the Graph variables box to specify the Y-variable. Then assign the y-variable from the Variable list box. Click on the **X cell** for the graph and assign the x-variable from the Variable	

	list box. Click the **OK** button to view the scatterplot. To compute a correlation coefficient in MINITAB, choose **Basic Statistics** from the **Stat** menu. From the Basic Statistics submenu, choose **Correlation**. Click on the **Variables** box and assign variables from the Variable List box. Click the **OK** button to compute the correlation table.	
SPSS	To make a scatterplot in SPSS choose **Interactive** from the **Graphs** menu. From the Interactive Graphs submenu, choose **Scatterplot**. In the Create Scatterplot dialog, drag variable names from the source list into the targets on the right. Each target describes a specific part or aspect of the plot. For example, drag a variable name to the y-axis target to specify the variable to display on the y-axis. Similarly, the x-axis target gets the name of the variable to display on the x-axis. To compute a correlation coefficient in SPSS choose **Correlate** from the **Analyze** menu. From the Correlate submenu, choose **Bivariate**. In the Bivariate Correlations dialog, use the arrow button to move variables between the source and target lists. Make sure the **Pearson** option is selected in the Correlation Coefficients field.	

Key Concepts

Scatterplots	A scatterplot shows the relationship between two quantitative variables measured on the same cases.
Looking at Scatterplots	• direction • form • scatter
x-variable, y-variable **explanatory variable, response variable**	In a scatterplot, you must choose a role for each variable. Assign to the y-axis the variable that you hope to predict or explain. Assign to the x-axis the variable that accounts for, explains, predicts, or is otherwise responsible for the y-variable.
Correlation	Correlation is a numerical measure of the direction and strength of a linear association

Skills:

After completing this lesson you should:

> *Think*
>
> - Recognize when interest in the pattern of possible relationship between two quantitative variables suggests making a scatterplot.
>
> - Know how to identify the roles of the variables and to place the response variable on the *y*-axis and the factor variable on the *x*-axis.
>
> - Know the Conditions for Correlation and how to check them.
>
> - Know that correlations are between –1 and +1, that each extreme indicates a perfect linear association.
>
> - Understand how the magnitude of the correlation reflects the strength of a linear association as viewed in a scatterplot.
>
> - Know that the correlation has no units.
>
> - Know that the correlation coefficient is not changed by changing the center or scale of either variable.
>
> - Understand that causation cannot be demonstrated by a scatterplot or correlation.
>
> *Show*
>
> - Know how to make a scatterplot by hand (for a small set of data) or with technology.
>
> - Know how to compute the correlation of two variables.
>
> - Know how to read a correlation table produced by a statistics program.
>
> *Tell*
>
> - Be able to describe the direction, form, and scatter of a scatterplot.
>
> - Be prepared to identify and describe points that deviate from the overall pattern.
>
> - Be able to use correlation as part of the description of a scatterplot.
>
> - Be alert to misinterpretations of correlation.
>
> - Understand that finding a correlation between two variables does not indicate a causal relationship between them. Beware the dangers of suggesting causal relationships when describing correlations.

Exercises

1 **Association** Suppose you were to collect data for each pair of variables. You want to make a scatterplot. Which variable would you use as the explanatory variable, and which as the response variable? Why? What would you expect to see in the scatterplot? Discuss the likely direction, form, and scatter.

    a) Apples: weight in grams, weight in ounces
    b) Apples: circumference (inches), weight (ounces)
    c) College freshmen: shoe size, grade point average
    d) Gasoline: number of miles you drove since filling up, gallons remaining in your tank

2 **Association** Suppose you were to collect data for each pair of variables. You want to make a scatterplot. Which variable would you use as the explanatory variable, and which as the response variable? Why? What would you expect to see in the scatterplot? Discuss the likely direction, form, and scatter.

    a) T- Shirts at a store: price each, number sold
    b) Skin diving: depth, water pressure
    c) Skin diving: depth, visibility
    d) Elementary school students: weight, score on a reading test

3 **Association** Suppose you were to collect data for each pair of variables. You want to make a scatterplot. Which variable would you use as the explanatory variable, and which as the response variable? Why? What would you expect to see in the scatterplot? Discuss the likely direction, form, and scatter.

    a) When climbing a mountain: altitude, temperature
    b) Ice cream cone sales, air conditioner sales
    c) People: age, grip strength
    d) Drivers: blood alcohol level, reaction time

4 **Association** Suppose you were to collect data for each pair of variables. You want to make a scatterplot. Which variable would you use as the explanatory variable, and which as the response variable? Why? What would you expect to see in the scatterplot? Discuss the likely direction, form, and scatter.

    a) Long distance calls: time (minutes), cost
    b) Distance from lightning, time delay of the thunder
    c) A streetlight: its apparent brightness, your distance from it
    d) Cars: weight of car, age of owner

5 **Scatterplots** Which of the scatterplots below show:

    a) little or no association?
    b) a negative association?
    c) a linear association?
    d) a moderately strong association?

     DRAFT: Do not distribute or copy

e) a very strong association?

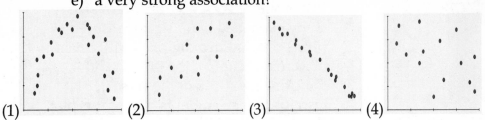

(1)   (2)   (3)   (4)

6   **Scatterplots** Which of the scatterplots below show:

a) little or no association?
b) a negative association?
c) a linear association?
d) a moderately strong association?
e) a very strong association?

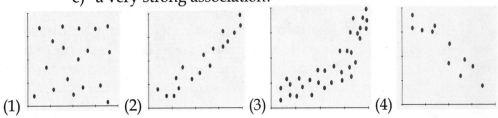

(1)   (2)   (3)   (4)

7   **Performance IQ scores** *vs.* **Brain size** A study examined brain size (measured as pixels counted in a digitized MRI image of a cross-section of the brains) and IQ (4 Performance scales of the Weschler IQ test) for college students. The scatterplot shows the Performance IQ scores *vs.* the brain size. Comment on the association between brain size and IQ as seen in this scatterplot.

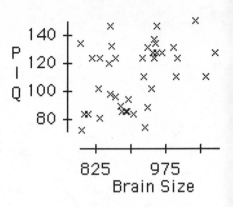

8   **Kentucky Derby** The fastest horse in Kentucky Derby history was Secretariat in 1973. The scatterplot shows speed (in miles per hour) of the winning horses each year. What do you see? In most sporting events, performances have improved and continue to improve, so surely we anticipate a positive direction. But what of the form? Has the performance increased at the same rate throughout the last 125 years?

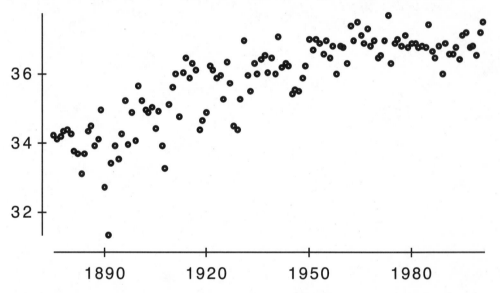

9   **Firing Pottery** A ceramics factory can fire 8 large batches of pottery a day. Sometimes in the process a few of the pieces break. In order to understand the problem better they record the number of broken pieces in each batch for three days, and then create the scatterplot shown.

a) Create a histogram showing the distribution of the number of broken pieces in the 24 batches of pottery examined.

b) Describe the distribution as shown in the histogram. What feature of the problem is more apparent in the histogram than in the scatterplot?

c) What aspect of the company's problem is more apparent in the scatterplot?

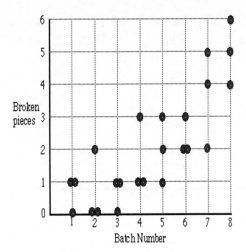

10 **Coffee Sales** Owners of a new coffee shop tracked sales for the first 20 days, and displayed the data in a scatterplot (by day):

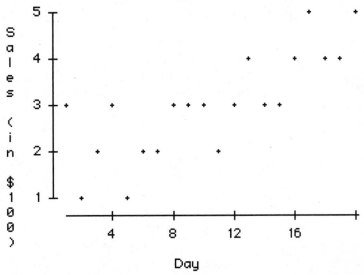

    a) Make a histogram of the daily sales since the shop has been in business.

    b) State one fact that is obvious from the scatterplot, but not from the histogram.

    c) State one fact that is obvious from the histogram, but not from the scatterplot.

11 **Matching** Here are several scatterplots. The calculated correlations are –0.923, --0.487, 0.006, and 0.777. Which is which?

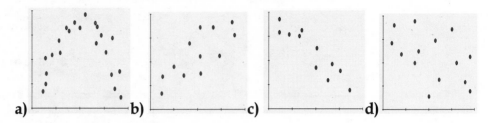

a)   b)   c)   d)

12 **Matching** Here are several scatterplots. The calculated correlations are –0.977, --0.021, 0.736, and 0.951. Which is which?

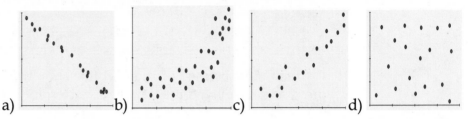

a)   b)   c)   d)

13 **Lunchtime** Does how long children remain at the lunch table help predict how much they eat? The table gives data on 20 toddlers observed over several months at a nursery school. Time is the average number of minutes a child spent at the table when lunch was served. Calories is the average number of calories the child consumed during lunch, calculated from careful observation of what the child ate each day.

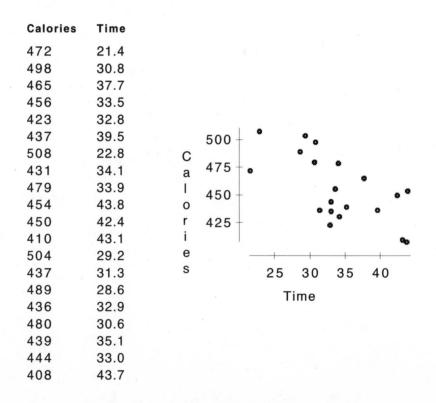

Calories	Time
472	21.4
498	30.8
465	37.7
456	33.5
423	32.8
437	39.5
508	22.8
431	34.1
479	33.9
454	43.8
450	42.4
410	43.1
504	29.2
437	31.3
489	28.6
436	32.9
480	30.6
439	35.1
444	33.0
408	43.7

Calories and time at the lunch table for Toddlers.

     DRAFT: Do not distribute or copy

a) Find the correlation for these data.
b) Suppose we were to record time at the table in hours rather than in minutes. How would the correlation change? Why?
c) Write a sentence or two explaining what this correlation means for these data. Remember to write about food consumption in toddlers rather than about correlation coefficients.
d) One analyst concluded, "It is clear from this correlation that toddlers who spend more time at the table eat less. Evidently something about being at the table causes them to lose their appetites." Explain why this explanation is not an appropriate conclusion from what we know about the data.

14 **Vehicle Weights** The Minnesota Department of Transportation installed a state-of-the art weigh-in-motion scale in the concrete surface of the eastbound lanes of Interstate 494 in Bloomington, Minnesota. After installation, a study was undertaken to determine whether the scale's readings correspond with the static weights of the vehicles being monitored. The table gives the static (assumed correct) weight of a test truck and the weight recorded by the new scale.

Weight-in-Motion	Static Weight
26	27.9
29.9	29.1
39.5	38
25.1	27
31.6	30.3
36.2	34.5
25.1	27.8
31	29.6
35.6	33.1
40.2	35.5

**Weight of a truck (thousands of pounds)
found by two different methods**

a) Make a scatterplot for these data.
b) Describe the direction, form and strength of the plot.
c) Write a few sentences telling what the plot says about the data. (Note: the sentences should be about weighing trucks, not about scatterplots.)
d) Find the correlation.
e) If the trucks were weighed in kilograms, how would this change the correlation? (1 kilogram = 2.2 pounds)

f) Do any points deviate from the overall pattern? What does the plot say about a possible recalibration of the weigh-in-motion scale?

15 **Fuel Economy** Here are advertised horsepower ratings and expected gas mileage for several 2001 vehicles.

Audi A4	170 hp	22 mpg	Buick LeSabre	205	20
Chevy Blazer	190	15	Chevy Prizm	125	31
Ford Excursion	310	10	GMC Yukon	285	13
Honda Civic	127	29	Hyundai Elantra	140	25
Lexus 300	215	21	Lincoln LS	210	23
Mazda MPV	170	18	Olds Alero	140	23
Toyota Camry	194	21	VW Beetle	115	29

a) Make a scatterplot for these data.
b) Describe the direction, form and strength of the plot.
c) Find the correlation between horsepower and miles per gallon.
d) Write a few sentences telling what the plot says about fuel economy.

16 **Drug Abuse** A survey was conducted in the US and 10 countries of Western Europe to determine the percentage of teenagers who had used marijuana and other drugs. The results are summarized in the table.

Country	% who have used	
	marijuana	other drugs
Czech Rep	22	4
Denmark	17	3
England	40	21
Finland	5	1
Ireland	37	16
Italy	19	8
No Ireland	23	14
Norway	6	3
Portugal	7	3
Scotland	53	31
USA	34	24

a) Create a scatterplot.
b) What is the correlation between the percent of teens who have used marijuana and the percent who have used other drugs?
c) Write a brief description of the association.
d) Do these results confirm that marijuana is a "gateway drug"; that is, that marijuana use leads to the use of other drugs? Explain.

17 **Burgers** Fast food is often considered unhealthy because it is often high in both fat and sodium. But are the two related? Here are the fat and

DRAFT: Do not distribute or copy

sodium contents of several brands of burgers. Create a scatterplot and find the correlation between fat content and sodium content. Write a description of the association.

Fat (gm)	19	31	34	35	39	39	43
Sodium (mg)	920	1500	1310	860	1180	940	1260

18 **Burgers** In the last exercise you found little association between the amounts of fat and sodium in fast food hamburgers. But what about fat and calories? Here are the data for the same burgers.

Fat (gm)	19	31	34	35	39	39	43
Calories	410	580	590	570	640	680	660

a) Create a scatterplot.
b) Find the correlation.
c) Describe the association.

19 **Attendance** American League baseball games are played under the designated hitter rule, meaning that weak-hitting pitchers do not come to bat. Baseball owners believe that the designated hitter means more runs scored which in turn means higher attendance. Is there evidence that more fans attend games if the teams score more runs? Data collected midway through the 2001 season indicates a correlation of 0.74 between runs scored and the number of people at the game.

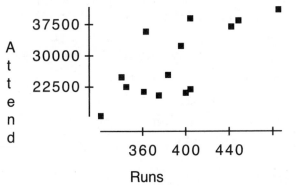

a) Does the scatterplot indicate that it is appropriate to calculate a correlation? Explain.
b) Describe the association between attendance and runs scored.
c) Does this prove that the owners are right, that more fans will come to games if the teams score more runs?

20 **2nd Inning** Perhaps fans are just more interested in teams that win? Are the teams that win necessarily those that score the most runs?

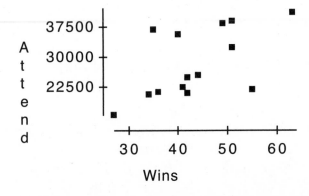

Correlation

	Wins	Runs	Attend
Wins	1.000		
Runs	0.680	1.000	
Attend	0.577	0.740	1.000

a) Do winning teams generally enjoy greater attendance at their home games? Describe the association.

b) Is attendance more strongly associated with winning or scoring runs? Explain.

c) How strongly is scoring more runs associated with winning more games?

21 **Politics** A candidate for office claims that "there is a correlation between television watching and crime." Criticize this statement in statistical terms.

22 **Association** A researcher investigating the association between two variables collected some data and was surprised when he calculated the correlation. He had expected to find a fairly strong association, yet the correlation was near 0. Discouraged, he didn't bother making a scatterplot. Explain to him how the scatterplot could still reveal the strong association he anticipated.

23 **Correlation Errors** Your economics professor assigns your class to investigate factors associated with the gross domestic product (GDP) of nations. Each student examines a different factor (such as life expectancy, literacy rate, etc.) for a few countries and reports to the class. Apparently some of your classmates do not understand statistics very well because you know several of their conclusions are incorrect. Explain the mistakes in their statements below.

a) "My correlation of –0.772 shows that there is almost no association between GDP and infant mortality rate."

b) "There was a correlation of 0.44 between GDP and continent."

c) "There was a very strong correlation of 1.22 between life expectancy and GDP."

d) "The correlation between literacy rate and GDP was 0.83. This proves that countries wanting to increase their standard of living should invest heavily in education."

24 **Sample survey** A polling organization is checking their data base to see if the two data sources they used sampled the same zip codes. The variable *datasource* = 1 if the data source is MetroMedia, 2 if the data source is DataQwest and 3 if it's RollingPoll. They find that the

correlation between 5 digit zipcode and *datasource* is -.0229. They conclude that the correlation is low enough to state that there is no dependency between zipcode and source of data. Comment.

25 **Baldness and Heart Disease** Medical researchers followed 1435 middle aged men for a period of 5 years, measuring the amount of baldness present (none=1, little=2, some=3, much=4, extreme = 5) and presence of heart disease (No=0, Yes= 1). They found a correlation of 0.089 between the two variables. Comment on their conclusion that this shows that baldness is not a possible cause of heart disease.

26 **Oil Production** The following table shows the oil production of the United States from 1949 to 2000 (in millions of barrels per year).
a) Find the correlation between year and production.
b) A reporter concludes that a low correlation between year and production shows that oil production has remained steady over the 50 year period. Do you agree with this interpretation? Explain.

year	oil	year	oil	year	oil	year	oil
1949	1841940	1962	2676189	1975	3056779	1988	2979123
1950	1973574	1963	2752723	1976	2976180	1989	2778773
1951	2247711	1964	2786822	1977	3009265	1990	2684687
1952	2289836	1965	2848514	1978	3178216	1991	2707039
1953	2357082	1966	3027763	1979	3121310	1992	2624632
1954	2314988	1967	3215742	1980	3146365	1993	2499033
1955	2484428	1968	3329042	1981	3128624	1994	2431476
1956	2617283	1969	3371751	1982	3156715	1995	2394268
1957	2616901	1970	3517450	1983	3170999	1996	2366017
1958	2448987	1971	3453914	1984	3249696	1997	2354831
1959	2574590	1972	3455368	1985	3274553	1998	2281919
1960	2574933	1973	3360903	1986	3168252	1999	2146732
1961	2621758	1974	3202585	1987	3047378	2000	2135062

27 *****Planets** Is there any pattern to the locations of the planets in our solar system? The table shows the average distance each of the nine planets is from the sun.

Planet	Position number	Distance from sun (million miles)
Mercury	1	36
Venus	2	67
Earth	3	93
Mars	4	142
Jupiter	5	484

Copyright © 2002, Dick De Veaux and Paul Velleman

Saturn	6	887
Uranus	7	1784
Neptune	8	2796
Pluto	9	3666

a) Make a scatterplot and describe the association (Remember: direction, form, scatter!)
b) Why would you not want to talk about the correlation between planet position and distance from the sun?
c) Make a scatterplot showing the logarithm of distance vs position. What is better about this scatterplot?

28 ***Internet Journals** The rapid growth of internet publishing is seen in number of electronic academic journals available during the last decade. [http://www.people.virginia.edu/~pm9k/libsci/charts.html]

Year	Number of Journals
1991	27
1992	36
1993	45
1994	181
1995	306
1996	1093
1997	2459

a) Make a scatterplot and describe the trend.
b) Re-express the data in order to make the association more nearly linear

DRAFT: Do not distribute or copy

8 Linear Regression

WHOPPERS® ARE NOT EXACTLY HEALTH FOOD[1]. But one Double Whopper with Cheese does provide 53 grams of protein—all the protein you need in a day. It also supplies 1020 Calories and 65 grams of fat. The Daily Value (based on a 2000 calorie diet) for fat is 65 grams. So after a double Whopper you'll want the rest of your calories that day to be fat free[2].

There are other items on the Burger King menu. How are their fat and protein related? The scatterplot of the fat (in grams) *versus* the protein (in grams) for foods sold at Burger King shows a positive, linear relationship with relatively little scatter.

Total fat (grams) versus protein (grams) for 30 items on the Burger King menu. The Double Whopper is in the upper right corner. It is extreme, but it is out of line? Fig 8.1

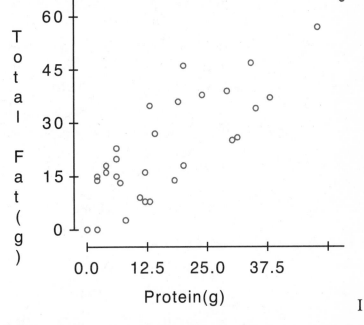

Who: Items on the Burger King menu

What: Protein content (g) and Total fat content (g)

How: Supplied by BK on request or at their web site.

If you want to get 25 grams of protein in your lunch, how much fat should you expect to consume at Burger King? The correlation between fat and protein is 0.83. That tells you that there's a strong linear association. But *strength* of the relationship is only part of the picture. The correlation says "There seems to be a linear association between these two variables," but it doesn't tell *what that association is*.

Models for Data

But, of course, we *can* say more. We can **model** the relationship with a line and give its equation. The equation will let us predict the fat content

---

[1] A whopper is Burger King's signature hamburger.

[2] Sorry about the fries.

DRAFT: Do not distribute or copy

"All models are wrong – but some are useful." George Box – famous statistician.

for any Burger King food, given its amount of protein. But clearly no line can go through all the points. Like all models of the real world, the line will be wrong – wrong in the sense that it can't match reality *exactly*. But it can still be useful. Like a physical model, it's something we can look at and manipulate in order to learn more about the real world.

Models help our understanding in many ways. Just as a model of an airplane in a wind tunnel can give insights even though it doesn't have every rivet, models of data give us summaries that we can learn from and use even though they don't fit each data value exactly. It's important to remember that they're only models of reality and not reality itself. But without models, what we can learn about the world at large is limited to only what we can say about the data we have at hand.

A model simplifies reality in order to help us to understand underlying patterns and relationships. Often models require numbers, which we call **parameters.** Choosing values for the parameters helps us mold the model to fit a particular situation.

We met our first model, the Normal model, in Chapter 6. We saw there that we can specify a Normal model with its mean (μ) and standard deviation (σ). These are the parameters of the Normal model.

For the Burger King foods, we might choose a linear model to describe the relationship between protein and fat. The **linear model** is just an equation of a straight line through the data. The points in the scatterplot don't all line up, but a straight line can summarize the general pattern with only a few parameters. This model can help us understand how the variables are associated.

Correlation and the Line

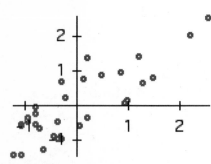

The Burger King scatterplot in z-scores. Fig 8.2

protein	fat
$\bar{x} = 17.2g$	$\bar{y} = 23.5g$
$s_x = 14.0g$	$s_y = 16.4g$

How can we get from the correlation coefficient to a linear model for the association? It turns out that it's not a very big step.

We'll start by standardizing the variables. We don't know μ and σ for either variable, but we can use the means and standard deviations of the data. What line would you choose to model the relationship of the standardized values? Let's start at the center of the scatterplot. How much protein and fat does a *typical* Burger King food item provide? If it has average protein content, $\bar{x}$, what about its fat content? If you guessed that its fat content should be about average, $\bar{y}$, as well, then you've discovered the first property of the line we're looking for. The line must go through the point $(\bar{x},\bar{y})$. So in the plot of z-scores, the line passes through the origin $(0, 0)$.

You might recall that the equation for a line that passes through the origin can be written with just a slope and no intercept:

DRAFT: Do not distribute or copy

$$y = mx$$

We'll need to change this formula in two ways. First we are working with the standardized values, z_x and z_y, not with x and y. So our equation becomes

$$z_y = m\, z_x.$$

But unlike the equation you learned in algebra, our points don't fall on the line, so this won't work for us. The line we want is a model predicting a value of z_y for each value of z_x, but it doesn't get it exactly right. A menu item whose standardized protein value is z_x, won't usually have a standardized fat value, z_y that falls right on the line.

So we need a way to write the predicted values from the model so we can distinguish them from the actual z_y values in the data. In Statistics, we do that by putting a hat on z_y. So we write the line as

$$\hat{z}_y = m z_x.$$

The line is a model. For a given z_x, it predicts a response value $\hat{z}_y$. So we call these $\hat{z}_y$'s **predicted values.**

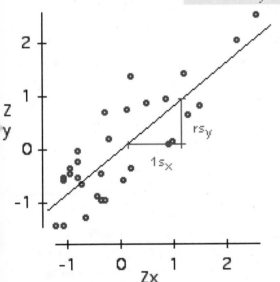

The value m is the **slope**; larger magnitude m's indicate steeper slopes, negative slopes show a negative association, and a slope of zero gives a horizontal line. Moving up one unit in z_x corresponds on the line to moving up m units in $\hat{z}_y$. So moving up one standard deviation in x corresponds to moving up m standard deviations in y.

It turns out that the best[3] choice for m is the correlation coefficient itself, r. So we can write

$$\hat{z}_y = r z_x.$$

Since the correlation between fat content and protein content is 0.83, the equation of the line drawn on the scatterplot of z-scores is

$$\hat{z}_y = 0.83 z_x.$$

Standardized fat *vs* standardized protein with the regression line. Each one standard deviation increase in *protein* results in a predicted increase of *r* standard deviations in *fat* from the model. Fig 8.3

Now we can use this model for prediction. For example, the double hamburger has 31g of protein. That's about 1

---

[3] You really shouldn't let us get away with so sweeping a statement. By "best" we have in mind a specific criterion that we promise to discuss in just a few pages. By "it turns out" what we mean is that a half a page of high school algebra will do the trick. But we didn't want to stop to do the math. If you really want to see the derivation, send the authors an email and we'll be happy to send it to you.

standard deviation above the mean. How much fat should you expect it to have? Putting 1.0 in for z_x in the model, gives a $\hat{z}_y$ value of .83. So, if you trust the model, you'd expect the fat content to be about .83 fat standard deviations above the mean fat level. Moving one standard deviation away from the mean in x moves us r standard deviations away from the mean in y.

If $r = 0$ there's no linear relationship. The line is horizontal, and no matter how many standard deviations you move in x, the predicted value for y doesn't change. On the other hand, if $r = 1.0$, there's a perfect linear association. In that case, moving any number of standard deviations in x moves exactly the same number of standard deviations in y. But, in general, moving any number of standard deviations in x moves r times that number of standard deviations in y.

How big can predicted values get?

Suppose you were told that a new male student was about to join the class, and you were asked to guess his height in inches. What would be your guess? A good guess would be the mean height of male students. Now suppose you are also told that this student has a grade point average of 3.9 – about 2 standard deviations above the mean GPA. Would that change your guess? Probably not. There's no correlation between GPA and height, so knowing the GPA value doesn't tell you anything and doesn't move your guess. (And the formula tells us that as well since it says that we should move 0 times 2 standard deviations from the mean.)

On the other hand, if you were told that, measured in centimeters, the student's height was 2 s.d.'s above the mean, you'd know his height in inches. There's a perfect correlation between height in inches and height in centimeters, so you know he's 2 s.d.'s above mean height in inches as well. (The formula would tell us to move 1.0 times 2 standard deviations from the mean.)

Sir Francis Galton was the first to speak of "regression", although others had fit lines to data by the same method.

The First Regression
Sir Francis Galton related the heights of sons to the heights of their fathers with a regression line. The slope of his line was less than 1. That is, sons of tall fathers were tall, but not as much above the average height as their fathers had been above their mean. Sons of short fathers were short, but generally not as far from their mean as their fathers. Galton interpreted the slope correctly as indicating a "regression" toward the mean height—and "regression" stuck as a description of the method he had used to find the line.

But what if you are told that the student is 2 s.d.'s above the mean in shoe size? Would you still guess that he's average height? No, you'd probably guess that he's taller than average since there's a positive correlation between height and shoe size. But would you guess that he's 2 standard deviations above the mean? When there was no correlation, we didn't move away from the mean at all. With a perfect correlation, we

DRAFT: Do not distribute or copy

moved our guess the full 2 standard deviations. But any correlation between these extremes should lead us to move somewhere between 0 and 2 standard deviations above the mean. (To be exact, the formula tell us to move 2*r standard deviations away from the mean).

Notice that we can't ever move more than 2 standard deviations away since r can't be bigger than 1.0. So, each predicted y tends to be closer to its mean (in standard deviations) than its corresponding x was. This property of the linear model is called **regression to the mean** and the line is called the **regression line**.

Working in Real Units

Why is correlation "r"?
In his original paper on correlation, Galton used r for the "index of co-relation" that we now call the correlation coefficient. He calculated it from the regression of y on x or of x on y after standardizing the variables, just as we have done. It is fairly clear from the text that he used r to stand for (standardized) regression.

protein	fat
$\bar{x} = 17.2g$	$\bar{y} = 23.5g$
$s_x = 14.0g$	$s_y = 16.4g$

$$b_1 = r\frac{s_y}{s_x}$$

We mean this literally. Get in the habit of identifying the units and writing down "y-units *per* x-unit" with the unit names put in place. You'll find it'll really help you to tell about the line.

When you read the Burger King menu, you probably don't think in z-scores. But you might want to know the fat content in grams for a specific amount of protein in grams.

Suppose you wanted to know how much fat should we *expect* in a double hamburger with 31 grams of protein? The mean protein content is 17 grams and the standard deviation is 14, so that item is 1 sd above the mean. Since r = 0.83 we predict the fat content will be 0.83 standard deviation above the mean fat content. Great. How much fat is that? Well, the mean fat content is 23.5g and the standard deviation of fat contents is 16.4, so we predict that the double hamburger will have 23.5 + .83 * 16.4 = 37.11 grams of fat.

So, we can always convert both *x* and *y* to z-scores, find the correlation, use $\hat{z}_y = rz_x$ and then convert $\hat{z}_y$ back to its original units so that we can understand the prediction. But can't we do this more simply?

Yes. Since r = 0.83 we know that for each increase of one standard deviation in protein we'll see an increase of about .83 standard deviations in fat. (One sd increase in *x* means an increase of *r* sd's in *y*). A one sd increase in protein mean 14 grams. And one sd in fat is 16.4 grams. So in actual units, for each increase of 14 grams of protein we'll increase .83*16.4 or 13.6 grams of fat. So for every *gram* of protein, we'll increase 0.97 grams of fat. (Because 13.6 /14 = .97) .

In other words, the slope of the line in *original units* is:

$$b_1 = \frac{rs_y}{s_x} = \frac{0.83 \times 16.4g\, fat}{14g\, protein} = 0.97\, grams\ of\ fat \text{ per } gram\ of\ protein .$$

The correlation coefficient, *r*, has no units, but the standard deviations carry the units of their respective variables, so this slope has units. To understand the slope, start with the phrase "*y-units* per *x-unit*" and put

Copyright © 2001, Dick De Veaux and Paul Velleman

the units into the expression. In our example, the slope is in *grams of fat* per *gram of protein*.

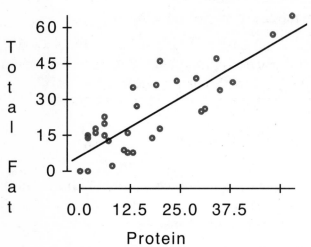

Burger King menu items in their natural units with the regression line. Fig 8.4

If the correlation were zero, the slope b_1 would be zero, and the intercept, b_0, would be just $\bar{y}$. And so the model would ignore x completely and just predict y to be its mean: $\hat{y} = \bar{y}$.

In going back to the real units, something else has changed besides the slope. Remember that the line has to go through the mean-mean point: $(\bar{x}, \bar{y})$. Unless x and y both just happen to have zero means, the line won't go through the origin. So we need to include a term (called the *y*-intercept) to adjust the level of the line. We write

$$\hat{y} = b_0 + b_1 x.$$

As we know already, the hat over the y (we say "y-hat") indicates values predicted from the model. In this equation, b_0 is the **intercept**, the value of y where the line crosses the y-axis. (Put in 0 for x in the equation to verify that the intercept is the $\hat{y}$ value when $x = 0$.)

How do we find b_0? Since the line has to go through $(\bar{x}, \bar{y})$, we can put the means into the equation and write: $\bar{y} = b_0 + b_1\bar{x}$.

The intercept is just $b_0 = \bar{y} - b_1\bar{x}$.

For the Burger King foods, it comes out to

$$b_0 = 23.5g\ fat - 0.97\frac{g\ fat}{g\ protein} \times 17.2\,g\ protein = 6.8g\ fat$$

Putting this back into the regression formula gives:

$$\hat{fat} = 6.8\,g\,fat + 0.97\frac{g\ fat}{g\ protein}\ protein$$

With the equation it's easy to answer the question for any menu item we want. For example, if we wanted to know the *predicted* fat content of the BK Broiler Chicken sandwich, which has 30 grams of protein, we could plug in 30 grams for the amount of protein and see that the predicted fat content is 6.8 + 0.97* 30 = 35.9 g fat.

Calculating a Regression Equation Step-by-Step

In Chapter 7 we examined a scatterplot of annual cost per person due to traffic delays against peak period freeway speed and saw that slower speeds were linearly associated with higher costs. That's all very well, but it doesn't answer the all-important (when in comes to costs) question "how much?" Given the peak period freeway speeds, what would we predict the annual cost per person to be? That's the kind of question that might be raised when a city considers budget items for highway improvement or for public transportation. And the answer lies in the regression model.

So let's find the regression model.

Think	**Variables:** Identify the variables and report the W's.	We have the annual cost per person ($) and the peak period freeway speed (mph) for 70 U.S. cities. The data come from the 2002 Urban Mobility Report issued by the Texas Transportation Institute.
	Plan: The condition we need to check is the one required for correlation—that we have a straight enough relationship. That's simple. We make a scatterplot.	The **straight enough condition** is satisfied as we can see from the scatterplot. We can reasonably fit a line to model this relationship.
Show	**Mechanics** Find the equation of the regression line.	Summary statistics give the building blocks of the calculation **Annual cost per person:** Mean = $298.96 Std dev = $180.830 **Peak Period freeway speed:** Mean = 54.34 mph Std dev = 4.494 mph r = -0.90

		$b_1 = r\dfrac{s_y}{s_x}$ and $b_0 = \bar{y} - b_1\bar{x}$. $b_1 = .90\dfrac{180.83}{4.494} = 36.21$ $b_0 = 298.96 - 36.21 \times 54.34 = -1677.92$
Tell	**Interpretation:** Discuss what you have found.	Traffic delays cost each urban area resident about $36 per year for each mile per hour the freeways are slowed at peak periods.

Residuals

A *negative* residual from a model means that the predicted value is larger than the actual data value. In other words, it is an **overestimate**.

Likewise, a *positive* residual shows a model value that is an **underestimate**.

These may seem backwards until you think about them.

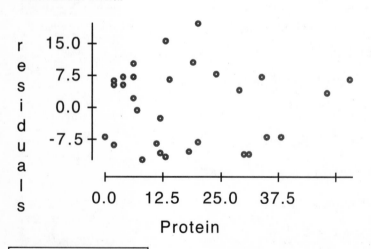

The residuals for the BK menu regression look appropriately boring. Fig 8.5

Of course, no model is perfect. The BK Broiler Chicken, which we predicted would have 35.9g of fat doesn't. In fact, it has 25g of fat. The difference between the observed value and its associated predicted value is called the **residual.** The residual at each data value tells us how far off our prediction is at that point. So the BK Broiler Chicken residual is

$$25 - 35.9 = -10.9 \text{ g of fat.}$$

We always subtract the predicted value from the observed one. The negative residual tells us that the actual fat content of the BK broiler chicken is about 11 grams *less* than the model predicts for a typical Burger King menu item with 30 grams of protein.

The linear model we are using assumes that the relationship between the two variables is a perfect straight line. The residuals are the part of the data that *hasn't* been modeled. We can write: *Data = Model + Residual*, or equivalently, Residual = Data – Model. Or, in symbols: $e = y - \hat{y}$. When we ask how well the model fits, we are really asking how much of the data is still in the residuals.

Residuals also help us to see whether the model makes sense. When a regression model is appropriate, it should model the underlying relationship. Nothing interesting should be left behind. So after we fit a regression model, we usually plot the residuals in the hope of finding…

nothing.

A scatterplot of the residuals *vs* the x-values should be the most boring scatterplot you've seen. It shouldn't have any interesting features, like a

DRAFT: Do not distribute or copy

We find the standard deviation of the residuals in almost the way you'd expect:

$$s_e = \sqrt{\dfrac{e^2}{n-2}}$$

We don't need to subtract the mean because $\bar{e} = 0$.
Why $n-2$ rather than $n-1$? We'll get back to you on that one.

direction, or shape. It should stretch horizontally, with about the same amount of scatter throughout. It should show no bends, and it should have no outliers. If you see any of these features, you need to follow up to find out what the regression model missed.

If the residuals show no interesting pattern when we plot them against x, we can look at how big they are. After all, we're trying to make them as small as possible. But since their mean is always zero, it is only sensible to look at how much they vary. The standard deviation of the residuals gives us a measure of how much the points spread out around the regression line.

For the Burger King foods, the standard deviation of the residuals is 9.3 g. fat. That looks about right in the scatterplot of residuals. The residual for the BK Broiler chicken was –10.9 g, just about what we'd expect.

R^2 — The Variation Accounted for

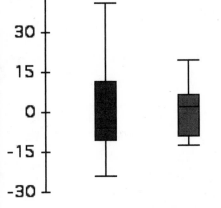

Total Fat residuals

Compare the variability of total fat, and the residuals from the regression. The means have been subtracted to make it easier to compoare spreads. The variation left in the residuals is unaccounted for by the model, but it is less than the variation in the original data. Fig 8.6

The variation in the residuals is the key to assessing how well the model fits. Let's compare the variation of the response variable to the variation of the residuals. The total fat has a standard deviation of 16.3 grams. The residuals' standard deviation is 9.2 grams. If the correlation were 1.0 and the model predicted the fat values perfectly, the residuals would all be zero and have no variation. We couldn't possibly do any better than that.

On the other hand, if the correlation were zero, the model would simply predict 23.5 g of fat (the mean) for all menu items. The residuals from that prediction would just be the observed fat values minus their mean. These residuals would have the same spread as the original *data* because, as we know, just subtracting the mean doesn't change the spread.

How well does the BK model do? Look at the boxplots. The variation in the residuals is smaller than in the data, but certainly bigger than zero. That's nice to know, but how much of the variation is still left in the residuals? If you had to put a number between 0 and 100% on the fraction of the variation left in the residuals, what would you say?

All regression models fall somewhere between the two extremes of zero correlation and perfect correlation. We'd like to gauge where our model falls. Can we use the correlation to do that? Well, a model with correlation -.5 is doing as well as one with correlation +.5. They just have different directions. But if we *square* the correlation coefficient, we'll get a value between 0 and 1, and the direction won't matter. It turns out that this works perfectly. The squared correlation, r^2, gives the fraction of the data's variance accounted for by the model and

Copyright © 2001, Dick De Veaux and Paul Velleman

Is a correlation of 0.80 twice as strong as a correlation of 0.40? Not if you think in terms of R^2. A correlation of 0.80 means an R^2 of $0.80^2 = 64\%$. A correlation of 0.40 means an R^2 of $0.40^2 = 16\%$ -- only a quarter as much of the variability accounted for. So a correlation of 0.80 gives an R^2 *four* times as strong as a correlation of 0.40 and accounts for four times as much of the variability

$1 - r^2$ is the fraction of the original variance left in the residuals. For the Burger King model, $r^2 = .83^2 = .684$, and $1 - r^2$ is $.316$, so 31.6% of the variance in total fat has been left in the residuals. How close was that to your guess?

All regression analyses include this statistic, although by tradition, it is written with a capital letter, R^2 and pronounced "R-squared". An R^2 of 0 means that none of the variance in the data is in the model; all of it is still in the residuals. It would be hard to imagine using that model for anything.

Because R^2 is a fraction of a whole, it is often given as a percentage.[4] For the Burger King data, R^2 is 68.4%.

How can we see that R^2 is really the Fraction of Variance accounted for by the model?

It's a simple calculation. The variance of the fat content of the Burger King foods is $16.4^2 = 265.48$. The variance of the residuals is 83.91. So as a fraction, that's $83.91/265.48 = 0.316$ or 31.6%. That's the fraction of the variance that is *not* accounted for by the model. So the fraction that *is* accounted for is $100\% - 31.6\% = 68.4\%$, just the value we got for R^2.

How Big Should R^2 be?

Some Extreme Tales: One major company developed a method to differentiate between proteins. To do so they had to distinguish between regressions with R^2 of 99.99 and 99.98%. For this application, 99.98% was not high enough.

The President of a financial services company reports that although his regressions give R^2 below 2%, they are highly successful because those used by his competition are even lower.

R^2 is always between 0% and 100%. But what's a "good" R^2 value? The answer depends on the kind of data you are analyzing and on what you want to do with it. There is no value for R^2 that automatically determines that the regression is "good." Data from scientific experiments often have R^2 in the 80% to 90% range and even higher. But data from observational studies and surveys often show relatively weak associations because it is so difficult to measure reliable responses. An R^2 of 50% to 30% or even lower might be taken as evidence of a useful regression. The standard deviation of the residuals can give us more information about the usefulness of the regression by telling us how much scatter there is around the line.

As we've seen, an R^2 of 100% is a perfect fit with no scatter around the line. Here, s_e would be zero. All of the variance is accounted for by the model and none is left in the residuals at all. This sounds great, but it's too good to be true for real data.

Along with the slope and intercept for a regression, you should always report R^2 so that readers can judge for themselves how successful the

---

[4] By contrast, we usually give correlation coefficients as decimal values between -1.0 and 1.0.

DRAFT: Do not distribute or copy

regression is at fitting the data. Statistics is about variation, and R^2 measures the success of the regression model in terms of the fraction of the variation of y accounted for by the regression. R^2 is the first part of a regression that many people look at because, along with the scatterplot, it tells whether the regression model is even worth thinking about.

Least Squares

The variation of the residuals is the key to the success of the model. But does our model try as hard as it can to make that variation small? Of course it does. Do you think we would have spent all this time on it if it weren't the best?[5]

Our line has the special property that the variation of its residuals is the smallest it can be for any straight line model for these data. No other line has this property. Speaking mathematically, we say that this line minimizes the sum of the squared residuals. This is why it is often called the **least squares regression** line.

Whenever we sum up squares of deviations, however, there's a danger. Outlying values contribute a great deal to large deviations and squaring them makes their influence that much greater. Even a single outlier can inflate a standard deviation dramatically. And we must be even more careful with least squares regression. Outlying points can dramatically change a regression model. They can even change the sign of the slope, misleading us about the underlying relationship between the variables. We'll see examples in the next chapter.

Assumptions and Conditions

The linear regression model is perhaps the most widely used model in all of Statistics. It has everything we could want in a model: two easily estimated parameters, a meaningful measure of how well the model fits the data, and the ability to predict new values. It even provides a self-check in plots of the residuals, to help us avoid silly mistakes.

But, like all models, linear models apply only when certain assumptions are true, so we'd better think about whether they're reasonable. Fortunately, we can check the conditions just by looking at simple plots.

---

[5] We promised earlier to tell you exactly the sense in which the regression line is "best". This is it. The regression line is the unique line that minimizes the variance of the residuals.

Copyright © 2001, Dick De Veaux and Paul Velleman

Linearity Assumption:

The linear model assumes that the relationship between the variables is linear[6]. If you try to model a curved relationship with a straight line, you'll usually get exactly what you deserve. But a scatterplot will let you check that the assumption is reasonable.

Check the scatterplot. The shape must be linear or we can't use regression at all.

The **Straight Enough Condition** is satisfied if the scatterplot looks reasonably straight[6]. It's also a good idea to check linearity again *after* computing the regression when we can examine the residuals. You should also check for outliers, which could change the regression. If the data seem to clump or cluster in the scatterplot, that could be a sign of trouble worth looking into further.

If the scatterplot is not straight enough, stop here. You can't use a linear model for *any* two variables, even if they are related. They must have a *linear* association or the model won't mean a thing. Some non-linear relationships can be saved by re-expressing the data to make the scatterplot more linear.

Regression Step-by-Step

Even if you hit the fast food joints for lunch, you should have a good breakfast. Researchers recorded facts about 77 breakfast cereals including the calories and sugar content (in grams) of a serving. Let's build a linear model to understand how calories are related to sugar content.

Think

Variables: Name the variables, report the W's, and specify the questions of interest.

We have two quantitative variables, *calories,* and *sugar* content, measured on 77 breakfast cereals. The units of measurement are calories and grams of sugar.

We are interested in the relationship between these two variables.

---

[6] Duh!

DRAFT: Do not distribute or copy

Plan: To check the conditions for a regression, always make a picture. Never fit a regression without looking at the scatterplot first.

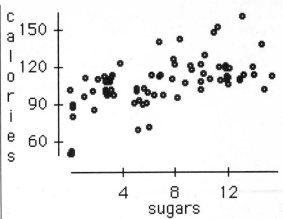

We can see from the scatterplot that the direction of the relationship is positive, and the form of the association is straight enough.

There are no obvious outliers or groups.

Because the **straight enough condition** is satisfied, we can fit a regression model to these data.

Summary statistics give the building blocks of the calculation

calories
mean = 107 calories
sd = 19.5 calories
sugars
mean = 7 grams
sd = 4.4 grams
Correlation
r = 0.564

Show **Mechanics:** If there are no clear violations of the condition, fit a straight line model of the form

$$\hat{y} = b_0 + b_1 x$$

to the data.

$b_1 = r \dfrac{s_y}{s_x}$ and $b_0 = \bar{y} - b_1 \bar{x}$.

For the cereals,

$b_1 = 0.564 \dfrac{19.5}{4.4} = 2.50$ and its units are *calories per gram of sugar.*

The intercept, b_0 is

$$b_0 = \bar{y} - b_1\bar{x} = 107 - 2.50 \times 7 = 89.5$$

and its units are *calories*.

So the least squares line is:

$$\hat{y} = 89.5 + 2.50\, x,$$

or $cal\hat{o}ries = 89.5 + 2.50\, sugar.$

Squaring the correlation gives

$$R^2 = 0.564^2 = 0.318 \text{ or } 31.8\%$$

Tell

Interpretation: Describe what the model says in words and numbers. Be sure to use the names of the variables and their units.

The key to interpreting a regression model is to start with the phrase "b_1 y-units per x-unit", substituting the estimated value of the slope for b_1 and the names of the respective units. The intercept is then a starting or base value.

R^2 gives the fraction of the variability of *y* accounted for by the linear regression model.

The scatterplot shows a positive, linear relationship and no outliers. The least squares regression line fit through these data has the equation

Predicted calories = 89.5 + 2.50 calories/gm x sugar.

The regression model says that cereals gain about 2.50 calories per gram of sugar starting from a base of 89.5 calories. The intercept in this regression can also be interpreted as predicting the calories in a sugar-free cereal.

The R^2 says that 31.8% of the variability in calories is accounted for by the linear regression on sugars.

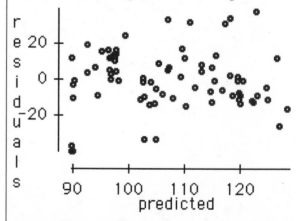

Think Again

Check again: Even though we looked at the scatterplot *before* fitting a regression model, a plot of the residuals is an essential part of any regression analysis because it is the best check for additional patterns and interesting quirks in the data.

The residuals show a horizontal direction, a shapeless form, and roughly equal scatter for all predicted values.

DRAFT: Do not distribute or copy

Reality Check: Is the Regression Reasonable?

Statistics don't come out of nowhere. They are based on data. The results of a statistical analysis should reinforce your common sense, not fly in its face. If the results are surprising, then either you've learned something new about the world or your analysis is wrong.

Whenever you perform a regression, think about the coefficients and ask whether they make sense. Is a slope of 2.5 calories per gram of sugar reasonable? That's hard to say right off. But, we know from the summary statistics that a typical cereal has about 100 calories and 7 grams of sugar. A gram of sugar contributes some calories (actually, 4, but you don't need to know that), so calories should go up with increasing sugar. So the direction of the slope seems right.

To see if the *size* of the slope is reasonable, a useful trick is to consider its order of magnitude. We'll start by seeing if decreasing the slope by a factor of 10 seems reasonable. Is 0.25 calories per gram of sugar enough? The 7 grams of sugar found in the average cereal would contribute less than 2 calories. That seems too small.

Now let's try inflating the slope by a factor of 10. Is 25 calories per gram reasonable? Then the average cereal would have 175 calories from sugar alone. But the average cereal only has 100 calories per serving, so that slope seems too big.

We have tried inflating the slope by a factor of 10 and deflating it by 10 and found both to be unreasonable. So, like Goldilocks, we're left with the value in the middle that's just right. And an increase of 2.5 calories per gram of sugar is certainly *plausible*.

The small effort of asking yourself whether the regression equation is plausible is repaid whenever you catch errors or avoid saying something silly or absurd about the data. It's too easy to take something that comes out of a computer at face value and assume that it makes sense.

Always be skeptical and ask yourself if the answer is reasonable.

What can go wrong

There are many ways in which data that appear at first to be a good candidate for regression analysis may be unsuitable. And there are ways that people use regression that can lead them astray. Here's an overview of the most common problems. We'll discuss these at length in the next chapter.

- ***Don't fit a straight line to a nonlinear relationship.*** Linear regression is only suited to relationships that are, well, *linear*. Fortunately, we can often improve the linearity easily by using re-expression. We'll come back to this topic in Chapter 10.

- ***Beware extraordinary points.*** Data values can be extraordinary in a regression in two ways. They can have y-values that stand off from the linear pattern suggested by the bulk of the data or extreme x-values. Both kinds of extraordinary points require attention.

- ***Don't extrapolate beyond the data.*** A linear model will often do a reasonable job of summarizing a relationship in the narrow range of observed x-values. And once we have a working model for the relationship, it's tempting to use it. But beware of predicting y-values for x-values that lie outside the range of the original data. The model may no longer hold there, so such **extrapolations** too far from the data are dangerous.

- ***Don't infer that x causes y just because there is a good linear model for their relationship.*** We have seen that when two variables are strongly correlated, it is often tempting to assume a causal relationship between them. Putting a regression line on a scatterplot tempts us even further, but it doesn't make the assumption of causation any more valid.

Don't Tell

The R^2 does **not** mean that height accounts for 42% of the pounds a person weighs. It is the *variation* in weight that is accounted for by the linear model.

Although R^2 measures the *strength* of the linear association, a high R^2 does not demonstrate the *appropriateness* of the regression. A single outlier or data that separate into two groups rather than a single cloud of points can make the R^2 seem quite large when, in fact, the linear regression model is simply inappropriate. Conversely, a low R^2 value may be due to a single outlier as well. It may be that most of the data fall roughly along a straight line with the exception of a single point.

Connections

We've talked about the importance of models before, but have only seen the Normal model as an example. The linear model is one of the most important models in statistics. Chapter 7 talked about the assignment of variables to the y and x axes. It didn't matter to correlation, but it does matter to regression because y is predicted by x in the regression model.

DRAFT: Do not distribute or copy

The connection of R^2 to correlation is obvious, although it may not be immediately clear that just by squaring the correlation we can learn the fraction of the variability of y accounted for by a regression on x. We'll return to this in subsequent chapters.

We made a big fuss about knowing the units of your quantitative variables. We didn't need units for correlation, but without the units we can't define the slope of a regression. A regression makes no sense if you don't know the Who, the What, and the Units of both of your variables.

We've summed squared deviations before when we computed the standard deviation and variance. That's not coincidental. They are closely connected to regression.

When we first talked about models, we noted that deviations away from a model were often interesting. Now we have a formal definition of these deviations as residuals.

Regression and the Computer

All statistics packages make a table of results for a regression. These tables may differ slightly from one package to another, but all are essentially the same — and all include much more that we need to know for now. Every computer regression table includes a section that looks something like this:

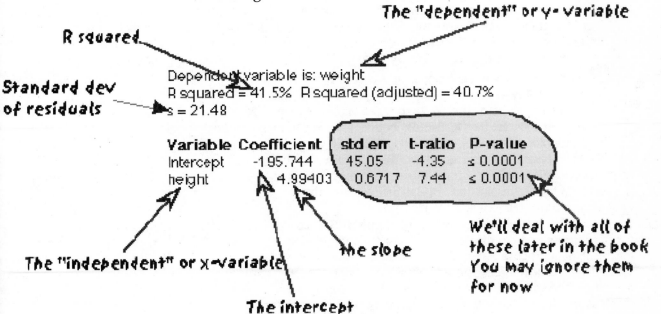

The slope and intercept coefficient are given in a table such as this one. Usually the slope is labeled with the name of the x-variable, and the intercept is labeled "Intercept" or "Constant". So the regression equation shown here is

$$\overset{\frown}{Weight} = -195.774 + 4.99403 \ Height$$

It is not unusual for statistics packages to give many more digits of the estimated slope and intercept than could possibly be estimated from the data. (The original data were reported to the nearest pound and inch.) Ordinarily, you should round the reported numbers to the same precision as the data. We will learn about the other numbers in the regression table later in the book. For now, all you need to be able to do is find the coefficients and the R^2 value.

This computer grid offers guidance for displaying a scatterplot and then computing a regression. Many of these programs can compute the regression without also making the scatterplot (sometimes with a different command in a different menu), but you didn't want to do that anyway because you planned to check the conditions.

Package	Commands & Location	Comments
Data Desk	To find and display a regression line in Data Desk, select the *y*-variable and the *x*-variable. In the **Plot** menu choose **Scatterplot**. From the scatterplot HyperView menu choose **Add Regression Line** to display the line. From the HyperView menu choose **Regression** to compute the regression.	Alternatively, find the regression first with the Regression command in the Calc menu. Click on the *x*-variable's name to open a menu that offers the scatterplot.
Excel	To find and display a regression line in Excel: Make a scatterplot of the data*. With the scatterplot frontmost, select **Add Trendline...** from the **Chart** menu. Click the **Options** tab and select **Display Equation on Chart**. Click **OK**.	*The computer grid for chapter 7 shows how to make a scatterplot. We don't repeat those steps here.
JMP	To find and display a regression in JMP choose **Fit Y by X** from the **Analyze** menu. Specify the *y*-variable in the Select Columns box and click the "**Y, Response**" button. Specify the *x*-variable and click the "**X, Factor**" button. Click **OK** to make a scatterplot. In the scatterplot window, click on the red triangle beside the heading labeled "Bivariate Fit..." and choose "**Fit Line**". JMP draws the least squares regression line on the scatterplot and displays the results of the regression in tables below the plot.	
Minitab	To find and display a regression line in MINITAB, choose **Regression** from the **Stat** menu. From the Regression submenu, choose **Fitted Line Plot**. In the Fitted Line Plot dialog, click in the **Response Y** box, and assign the *y*-variable from the Variable list. Click in the **Predictor X** box, and assign the *x*-variable from the Variable list. Make sure that the Type of Regression Model is set to Linear. Click the **OK** button.	
SPSS	To find and display a regression line in SPSS, choose **Interactive** from the **Graphs** menu. From the Interactive Graphs submenu, choose **Scatterplot**. In the Create Scatterplot dialog, drag the *y*-variable into the **y-axis target**, and the *x*-variable into the **x-axis target**. Click on the **Fit** tab. Choose **Regression** from the **Method** popup menu. Click the **OK** button.	

DRAFT: Do not distribute or copy

Key Concepts

Model	An equation or formula that simplifies and represents reality.
Parameter	The numbers in the model that have to be chosen to explicitly determine the value of the model.
Linear Model	A linear model is an equation of the form $$\hat{y} = b_0 + b_1 x$$ To interpret a linear model we need to know the variables (along with their "W's") and their units
Predicted Values	The values of $\hat{y}$ found for each x value in the data. Predicted values are found by substituting the x-value in the regression equation and solving for $\hat{y}$. The predicted values are the values on the fitted line; the points $(x, \hat{y})$ all lie exactly on the fitted line.
Slope	The slope gives a value in "y-units per x-unit"
Regression to the Mean	Because the correlation is always less than 1.0, each predicted y tends to be fewer standard deviations from its mean than its corresponding x was from its mean. This is called regression to the mean.
Intercept	The intercept gives a starting value in y-units. It's the $\hat{y}$-value when x is 0.
Residuals	Residuals are the differences between data values and the corresponding values predicted by the regression model – or , more generally, values predicted by any model. Residual = Observed value – Predicted value
R^2	• R^2 is the squared of the correlation between y and x. • R^2 gives the fraction of the variability of y accounted for by the least squares linear regression on x. • R^2 is an overall measure of how successful the regression is in linearly relating y to x.
Least Squares	The least squares criterion specifies the unique line that minimizes the variance of the residuals, or equivalently, the sum of the squared residuals.
Regression Line	The particular linear equation, $$\hat{y} = b_0 + b_1 x$$ that satisfies the least squares criterion is called the least squares regression line. Casually, we often just call it the

	regression line.
Examining Residuals	To check whether a linear model is appropriate, it is usually best to plot the residuals. A histogram of the residuals can check for multiple modes and *y*-outliers. A scatterplot of residuals against predicted values can reveal bends, groups, and model outliers.

Skills

When you complete this lesson you should:

Think

- Be able to identify response (*y*) and explanatory (*x*) variables in context.

- Understand how a linear equation summarizes the relationship between two variables.

- Recognize when a regression should be used to summarize a linear relationship between two quantitative variables.

- Be able to judge whether the slope of a regression makes sense.

- Know how to examine your data for violations of the straight enough condition that would make it inappropriate to compute a regression.

- Understand that the least squares slope is easily affected by extreme values.

- Know that residuals are the differences between the data values and the corresponding values predicted by the line and that the *least squares criterion* finds the line that minimizes the sum of the squared residuals.

- Know how to use a plot of residuals against predicted values to check the straight enough condition or look for outliers.

Show

- Know how to find a regression equation from the summary statistics for each variable and their correlation.

- Know how to find a regression equation using your statistics software and how to find the slope and intercept values in the regression output table.

- Know how to use regression to predict a value of *y* for a given *x*.

- Know how to compute the residual for each data value and to display them.

DRAFT: Do not distribute or copy

> *Tell*
>
> - Be able to write a sentence explaining what a linear equation says about the relationship between y and x, basing it on the fact that the slope is given in *y-units per x-unit*.
>
> - Understand how the correlation coefficient and the regression slope are related. Know how R^2 describes how much variation in y is accounted for by its linear relationship with x.
>
> - Be able to describe a prediction made from a regression equation, relating the predicted value to the specified x-value.

Exercises

1. **Regression equations** Fill in the missing information in the table below.

$\bar{x}$	s_x	$\bar{y}$	s_y	r	$\hat{y} = b_0 + b_1 x$
a) 10	2	20	3	0.5	
b) 2	0.06	7.2	1.2	-0.4	
c) 12	6			-0.8	$\hat{y} = 200 - 4x$
d) 2.5	1.2		100		$\hat{y} = -100 + 50x$

2. **More regression equations** Fill in the missing information in the table below.

$\bar{x}$	s_x	$\bar{y}$	s_y	r	$\hat{y} = b_0 + b_1 x$
a) 30	4	18	6	-0.2	
b) 100	18	60	10	0.9	
c)	0.8	50	15		$\hat{y} = -10 + 15x$
d)		18	4	-0.6	$\hat{y} = 30 - 2x$

3. **Residuals** Tell what each of the residual plots below indicates about the appropriateness of the linear model that was fit to the data.

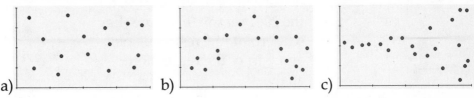

a)　　　　　　　　　　b)　　　　　　　　　　c)

4. **Residuals** Tell what each of the residual plots below indicates about the appropriateness of the linear model that was fit to the data.

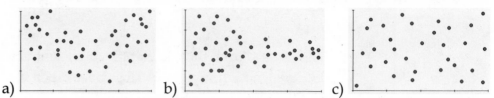

a)　　　　　　b)　　　　　　c)

5. **Least Squares** Consider the four points (10,10), (20,50), (40,20), and (50,80). The line of best fit is $\hat{y} = 7.0 + 1.1x$. Use these data to explain what "least squares" means.

6. **Least Squares** Consider the four points (200,1950), (400,1650), (600,1800), and (800,1600). The line of best fit is $\hat{y} = 1975 - 0.45x$. Use these data to explain what "least squares" means.

7. **Real Estate** A random sample of records of sales of homes from Feb 15 to Apr 30, 1993 from the files maintained by the Albuquerque Board of Realtors gives the price and size (in square feet) of 117 homes. A regression to predict price (in thousands of dollars) from size has an R-squared of 71.4%. The residuals plot confirmed that a linear model is appropriate.
   a) What are the variables and units in this regression? What units does the slope have?
   b) Write a sentence summarizing what the R-squared value says about this regression.
   c) Do you think the slope is positive or negative? Explain.
   d) What is the correlation between size and price?
   e) What would you predict about the price of a home one standard deviation above average in size?
   f) What would you predict about the price of a home two standard deviations below average in size?

8. **Baseball** In the last chapter you looked at the relationship between the number of games won by American League baseball teams and the average attendance at their home games for the first half of the 2001 season. Here are the scatterplot, the residuals plot, and part of the regression analysis.

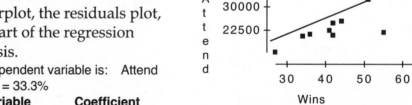

   Dependent variable is:　Attend
   R2 = 33.3%

Variable	Coefficient
Constant	5773.27
Wins	517.609

   a) Do you think a linear model is appropriate here? Explain.
   b) Interpret the meaning of R² in this context.

c) What is the correlation between wins and average attendance?

d) What would you predict about the average attendance for a team that is two standard deviations above average in games won?

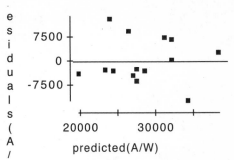

e) If a team is one standard deviation below average in attendance, what would you predict about the number of games the team has won?

9. **More Real Estate** Consider the Albuquerque home sales from Exercise 7 again. The regression analysis gives the model

$$\widehat{price} = 47.82 + 0.061size.$$

a) Explain what the slope of the line says about housing prices and house size.

b) What price would you predict for a 3000 square-foot house in this market?

c) A real estate agent shows a potential buyer a 1200 square foot home, saying that the asking price is $6000 less than what one would expect to pay for a house of this size. What is the asking price, and what is the $6000 called?

10. **2nd Inning** Refer again to the regression analysis for attendance and games won by American League baseball teams, seen in Exercise 8.

a) Write the equation of the regression line.

b) Estimate the average attendance for a team with 50 wins.

c) Interpret the meaning of the slope of the regression line in this context.

d) In general, what would a negative residual mean in this context?

e) The St Louis Cardinals are not included in this data because they are a National League team. At the time these data were collected they had won 43 games, and averaged 38988 fans at their home games. Calculate the residual for this team, and explain what it means.

11. **What slope?** If you create a regression model for predicting the weight of a car (in pounds) from its length (in feet), is the slope most likely to be 3, 30, 300, or 3000? Explain.

12. **What slope?** If you create a regression model for estimating the height of a pine tree (in feet) based upon the circumference of its trunk (in inches), is the slope most likely to be 0.1, 1, 10, or 100? Explain.

13. **Misinterpretations** A biology student who created a regression model to use a bird's height when perched for predicting its wingspan made these two statements. Assuming the calculations were done correctly, explain what is wrong with each interpretation.
    a) My R^2 of 93% shows that this linear model is appropriate.
    b) A bird 10 inches tall will have a wingspan of 17 inches.

14. **More misinterpretations** A sociology student investigated the association between a country's literacy rate and life expectancy, then drew the conclusions listed below. Explain why each statement is incorrect. (Assume that all the calculations were done properly.)
    a) The literacy rate determines 64% of the life expectancy for a country.
    b) The slope of the line shows that an increase of 5% in literacy rate will produce a 2-year improvement in life expectancy.

15. **ESP** People who claim to "have ESP" participate in a screening test in which they have to guess which of several images someone is thinking of. You and a friend both took the test. You scored 2 standard deviations above the mean and your friend scored one standard deviation below the mean. The researchers offer everyone the opportunity to take a retest.
    a) Should you choose to take this retest? Explain.
    b) Now explain to your friend what his decision should be and why.

16. **SI Jinx** Players in any sport who are having great seasons, turning in performances that are much better than anyone might have anticipated, often are pictured on the cover of *Sports Illustrated*. Frequently their performances then falter somewhat, leading some athletes to believe in a "Sports Illustrated jinx". Similarly it is common for phenomenal rookies to have less stellar second seasons – the so-called "sophomore slump". While fans, athletes, and analysts put forth many theories about what leads to such declines, a statistician might simply argue that this is an example of regression toward the mean. Explain.

17. **SAT Scores** Because doing the SAT-Math problems also involves the ability to read and understand the questions, can a person's verbal score be used to predict their math score? Verbal and math SAT scores of a high school graduating class are displayed in the scatterplot, with the line of best fit added.

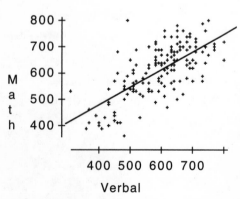

    a) Describe the relationship.
    b) Are there any students whose scores do not seem to fit the overall pattern?
    c) For these data, $r = 0.685$. Interpret this statistic.
    d) These verbal scores averaged 596.3 with a standard deviation of 99.5, and the math scores averaged 612.2 with a standard deviation of 96.1. Write the equation of the line

DRAFT: Do not distribute or copy

of regression.
e) Interpret the slope of this line.
f) Predict the math score of a student with a verbal score of 500.
g) A few students every year score a perfect 1600. Based on this model, what would that student's residual be for her math score?

18. **Success in College** Colleges use SAT scores in the admissions process because they believe these scores provide some insight into how a high school student will perform at the college level. Suppose the entering freshmen at a certain college have mean combined SAT scores of 1222 with standard deviation 83. First semester these students attained a mean GPA of 2.66 with standard deviation 0.56. A scatterplot showed the association to be reasonably linear, and the correlation between SAT score and GPA was 0.47.
a) Write the equation of the regression line.
b) Explain what the y – intercept of the regression line indicates.
c) Interpret the slope of the regression line.
d) Predict the GPA of a freshman who scored a combined 1400.
e) Based upon these statistics, how effective do you think SAT scores would be in predicting academic success during first semester of the freshman year at this college? Explain.
f) As a student, would you rather have a positive or a negative residual in this context? Explain.

19. **SAT, Take 2** Suppose we wanted to use SAT math scores to estimate verbal scores based on the information in Exercise 17.
a) What is the correlation in this direction?
b) Write the equation of the line of regression predicting verbal scores from math scores.
c) In general, what would a positive residual mean in this context?
d) A person tells you her math score was 500. Predict her verbal score.
e) Using that predicted verbal score and the equation you created in Exercise 17, predict her math score.
f) Why doesn't the result in part e) come out to 500?

20. **Success, Part 2** Based on the statistics for college freshmen given in Exercise 22, what SAT score might be expected among freshman who attained a first semester GPA of 3.0?

21. **Used Cars** Classified ads in the Ithaca Journal offered several used Toyota Corollas for sale. Listed below are the ages of the cars and the advertised prices.

Age (years)	Prices advertised
1	12995, 10950
2	10495
3	10995, 10995

Copyright © 2001, Dick De Veaux and Paul Velleman

4	6995, 7990
5	8700, 6995
6	5990, 4995
9	3200, 2250, 3995
11	2900, 2995
13	1750

a) Make a scatterplot for these data.
b) Describe the association between age and price of a used Corolla.
c) Do you think a linear model is appropriate?
d) Computer software says that R-sq = 0.894. What is the correlation between age and price?
e) Explain the meaning of R-squared in this context.
f) Why doesn't this model explain 100% of the variability in the price of a used Corolla?

22. **Drug Abuse** In the exercises of the last chapter you examined results of a survey conducted in the US and 10 countries of Western Europe to determine the percentage of teenagers who had used marijuana and other drugs. Here is the scatterplot. Summary statistics showed that the mean percent that had used marijuana was 23.9%, with a standard deviation of 11.6%. An average of 15.6% of teens had used other drugs, with a standard deviation of 10.2%.

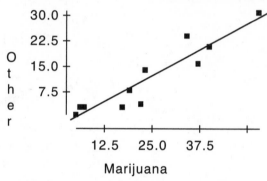

a) Do you think a linear model is appropriate? Explain.
b) For this regression, R-squared is 87.3%. Interpret this statistic in this context.
c) Write the equation you would use to estimate the percentage of teens who use other drugs from the percent who have used marijuana.
d) Explain in context what the slope of this line means.
e) Do these results confirm that marijuana is a "gateway drug"; that is, that marijuana use leads to the use of other drugs?

23. **More Used Cars** Use the advertised prices for Toyota Corollas given in Exercise 21 to create a linear model for the relationship between a car's age and its price.
a) Find the equation of the regression line.
b) Explain the meaning of the slope of the line.
c) Explain the meaning of the y - intercept of the line.
d) If you want to sell a 7-year old Corolla, what price seems appropriate?

e) You have a chance to buy one of two cars. They are about the same age and appear to be in equally good condition. Would you rather buy the one with a positive residual or a negative residual? Explain.

f) You see a "For Sale" sign on a 10-year old Corolla stating the asking price as $1500. What is the residual?

g) Would this regression model be useful in establishing a fair price for a 20-year old car? Explain.

24. **Veggie Burgers** Recently Burger King introduced a meat-free burger. The nutrition label is shown here.

a) Use the regression model created in this chapter, $\hat{fat} = 6.8 + 0.97\,protein$, to predict the fat content of this burger from its protein content.

b) What is its residual? How would you explain the residual?

c) Write a brief report about the fat and protein content of this new menu item. Be sure to talk about the variables by name and in the correct units.

Nutrition Facts

lories	330
t	10g*
dium	760g
gars	5g
otein	14g
rbohydrates	43g
etary Fiber	4g
olesterol	0

* (2 grams of saturated fat)

COMMENDED DAILY VALUES*
sed on a 2,000-calorie/day diet)

n	20%
tamin A	10%
tamin C	10%
lcium	6%

25. **Burgers** In the last chapter you examined the association between the amounts of fat and calories in fast food hamburgers. Here are the data:

Fat (gm)	19	31	34	35	39	39	43
Calories	410	580	590	570	640	680	660

a) Create a scatterplot of calories vs. fat content.

b) Interpret the value of r^2 in this context.

c) Write the equation of the line of regression.

d) Use the residuals plot to explain whether your linear model appropriate.

e) Explain the meaning of the y-intercept of the line.

f) Explain the meaning of the slope of the line.

g) A new burger containing 28 grams of fat is introduced. According to this model its residual for calories is +33. How many calories does the burger have?

26. **Chicken** Chicken sandwiches are often advertised as a healthier alternative to beef because many are lower in fat. Tests on eleven brands of fast food chicken sandwiches produced the following summary statistics and scatterplot:

	Fat (gm)	Calories
Mean	20.6	472.7
St. Dev.	9.8	144.2
Correlation	0.947	

a) Do you think a linear model is appropriate in this situation?

b) Describe the strength of this association.

c) Write the equation of the line of regression.

d) Explain the meaning of the slope
e) Explain the meaning of the *y*-intercept.
f) What does it mean if a certain sandwich has a negative residual?
g) If a chicken sandwich and a burger each advertised 35 grams of fat, which would you expect to have more calories? (See Exercise 25.)
h) MacDonald's Filet-O-Fish sandwich has 26 grams of fat and 470 calories. Does the fat/calorie relationship in this sandwich appear to be very different from that found in chicken sandwiches or in burgers (see Exercise 25)? Explain.

27. **A second helping of Burgers** In exercise 25 you created a model that can estimate the number of calories in a burger when the fat content is known.

a) Explain why you cannot use that model to estimate the fat content of a burger with 600 calories.

b) Estimate the fat content of a burger with 600 calories using an appropriate model.

28. **Cost of Living** The *Worldwide Cost of Living Survey City Rankings* determine the cost of living in the 25 most expensive cities in the world. These rankings scale New York City as 100, and express the cost of living in other cities as a percentage of the New York cost. For example, the table indicates that in Tokyo the cost of living was 65% higher than New York in 2000, but dropped to only 34% higher than NY in 2001. [http://www.finfacts.com/costofliving.htm]

CITY	2001	2000	CITY	2001	2000
Tokyo	134.0	164.9	Shenzhen	90.8	100.1
Moscow	132.4	136.1	Ho Chi Minh City	90.4	92.7
Hong Kong	130.0	141.5	Singapore	86.4	94.7
Beijing	124.4	138.3	White Plains, NY	85.5	84.0
Osaka	116.7	143.6	Tel Aviv	85.0	88.7
Shanghai	114.3	128.0	San Francisco	84.4	83.7
St. Ptsbg, Russia	106.5	109.7	Chicago	84.3	82.7
New York	100.0	100.0	Kiev	83.8	78.2
Guangzhou	97.4	107.9	Beirut	83.8	86.2
Seoul	95.3	111.1	Buenos Aires	83.6	91.0
Hanoi	94.3	94.9	Los Angeles	83.4	83.1
Taipei	92.9	102.8	Miami	83.0	83.8
London	92.9	106.9			

a) Here is a scatterplot; describe the association between costs of living in 2000 and 2001.

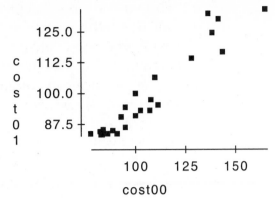

b) The correlation is 0.957. Find and interpret the value of R-squared.

c) The regression equation predicting the 2001 cost of living from the 2000 figure is $\hat{cost01} = 25.41 + 0.69 * cost00$. Use this equation to find the residual for Moscow.

d) Explain what the residual means.

29. **Cell Phones** Most people prefer digital cell phone service to analog because it is clearer and more private. Nonetheless, many calls are switched to analog channels because digital lines are busy, or because the calls are between people with different carriers. These analog calls require more power, so they are harder on phone batteries. How much battery time do you lose when making analog calls?

Consumer Reports tested seven popular brands of cell phones, comparing digital and analog talk times. The scatterplot appears to show a linear relationship with $r = 0.94$ and regression equation $\hat{Anl} = -5.1 + 0.44dig$.

a) If you have a cell phone claiming to provide 200 minutes of digital calls between battery chargings, how many minutes of analog calling would you expect to get?

b) How much faith do you place in that prediction? Explain.

c) Explain what the slope of the line means in this context.

d) If a certain brand of battery has a positive residual, what does that mean in this context?

30. **Candy** The table shows the increase in Halloween candy sales over a seven year period. Using these data, predict the amount of sales for 2002. Discuss the appropriateness of your model and your faith in the prediction. [National Confectioners Association]

Year	Halloween Candy Sales (millions of dollars)
1995	1.474
1996	1.660
1997	1.708
1998	1.787
1999	1.896
2000	1.985
2001	2.035

Copyright © 2001, Dick De Veaux and Paul Velleman

31. **Global Warming** Scientists have observed that the climate on earth is getting warmer. The most common theory relates an increase in atmospheric levels of carbon dioxide (CO2), a greenhouse gas, to increases in temperature. Here is a scatterplot showing the mean annual CO2 concentration in the atmosphere measured in parts per million (ppm) at the top of Mona Loa in Hawaii, and the mean annual air temperature over both land and sea across the globe, in degrees C.

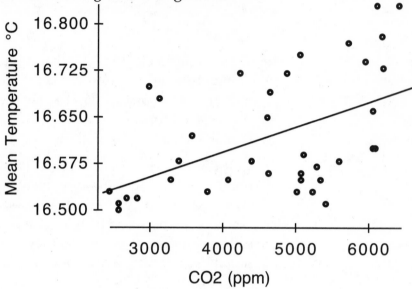

A regression predicting temperature from CO2 level, produces the following output table (in part):

Dependent variable is:Mean Temperature
R squared = 25.8%
s = 0.0854

Variable	Coefficient	SE(Coeff)	t-ratio	P-Value
Constant	16.4328	0.0557	295	≤ 0.0001
CO2	4.05300e-5	0.0000	3.49	0.0013

a) What is the correlation between CO2 level and temperature?
b) Explain the meaning of R-squared in this context.
c) Give the regression equation.
d) What is the meaning of the slope in this equation?
e) What is the meaning of the y-intercept of this equation?
f) Here is a scatterplot of the residuals vs CO2 level. Does this plot show evidence of the violation of any assumptions behind the regression? If so, which ones?

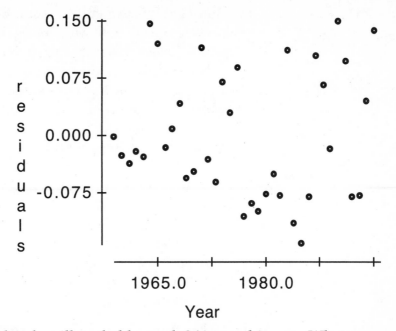

g) CO2 levels will probably reach 364ppm this year. What mean temperature does the regression predict from that information?

32. **Birth Rates** The table shows the number of live birth per 1000 women aged 15 - 44 years in the U.S. since starting in 1965. [National Vital Statistics Report, April 2001]

Year	1965	1970	1975	1980	1985	1990	1995	1999
Rate	19.4	18.4	14.8	15.9	15.6	16.4	14.8	14.5

a) Make a scatterplot and describe the general trend in birth rates.
b) Find the equation of the line of regression.
c) Check to see if the line is an appropriate model. Explain.
d) Interpret the slope of the line.
e) The table gives rates only at 5-year intervals. Estimate what the rate was in 1978.
f) In 1978 the birth rate was actually 15.0. How close did your model come?
g) Predict what the birth rate will be in 2005. Comment on your faith in this prediction.
h) Predict the birth rate for 2020. Comment on your faith in this prediction.

33. **Body Fat** It is difficult to accurately determine a person's body fat percentage without immersing them in water. Researchers hoping to find easy ways to make a good estimate immersed 20 male subjects, then measured their waists and recorded their weights. Data is shown at the left.

Waist (in)	Weight (lb)	Body Fat (%)
32	175	6
36	181	21
38	200	15
33	159	6
39	196	22
40	192	31
41	205	32
35	173	21
38	187	25
38	188	30
33	188	10
40	240	20
36	175	22
32	168	9
44	246	38
33	160	10
41	215	27
34	159	12
34	146	10
44	219	28

a) Create a model to predict body fat from weight.
b) Do you think a linear model is appropriate? Explain.
c) Interpret the slope of your model.
d) Is your model likely to make reliable estimates? Explain.
e) What is the residual for a person who weighs 190 pounds and is 21% body fat?

34. **Body Fat, Again** Would a model that uses the person's waist size be able to predict their percentage of body fat more accurately? Create and analyze that model.

35. **Hard Water** In an investigation of environmental causes of disease, data were collected on the annual mortality rate (deaths per 100,000) for males in 61 large towns in England and Wales. In addition, the water hardness was recorded as the calcium concentration (parts per million, ppm) in the drinking water. The following display shows the relationship between mortality and calcium concentration for these towns:

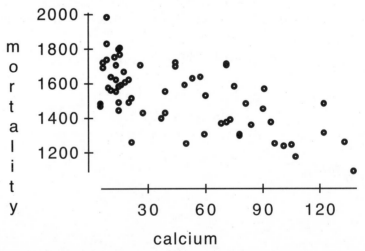

a) Describe what you see in this scatterplot, in context.
b) Here is the regression analysis of mortality and calcium concentration. What is the regression equation?

DRAFT: Do not distribute or copy

Dependent variable is: **mortality**
R squared = 43%
s = 143.0

Variable	Coefficient	SE(Coeff)	t-ratio	P-value
Constant	1676	29.30	57.2	≤ 0.0001
calcium -	3.23	0.48	-6.66	≤ 0.0001

c) Interpret the slope and *y*-intercept of the line, in context.

d) The largest residual, with a value of -348.6, is for the town of Exeter. Explain what this value means.

e) The hardness of Derby's municipal water is about 100 ppm of Calcium. Use this equation to predict the mortality rate in Derby.

f) Explain the meaning of R-squared in this situation.

36. **Gators** Wildlife researchers monitor many wildlife populations by taking aerial photographs. Can they estimate the weights of alligators accurately from the air? Here is a regression analysis of the weight of alligators (in pounds) and their length (in inches) based on data collected from captured alligators.

Dependent variable is: weight
R squared = 83.6%
s = 54.01

Variable	Coefficient	SE(Coeff)	t-ratio	P-Value
Constant	-393.	47.53	-8.27	≤ 0.0001
Length	5.9	0.5448	10.8	≤ 0.0001

a) Did they choose the correct variable to use as the dependent variable and the predictor? Explain.

b) What is the correlation between an alligator's length and weight?

c) Write the regression equation.

d) Interpret the slope of the equation in this context.

e) Do you think this equation will allow the scientists to make accurate predictions about alligators? What part of the regression analysis indicates this? What additional concerns do you have?

37. **Internet** The rapid growth of internet publishing is seen in number of electronic academic journals available during the last decade. Explain why you cannot use the methods of this chapter to model this growth.

[http://www.people.virginia.edu/~pm9k/libsci/charts.html]

Year	Number of Journals
1991	27
1992	36
1993	45
1994	181
1995	306
1996	1093
1997	2459

38. **Oil Production** In the exercises for Chapter 7, you looked at the oil production of the United States from 1949 to 2000. Here are the data again:

year	oil	year	oil	year	oil	year	oil
1949	1841940	1962	2676189	1975	3056779	1988	2979123
1950	1973574	1963	2752723	1976	2976180	1989	2778773
1951	2247711	1964	2786822	1977	3009265	1990	2684687
1952	2289836	1965	2848514	1978	3178216	1991	2707039
1953	2357082	1966	3027763	1979	3121310	1992	2624632
1954	2314988	1967	3215742	1980	3146365	1993	2499033
1955	2484428	1968	3329042	1981	3128624	1994	2431476
1956	2617283	1969	3371751	1982	3156715	1995	2394268
1957	2616901	1970	3517450	1983	3170999	1996	2366017
1958	2448987	1971	3453914	1984	3249696	1997	2354831
1959	2574590	1972	3455368	1985	3274553	1998	2281919
1960	2574933	1973	3360903	1986	3168252	1999	2146732
1961	2621758	1974	3202585	1987	3047378	2000	2135062

a) Fit a least squares regression line to oil production by year
b) Using this regression line, predict United States oil production in the year 2001.
c) Does the prediction in part b) look reasonable? Comment.
d) Do you think the line is an appropriate model? Comment.

9 Regression Wisdom

REGRESSION MAY BE THE MOST WIDELY USED statistics method. It is used every day throughout the world to predict customer loyalty, numbers of admissions at hospitals, sales of automobiles, and many other things. But, because regression is so widely used, it's also widely abused and misinterpreted. This chapter presents examples of regressions in which things are not quite as simple as they may have seemed at first, and shows how you can still use regression to discover what the data have to say.

Sifting Residuals for Groups

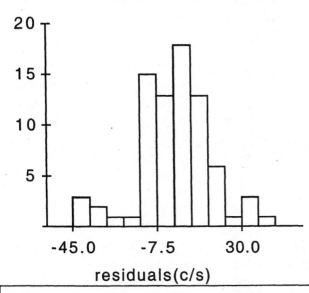

A histogram of the regression residuals shows small modes both above and below the central large mode. These may be worth a second look. Fig 9.1

No regression analysis is complete without a display of the residuals to check that the linear model is reasonable. Because the residuals are what is "left over" after the model describes the relationship, they often reveal subtleties that were not clear from a plot of the original data. Sometimes these are additional details that help confirm or refine our understanding. Sometimes they reveal violations of the regression conditions that require our attention.

In the Step by Step analysis of the cereal data from Chapter 8, we examined a scatterplot of the residuals. Our first impression was that it had no particular structure—a conclusion that supported using the regression model. But let's look again.

It's often a good idea to look at a histogram. How would you describe its shape? It looks like there might be small modes at both sides of the central body of the data. There is a group of cereals that seem to stand out as having large negative residuals, with fewer calories than we might have predicted. The calories in these cereals were overestimated by the model. Whenever we suspect multiple modes, we ask whether they are somehow different.

Let's look more carefully at the residual scatterplot. Here's that same residual plot with the points in those modes marked. Now we can see that those two groups stand away from the central pattern in the scatterplot. If we go back to the dataset, we find that the high residual cereals are Just Right Fruit & Nut, Muesli Raisins, Dates & Almonds, Muesli Raisin, Peaches, & Pecans,

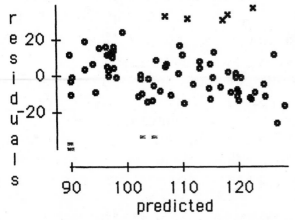

A scatterplot of the residuals versus predicted values for the cereal regression. The [first color] points are overestimated, while the [second color] points are underestimated. Is there something special about these cereals? Fig 9.2

9–1

Mueslix Crispy Blend, and Nutri-Grain Almond Raisin. Do these cereals seem to have something in common? These high-calorie cereals all present themselves as "healthy". This might be surprising, but in fact, "healthy" cereals often contain more fat and therefore more calories than we might expect by looking at their sugar content alone.

The low residual cereals are Puffed Rice, Puffed Wheat, three bran cereals, and Golden Crisps. These cereals have fewer calories than we would expect based on their sugar content. We might not have grouped these cereals together before. What they have in common is a low calorie count relative to their sugar content—even though their sugar contents are quite different.

These observations may not lead us to question the overall linear model, but they do help us to understand that other factors may be part of the story. An examination of residuals often leads us to discover groups of observations that are different from the rest.

When we discover that there is more than one group in a regression, we may decide to analyze the groups separately, using a different model for each group. Or we can stick with the original model, and simply note that there are groups that are a little different. Either way, the model will be wrong, but useful and so it will improve our understanding of the data.

Subsets

An important unstated condition for fitting models: **All the data must come from the same group.**

The residuals plot suggests that there may be different "types" of breakfast cereals. Cereal manufacturers aim cereals at different segments of the market. Supermarkets and cereal manufacturers try to attract different customers by placing different types on each shelf. Cereals for kids tend to be at kids' eye level. Toddlers wouldn't be likely to grab a box from the shelf and beg "Mom, can we please get this All-Bran with Extra Fiber?"

Should we take this extra information into account in our analysis? Here's the scatterplot of calories and sugar, colored according to the shelf on which the cereals were found and with a separate regression line fit for each. Now we can see that the top shelf is different. We might want to report two regressions, one for the top shelf and

Calories and sugars colored according to the shelf on which the cereal was found in a super market, with regression lines fit for each shelf individually. Do these data appear homogeneous? That is, do the cereals seem to all be from the same population of cereals? Or are there different kinds of cereals that we might want to consider separately? Fig 9.3

DRAFT: Do not distribute or copy

one for the bottom two shelves.

Getting the "Bends"

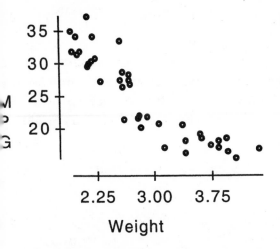

Fuel efficiency (mpg) versus weight (1000's of pounds) shows a strong, apparently linear, negative trend. Fig 9.4

The fundamental assumption for working with a linear model is that the relationship you are modeling is, in fact, linear. That sounds obvious. But when you fit a regression, you can't take it for granted. And often it is hard to tell it is straight from the scatterplot you looked at before you fit the regression model. Sometimes you can't see a bend in the relationship until you plot the residuals.

Here are the weights (in 1000's of pounds) and fuel efficiencies (measured in miles per gallon) of 38 cars. We know, from common sense, and from physics that heavier cars generally need more fuel to move. The scatterplot looks sort of linear with a moderately strong negative association (R^2 = 81.6%). The linear regression equation:

$$m\hat{p}g = 48.7 - 8.4\ weight$$

says that fuel efficiency drops by 8.4 mpg per 1,000 pounds of weight, starting from a value of 48.7 mpg (presumably for a weightless car).

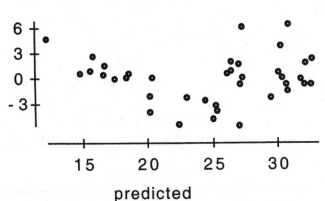

Regression residuals plotted against predicted values reveals a bend. It was in the original plot, but is easier to see here. Fig 9.5

The scatterplot of the residuals against the predicted values holds a surprise. This plot should have no pattern. But instead, there is a bend, starting high on the left, dropping down in the middle of the display, and then rising again at the right. Graphs of residuals often reveal patterns such as this that were hard to see in the original scatterplot.

Look back at the original scatterplot. The scatter of points isn't really straight. There's a slight bend to the plot. But the bend is much easier to see in the residuals. Even though it means checking the straight enough condition *after* we find the regression, it is always a good idea to plot the residuals.

Extrapolation: Reaching Beyond the Data

Linear models give a predicted value for each case in the data. Put a new x-value into the equation and it gives a predicted value, $\hat{y}$, to go with it. But when the new x value lies far from the data we used to build the regression, how trustworthy is the prediction?

The simple answer is that the farther the new x-value is from $\bar{x}$, the less trust we should place in the predicted value. Once we venture into new x territory, such a prediction is called an **extrapolation**. Extrapolations are dubious because they require the additional — and very questionable — assumption that nothing about the relationship between x and y changes even at extreme values of x.

Extrapolations can get you into deep trouble. The U.S. Census Bureau reports the median age at first marriage for men and women. Here is a regression of age at first marriage against year of the century (1900 is 0) for selected years reported on for the first part of the 20th century; 1900 to 1940:

R squared = 92.6%

s = 0.2417

Variable	Coefficient	SE(Coeff)	t-ratio	P-value
Constant	25.7	0.1313	195	≤ 0.0001
year	-0.04	0.0058	-7.07	0.0021

The regression equation is

$$\hat{age} = 25.7 - 0.04\,year$$

The slope of -0.04 years of age per year of the century shows that first marriage age was falling at a rate of about 4 years per century. That is, people were getting married for the first time at younger and younger ages. In these data, the intercept can be interpreted as the predicted age at first marriage in 1900 (year 0). The high R^2 suggests a strong linear pattern. But can we extrapolate?

When *year* counts from 0 in 1900, the year 2000 is "100". Substituting 100 for year, we find that the model predicts a first marriage age of 25.7 – 0.04 x 100 = 21.7. But in fact, by the year 2000, the median age at first marriage for men was almost 27 years. What's gone wrong?

Here's a scatterplot of the mean age at first marriage for men for the *entire* 20th century:

DRAFT: Do not distribute or copy

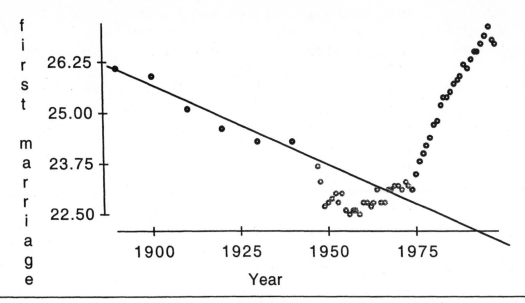

Mean age at first marriage (years of age) for men in the United States vs Year. The regression line is fit only to the first 4 decades of the 20th century, which looked nicely linear. But the linear pattern could not have continued, and in fact changed in direction, steepness, and strength. Fig 9.6

Now we can see why the extrapolation failed. Although the trend in age at first marriage has been linear for parts of the century, it has not followed the same linear model over the entire century.

Predicting the Future

"Prediction is difficult, especially about the future" Niels Bohr, Danish Physicist.

Extrapolation is always dangerous. But when, as in the marriage age predictions, the x-variable in a linear model is *time*, extrapolation becomes an attempt to peer into the future. People have always wanted to see into the future. And we can foresee that they will always want to see into the future. In the past, seers, oracles and wizards were called on to predict the future, and mediums, fortunetellers, and Tarot card readers still find many customers. The clever ones usually phrase their predictions ambiguously so they can claim to be right no matter how things actually turn out.

Those with a more scientific turn of mind may spurn such methods—and then turn around and use a linear model based on time to predict into the future. That's just using a digital crystal ball. Linear models are based on the x-values of the data at hand, and cannot be trusted beyond that span. Some phenomena do exhibit a kind of "inertia" that allows us to guess that current systematic behavior will continue outside of this range. But when x is time you should be especially wary. Such regularity can't be counted on in phenomena such as stock prices, sales figures, hurricane tracks, or public opinion.

Extrapolating from current trends is not a mistake made only by regression beginners or the naïve. Professional forecasters are prone to the same mistakes and sometimes the errors are striking. In the mid 1970's, in the midst of an energy crisis, oil prices surged and long lines at gas stations were common. In 1970, oil cost about $3 a barrel. A few years later it had surged to $15. In 1975, a survey of 15 top econometric forecasting models, (built by groups that included Nobel prize-winning economists), found predictions for 1985 oil prices that ranged from $50 to $200 a barrel (in 1975 dollars). How close were these forecasts? Well, oil prices were actually *lower* in 1985 than in 1975, after accounting for inflation. No one predicted that. No one. The forecasts had all been made *assuming* oil prices would continue to rise at the same rate or even faster. By the year 2000, oil prices averaged about $7 a barrel in 1975 dollars ($28 a barrel in 2000 dollars).

Of course, knowing that extrapolation is dangerous doesn't stop people. The temptation to see into the future is hard to resist. So our more realistic advice is this:

> If you *must* extrapolate into the future, at least *don't believe that the prediction will come true.*

Outliers

The outcome of the year 2000 Presidential election was determined in Florida amid much controversy. The main race was between George W. Bush and Al Gore, but two minor candidates played a significant role. To the political right of the main party candidates was Pat Buchanan, while to the political left could be found Ralph Nader. Generally, Nader earned more votes than Buchanan throughout the state. We would expect counties with larger vote totals to give more votes to each candidate. Here's a regression relating Buchanan's vote totals by county in the state of Florida to Nader's:

Dependent variable is: Buchanan vote

R squared = 42.8%

s = 343.0

Variable	Coefficient	SE(Coeff)	t-ratio	P-value
Constant	50.3	51.6	0.97	0.3341
Nader vote	0.14	0.02	6.97	≤ 0.0001

The regression model,

$$\widehat{Buchanan} = 50.3 + 0.14\,Nader,$$

says that in each county, Buchanan received about 0.14 times (or 14% of) the vote Nader received, starting from a base of 50.3 votes.

This seems like a reasonable regression with an R^2 of almost 43%. But we've violated the three Laws of Data Analysis by going straight to the regression table without making a picture.

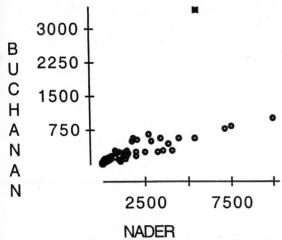

ces received by Buchanan against votes for
der in all Florida counties in the Presidential
ction of 2000. The [second color] point is Palm
ach County, home of the "butterfly ballot". Fig

Here's a scatterplot that shows the vote for Buchanan in each county of Florida plotted against the vote for Nader. The outlying point is Palm Beach county.

The so-called "butterfly ballot", used only in Palm Beach county, was a source of controversy. It has been claimed that the format of this ballot confused voters so that some who intended to vote for the Democrat, Al Gore, punched the hole on the other side of his name and, as a result, voted for Buchanan.

The scatterplot shows a strong, positive, linear association, and one striking point. With Palm Beach removed from the regression, the R^2 jumps from 42.8% to 82.1% and the slope of the line changes to 0.1, suggesting that Buchanan received only about 10% of the vote that Nader received. With over 82% of the variability of the Buchanan vote accounted for, the model when Palm Beach is omitted certainly fits better. The exception represented by Palm Beach county now stands out, not as a Buchanan stronghold, but rather as a clear violation of the model that begs for explanation.

> Nature is no where accustomed more openly to display her secret mysteries than in cases where she shows traces of her workings apart from the beaten path." - William Harvey (1657)

Outlying points can strongly influence a regression. Even a single point far from the body of the data can dominate the analysis. Points can be outliers because their x-value is extraordinary, because their y-value is extraordinary, or because they deviate from the regression model. A point can stand away from the regression model without being an outlier in either x or y. Any point that stands away from the others can be called an **outlier** and deserves your special attention. We sometimes speak of x-outliers, y-outliers, and *model*-outliers as a shorthand way of emphasizing how a point is extraordinary, but in real data, it is not always clear that a particular point falls in one or another of these categories.

The Palm beach county data point is an outlier in y because the Buchanan vote is far greater than for any other county. But it is also a model outlier because it is far from the regression line. Model outliers are usually easy to see in a scatterplot of the residuals against either x or predicted values. That's another reason to never consider a regression analysis complete until a scatterplot of the residuals against the predicted values has been made and looked at. As with this example, removing a model outlier usually increases the R^2.

Whenever you have—or suspect that you have—model outliers, you should fit the linear model to the *other* points alone and then compare the resulting regression models to understand how the outlying points

> For whoever knows the ways of Nature will more easily notice her deviations; and, on the other hand, whoever knows her deviations will more accurately describe her ways.
> -- Francis Bacon (1561-1626)

affect the model. On one hand, a model dominated by a single point is unlikely to be useful for understanding the rest of the cases. On the other hand, the best way to understand outliers is against the background of the model established by the other data values. (That insight's at least 400 years old. See the sidebar.) But don't give into the temptation to simply delete points that don't fit the line without examining and discussing them. Outliers — and especially model outliers — often tell us more about the data and the model than any other points. And arbitrarily deleting outliers will artificially inflate the R² and give a false sense of how well the model fits the data.

Points that are extraordinary in their *x*-value can especially influence a regression model. We say that they have high **leverage**. The physical image of a lever is exactly right. We know the line must pass through $(\bar{x}, \bar{y})$, so you can picture that point as the fulcrum of the lever. Just as sitting farther from the hinge on a see-saw gives you more leverage to pull it your way, points with values far from the mean of *x* pull more strongly on the regression line.

When a point with high leverage lines up with the rest of the data it doesn't influence the slope but it does increase the R². So removing a point that is an *x*-outlier (high leverage) but not a model outlier can actually *decrease* your R². But even a single high-leverage point that is also a model outlier can change the regression model radically.

George W. Bush won Florida (and thus, the Presidency) by only a few hundred votes, so the Palm Beach county residual is big enough to be meaningful. Most outliers don't determine a Presidency, but all are worth examining and trying to understand. When we investigate an outlier we often learn more about the situation than we could have learned from the model alone.

Influential Points

Bozo's extraordinarily large shoes give his data point high leverage in the regression. Wherever Bozo's IQ falls, the regression line will follow. Fig 9.8

High leverage points that are also model outliers can have a shocking affect on the regression. Here's a plot of IQ against shoe size again from the fanciful study of intelligence and foot size in comedians we saw in Chapter 7. The linear regression output shows:

Dependent variable is: IQ
R squared = 24.8%

Variable	Coefficient	SE(Coeff)	t-ratio	P-value
Constant	93.3265	3.106	30.0	≤ 0.0001
Shoe size	2.08318	0.3664	5.69	≤ 0.0001

Although this is a silly example, it illustrates an important and common potential problem. Almost all of the variance accounted for ($R^2 = 24.8\%$), is due to *one* point, namely Bozo. Without Bozo, there is little correlation between shoe size and IQ. Look what happens to the regression when we take him out:

Response variable is: IQ
R squared = 0.7%

Variable	Coefficient	SE(Coeff)	t-ratio	P-value
Constant	105.458	4.282	24.6	< 0.0001
Shoe size	0.460194	0.5427	0.848	0.3985

The R^2 value is now 0.7%-- a very weak linear relationship (as one might expect!). One single point exhibits a great influence on the regression analysis.

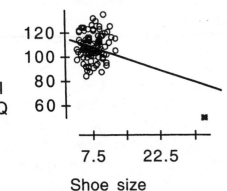

I
Q

7.5   22.5

Shoe size

> If Bozo's IQ were low, the regression slope would change from positive to negative. A single influential point can change a regression model drastically.
> Fig 9.9

What would have happened if Bozo hadn't shown his comic genius on IQ tests? Suppose his measured IQ had been only 50. The slope of the line drops from 0.96 points/shoe size to –0.69 points /shoe size. No matter where Bozo's IQ is, the line tends to follows it because his shoe size, being so far from the mean shoe size, makes this a high leverage point.

> **Warning:**
> Influential points can hide in plots of residuals. Points with high leverage pull the line close to them, so they often have small residuals. You'll see influential points more easily in scatterplots of the original data or by finding a regression model with and without the points.

You can often see high leverage points best in the original scatterplot of the data. But it isn't always clear what to do with them. Sometimes these are data values that you had to work hard to get, and they may say more about the relationship between y and x than any of the other data values. At other times, high leverage points are values that really don't belong with the rest of the data. Such points should probably be omitted, and a linear model found without them for comparison. The situation may lie between these two extremes. A data value may be far from the other x values, and therefore a point with high leverage, but it may not be clear whether it belongs. When it doubt, it's usually best to perform and compare the two regressions.

Lurking Variables and Causation

> One common way to interpret a regression slope is to say that "a change of 1 unit in x results in a change of b1 units in y." This way of saying things encourages causal thinking. Beware.

In Chapter 7, we tried to make it clear that no matter how strong the correlation is between two variables, there is no simple way to show that one variable causes the other. Putting a regression line through a cloud of points just increases the temptation to think and to say that the x-variable *causes* the y-variable. But just to make sure, let's repeat the point again. No matter how strong the association, no matter how large the R^2 value, no matter how straight the line, there is no way to conclude from a regression alone that one variable *causes* the other. There is always the possibility that some third variable is driving both of the variables you have observed. With observational data, as opposed

Copyright © 2001, Dick De Veaux and Paul Velleman

to data from a designed experiment, there is no way to be sure that a **lurking variable** is not the cause of any apparent association.

Here's an example. The scatterplot shows the life expectancy (average between men and women, in years) for each of 41 countries of the world, plotted against the square root of the number of doctors per person in the country. (We've taken the square root to make the relationship linear. It's not a big deal. Without the re-expression the plot is too curved to fit a straight line. The square root is not the point. The point is that life expectancy goes up with doctors. You can learn more about re-expression in regression in more detail in the next chapter.)

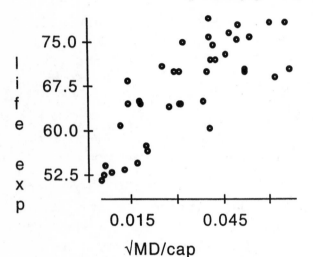

The relationship between life expectancy (years) and availability of doctors (as √doctors per capita) for countries of the world shows a strong, positive, linear association. Fig 9.10

The strong positive association (r = 0.79; R^2 = 62.4%) seems to confirm our expectation that more doctors per person improves healthcare, leading to longer lifetimes and a larger life expectancy. The strength of the association would *seem* to argue that we should send more doctors to developing countries to increase life expectancy.

But now we are asking about the consequences of a change. If we increase the number of doctors, should we predict that the life expectancy will increase? This is a *causal* explanation, arguing that adding doctors *causes* greater life expectancy. But these are observed data. Could there be another explanation of the association?

Let's consider another variable. Here is a very similar looking scatterplot, again with life expectancy as the *y*-variable, but this time the *x*-variable is the square root of the number of televisions per person in each country. The positive association shown in this scatterplot is even *stronger* than the association in the previous plot (r = 0.85; R^2 =72.3%). We can fit the linear model, and quite possibly use the number of TV's as a way to predict life expectancy. But should we conclude that increasing the number of televisions actually extends lifetimes? If so, we should send TV's to developing countries instead of doctors. Not only is the correlation with life expectancy higher, but televisions are much cheaper than doctors.

What's wrong with this reasoning? Maybe we were a bit hasty earlier when we concluded that *doctors* cause longer lives. Maybe there's a lurking variable here. Countries with higher standards of

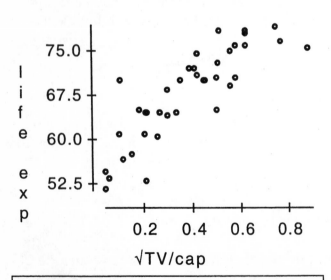

To increase life expectancy, don't send doctors, send TV's; they're cheaper and more fun. Or maybe that's not the right interpretation of this scatterplot of life expectancy against availability of TV's (as √TV's per capita) Fig 9.11

9-1

living have both longer life expectancies *and* more doctors. Could higher living standards *cause* the other variables? If so, then improving living standards might be expected to prolong lives, increase the number of doctors, and increase the number of TV's.

From this example, you can see how easy it is to fall into the trap of mistakenly inferring causality from a regression. For all we know, doctors (or TV's!) *do* increase life expectancy. But we can't tell that from these data no matter how much we'd like to. Resist the temptation to conclude that *x*-causes *y* from a regression, no matter how obvious it seems that it does.

Working with Summary Values

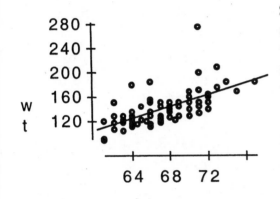

Weight (pounds) against height (inches) for a sample of men. There's a strong, positive, linear association. Fig 9.12

Scatterplots of statistics summarized over groups tend to show less variability than we would see if we measured the same variable on individuals. This is because the summary statistics themselves vary less than the data on the individuals do, a fact we will make more specific in coming chapters.

We looked in chapter 7 at the heights and weights of individual students. There we saw a correlation of .644, so R^2 is 41.5%.

Suppose, instead of data on individuals, we had been given only the mean weight for each height value. The scatterplot of mean weight by height would show less scatter. And the R^2 would increase to 80.1%

Scatterplots of summary statistics show less scatter than the baseline data on individuals, and can give a false impression of how well a line summarizes the data. There is no simple correction for this phenomenon. Once we are given summary data, there is no simple way to get the original values back.

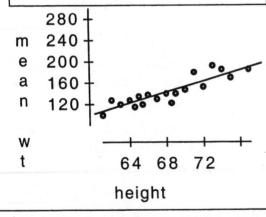

Mean weight (pounds) shows a stronger linear association with height than did the weights of individuals. Means vary less than individual values. Fig 9.13

In the life expectancy and TV's example, we have no good measure of exposure to doctors or to TV on an individual basis. But if we did, we should expect the scatterplot to show more variability and the corresponding R^2 to be larger. The bottom line is that you should be a bit suspicious of conclusions based on regressions of summary data. They may look better than they really are.

What Can Go Wrong

This entire chapter has held warnings about things that can go wrong in a regression analysis. So let's just recap. When you make a linear model:

- *Make sure the relationship is straight.* Check the straight enough condition. Always examine the residuals, and pay special attention to the most extreme residuals because they may have something to add to the story told by the linear model Check the residuals for evidence that the linearity condition has failed. It's often easier to see deviations from a straight line in the residual plot than in the scatterplot of the original data.

- *Beware of extrapolating.* Beware extrapolation beyond the *x*-values that were used to fit the model. Although it is common to use linear models to extrapolate, the practice is dangerous.

- *Beware especially of extrapolating into the future!* Be especially cautious about extrapolating into the future with linear models in which the *x*-variable is time. Predicting the future is particularly tempting and particularly dangerous.

- *Be on guard for different groups in your regression.* Check for evidence that the data consist of separate subsets. If you find subsets that behave differently, consider fitting a different linear model to each subset.

- *Look for outliers.* Outliers are special points that always deserve attention and that may well reveal more about your data than the rest of the points combined. Always look for them and try to understand why they stand apart. A scatterplot of the data is a good way to see outliers in *y* and *x*. A scatterplot of the residuals against the predicted values is a good tool for finding model outliers.

- *Beware of high leverage points, and especially of those that are influential.* High leverage points (*x*-outliers) that are also model outliers can alter the regression model a great deal. The resulting model may say more about one or two points than about the overall relationship.

- *Consider comparing two regressions.* To see the impact on a regression of outliers, it is often wise to run two regressions, one with and one without the extraordinary points and then to discuss the differences.

- *Treat outliers honestly.* If you remove enough carefully selected points, you can always get a regression with a high R^2 eventually. But it won't give you much understanding. Some data are just not simple enough for a linear model to fit very well. When that happens, report it and stop.

- *Beware of lurking variables.* Think about lurking variables before interpreting a linear model. It is particularly tempting to explain a strong regression by thinking that the *x*-variable *causes* the *y*-variable. A linear model fitted to observational data can never demonstrate such

DRAFT: Do not distribute or copy

causation, in part because it cannot eliminate the chance that a lurking variable has caused the variation in both *x* and *y*.

- *Watch out when dealing with data that are summaries.* Be cautious in working with data values that are themselves summaries such as means or medians. Summary statistics are less variable than the raw data on which they are based, so they tend to inflate the impression of the strength of a relationship.

Key Concepts

Subsets	One unstated condition for finding a linear model is that the data be homogeneous. If, instead, the data consist of two or more groups that have been thrown together, it is usually best to fit different linear models to each group than to try to fit a single model to all of the data. Displays of the residuals can often help you find subsets in the data.
Extrapolation	Although linear models provide an easy way to predict values of y for a given value of x, it is unsafe to predict for values of x far from the ones used to find the linear model equation. Such extrapolation may pretend to see into the future, but the predictions should not be trusted.
Outlier	Any data point that stands away from the others can be called an outlier. In regression, outliers can be extraordinary in x, in y, and in failing to fit the model.
Leverage	Data points that are outliers in x because their x-value is far from the mean of x are said to exert leverage on a linear model. High leverage points pull the line close to them, and so they can have a large effect on the line, sometimes completely determining the slope and intercept.
Influential Point	A point that has high leverage and is also a model outlier is called an influential point. Omitting an influential point from the data usually results in a very different regression model.
Lurking Variables	Because we can never be certain that observational data is not hiding a lurking variable that influences both x and y, it is never safe to conclude that a linear model demonstrates a causal relationship, no matter how strong the linear association.

Skills

Upon completing this lesson you should:

Think

- Understand that we cannot fit linear models or use linear regression if the underlying relationship between the variables is not itself linear.

- Understand that data used to find a model must be homogeneous. Look for subgroups in data before you find a regression, and analyze each separately.

- Know the danger of extrapolation beyond the range of the x-values used to find the linear model, and especially when the extrapolation tries to predict into the future.

- Understand that outliers can be in the x or y direction, and can also be deviation from the regression model. Understand that points that are outliers in different ways can have different effects on the regression model.

- Look for lurking variables whenever considering the association between two variables. Understand that a strong association does not mean that the variables are causally related.

Show

- Know how to display residuals from a linear model by making a scatterplot of residuals against predicted values or against the x variable, and know what patterns to look for in the picture.

- Know how to look for outliers in a regression by examining a scatterplot of the data, and to look for model outliers by examining a scatterplot of the residuals against the predicted values. Understand how removing outliers can affect the regression model.

- Know how to look for high leverage points by examining the x-values or in a scatterplot of the data, and understand how they can affect a linear model.

Tell

- Include diagnostic information as part of your report of a regression.

- Report any high leverage points.

- Report any outliers. Consider reporting analyses with and without outliers included.

- Include appropriate cautions about extrapolation when reporting predictions from a linear model.

- Discuss any possible lurking variables.

Exercises

1. **Marriage Age** We've looked at the ages of men at first marriage. How about women? Is there evidence that the age at which women get married has changed over the past 100 years? The scatterplot shows the trend in age at first marriage for American women.

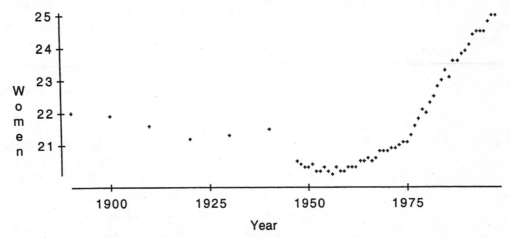

a) Do you think there is a clear pattern? Describe the trend.
b) Is the association strong?
c) Is the correlation high? Explain.
d) Do you think a linear model is appropriate for these data? Explain.

2. **Ages of Couples** The graph shows the ages of both men and women at first marriage.

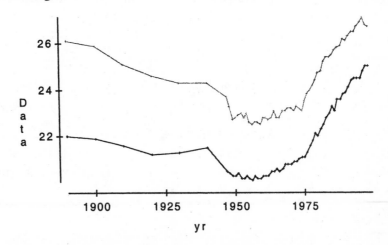

Clearly the pattern for males is very similar to the pattern for females. But are the two lines getting closer together?

Here is a timeplot showing the *difference* in average age (man – woman) at first marriage, the regression analysis, and the associated residuals plot.

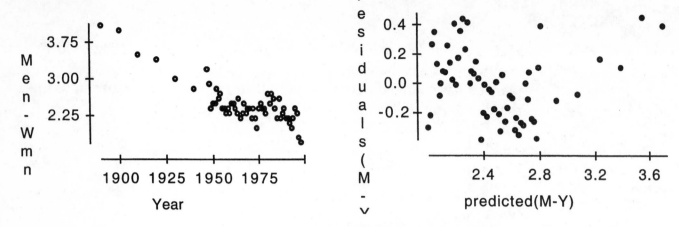

Dependent variable is: Men-Wmn
R squared = 71.6%

Variable	Coefficient	SE(Coeff)
Constant	33.4830	2.606
Year	-0.015756	0.0013

a) What is the correlation between age difference and year?
b) Interpret the slope of this line.
c) Predict the average age difference in 2010.
d) Describe reasons why you might not place much faith in that prediction.

3. **Marriage age Revisited** Suppose you wanted to predict the trend in marriage age for American women into the early part of this century.
   a) How could you use the data graphed in Exercise 1 to get a good prediction? Marriage ages in selected years starting in 1900 are listed below. Use all or part of these data to create an appropriate model for predicting the average age at which women will first marry in 2005.
      1900 – 1940 (10 yr intervals): 21.9, 21.6, 21.2, 21.3, 21.5, 20.3
      1955 – 1995 (5 yr intervals): 20.2, 20.2, 20.6, 20.8, 21.1, 22.0, 23.3, 23.9, 24.5
   b) How much faith do you place in this prediction? Explain.
   c) Do you think your model would produce an accurate prediction about your grandchildren, say 50 years from now? Explain.

4. **Ages of Couples, Again** Is the trend of decreasing difference in age at first marriage seen in Exercise 2 stronger recently? Here are the scatterplot, residuals plot, and regression analysis using only the data from 1975 through 1998.

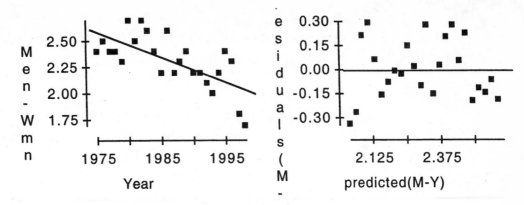

Dependent variable is: Men-Wmn
Cases selected according to post75
R squared = 46.3%

Variable	Coefficient	s.e. of Coeff
Constant	49.9021	10.93
Year	-0.023957	0.0055

a) Why is R-squared higher for the first model (in Exercise 2)?
b) Is the new linear model appropriate for the post-1975 data? Explain.
c) What does the slope say about marriage ages since 1975?
d) Explain why it is not reasonable to interpret the y-intercept.

5. **Good Model?** In justifying his choice of a model, a student wrote, "I know this is the correct model because $R^2 = 99.4\%$."
   a) Is this reasoning correct? Explain.
   b) Does this model allow the student to make accurate predictions? Explain.

6. **Bad Model?** A student who has created a linear model is disappointed to find that her R-squared value is a very low 13%.
   c) Does this mean that a linear model is not appropriate? Explain.
   d) Does this model allow the student to make accurate predictions? Explain.

7. **Reading** To measure progress in reading ability students at an elementary school take a reading comprehension test every year. Scores are measured in "grade level" units; that is, a score of 4.2 means that a student is reading at slightly above the expected level for a fourth grader. The school principal prepares a report to parents that includes a graph showing the mean reading score for each grade. In his comments he points out that the strong positive trend

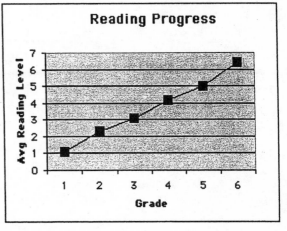

demonstrates the success of the school's reading program.
a) Does this graph indicate that students are making satisfactory progress in reading? Explain.
b) What would you estimate the correlation between grade and average reading level to be?
c) If instead of this plot showing average reading levels the principal had produced a scatterplot showing the reading levels for all the individual students, would you expect the correlation to be the same, higher, or lower? Explain.
d) While the principal did not do a regression analysis, someone as statistically astute as you might do that. (But don't bother.) What value of the slope of that line would you view as demonstrating acceptable progress in reading comprehension? Explain.

8. **Grades** A college admissions officer, defending the college's use of SAT scores in the admissions process, produced the graph below. It shows the mean GPA's for last year's freshmen, grouped by SAT scores. How strong is the evidence that SAT score is a good predictor of GPA? What concerns you about the graph, the statistical methodology, or the conclusions reached?

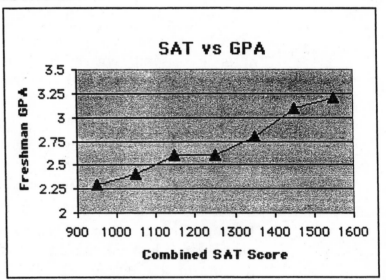

9. **Heating** After keeping track of his heating expenses for several winters, a homeowner believes he can estimate the monthly cost C from the average daily Fahrenheit temperature using the model $\hat{C} = 133 - 2.13temp$. The residuals plot for his data is shown.

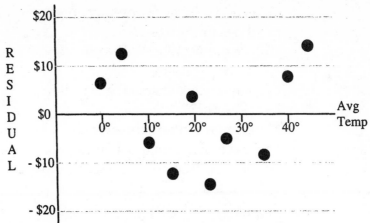

a) Interpret the slope of the line in this context.
b) Interpret the *y*-intercept of the line in this context.
c) During months when the temperature stays around freezing, would you expect cost predictions based on this model to be accurate, too low, or too high? Explain.
d) What heating cost does the model predict for a month that averages 10°?
e) During one of the months on which the model was based the temperature did average 10°. What were the actual heating costs for that month?
f) Do you think the homeowner should use this model? Explain.
g) Would this model be more successful if created using degrees Celsius? Explain.

10. **Speed** How does the speed at which you drive impact your fuel economy? To find out researchers drove a compact car for 200 miles at speeds ranging from 35 to 75 miles per hour. From their data they created the model $\hat{mpg} = 32 - 0.1mph$ and created this residuals plot:

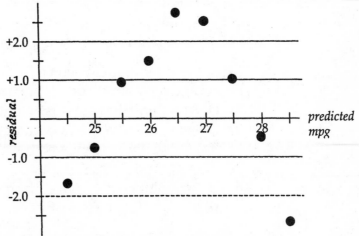

a) Interpret the slope of this line in context.
b) Explain why it is silly to attach any meaning to the *y*-intercept.

   c) When this model predicts high gas mileage, what can you say about those predictions?

   d) What gas mileage does the model predict when the car is driven at 50 miles per hour?

   e) What was the actual gas mileage when the car was driven at 45 miles per hour?

   f) Do you think there appears to be a strong association between speed and fuel economy? Explain.

   g) Do you think this is the appropriate model for that association? Explain.

11. **Unusual Points** Each of the scatterplots below shows a cluster of points and one "stray" point. For each, answer these questions:
   1) Do you think that point is an outlier?
   2) Do you think that point is an influential point?
   3) If that point were removed from the data would the correlation increase or decrease? Explain
   4) If that point were removed from the data would the slope of the regression line increase or decrease? Explain.

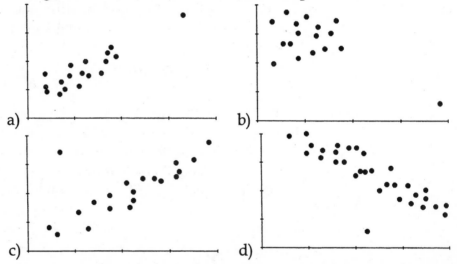

12. **More Unusual Points** Each of the scatterplots below shows a cluster of points and one "stray" point. For each, answer these questions:
   1) Do you think that point is an outlier?
   2) Do you think that point is an influential point?
   3) If that point were removed from the data would the correlation increase or decrease? Explain
   4) If that point were removed from the data would the slope of the regression line increase or decrease? Explain.

      DRAFT: Do not distribute or copy

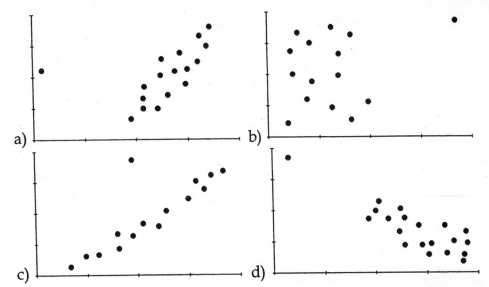

13. **The Extra Point** The scatterplot shows five [color 1] data points at the left. Not surprisingly the correlation for these points is $r = 0$. Suppose *one* additional data point is added at one of the five positions noted below. Match each point (a – e) with the correct new correlation from the list given.

(1) –0.90

(2) –0.40

(3) 0.00

(4) 0.05

(5) 0.75

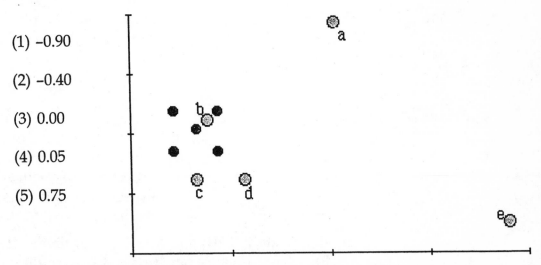

14. **The Extra Point Revisited** The original five points in Exercise 13 produce a regression line with slope 0. Match each of the points (a – e) with the slope of the line after that one point is added.

(1) –0.45   (2) –0.30   (3) 0   (4) 0.05   (5) 0.85

15. **Gestation** For women, pregnancy lasts about 9 months. In other species of animals the length of time from conception to birth varies. Is there any evidence that gestation period is related to the animal's lifespan? The first scatterplot shows gestation period (in days) versus lifespan (in years) for 18 species of mammals. The highlighted point at the far right represents humans.

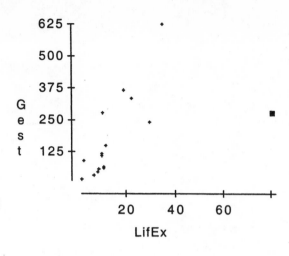

a) For these data r = 0.54, not a very strong relationship. Do you think the association would be stronger or weaker if humans were removed? Explain.

b) Is there a reasonable justification for removing humans from the data set? Explain.

c) Here is the scatterplot and regression analysis for the 17 non-human species. Comment on the strength of the association.

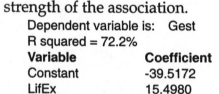

    Dependent variable is: Gest
    R squared = 72.2%

Variable	Coefficient
Constant	-39.5172
LifEx	15.4980

d) Interpret the slope of the line.

e) Some species of monkeys have a life expectancy of about 20 years. Estimate the expected gestation period of one of these monkeys.

16. **Elephants and Hippos** We removed humans from the scatterplot in Exercise 15 because our species was an outlier in life expectancy. The resulting scatterplot shows two points that now may be of concern. The point in the upper right corner of this scatterplot is for elephants, and the other point at the far right is for hippos.

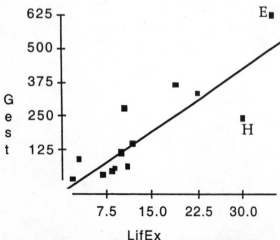

a) By removing one of these points we could make the association appear to be stronger. Which point? Explain.

b) Would the slope of the line increase or decrease?

c) Should we just keep removing animals to increase the strength of the model? Explain.

d) If we remove elephants from the scatterplot the slope of the regression line becomes 11.6 days per

DRAFT: Do not distribute or copy

year. Do you think elephants were an influential point? Explain.

17. **Law Enforcement** Federal employees with the authority to carry firearms and make arrests are sometimes assaulted, injured, or killed. The table below summarizes the rates of assault and injury (or death) for these employees for five years, 1995-1999. Can the assault rate be used to predict injuries or deaths?

Agency	Assaults (per 1000)	Killed-Injured (per 1000)
BATF	31.1	2.2
Capitol Police	5.0	3.6
Customs Service	9.7	5.1
DEA	17.9	1.1
FBI	3.9	1.2
INS	14.1	2.5
IRS	1.7	0.2
US Marshall Service	9.7	3.0
National Park Service	38.7	15.0
Postal Service	5.7	2.9
Secret Service	9.7	3.0

18. **Smoking** The Centers for Disease Control and Prevention track cigarette smoking in the U. S. How has the percentage of people who smoke changed since the danger became clear during the last half of the 20th century? The table below shows percentages of smokers among of males 18 – 24 years of age, as estimated by surveys. Create a model to describe the changes in smoking rate. Justify decisions you make in using these data to construct your model.

Year	PerCent	Year	PerCent
1965	54.1%	1992	28.0
1974	42.1	1993	28.8
1979	35.0	1994	29.8
1983	32.9	1995	27.8
1985	28.0	1997	31.7
1990	26.6	1998	31.3

19. **Illegitimate Births** The National Center for Health Statistics reported the data below, showing the percentage of all births that are to unmarried women for selected years between 1980 and 1998. Create a model that describes this trend. Justify decisions you make about how to best use these data.

Year	1980	1985	1990	1991	1992	1993	1994	1995	1996	1997	1998
%	18.4	22.0	28.0	29.5	30.1	31.0	32.6	32.2	32.4	32.4	32.8

20. **Life Expectancy** Data from the World Bank for 26 Western Hemisphere countries can be used to examine the association between female life expectancy and the average number of children women give birth to.

Country	Births/ woman	Life Exp.	Country	Births/ woman	Life Exp.
Argentina	2.5	77	Bahamas	2.2	77
Barbados	1.8	78	Belize	3.5	74
Bolivia	4.0	64	Brazil	2.2	71
Canada	1.5	82	Chile	2.2	79
Colombia	2.7	74	Costa Rica	2.5	79
Dom. Rep.	2.8	73	Ecuador	3.1	71
El Salv.	3.2	72	Guatemala	4.7	68
Jamaica	2.5	77	Honduras	4.0	72
Mexico	2.8	75	Nicaragua	3.6	71
Panama	2.5	76	Paraguay	4.0	72
Peru	3.1	71	PuertoRico	3.1	71
U. S.	2.1	80	Uruguay	2.3	78
Venezuela	2.9	76	Virgin Is.	2.4	79

a) Create a scatterplot relating these two variables and describe the association.

b) Are there any countries that do not seem to fit the overall pattern?

c) Find the correlation, and interpret the value of R^2.

d) Find the equation of the line of regression.

e) Is the line an appropriate model? Describe what you see in the residuals plot.

f) Interpret the slope and the y - intercept of the line.

g) If government leaders wanted to increase life expectancy in their country should they encourage women to have fewer children? Explain.

21. **Inflation** The Consumer Price Index tracks the prices of consumer goods in the U.S., as shown in the table. It indicates, for example, that the average item costing $17.90 in 1928 cost $168.80 in the year 2000.

a) Make a scatterplot showing the trend in consumer prices. Describe what you see.

b) Be an economic forecaster: project increases in the cost of living over the next decade. Justify decisions you make in creating your model.

c) Sometimes re-expressing the data can reveal interesting information concealed there. Create a new variable containing the logarithm of the CPI. Plot log(CPI) against year. What historical events had a clear impact on the cost of living? (The next chapter explores more advantages that may arise by re-expressing data.)

Year	CPI
1916	10.4
1920	16.5
1924	17.3
1928	17.9
1932	12.9
1936	14.2
1940	13.9
1944	17.4
1948	23.7
1952	26.5
1956	26.8
1960	29.3
1964	30.9
1968	34.1
1972	41.1
1976	55.6
1980	77.8
1984	101.9
1988	115.7
1992	138.1
1996	154.4
2000	168.8

10 Re-expressing Data:
It's easier than you think

WE HAVE SEEN SEVERAL CASES WHERE A simple re-expression of the data, such as taking a logarithm or looking at the reciprocal (*1/y*), makes the data much easier to understand. Many of our tools for displaying and summarizing data work only when the data meet certain conditions. Linear models raise the stakes even further. We cannot use a linear model unless the relationship between the two variables is linear. Often re-expression can save the day, straightening bent relationships so that we can fit and use a simple linear model. It turns out that finding a useful re-expression is probably easier than you think. This chapter shows how to find re-expressions in a simple systematic way.

Sometimes when we use re-expressions, we hear people say, "Wait a minute. If you're allowed to do anything you want to the data, you can make them show anything you want. The original data weren't measured in square roots! You're cheating." The fact is, it's not cheating, and re-expression is something that you do everyday. The point of this chapter is to show you how to find re-expressions easily and to show you that not only is it incredibly useful, but it's easy and natural as well. The material in this chapter is not needed explicitly for any subsequent chapter. But it makes all of them more useful by allowing more data to satisfy the conditions of each method we will discuss.

Straightening Relationships

The relationship between fuel efficiency measured in miles per gallon and weight measured in pounds looks fairly linear at first. It isn't surprising that lighter cars get better gas mileage. And with an R^2 of 81.6% the regression line might seem like a good fit. But a look at the residual plot shows a problem.

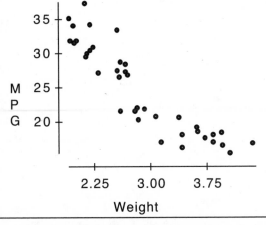

Fuel efficiency vs Weight for 38 cars as reported by *Consumer Reports*. The plot shows a negative direction, roughly linear shape, and strong relationship. Fig 10.1

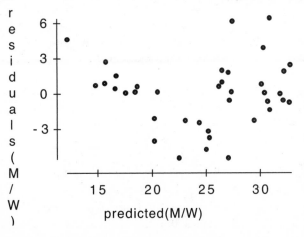

The residuals from a regression of fuel efficiency on weight reveal a bent shape when plotted against the predicted values. Looking back at the original scatterplot you may be able to see the bend. Fig 10.2

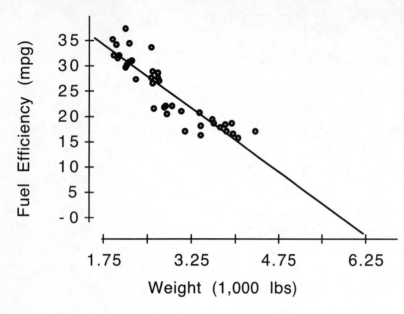

Fuel Efficiency (mpg) vs Weight (1,000 lbs)

Extrapolating the regression line gives an absurd answer even for vehicles that weigh as little as 6,000 pounds.
 Fig 10.3

"Gallons per hundred miles—what an absurd way to measure fuel efficiency! "Who would ever do it that way?"

Not all re-expressions are easy to understand, but in this case, the answer is "Everyone except U.S. drivers." Most of the world measures fuel efficiency in liters per 100 kilometers (L/100Km). This is the same reciprocal form (fuel amount per distance driven) and differs from Gal/100mi only by a constant multiple of about 2.38.

It has been suggested that most of the world says "I've got to go 100 Km, how much gas do I need?" But Americans say "I've got 10 gallons in the tank. How far can I drive?"

In much the same way, re-expressions "think" about the data differently but don't change what they mean.

The pattern is clearly bent. Now, looking back at the first scatterplot, you can probably see the slight bending. And think about the regression line through the points. How heavy would a car have to be to have a predicted gas mileage of 0? Looks like the fuel efficiency would go negative by about 6.00 (6000 pounds). The Lincoln Navigator 4-door wagon weighs in at 5994 pounds. It is hardly known for fuel efficiency, but it does get more than the *minus* 1 mpg this regression would predict. Extrapolation is always dangerous, but it's even more dangerous when the model is wrong because wrong models tend to do even worse the farther you get from the middle of the data.

The bend in the relationship between fuel efficiency and weight is the kind of failure to satisfy the conditions for an analysis that we have repaired before by re-expressing the data, and that method works here too. Instead of looking at miles per gallon, we can take the reciprocal and work with gallons per hundred miles)[1]

---

[1] The reciprocal is the part of this re-expression that makes the relationship more linear. Multiplying by 100 to get gallons per 100 miles simply makes the numbers easier to think about. You might have a good idea of how many gallons your car needs to drive 100 miles, but probably a much poorer sense of how much gas you need to go just one mile.

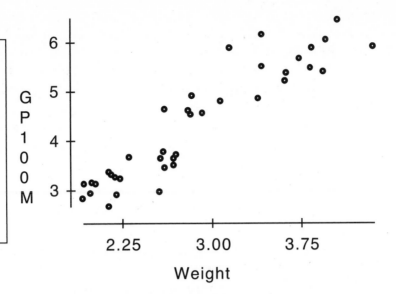

The reciprocal (1/y), is measured in gallons per mile. Gallons per 100 miles gives more natural numbers. The reciprocal, is more nearly linear against weight than the original variable, but it changes the direction of the relationship. Fig 10.4

The direction of the association is positive now since we're measuring gas *consumption* and heavier cars consume more gas per mile. The R^2 is now 85.8%, but the real gain is that the relationship is much straighter, as we can see from a scatterplot of the regression residuals.

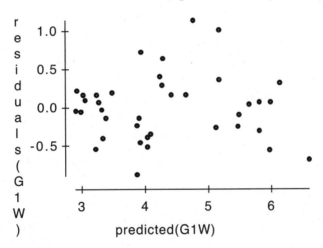

The residuals from the regression of gallons per 100 miles on weight show no pattern or trend. Fig 10.5

This is more the kind of boring scatterplot (no direction, no particular form, no outliers, no bends) that we hope to see in a scatterplot of residuals, so we have reason to think that the straight enough condition is now satisfied.

What does the reciprocal model say about the Navigator? The regression line fit to the scatterplot of Gallons per 100 miles vs weight predicts somewhere near 9.1 for a car weighing 5995 pounds. What does this mean? It means the car is predicted to use 9.1 gallons for every 100 miles, or in other words $\dfrac{100\ miles}{9.1\ gallons} = 11.0\ mpg$. That's a much more reasonable prediction.

Everybody Does It

Scientific laws often include simple re-expressions. Einstein's e = mc^2 includes a square re-expression. In Psychology, Fechner's Law states that sensation increases as the logrithm of stimulus intensity, S = k log R.

You may not be aware of it, but you use re-expressions in everyday life. How fast can you go on a bicycle? If you measure your speed you probably do it in distance per time (miles per hour or kilometers per hour). In 2000, during a 25-mile-long time trial in the Tour de France, Lance Armstrong *averaged* over 33.5 mph (53.9 km per hr). You probably realize that that's a tough act to follow. It's fast. You can tell that at a glance because you have no trouble thinking in terms of distance covered per time.

OK, then, if you averaged 12.5 miles per hour (20.1 km per hr) for a mile *run*, would that be fast? Would it be fast for a 100 meter dash? Even if you run the mile often, you probably have to stop and calculate. Although we measure speed of bicycles in distance per time, we don't usually measure running speed that way. Instead, we use the *reciprocal*, time per distance (minutes per mile, seconds per 100 meters, *etc.*). Running a mile in under 5 minutes (12 miles per hour) is fast. A mile at 16 miles per hour would be a world record (that's a 3 minute 45 second mile.)

How fast can a human being run?

The world record for the 200 meters is 19.32 sec. (Michael Johnson 1996). That's 23.4 mph (37.3 kph)! Most people can't even *bicycle* faster than about 19 or 20 mph. Of course, sprinters can't keep up that speed for very long. If they could, they could run a 2:34 mile.

The point is that there is no *natural* way to measure speed. In some cases we use distance traveled per time and in other cases we use the reciprocal. It's just because we're used to thinking that way in each case, not because one way is correct. The important fact to realize is that the way these quantities are measured is not sacred. It's usually just convenience or custom. When we re-express a quantity to make it satisfy certain conditions that we want, we may either leave it in those new units when we explain the analysis to others, or we may transform back to the original units.

Other examples of common variables that re-express a crude measurement include the Richter scale of earthquake strength, the decibel scale for sound intensity, the f-Stop scale for camera aperture openings, and the gauges of shotguns.

Careful re-expression is a common practice that can simplify patterns and relationships.

Goals of Re-expression

We re-express data for several reasons. Each of these goals is an aspect of the larger goal of making the data more suitable for analysis by our

DRAFT: Do not distribute or copy

methods.[2] We'll illustrate each goal with an example from data about large companies.

Goal 1: Make the distribution of a variable (as seen in its histogram, for example) more symmetric. It is easier to summarize the center of a symmetric distribution, and for nearly symmetric distributions we can use the mean and standard deviation. If the distribution is unimodal, then the resulting distribution may be closer to the Normal model, allowing us to use the 68-95-99.7 rule. We saw an example of this in Chapter 4.

Who: 77 Large Companies
What: Assets, Sales, and market sector
How: Public records
When: 1986
Why: Reported by *Forbes* magazine in reporting on the Forbes 500 for that year.

Here are the Assets of these companies (in $100,000)

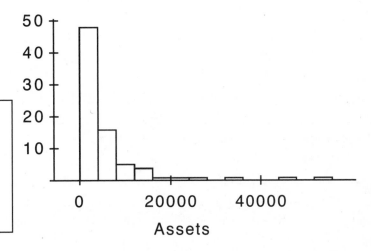

The distribution of the Assets of large companies is skewed to the right. Data on wealth often look like this. Fig 10.6

The skewed distribution is made much more symmetric by taking logs:

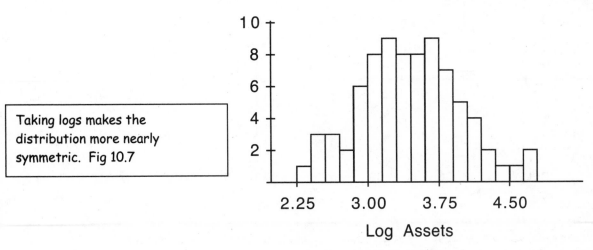

Taking logs makes the distribution more nearly symmetric. Fig 10.7

Goal 2: Make the spread of several groups (as seen in side-by-side boxplots) more alike, even if their centers differ. Groups that share a common

---

[2] Yes, there are other methods that we could use for bent relationships, but they are more complicated, don't work as well, and don't give us as much information. And often they use models that are not as useful for understanding.

spread are easier to compare. We will see analysis methods later in the book that can be applied only to groups with a common standard deviation. We saw an example of re-expression for comparing groups with boxplots in Chapter 5.

Here are the Assets of these companies by Market sector:

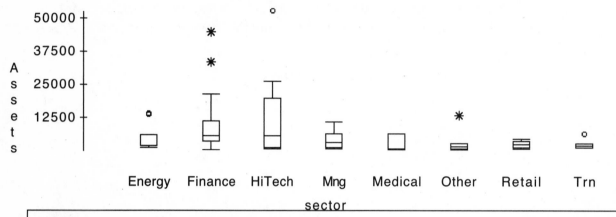

Assets of large companies by market sector. It is hard to compare centers or spreads and there seem to be a number of high outliers.   Fig 10.8

Taking logs makes the individual boxplots more symmetric and gives them spreads that are more nearly equal.

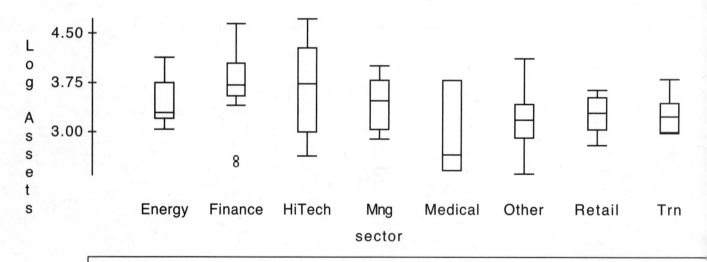

After re-expressing by logs, it is much easier to compare across market sectors. The boxplots are symmetric, most have similar spreads, and the companies that seemed to be outliers before are no longer extraordinary. Two new outliers have appeared in the Finance sector. They are the only companies in that sector who are not banks. Perhaps they don't belong there.   Fig 10.9

This makes it easier to compare assets across market sectors. It can also reveal problems in the data. Some companies that looked like outliers on the high end, turned out to be more typical. But two companies in the Finance sector now stick out. They are not banks like the rest of the companies in that sector, and may have been placed in the wrong sector, but we couldn't see that in the original data.

Goal 3: Make the form of a scatterplot more nearly linear. Linear scatterplots are easier to describe. We saw an example of scatterplot straightening in Chapter 7. But the greater value of re-expression to straighten a relationship is that we can fit a linear model once the relationship is straight.

Here are Assets against the logarithm of sales.

Assets vs Log Sales shows a positive association (bigger sales goes with bigger assets), but a bent shape. Fig 10.10

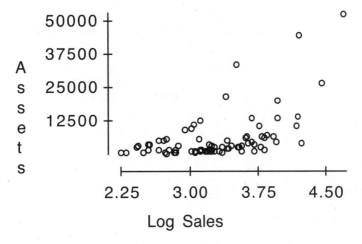

The plot shows a clear bend. Taking logs makes things much more linear.

Log Assets against Log Sales shows a clean, positive, linear association. And the variability at each value of *x* is about the same.
   Fig 10.11

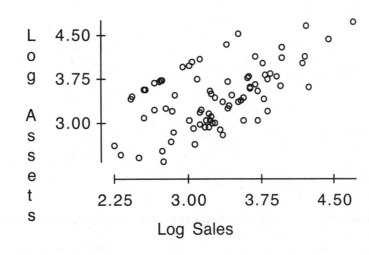

Goal 4: Make the scatter in a scatterplot spread out evenly rather than following a fan shape. Having an even scatter is a condition of many of the methods of statistics, as we will see in later chapters. This goal is closely related to Goal 2. But it often comes along with Goal 3. Indeed, a glance back at the scatterplots shows that the plot for Assets is much more spread out on the

right than on the left, while the plot for Log assets has roughly the same variation in Log Assets for any *x*-value.

The Ladder of Powers

We've seen that taking logs or reciprocals can really simplify an analysis. But how do we know which re-expression to use? We could use trial and error to choose a re-expression, but there's an easier way. We can choose our re-expressions from a family of r simple e-expressions that move data toward our goals in a consistent way. This family includes the most common ways to re-express data. And, more important, the members of the family line up in order so that the farther you move away from the original data (the "1" position), the greater the effect on the data. This fact lets you search systematically for a re-expression that works, stepping a bit farther from "1" or taking a step back toward "1" as you see the results.

But where to start? It turns out that certain kinds of data are more likely to be helped by particular re-expressions. Knowing that, gives you a good place to start your search for a re-expression.

We call this collection of re-expressions the **Ladder of Powers**. Each power is specified as a single value as follows:

Power	Name	Comment
2	The square of the data values	Try this for unimodal distributions that are skewed to the left.
1	The raw data -- no change at all. This is "home base." The farther you step from here up or down the ladder, the greater the effect.	Data that can take on both positive and negative values with no bounds are less likely to benefit from re-expression.
1/2	The square root of the data values	Counts often benefit from a square root re-expression. For counted data, start here.
"0"	Although mathematicians define the "0th" power differently[3], for us the place is held by the logarithm. You may feel uneasy about logarithms.	Measurements that cannot be negative, and especially values that grow by percentage increases such as salaries or populations often benefit from a log re-expression. When in

---

[3] You may remember that for any number, y, $y^0 = 1$. This is not a very exciting transformation for data; every data value would be the same. We use the logarithm in its place.

DRAFT: Do not distribute or copy

	Don't worry, the computer or calculator does the work.[4]	doubt, start here. If your data have zeros, try adding a small constant such as 1/6 to all values before finding the logs.
-1/2	The reciprocal square root.	An uncommon re-expression, but sometimes useful. Changing the sign to take the *negative* of the reciprocal square root preserves the direction of a relationship, which can be a bit simpler.
-1	The reciprocal.	Ratios of two quantities (miles per hour, for example) often benefit from a reciprocal. (You have about a 50-50 chance that the original ratio was taken in the "wrong" order for simple statistical analysis and would benefit from re-expression.) Often, the reciprocal will have simple units (hours per mile). Change the sign to preserve the direction of a relationship. If your data have zeros, try adding a small constant such as 1/6 to all values before finding the square roots.

The ladder of powers orders the *effects* that the re-expressions have on data. If you try, say, taking the square roots of all the values in a variable and it helps, but not enough, then moving further down the ladder to the logarithm or reciprocal root will have a similar effect on your data, but even stronger. If you go too far, you can always back up. But don't forget, once you take a negative power, the *direction* of the relationship will change. That's OK. You can always change the sign of the response if you want to keep the same direction.

A generation ago, before desktop computers and powerful calculators were available, finding a suitable re-expression was a major undertaking, often given as an end of semester project. Now, it's usually no harder than the push of a button, making it easy to search for a suitable re-expression.

Re-expressing to Straighten a Scatterplot, Step by Step

We have noted that scatterplots with a linear shape let us fit linear models. Here's a simple example.

---

[4] Your calculator or software package probably gives you a choice between "base 10" logarithms and "natural (base e)" logarithms. Don't worry about that. It doesn't matter at all which you use; they have exactly the same effect on the data. If you want to choose, then base 10 logarithms can be a bit easier to interpret.

Standard (monofilament) fishing line comes in a range of strengths, usually expressed as "test pounds". Five-pound test line, for example, can be expected to withstand a pull of up to five pounds without breaking. The convention in selling fishing line is that the price of a spool doesn't vary with strength. Instead, the length of line on the spool varies. But, because higher test pound line is thicker, spools of fishing line hold about the same amount of material. Some spools hold line that is thinner and longer, some fatter and shorter. Here's a scatterplot of the length and strength of spools of monofilament line manufactured by the same company and sold for the same price at one store:

How are the length on the spool and the strength related? And what re-expression will straighten the relationship?

Think

Variables: Name the variables, report the W's, and specify the questions of interest.

We have the length (in ft) and "pound test" (in pounds?) of monofilament fishing line sold by a single vendor at a particular store. Each case is a different strength of line, but all spools of line sell for the same price.

Plan:

Examine the relationship for bends.

Check that even if there is a curve, the overall pattern does not reach a minimum or maximum and then turn around and go back. A bend like that cannot be fixed by re-expression.

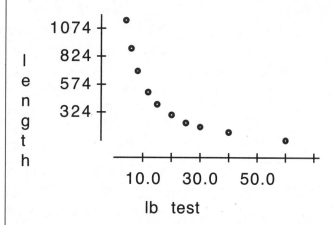

The plot shows a negative direction and an association that has little scatter, but is not straight.

Mechanics:

Try a re-expression.

Show

The lesson of the ladder of powers is that if we are moving in the right direction but have not had sufficient effect, we should go farther along the ladder. This example shows

Here is a plot of the square root of length against strength:

DRAFT: Do not distribute or copy

improvement, but is still not straight.

(Because length is an amount of something and cannot be negative, we probably should have started with logs. This plot is here in part to illustrate how the ladder of powers works.)

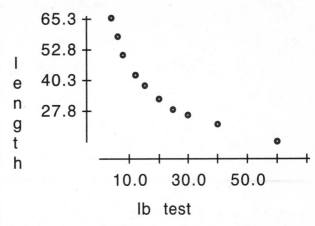

The plot is less bent, but still not straight.

The scatterplot of the logarithm of length against test weight is still less bent:

Stepping from the 1/2 power to the "0" power, we try the logarithm of length against strength:

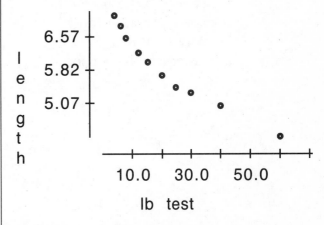

This is much better, but still not straight, so we take another step to the "-1" power, or reciprocal. (To keep the direction consistent, we'll change the sign and re-express to –1/yards.)

Because the straightness is improving, we know we are moving in the right direction. Because the plot of the logarithms is not yet straight, we know we haven't gone far enough.

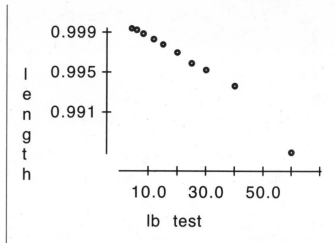

Hmm, maybe we moved too far along the ladder.

A half-step back is the –1/2 power: the reciprocal square root. Let's try it:

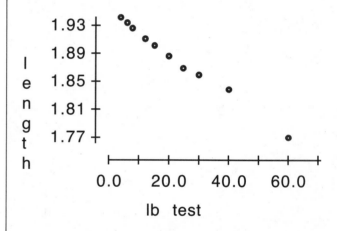

We may have to choose between two adjacent re-expressions. For most data analyses, it really doesn't matter which we choose.

It is hard to choose between the last two alternatives. Either of the last two choices is good enough for our purposes. We'll choose the –1/2 power.

Tell

Discussion: Specify your choice of re-expression. If there is some natural interpretation (as for gallons per 100 miles) give that.

We can use the linear model to predict the length of a spool of, say 35 pound test line. We find that

$$1/\sqrt{length} = 0.026 + 0.00148*35 = 0.0778$$

We can leave the analysis in these units (1/√yards). Often the new units are as reasonable as the original. But, we might want to re-express this back into yards. We can use this model to predict that a 35 pound test line, *1/√length* will be *0.0778*. But how much line is that? Fortunately each of the re-expressions in the ladder of powers can be reversed.

DRAFT: Do not distribute or copy

We can reverse the process by first taking the reciprocal to get $\sqrt{length}$ = $1/.0778$ and then squaring to get back to *length* in its original units:

$$length = \left(\frac{1}{0.0778}\right)^2 = 165 \text{ yards.}$$

This may be the most painful part of the re-expression. Getting back to the original units can sometimes be a little work. But, nevertheless, it's worth the effort to always consider re-expression. Re-expressions can often vastly improve a statistical analysis or model.

Multiple Benefits

We often choose a re-expression for one reason and then discover that it has helped other aspects of an analysis. For example, we might re-express a variable to make its histogram more nearly symmetric. It wouldn't be surprising to find that the same re-expression also straightens scatterplots or make spreads more nearly equal. This phenomenon is one reason to encourage that data re-expression should be used more often. Sometimes there is an obvious "best" or "right" re-expression for a variable. For example, it makes sense that things that tend to grow by a constant percentage so that larger values grow faster (populations, bacteria counts, wealth) will grow exponentially. Logarithms straighten out the exponential trend and pull in the long right tail in the histogram.

We saw just this phenomenon in the companies example earlier. Each of our goals was met by re-expressing Assets with logarithms. That single re-expression improved all four of the goals at the same time. That turns out not to be all that unusual.

Measurement errors are often larger when measuring larger quantities than when measuring smaller ones. (The error in your height may be only a centimeter or two, but the error in the height of a tree could be ten times that much.) Here, again, logarithms are likely to help. Measurements of rates (time to complete a task) are often plagued by infinities for those who just never finish. The reciprocal of "minutes per task" is "tasks per minute" -- a speed measure. And the unfinished tasks that once took "infinite" time now simply rate a zero speed. Here again, the re-expression seems natural.

But in other cases, the only evidence we have to favor re-expression is that it seems to work well and that it leads to simpler models. Often we can find a re-expression for a variable that simplifies its analysis in

KISS?

If you think that simpler explanations and simpler models are more likely to give a true picture of the way things work, then you should look for opportunities to re-express your data and simplify your analyses.

The general principle that simpler explanations are likely to be the better ones is known as Occam's Razor after the English philosopher and theologian William of Occam (1284-1347). The modern colloquial version is KISS: Keep it simple, stupid.

several ways at once, making its distribution symmetric, making it linear in terms of other variables of interest, or stabilizing its variance. If so, re-expressing it certainly simplifies our efforts to analyze and understand it.

Re-expression and the Computer

Computers and calculators make it easy to re-express data. Most statistics packages offer a way to re-express and compute with variables. Some packages permit you to specify the power of a re-expression with a slider or other moveable control, possibly while watching the consequences of the re-expression on a plot or analysis. This, of course, is a very effective way to find a good re-expression.

What Can Go Wrong

- *Beware of multiple modes.* Re-expression can often make a skewed unimodal histogram more nearly symmetric, but it cannot pull separate modes together. A suitable re-expression may, however, make the separation of the modes clearer, simplifying their interpretation.

- *Watch out for scatterplots that turn around.* Re-expression can straighten many bent relationships, but not those that go up and then down or down and then up. Of course, you should still refuse to analyze the data with methods that require a linear form.

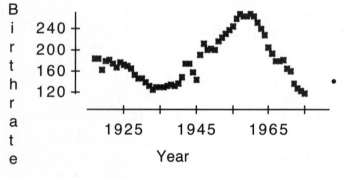

The shape of the scatterplot of birthrates (births per 100,000 women) in the U.S. shows an oscillation that cannot be straightened by re-expressing the data.   Fig 10.12

- *Watch out for negative data values.* It is impossible to re-express negative values by any power that is not positive on the ladder of powers or to re-express values that are zero for powers between 0 and –1. Most statistics programs will just mark such values "missing" if they cannot be re-expressed. But that might mean that when you try a re-expression, you inadvertently lose a bunch of data values. The effect of that loss may be surprising and may substantially change your analysis. Because you are likely to be working with a computer package or calculator, take special care that you have not lost otherwise good data values when you chose a re-expression.

One possible cure if the negative values are not very far below zero is to add a small constant (1/2 and 1/6 are both used) to all the data values to bring the minimum up above zero.

- *Watch for data far from one.* Data values that are all very far from 1 may not be much affected by re-expression unless the range is very large. Re-expressing numbers between 1 and 100 will have a much greater effect than re-expressing numbers between 100,001 and 100,100. If all the data values are large (for example, working with years), consider subtracting a constant to bring them back near to 1. (For example, consider "years since 1950" as an alternative variable to re-express.)

- ***Don't stray too far from the Ladder.*** Finally, it's wise not to stray too far from the powers that we suggest in the ladder of powers. Taking the y-values to an extremely high power may artificially inflate R^2, but it won't give a useful or meaningful model, so it doesn't really simplify anything. It's better to stick to powers between 2 and –2. Even in that range, you should prefer the simpler powers in the ladder to those in the cracks. A square root is easier to understand than the .413 power. That simplicity may compensate for a slightly less straight relationship.

Key Concepts

Re-express data	
	- To improve symmetry
	- To make several groups have more nearly equal spreads
	- To make the form of a scatterplot more nearly linear
	- To make a scatterplot have a more nearly consistent spread throughout

Skills

When you complete this lesson you should:

Think

- Recognize when a well-chosen re-expression may help you improve and simplify your analysis.

- Understand the value of re-expressing data to improve symmetry, constant variance, or linearity.

- Recognize when the pattern of the data indicates that no re-expression can improve the structure of the data.

Show

- Know how to re-express data with powers and how to find an effective re-expression for your data using your statistics software or calculator.

- Be able to reverse any of the common re-expressions to put a predicted value or residual back into the original units.

> *Tell*
>
> - Be able to describe a summary or display of a re-expressed variable making clear how it was re-expressed and giving its re-expressed units.
>
> - Be able to describe a regression model fit to re-expressed data in terms of the re-expressed variables.

Exercises

1. **Models** For each of the models listed below predict y when $x = 2$.
   a) $\hat{y} = 1.2 + 0.8x$
   b) $\ln \hat{y} = 1.2 + 0.8x$
   c) $\sqrt{\hat{y}} = 1.2 + 0.8x$
   d) $\dfrac{1}{\hat{y}} = 1.2 + 0.8x$
   e) $\hat{y} = 1.2x^{0.8}$

2. **More Models** For each of the models listed below predict y when $x = 2$.
   a) $\hat{y} = 1.2 + 0.8 \log x$
   b) $\log \hat{y} = 1.2 + 0.8x$
   c) $\hat{y} = 1.2 + 0.8\sqrt{x}$
   d) $\hat{y} = 1.2(0.8^x)$
   e) $\hat{y} = 0.8x^2 + 1.2x + 1$

3. **Gas Mileage** As the example in the chapter indicates, one of the important factors determining a car's fuel efficiency is its weight. Let's examine this relationship again, for 11 cars.
   a) Describe the association between these variables shown in the scatterplot.

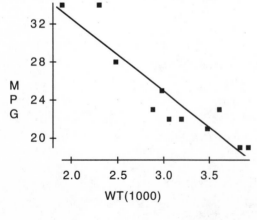
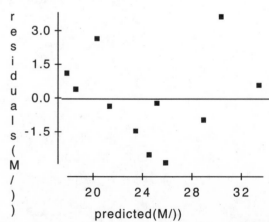

   b) Here is the regression analysis for the linear model. What does the slope of the line say about this relationship?
   Dependent variable is: MPG

DRAFT: Do not distribute or copy

R squared = 85.9%

Variable	Coefficient
Constant	47.9636
WT(1000)	-7.65184

c) Do you think this linear model is appropriate? Use the residuals plot above to explain your decision.

d) Let's try a reexpressed variable: gallons per hundred miles. Use the new residuals plot to explain why this model appears to be better.

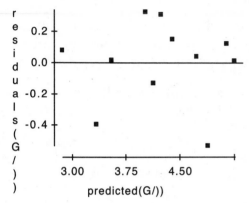

residuals (G/))

predicted(G/))

Dependent variable is: Gal/100

R squared = 89.2%

Variable	Coefficient
Constant	0.624932
WT(1000)	1.17791.

e) Using the regression analysis above, write an equation of this model.

f) Interpret the slope of this line.

g) Based on this model, how many miles per gallon would you expect a 3500 pound car to get?

4. **Pressure** Scientist Robert Boyle examined the relationship between the volume in which a gas is contained and the pressure in that container. He used a cylindrical container with a movable top that could be raised or lowered to change the volume. He measured the height by counting equally spaced marks on the cylinder, and measured the pressure in inches of mercury (as in a barometer). Some of his data is listed below. Create an appropriate model.

Height	48	44	40	36	32	28	24	20	18	16	14	1
Pressure	29.1	31.9	35.3	39.3	44.2	50.3	58.8	70.7	77.9	87.9	100.4	11

5. **Brakes** The table below shows stopping distances in feet for a car tested three times at each of 5 speeds. We hope to create a model that predicts stopping distance from the speed of the car.

Speed (mph)	Stopping distance (ft)
20	64, 62, 59
30	114, 118, 105
40	153, 171, 165
50	231, 203, 238
60	317, 321, 276

a) Explain why a linear model is not appropriate.

b) Reexpress the data to straighten the scatterplot.

c) Create an appropriate model.

d) Estimate the stopping distance for a car traveling 55 mph.

e) Estimate the stopping distance for a car traveling 70 mph.

f) How much confidence do you place in these predictions? Why?

Copyright © 2001, Dick De Veaux and Paul Velleman

6. **Pendulum** A student experimenting with a pendulum counted the number of full swings the pendulum made in 20 seconds for various lengths of string. Her data is shown below.

Length (inches)	6.5	9	11.5	14.5	18	21	24	27	30	37.5
Number of swings	22	20	17	16	14	13	13	12	11	10

   a) Explain why a linear model is not appropriate for using the length of a pendulum to predict the number of swings in 20 seconds.
   b) Reexpress the data to straighten the scatterplot.
   c) Create an appropriate model.
   d) Estimate the number of swings for a pendulum with a 4″ string.
   e) Estimate the number of swings for a pendulum with a 48″ string.
   f) How much confidence do you place in these predictions? Why?

7. **Baseball Salaries** Ballplayers have been signing ever larger contracts. The highest salaries (in million of dollars per season) for some notable players are given in the table below.

Player	Year	Salary
Nolan Ryan	1980	1 million
George Foster	1982	2.04
Kirby Puckett	1990	3
Jose Canseco	1990	4.7
Roger Clemens	1991	5.3
Ken Griffey, Jr.	1996	8.5
Albert Belle	1997	11
Pedro Martinez	1998	12.5
Mike Piazza	1999	12.5
Mo Vaughn	1999	13.3
Kevin Brown	1999	15
Carlos Delgado	2001	17
Alex Rodriguez	2001	25.2

   a) Reexpress the data to straighten the scatterplot.
   b) Create an appropriate model for the trend in salaries.
   c) Predict a superstar salary for 2005.

8. **Planet Distances and Years** The table shows the average distance of each of the nine planets from the sun, and the length of the year (in earth years).

	Position number	Distance from sun (million miles)	Length of year (Earth years)
Mercury	1	36	0.24
Venus	2	67	0.61
Earth	3	93	1.0
Mars	4	142	1.88
Jupiter	5	484	11.86
Saturn	6	887	29.46
Uranus	7	1784	84.07
Neptune	8	2796	164.82
Pluto	9	3666	247.68

DRAFT: Do not distribute or copy

a) Plot the length of the year against the distance from the sun. Describe the shape of your plot.

b) Re-express one or both variables to straighten the plot. Use the re-expressed data to create a model to describe the length of a planet's year based upon its distance from the sun.

c) Comment on how well your model fits the data.

9. **Planet Distances and Order** Let's look again at the pattern in the locations of the planets in our solar system seen in the table above.

a) Use re-expressed data to create a model for the distance from the sun based on the planet's position.

b) There is some debate among astronomers as to whether Pluto is truly a planet or actually a large member of the Kuiper Belt of comets and other icy bodies. Does your model suggest that Pluto may not belong in the planet group? Explain.

10. **Planets, Part 3** The asteroid belt between Mars and Jupiter may be the remnants of a failed planet. If so, then Jupiter is really in position 6, Saturn is 7, and so on. Repeat Exercise 9 using this revised method of numbering the positions. Which method seems to work better?

11. **Quaoar, Planets, Part 4** In June 2002 Caltech astronomers Chad Trujillo and Mike Brown discovered a new large body in orbit about the sun, a billion miles beyond Jupiter. Named Quaoar (pronounced kwa-whar) after a Native American god, it is about one-tenth the diameter of Earth. Quaoar orbits the sun once every 288 years at a distance of about 4 billion miles. Astronomers have classified it as a member of the Kuiper Belt, rather than as a planet.

a. How does Quaoar's distance from the sun compare to the prediction made by your model(s) for planets?

b. There are other reasons for suspecting that Pluto is unlike other planets. For example, its orbit is tilted relative to the plane in which other planetary orbits are found. And its orbit is very eccentric, passing both inside the orbit of Neptune and outside the orbit of Quaoar. Omit Pluto from your count of planets, and consider Quaoar as a candidate for the next planet beyond Neptune. Now how well does your model to predict (re-expressed) distance from position number fit?

12. **Models and Laws, Planets Part 5** The model you found in Exercise 8 is a relationship noted by Kepler as his Third Law of Planetary Motion. It was subsequently explained as a consequence of Newton's law of Gravitation. The models for Exercises 9 – 11 relate to what is sometimes called the Titius-Bode "law", a pattern noticed in the 18th century, but lacking any scientific explanation.

Compare how well the re-expressed data are described by their respective linear models. What aspect of the model of Exercise 8 suggests that we have found a physical law? In the future, we may learn enough about a planetary system around another star to tell whether the Titius-Bode pattern applies there. How would it change your opinion about whether this is a real natural "law" to discover that another planetary system followed the same pattern? What would you think if the next system we find does not follow this pattern?

13. **Logs (not logarithms)** The value of a log is based on the number of "board feet" of lumber the log may contain. (A board foot is the equivalent of a piece of wood one inch thich, 12 inches wide, and one foot long. For example, a 2"x4" 12 feet long contains 8 board feet.) To estimate the amount of lumber in a log buyers measure the diameter inside the bark at the smaller end. Then they look in a table based on the Doyle Log Scale. The table below shows the estimates for logs 16 feet long. [muextension.missouri.edu/xplor/agguides/forestry/g05050.htm]

Diameter of log	8"	12"	16"	20"	24"	28"
Board feet	16	64	144	256	400	576

a) What model does this scale use?
b) How much lumber would you estimate a log 10 inches in diameter to contain?
c) What does this model suggest about logs 36" in diameter?

14.   **Weightlifting** Listed below are the gold medal winning men's weightlifting performances at the 2000 Olympics.

Weight Class (kg)	Winner (country)	Weight Lifted (kg)
56	Mutli (Turkey)	305
62	Pechalov (Croatia)	325
69	Boevski (Bulgaria)	357.5
77	Xugang (China)	367.5
85	Dimas (Greece)	390
94	Kakiasvilas (Greece)	405
105	Tavakoli (Iran)	425

a) Create a linear model for the amount lifted in each weight class.
b) Check the residuals plot. Is your linear model appropriate?
c) Create a better model.
d) Explain why you think your model is better.
e) Based on your model, which of the medallists turned in the most surprising performance? Explain.
f) Consider that competitor to be an outlier. Eliminate that data point and recreate your model.

DRAFT: Do not distribute or copy

g) Using this revised model, how much would you have expected the outlier competitor to lift?

h) Explain the meaning of the residual for that competitor.

15. **Life Expectancy** The data below lists the life expectancy for white males in the U.S. every 10 years during the last century (1910, 1920, etc.). Create a model to predict future increases in life expectancy. [National Vital Statistics Report]

   48.6, 54.4, 59.7, 62.1, 66.5, 67.4, 68.0, 70.7, 72.7, 74.9

16. **Tree Growth** A 1996 study examined the growth of grapefruit trees in Texas, determining the average trunk diameter (in inches) for trees of varying ages. [http://primera.tamu.edu/kcchome/pubs/treesize.htm]

Age (yr)	2	4	6	8	10	12	14	16	18	20
Diameter	2.1	3.9	5.2	6.2	6.9	7.6	8.3	9.1	10.0	11.4

a) Create a good model for this growth.

b) If data had been given for individual trees instead of averages, would you expect the fit to be stronger, less strong, or about the same? Explain.

17. **Slower is Cheaper?** Researchers studying how a car's gas mileage varies with its speed drove a compact car 200 miles at various speeds on a test track. Their data are shown in the table. Create an appropriate model.

Speed (mph)	35	40	45	50	55	60	65	70	75
Miles per gal	25.9	27.7	28.5	29.5	29.2	27.4	26.4	24.2	22.8

a) Create a model that fits these data.

b) Do you think this model is appropriate? Why?

c) Discuss the strength of your model.

d) Do you think the model will produce accurate predictions about the gas mileage people get in daily driving? Explain.

18. **Orange Production** The table below shows that as the number of oranges on a tree increases, the fruit tend to get smaller. Create a model for this relationship.
   [http://primera.tamu.edu/kcchome/pubs/treesize.htm]

Number of oranges/tree	Average Weight/Fruit(lb)
50	.60
100	.58
150	.56
200	.55
250	.53
300	.52
350	.50
400	.49
450	.48

Copyright © 2001, Dick De Veaux and Paul Velleman

500	.46
600	.44
700	.42
800	.40
900	.38

19.   **Years to Live** Insurance companies and other organizations use actuarial tables to estimate the remaining lifespan of their customers. Below are the estimated additional years of life for black males in the U.S., according to a 1999 National Vital Statistics Report.

Age	10	20	30	40	50	60	70	80	90	100
Yrs left	59.2	49.6	40.7	31.9	24.0	17.2	11.6	7.2	4.4	2.8

a) Create an appropriate model.
b) Predict the lifespan of an 18 year old black male.

20.   **Oil Production (again)** Here are the data on U.S. oil production first seen in Exercise 26 of Chapter 7.
a) Transform the *y* variable so that the relationship is more nearly straight.
b) How successfully might a model based on your transformed data predict the future of US oil production? Explain.

year	oil	year	oil	year	oil	year	oil
1949	1841940	1962	2676189	1975	3056779	1988	2979123
1950	1973574	1963	2752723	1976	2976180	1989	2778773
1951	2247711	1964	2786822	1977	3009265	1990	2684687
1952	2289836	1965	2848514	1978	3178216	1991	2707039
1953	2357082	1966	3027763	1979	3121310	1992	2624632
1954	2314988	1967	3215742	1980	3146365	1993	2499033
1955	2484428	1968	3329042	1981	3128624	1994	2431476
1956	2617283	1969	3371751	1982	3156715	1995	2394268
1957	2616901	1970	3517450	1983	3170999	1996	2366017
1958	2448987	1971	3453914	1984	3249696	1997	2354831
1959	2574590	1972	3455368	1985	3274553	1998	2281919
1960	2574933	1973	3360903	1986	3168252	1999	2146732
1961	2621758	1974	3202585	1987	3047378	2000	2135062

21.   **Internet** It is often difficult to find the ideal model for situations in which the data are strongly curved. The table below shows the rapid growth of the number of academic journals published on the internet during the last decade.
[http://www.people.virginia.edu/~pm9k/libsci/charts.html]

Year	Number of Journals
1991	27
1992	36
1993	45

1994	181
1995	306
1996	1093
1997	2459

a) Try to create a good model to describe this growth.
b) Use your model to estimate the number of electronic journals in the year 2000.
c) Comment on your faith in this estimate.

Exploring Relationships

Quick Review

You have now survived your second major unit of Statistics. Here's a brief summary of the key concepts and skills:

➢ Data come in two flavors: categorical and quantitative.

➢ To explore relationships in categorical data, check out Chapter 3.

➢ To explore relationships in quantitative data:

- Make a picture. Use a scatterplot. Put the explanatory variable on the x-axis and the response variable on the y-axis.

- Describe the association in terms of direction, form, and scatter.

- The amount of scatter determines the strength of the association.

- If as one variable increases so does the other, the association is positive. If one increases as the other decreases it's negative.

- If the form of the association is linear, calculate a correlation to measure its strength numerically, and do a regression analysis to model it.

- Correlations closer to –1 or +1 indicate stronger linear associations. Correlations near 0 indicate weak linear relationships, but other forms of association may still be present.

- The least squares regression line estimates values of the response variable from values of the explanatory variable.

- Residuals are the difference between the true value of the response variable and the value predicted by the regression model.

- The slope of the line is a rate of change, best described in "y-units" per "x-unit".

- R^2 gives the percentage of the variation in the response variable that is accounted for by the model.

- The standard deviation of the residuals measures the amount of scatter around the line.

- Outliers and influential points can distort any of our models.

- If you see a pattern (a curve) in the residuals plot, your chosen model is not appropriate; use a different model. You may, for example, straighten the relationship by re-expressing one of the variables.

- To straighten bent relationships, re-express the data using logarithms or a power (squares, square roots, reciprocals, etc.).

- Always remember that an association is not necessarily an indication that one of the variables causes the other.

One must learn by doing the thing; though you think you know it, you have no certainty until you try. Sophocles 495-406 BC

Need more help with some of this? Try rereading some sections of Chapters 7 - 10. And turn this page for more opportunities to review these concepts and skills.

Exercises

1. **College** Every year US *News and World Report* publishes a special issue on many US colleges and universities. The scatterplots below have Student/Faculty Ratio (number of students per faculty member) for the colleges and universities the *y*-axes plotted against 4 other variables. The correct correlations for these scatterplots appear in this list. Match them.

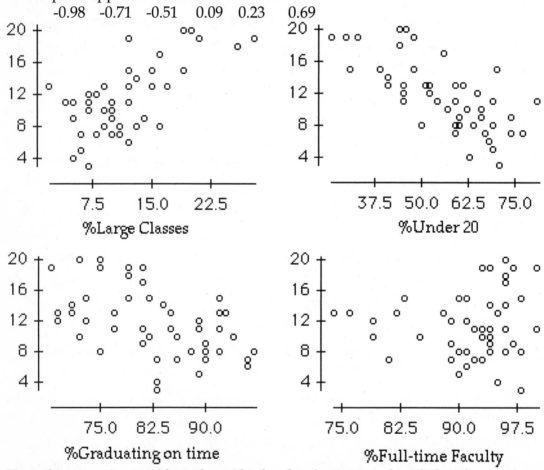

-0.98   -0.71   -0.51   0.09   0.23   0.69

2. **Togetherness** Are good grades in high school associated with family togetherness? A simple random sample of 142 high school students was asked how many meals per week their families ate together. Their responses produced a mean of 3.78 meals per week, with a standard deviation of 2.2. Researchers then matched these responses against the students' grade point averages. The

scatterplot appeared to be reasonably linear, so they created a line of regression. No apparent pattern emerged in the residuals plot. The equation of the line was $\hat{gpa} = 2.73 + 0.11 meals$.

a) Interpret the y-intercept in this context.
b) Interpret the slope in this context.
c) What was the mean GPA for the students in this study?
d) If a student in this study had a negative residual, what did that mean?
e) Upon hearing of this study a counselor recommended that parents who want to improve the grades their children get should get the family to eat together more often. Do you agree with this interpretation? Explain.

3. **Wines** Shown below are the scatterplot and regression analysis for case prices of 36 wines produced in the Finger Lakes region and the ages of vineyards that produced them.

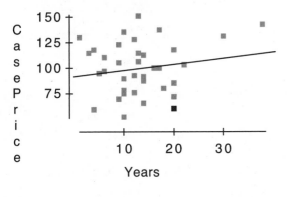

Dependent variable is: **CasePrice**
R squared = 2.7%

Variable	Coefficient
Constant	92.7650
Years	0.567284

a) Does it appear that vineyards in business longer produce more costly wines? Explain.
b) What does this analysis tell us about wines worldwide?
c) Write the regression equation.
d) Explain why that equation is essentially useless.

4. **More Wine** Instead of age, perhaps the size of the winery (in acres) is associated with the value of the wine. Here is the scatterplot:

a) Do you see any evidence of an association?
b) What concern do you have about this scatterplot?
c) If the black data point is removed, would you expect the correlation to increase or decrease? Explain.
d) If the [second color] data point is removed, would you expect the slope of the line to increase or decrease? Explain.

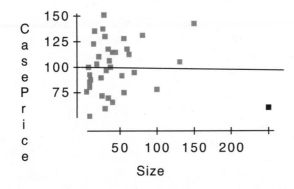

Year	Twin Births
1981	70049
1982	71631
1983	72287
1984	72949
1985	77102
1986	79485
1987	81778
1988	85315
1989	90118
1990	93865
1991	94779
1992	95372
1993	96445
1994	97064
1995	96736
1996	100750
1997	104137

5. **More Twins?** As the table shows, the number of twins born in the US has been increasing. [JAMA 2000:284:335-341]
   a) Find the equation of the regression line for predicting the number of twin births.
   b) Explain in this context what the slope of this line means.
   c) Predict the number of twin births in the US for the year 2002. Comment on your faith in that prediction.
   d) Comment on the residuals plot.

6. **Dow Jones** When the Dow Jones stock index first reached 10,000, the *NY Times* reported the dates on which the Dow crossed each of the "thousand" marks, starting with reaching 1000 in 1972. A regression of the Dow prices on year looks (in part) like this:

   Dependent variable is: **dow**
   R squared = 65.8%
   Variable   Coefficient
   Constant   -603335
   year   305.471

   a) What is the correlation between the Dow index and the year?
   b) Write the regression equation.
   c) Explain in this context what the equation says.
   d) Your answer to the previous question should have turned up an important weakness in the Dow average. What does the Dow lack as a measurement that makes interpreting the regression equation problematic?
   e) Here's a scatterplot of the residuals. Which assumption(s) of the regression analysis appear to be violated?

   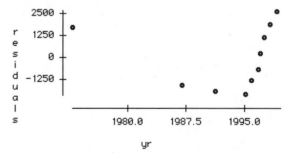

7. **Acid Rain** Biologists studying the effects of acid rain on wildlife collected data from 163 streams in the Adirondack Mountains. The recorded the pH (acidity) of the water and the BCI, a measure of biological diversity. Here's a scatterplot of BCI against pH. They calculated R-sq = 27%.

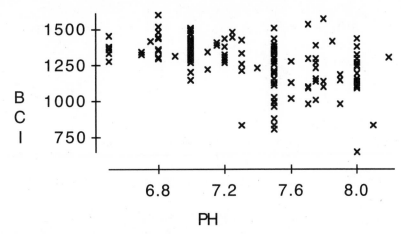

a) What is the correlation between pH and BCI.
b) Describe the association between these two variables.
c) If a stream has average pH, what would you predict about the BCI?
d) In a stream where the pH is 3 standard deviations above average, what would you predict about the BCI?

8. **Manatees** Marine biologists warn that the growing number of powerboats registered in Florida threatens the existence of manatees. The Feb 12, 2002 *NY Times* reported these data:
[http://www.nytimes.com/2002/02/12/science/12MANA.html]

Year	Manatees Killed	Powerboat Registrations (in 1000s)
1982	13	447.0
1983	21	459.6
1984	24	481.0
1985	16	497.9
1986	24	512.6
1987	20	512.3
1988	15	526.5
1989	34	558.6
1990	33	585.3
1992	33	613.5
1993	39	645.5
1994	43	675
1995	50	711
1996	47	719
1997	53	716
1998	38	716
1999	35	716
2000	49	735
2001	81	860

a) In this context, which do you think is the explanatory variable?
b) Make a scatterplot of these data and describe the association you see.
c) Find the correlation between boat registrations and manatee deaths.
d) Interpret the value of R-squared.

e) Does your analysis prove that powerboats are killing manatees?

9. **A Manatee Model** Continue your analysis of the manatee situation from the last exercise.

   a) Create a linear model of the association between manatee deaths and powerboat registrations.
   b) Interpret the slope of your model.
   c) Interpret the y-intercept of your model.
   d) How accurately did your model predict the high number of manatee deaths in 2001?
   e) Which is better for the manatees, positive residuals or negative residuals? Explain.
   f) What does your model suggest about the future for the manatee?

10. **Grades** A statistics professor created a linear regression equation to predict students' final exam scores from their midterm exam scores. The regression equation was: $\widehat{fin} = 10 + 0.9mid$

    a) If Susan scored a 70 on the midterm, what did the professor predict for her score on the final?
    b) Susan got an 80 on the final. How big is her residual?
    c) Suppose that the standard deviation of the final was 12 points and the standard deviation of the midterm was 10 points. What is the correlation between the two tests?
    d) How many points would someone need to score on the midterm to have a predicted final score of 100?
    e) Suppose someone scored 100 on the final. Explain why you cannot estimate this student's midterm score from the information given.
    f) One of the students in the class scored 100 on the midterm, but got overconfident, slacked off, and only scored 15 on the final exam. What is the residual for this student?
    g) No other student in the class "achieved" such a dramatic turnaround. If the professor decides not to include this student's scores when constructing a new regression model, will the R-squared value of the regression increase, decrease, or remain the same? Explain briefly.
    h) Will the slope of the new line increase or decrease?

11. **Traffic** Highway planners investigated the relationship between traffic density (number of automobiles per mile) and the average speed of the traffic on a moderately large city thoroughfare. The data were collected at the same location at 10 different times over a span of 3 months. They found a mean traffic density of 68.6 cars per mile with standard deviation 27.07 cpm. Overall the cars' average speed was 26.38 mph with standard deviation 9.68 mph. These researchers found the regression line for these data to be $\widehat{speed} = 50.55 - 0.352cars$.

    a) What is the value of the correlation coefficient between *speed* and *cars*?
    b) What percent of the variation in average speed is explained by traffic density?
    c) Predict the average speed of traffic on the thoroughfare when the traffic density is 50 automobiles per mile.

d) What is the value of the residual for a traffic density of 56 cars/mile with an observed speed of 32.5 mph?

e) The data set initially included the point *cars* =125 cpm, *speed* = 55 mph. This point was considered an outlier and was not included in the analysis. Will the slope increase, decrease or remain the same if we redo the analysis and include this point?

f) Will the correlation increase, decrease or remain the same if we redo the analysis and include this point (125,55)?

g) A European member of the research team measured the speed of the cars in kilometers per hour (1 km ~ 0.62 miles), and the traffic density in cars/km. Find the value of his calculated correlation between speed and density.

12. **Cramming** One Thursday researchers gave students enrolled in a section of basic Spanish a set of 50 new vocabulary words to memorize. On Friday the students took a vocabulary test. When they returned to class the following Monday they were retested – without advance warning. Both sets of test scores for the 28 students are shown.

a) What is the correlation between Friday and Monday scores?

b) What does a scatterplot show about the association between the scores?

c) What does it mean for a student to have a positive residual?

d) What would you predict about a student whose Friday score was one standard deviation below average?

e) Write an equation of the regression line.

f) Predict the Monday score of a student who earned a 40 on Friday.

FRI	MON
42	36
44	44
45	46
48	38
44	40
43	38
41	37
35	31
43	32
48	37
43	41
45	32
47	44
50	47
34	34
38	31
43	40
39	41
46	32
37	36
40	31
41	32
48	39
37	31
36	41

13. **Correlations** What factor most explains differences in gas mileage among cars? Here is a correlation matrix exploring that relationship for the car's weight, horsepower, engine size (displacement), and number of cylinders.

Pearson Product-Moment Correlation

No Selector

	MPG	Weight	Horse...	Displ...	Cylin...
MPG	1.000				
Weight	-0.903	1.000			
Horsepower	-0.871	0.917	1.000		
Displacem...	-0.786	0.951	0.872	1.000	
Cylinders	-0.806	0.917	0.864	0.940	1.000

a) Which factor seems most strongly associated with fuel economy (miles per gallon)?
b) What does the negative correlation indicate?
c) Explain the meaning of R-squared for that relationship.

14. **Autos Revisited** Look again at the correlation table for cars in the last exercise.
    a) Which two variables in the table exhibit the strongest association?
    b) Is that strong association necessarily cause-and-effect? Offer at least two explanations why that association might be so strong.
    c) Engine displacements for US-made cars are often measured in cubic inches. For many foreign cars the units are either cubic centimeters or liters. How will the choice of units affect the calculated correlations involving displacement?
    d) What would you predict about the fuel economy of a car whose engine displacement is one standard deviation above the mean?

15. **Cars, One More Time!** Can we predict the horsepower of the engine manufacturers will put in a car by knowing the weight of the car? Here are the regression analysis and residuals plot.

Dependent variable is: Horsepower
R squared = 84.1%
s = 10.68

Variable	Coefficient	SE(Coeff)	t-ratio	P-value
Constant	3.49834	7.319	0.478	0.6356
Weight	34.3144	2.484	13.8	≤ 0.0001

a) Write the equation of the regression line.
b) Do you think the car's weight is measured in pounds, or thousands of pounds? Explain.
c) Do you think this linear model is appropriate? Explain.
d) The highest point in the residuals plot, representing a residual of 22.5 horsepower, is for a Chevy weighing 2595 pounds. How many horsepower does this car have?

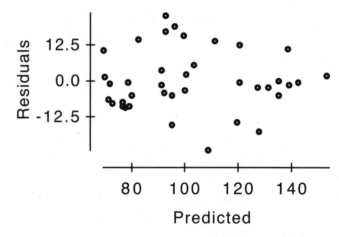

16. **Colorblind** Although there are some women who are colorblind, this condition is primarily found in men. Why is it wrong to say there is a strong correlation between gender and colorblindness?

17. **Old Faithful** There is some evidence that eruptions of Old Faithful can best be predicted by knowing the duration of the previous eruption.
    a) Describe what you see in the scatterplot of intervals between eruptions vs duration of the previous eruption.

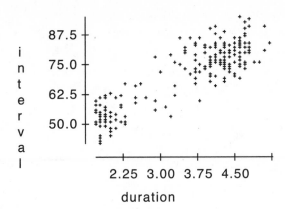

interval

duration

b) Write the equation of the line of best fit. Here is the regression analysis:

Dependent variable is: interval
R squared = 77.0%
s = 6.159

Variable	Coefficient	SE(Coeff)	t-ratio	P-value
Constant	33.9668	1.428	23.8	≤ 0.0001
duration	10.3582	0.3822	27.1	≤ 0.0001

c) Carefully explain what the slope of the line means in this context.
d) How accurate do you expect predictions based on this model to be? Cite evidence from the regression analysis.
e) If you just witnessed an eruption that lasted 4 minutes, how long do you predict you will have to wait to see the next eruption?
f) So you waited, and the next eruption came in 79 minutes. Use this an example to explain what a residual is.

18. **Which Croc?** The ranges inhabited by the Indian gharial crocodile and the Australian saltwater crocodile overlap in Bangladesh. Suppose a very large crocodile skeleton is found there, and we wish to determine which species the animal was. Wildlife scientists have measured the lengths of the heads and the complete bodies of several crocs (in centimeters) of each species, creating the regression analyses below:

Indian Crocodile		Australian Crocodile	
Dependent variable is: IBody		Dependent variable is: ABody	
R squared = 97.2%		R squared = 98.0%	
Variable	Coefficient	Variable	Coefficient
Constant	-69.3693	Constant	-20.2245
IHead	7.40004	AHead	7.71726

a) Do the associations between the sizes of the heads and bodies of the two species appear to be strong? Explain.
b) In what ways are the two relationships similar? Explain.
c) What is different about the two models? What does that mean?
d) The crocodile skeleton found had a head length of 62 centimeters, and a body length of 380 centimeters. Which species do you think it was? Explain why.

19. **How old is that tree?** One can determine how old a tree by
counting its rings, but that requires cutting the tree down.
Can we estimate the age simply from its diameter? A forester
measured 27 trees of the same species that had been cut
down, and counted the rings to determine their ages.

a) Find the correlation between diameter and age. Does this
suggest that a linear model may be appropriate? Explain.

b) Create a scatterplot and describe the association.

c) Create the linear model.

d) About how many inches per year does this model suggest
these trees grow?

e) Check the residuals. Explain why a linear model is
probably not appropriate.

f) If you used this model, would it generally overestimate or
underestimate the ages of very large trees? Explain.

20. **Improving Trees** In the last exercise you saw that the linear
model had some deficiencies. Let's create a better model.

a) Perhaps the cross-sectional area of a tree would be a better
predictor of its age. Since area is measured in square units,
try re-expressing the data by squaring the diameters. Does
the scatterplot look better?

b) Create a model that predicts age from the square of
diameter.

c) Check the residuals plot for this new model. Is this model
more appropriate? Why?

d) Estimate the age of a tree 18″ in diameter.

Diameter (inches)	Age (years)
1.8	4
1.8	5
2.2	8
4.4	8
6.6	8
4.4	10
7.7	10
10.8	12
7.7	13
5.5	14
9.9	16
10.1	18
12.1	20
12.8	22
10.3	23
14.3	25
13.2	28
9.9	29
13.2	30
15.4	30
17.6	33
14.3	34
15.4	35
11	38
15.4	38
16.5	40
16.5	42

21. **New Homes** A real estate agent collects data to develop a model that will use the
size of a new home (in square feet) to predict its sale price (in thousands of
dollars). Which of these is most likely to be the slope of the regression line: 0.008,
0.08, 0.8, or 8? Explain.

22. **Smoking and Pregnancy** The organization *KidsCount* monitors issues related to
children. The table shows a 50-city average of the percent of expectant mothers
who smoked cigarettes during their pregnancies.

a) Create a scatterplot and describe the trend you see.

b) Find the correlation.

c) How is the value of the correlation affected by the fact that
the data are averages rather than percentages for each of
the 50 cities?

d) Write a linear model and interpret the slope in this context.

23. **No Smoking?** The downward trend in smoking you saw in
the last exercise is good news for the health of babies, but will
it ever stop?

a) Explain why you cannot use the linear model you created
above to see when smoking during pregnancy will cease

Year	% smoke while preg
1990	17.7
1991	17.0
1992	16.0
1993	14.9
1994	13.9
1995	12.7
1996	11.9
1997	11.2
1998	10.8
1999	10.4

altogether.

b) Create a model that could estimate the year in which the level of smoking would be 0%.

c) Comment on the reliability of such a prediction.

24. **Tips** It is commonly believed people use tips to reward good service. A researcher for the hospitality industry examined tips and ratings of service quality from 2,645 dining parties at 21 different restaurants. The correlation between ratings of service and tip percentages was 0.11. [Gratitude and gratuity. Journal of Socio-Economics, 29, 203-214.]

a) Describe the relationship between quality of service and tip size.

b) Find and interpret the value of R-squared in this context.

25. **Move South?** Data from 50 large US cities shows the mean January temperature and the latitude. Describe what you see in the scatterplot.

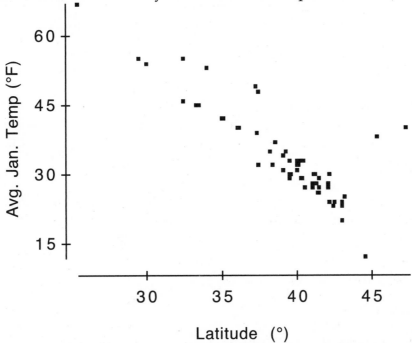

26. **Correlations** A study of living conditions in 55 large US cities found the mean January temperature (degrees Fahrenheit), altitude (feet above sea level), and latitude (degrees north of the equator). Here is the correlation matrix.

Correlations	JanTemp	Latitude	Altitude
JanTemp	1.000		
Latitude	-0.848	1.000	
Altitude	-0.369	0.184	1.000

a) Which seems to be more useful in predicting January temperature, altitude, or latitude? Explain.

b) If the temperature were measured in degrees Celsius, what would the correlation between temperature and latitude be?

c) If the temperature were measured in degrees Celsius and altitude in meters, what would the correlation be? Explain.

d) What would you predict about the January temperatures in a city that is two standard deviations higher than the average altitude?

27. **Winter in the City** Summary statistics for the data relating the latitude and average January temperature for 55 large US cities are given below.

Variable	Mean	StdDev	Correlation
Latitude	39.02	5.42	-0.848
JanTemp	26.44	13.49	

a) What percent of the variation on January temperatures can be explained by variation in latitude?
b) What does the fact that the correlation is negative indicate?
c) Write the equation of the line of regression for predicting January temperature from latitude.
d) Explain what the slope of the line means.
e) Do you think the y-intercept of the line is meaningful? Explain.
f) The latitude of Denver is 40°N. Predict the mean January temperature there.
g) If the residual for a city is positive, what does that mean?

28. **Depression** The September 1998 issue of the *American Psychologist* published an article by Kraut *et al.* Reporting on an experiment examining "the social and psychological impact of the Internet on 169 people in 73 households during their first 1 to 2 years on-line." In the experiment, a sample of households were offered free internet access for one or two years in return for allowing their time and activity on-line to be tracked. The members of the households who participated in the study were also given a battery of tests at the beginning and again at the end of the study. The conclusion of the study made news headlines: those who spent more time on-line tended to be more depressed at the end of the experiment. Although the paper reports a more complex model, the basic result can be summarized in the following regression of *Depression* (at the end of the study, in "depression scale units") vs *Internet use* (in mean hours per week.)

Dependent variable is: Depression T3
R squared = 4.6%
s = 0.4563

Variable	Coefficient	SE(Coeff)	t-ratio	P-Value
Constant	0.5655	0.0399	14.2	≤ 0.0001
Internet use	0.0199	0.0072	2.76	0.0063

The news reports about this study clearly concluded that using the internet causes depression. Discuss whether such a conclusion can be drawn from this regression. If so, discuss the supporting evidence. If not, say why not.

29. **Jumps** How are Olympic performances in various events related? The plot shows winning long jump and high jump distances, in inches, for the 20th century Olympic Games.

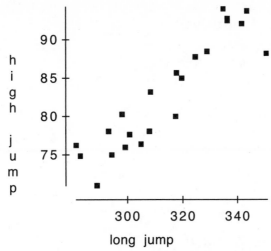

long jump

a) Describe the association.
b) Do long jump performances somehow influence the high jumpers? How do you account for the relationship you see?
c) The correlation for the given scatterplot is 0.92, but at the Olympics these jumps are actually measured in meters rather than inches. Does that make the actual correlation higher or lower?
d) What would you predict about the long jump in a year when the high jumper jumped one standard deviation better than the average high jump?

30. **Modeling Jumps** Here are the summary statistics for the Olympic long jumps and high jumps displayed in the scatterplot above.

Event	Mean	StdDev	Correlation
long jump	314.10	20.71	0.917
high jump	83.04	7.26	

a) Write the equation of the line of regression for estimating high jump from long jump.
b) Interpret the slope of the line.
c) In a year when the long jump is 340 inches, what high jump would you predict?
d) Why can't you use this line to estimate the long jump for a year when you know the high jump was 85 inches?
e) Write the equation of the line you need to make that prediction.

31. **French** Consider the association between a student's score on a French vocabulary test and the weight of the student. What direction and strength of correlation would you expect in each of the following situations? Explain.
a) The students are all in the third grade.
b) The students are in third through twelfth grades in the same school district.
c) The students are in 10th grade, in France.
d) The students are in third through twelfth grades in France.

32. **Twins** Twins are often born after a pregnancy that lasts less than 9 months. The graph from the *Journal of the American Medical Association* shows the rate of preterm twin births in the United States over the past 20 years. In their study

JAMA categorized mothers by the level of prenatal medical care they received: inadequate, adequate, or intensive.

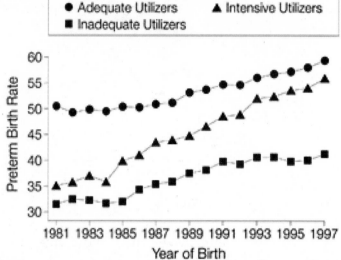

Preterm Birth Rate per 100 Live Twin Births Among US Twins by Intensive, Adequate, and Less Than Adequate Prenatal Care Utilization, 1981-1997 (*JAMA*. 2000;284:335-341)

a) Describe the overall trend in pre-term twin births.
b) Describe any differences you see in this trend depending on the level of prenatal medical care the mother received.
c) Should expectant mothers be advised to cut back on the level of medical care they seek in the hope of avoiding pre-term births? Explain.

33. **Lunchtime** Create and interpret a model for the toddlers' lunchtime data presented in chapter 7. The table shows the number of minutes the kids stayed at the table and the number of calories they consumed for lunch.

Calories	Time
472	21.4
498	30.8
465	37.7
456	33.5
423	32.8
437	39.5
508	22.8
431	34.1
479	33.9
454	43.8
450	42.4
410	43.1
504	29.2
437	31.3
489	28.6
436	32.9
480	30.6
439	35.1
444	33.0
408	43.7

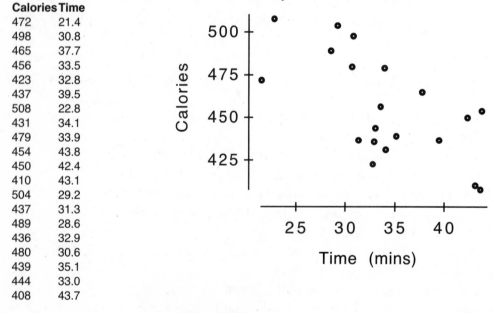

34. **Gasoline** Since clean air regulations have dictated the use of unleaded gasoline, the supply of leaded gas in New York State has diminished. The table below was given on the August 2001 New York State Math B exam, a statewide achievement test for high school students.

Year	1984	1988	1992	1996	2000
Gallons (1000's)	150	124	104	76	50

   a) Create a linear model to predict the number of gallons that will be available in 2005.
   b) The Exam then asked students to estimate the year when leaded gasoline will first become unavailable, expecting them to use the model from part (a) to answer the question. Explain why that method is incorrect.
   c) Create a model that *would* be appropriate for that task, and make the estimate.
   d) The "wrong" answer from the other model is fairly accurate in this case. Why?

35. **Tobacco and Alcohol** Are people who use tobacco products more likely to consume alcohol? Here are data on household spending taken by the British Government on 11 regions in Great Britain. Do tobacco and alcohol spending appear to be related? What questions do you have about these data? What conclusions can you draw?

Region	Alcohol	Tobacco
North	6.47	4.03
Yorkshire	6.13	3.76
Northeast	6.19	3.77
East Midlands	4.89	3.34
West Midlands	5.63	3.47
East Anglia	4.52	2.92
Southeast	5.89	3.2
Southwest	4.79	2.71
Wales	5.27	3.53
Scotland	6.08	4.51
Northern Ireland	4.02	4.56

36. **Football Weights** The Sears Cup honors institutions that maintain a broad-based athletic program, achieving success in many sports, both men's and women's. Since its Division III inception in 1995, Williams College has won the Sears Cup in every year except one. Their football team has a .853 winning record under their current coach. Why does the football team win so much? Is it because they are heavier than their opponents? The table shows the average team weights for selected years from 1973 to 1993.

Year	Weight
1973	185.5
1975	182.4
1977	182.1
1979	191.1
1981	189.4
1983	192.0
1987	196.9
1989	202.9
1991	206.0
1993	198.7

   a) Fit a straight line to the relationship between weight and year.
   b) Does a straight line seem reasonable?
   c) Predict the average weight of the team for the year 2003. Does this seem reasonable?
   d) What about the prediction for the year 2103? Explain.
   e) What about the prediction for the year 3003? Explain.

37. **Football again** In exercise 32 you looked at weights of the William College football team versus year. The predictions did not seem reasonable because weights cannot keep increasing at the same rate forever. Maybe a transformation would help to make the predictions more reasonable. Try to find such a re-expression that is consistent with the data, but makes the predictions more believable.

38. **Williams vs Texas** Here are the average weights of the football team for the University of Texas for various years in the 20th century.

Year	Weight
1905	164
1919	163
1932	181
1945	192
1955	195
1965	199

   a) Fit a straight line to the relationship of Weight by Year for Texas footballers.

   b) According to these models, in what year will the Williams College team first weigh more than the University of Texas team?

   c) Do you believe this? Explain.

39. **Vehicle Weights** The Minnesota Department of Transportation installed a state-of-the art weigh-in-motion scale in the concrete surface of the eastbound lanes of Interstate 494 in Bloomington, Minnesota. In theory this scale would allow observers to weigh large trucks without stopping them. After installation, a study was undertaken to determine whether the scale's readings correspond with the true weights of the vehicles being monitored. In Exercise 14 of chapter 7 you examined the scatterplot for the data they collected, finding the association to be approximately linear with R-squared = 93%. Their regression equation is $\widehat{Wt} = 10.85 + 0.64scale$, where both the scale reading and the predicted weight of the truck are measured in thousands of pounds.

   a) Estimate the weight of a truck if this scale read 31,200 pounds.

   b) If that truck actually weighed 32,120 pounds, what was the residual?

   c) If the scale reads 35,590 pounds, and the truck has a residual of –2,440 pounds, how much does it actually weigh?

   d) In general, do you expect estimates made using this equation to be reasonably accurate? Explain.

   e) If the police plan to use this scale to issue tickets to trucks that appear to be overloaded, will negative or positive residuals be a greater problem? Explain.

40. **Least Squares** Consider the four points (12,800), (24,680), (36,740), and (48,660). The line of best fit is $\hat{y} = 810 - 3x$. Use these data to explain what "least squares" means.

41. **Models** Find the predicted value of y using each model for $x = 10$.

   a) $\hat{y} = 2 + 0.8\ln x$

   b) $\log \hat{y} = 5 - 0.23x$

   c) $\dfrac{1}{\sqrt{\hat{y}}} = 17.1 - 1.66x$

42. **Profit** How are a company's profits related to its sales. Let's examine data from 71 large US corporations. All amounts are in millions of dollars.
   a) Here are histograms of profits and sales, and the histograms of the logarithms of profits and sales. Why are the re-expressed data better for regression?

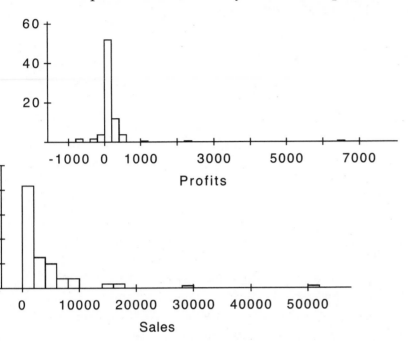

Profits

Sales

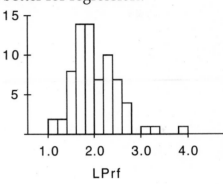

LPrf

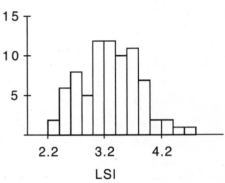

LSl

   b) Here are the scatterplot and residuals plot for the regression of logarithm of profits vs log of sales. Do you think this model is appropriate? Explain.

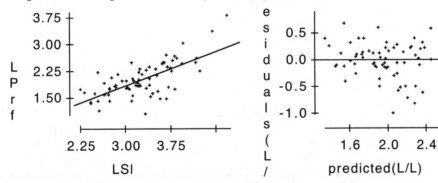

   c) Here is the regression analysis. Write the equation.

   Dependent variable is: Log Profit
   R squared = 48.1%
   Variable   Coefficient
   Constant   -0.106259
   LogSales   0.647798

   d) Use your equation to estimate profits earned by a company with sales of 2.5 billion dollars. (That's 2500 million …)

43. **Down the Drain** Most water tanks have a drain plug so that the tank may be emptied when it is to be moved or repaired. How long it takes a certain size tank to drain depends on the size of the plug, as shown in the table. Create a model.

Diameter of plug (inches)	Drain time (minutes)
$\frac{3}{8}$	140
$\frac{1}{2}$	80
$\frac{3}{4}$	35
1	20
$1\frac{1}{4}$	13
$1\frac{1}{2}$	10
2	5

44. **Chips** A startup company has developed an improved electronic chip for use in laboratory equipment. They need to project the manufacturing cost, so they develop a spreadsheet model that takes into account the purchase of production equipment, overhead, raw materials, depreciation, maintenaace, and other business costs. The spreadsheet estimates the cost of producing 10,000 – 200,000 chips per year, as seen in the table. Develop a regression model to predict costs based on the level of production.

Chips produced (1000s)	Cost per chip
10	146.10
20	105.80
30	85.75
40	77.02
50	66.10
60	63.92
70	58.80
80	50.91
90	47.22
100	44.31
120	42.88
140	39.05
160	37.47
180	35.09
200	34.04

III Gathering Data

11 Understanding Randomness

WE ALL KNOW WHAT IT MEANS FOR SOMETHING TO BE RANDOM. OR DO WE? Many children play games that rely on chance outcomes. Rolling dice, spinning spinners, shuffling cards, even choosing someone to be "it" with a counting rhyme ("one potato, two potato, …"), all select at random. Adult games use randomness as well, from card games, to lotteries to Bingo. What is the most important aspect of the randomness in these games? It must be fair.

What is it about the outcomes being random that makes random selection seem fair? It turns out it's really two things. First, part of what helps make it fair is that nobody can guess the outcome before it happens. And when we want things to be fair, usually some underlying set of outcomes will be equally likely (although in many games some combinations of outcomes are more likely than others.)

Randomness is not always what we might think of as "at random". Random outcomes have a lot of structure, especially when viewed in the long run. And, as we will see, randomness is an essential tool of Statistics. In fact, statisticians don't think of randomness as the annoying tendency of things to be unpredictable or haphazard. Statisticians use randomness as a tool. In fact, without deliberately applying randomness we could not do most of statistics and this book would stop right about here[1].

But truly random values are surprisingly hard to get. Just to see how fair humans are at selecting, pick a number at random from the next page. Go ahead. Turn the page, look at the numbers quickly and pick a number at random.

Ready?

Go.

---

[1] But don't get your hopes up.

1 2 3 4

Did you pick 3? If so, you've got company. More than 2/3 of all people pick the number 3. About 20% pick either 2 or 4. If you picked 1, well, consider yourself a little different. Only about 5% choose 1. Psychologists have proposed reasons for this phenomenon, but for us, it will simply serve as a lesson that we've got to find a better way to choose things at random.

It's Not Easy Being Random

So how should we generate random numbers? It is surprisingly difficult to generate random values even when they are equally likely.

Appeared
10/25/01

Aren't you done shuffling yet?

Even something as common as card shuffling may not be as random as you might think. If you drag your feet cards by the usual method in which you split the deck in half and try to let cards fall roughly alternately from each half, you're doing a "riffle shuffle".

How many times should you shuffle cards to make the deck random? A surprising fact was discovered by statisticians Persi Diaconis, Ronald Graham, and W.M. Kantor. It actually takes *seven* shuffles. Fewer than seven leaves order in the deck, but after that, more shuffling does little good. But most people don't shuffle that many times.

When computers were first used to generate hands in bridge tournaments, some professional bridge players complained that the computer was making too many "weird" hands; hands with 10 cards of one suit for example. Suddenly these hands were appearing more often than players were used to. Clearly the computer was doing something wrong. But, it turns out that it's humans who hadn't been shuffling enough to make the decks really random.

Computers have become a popular way to generate random numbers. But, even though they often do much better than humans, computers can't generate truly random numbers either. Computers follow programs. Start a computer from the same place and it will always follow exactly the same path. So numbers generated by a computer program are not truly random. Technically, "random" numbers generated this way are pseudorandom numbers. Because pseudorandom values are generated in a fixed sequence and because computers can represent only a finite number of distinct values, the sequence of pseudorandom numbers must eventually repeat itself. But pseudorandom values are good enough for most purposes because they are virtually indistinguishable from truly random numbers.

But there are ways to generate random numbers that are both equally likely and truly random. In the past, entire books of carefully generated random numbers were published. The books never made the best-seller lists and probably didn't make for great reading, but they were quite valuable to those who needed truly random values. Today, we can avoid these books and find truly random digits from several Internet sites. The sites use a variety of methods to generate these random numbers. One method uses the timings of the decay of a radioactive element to choose random times. Another uses the random changes of lava lamps. (See this book's website for URL's.). These sites will give you a random string of digits such as these:

2217726304387410092537086270581997622725849795907032825001108963
3217535822643800292254644943760642389043766557204107354186024508
8906427308645681412198226653885873285801699027843110380420067664
8740522639824530519902027044464984322000946238678577902639002954
8887003319933147508331265192321413908608674496383528968974910533
6944182713168919406022181281304751019321546303870481407676636740
6070204916508913632855351361361043794293428486909462881431793360
7706356513310563210508993624272872250535395513645991015328128202

You probably have more interesting things to download than a few million random digits. But we'll discuss ways to use such random digits to apply randomness to real situations soon. The best ways we know to generate data that give a fair and accurate picture of the world rely on randomness, and even the ways in which we draw conclusions from that data depend on the randomness too.

Practical Randomness

Suppose a cereal manufacturer puts pictures of famous athletes in boxes of their cereal, a common marketing ploy. They announce that 20% of the boxes contain a picture of Tiger Woods, 30% a picture of Lance Armstrong, and the rest a picture of Serena Williams. You want all three pictures. How many boxes of the cereal do you expect to have to buy in order to get the complete set?

How can we answer questions like this? Well, one way is to go buy hundreds of boxes of cereal to see what might happen. But let's not go there. Instead we'll consider using a random model. Why random? When we pick a box of cereal off the shelf we don't know what picture is inside. That's clear. We'll assume that the pictures are randomly placed in the boxes and the boxes distributed randomly to stores around the country. But why a model? We'll use a model to generate random values. To do that we'll need to make some assumptions about how they work. The assumption we'll work with here is that the underlying random events (we'll use random digits from 0 to 9) are equally likely to occur. With this model we can pretend we've bought sequences of cereal boxes and simulate the outcomes—even though these outcomes (which card we get) are not equally likely—to see what happens.

A Simulation

We want to use this simulation to give us some insight into how many boxes of cereal we might have to open until we get all three cards. We'll pretend to buy cereal and the random numbers will tell us what happened. Like any model, the simulation will be imperfect, but we hope the results we get will help us understand the situation. A simulation consists of a collection of things that happen at random. There is a situation that is repeated. These situations are called the components of the simulation. Each component has a set of possible outcomes. In our cereal example, the component is the selection of a particular box of cereal and the outcome is the type of card in the box. Here are the steps for making a simulation in general:

1   Identify the component to be repeated.

In this case, our component is the selection of a box of cereal.

2. Explain how you will model the outcome.

The digits from 0 to 9 are equally likely to occur. Because 20% of the boxes contain Tiger's picture, we'll use two of the ten digits to represent that outcome. Three of the ten digits can model the 30% of boxes with Lance Armstrong cards, and the remaining five digits can represent the 50% of boxes with Serena. One possible assignment of the digits is:

0, 1 = Woods   2, 3, 4 = Armstrong   5, 6, 7, 8, 9 = Williams

3. Explain how you will simulate the run.

A run is the sequence of events that we are pretending will take place. In this case we want to pretend to open cereal boxes until we have one of each picture. We do this by looking at each random number and indicating what outcome it represents. We continue until we have encountered all three pictures.

For example, the random number sequences 29240 would mean you get Lance's picture (2) in the first box you open, Serena's picture (9) in the next box, two more Armstrong pictures (2, 4) in the next two boxes, and then the Tiger Woods picture (0) you needed to complete your collection.

Since we've gotten all three pictures, we've finished one run of the simulation.

4. State clearly what the response variable is.

What are we interested in? We want to know how many boxes it takes to get all three pictures. This is the response variable. In the sample run above, the response value is 5 boxes.

5. Perform several runs.

A simulation is cheaper than really buying cereal, and the more runs you do the better. For example, consider the third line of random digits shown earlier:

89064 2730 8645681 41219 822665388587328580 169902 78431 10380420067664…

89064 2730 8645681 41219 82266538858732858016990278431103080420067664

Let's create a chart to keep track of what happened.

6. Analyze the response variable.

Run number	Outcomes	y = Number of boxes
1	**89064** = **Serena**, Serena, **Tiger**, Serena, **Lance**	5
2	**2730** = **Lance**, **Serena**, Lance, **Tiger**	4
3	**8645681** = **Serena**, Serena, **Lance**, …, **Tiger**	7
4	**41219** = **Lance**, **Tiger**, Lance, Tiger, **Serena**	5
5	**822665388587328580** = **Serena**, **Lance**, …, **Tiger**	18

To answer the question, you need to analyze the response variable in a number of ways. You know how to do this. In this case, we wanted to know how many boxes we might expect to buy. In our first 5 runs we needed 5, 4, 7, 5, and then 18 for an average of 7.8 boxes.

7. State your conclusion (in the context of the problem, as always)

Based upon our simulation we estimate that customers who want the complete set of sports star pictures will buy an average of 7.8 boxes of cereal.

If you fear that this may not be a very accurate estimate because we only ran five trials, you are absolutely correct. The more trials the better, and five is woefully inadequate. Twenty trials is probably a reasonable minimum if you are doing this by hand. Even better, use a computer, and do a few hundred trials.

DRAFT: Do not distribute or copy

Simulation Step by Step.

Fifty-seven students participated in a lottery for a particularly desirable dorm room—a triple with a fireplace and private bath in the tower. Twenty of the participants were members of the same varsity team. When all three winners were members of the team, the other students cried foul. Use a simulation to determine whether an all-team outcome could reasonably be expected to happen if everyone had a fair shot at the room.

Think	**Components:** Identify the components.	A component is the selection of a student.
	Outcomes: State how your will model the random occurrence of an outcome.	We can't use just the digits from 0 to 9 because the proportions of the outcomes we are simulating are n(...) multiples of 10%. We have 20 and 37 students in the two groups. We can simulate outcomes for them by looking at *two-* digit random numbers: Let 00 - 19 represent the varsity applicants Let 20 - 56 represent the other applicants Skip 57 – 99. If we get a number in this range, we'll throw it away and go back for another random number.
	Trial: Define a trial and its response variable.	Identify pairs of digits as V or N until 3 people are chosen, ignoring repeated numbers because we can't put the same person in the room twice. The response variable is whether or not all selected students are on the Varsity team.

Show **Mechanics:**

Run several trials

Trial number	Outcomes	All varsity?
1	74 02 94 39 02 77 55 X V X N X X N	no
2	18 63 33 25 V X N N	no
3	05 45 88 91 56 V N X X N	no
4	39 09 07	

	N V V	no
5	65 39 45 95 43	
	X N N X N	no
6	98 95 11 68 77 12 17	
	X X V X X V V	yes
7	26 19 89 93 77 27	
	V V X X X N	no
8	23 52 37	
	V N N	no
9	16 50 83 44	
	V N X N	no
10	74 17 46 85 09	
	X V N X V	no

Estimate:

Summarize the results across all trials.

"All varsity" occurred once, or 10% of the time.

Tell

Interpretation: Describe what the simulation shows and draw your conclusions about the real world.

In our simulation of "fair" room draw, the three people chosen were all varsity team members only 10% of the time. While this result *could* happen, it is not particularly likely. We might be suspicious, but we'd need many more trials and a smaller chance of the all-varsity outcome before we would make an accusation of unfairness.

What Can Go Wrong?

- *Don't overstate your case.* Let's face it: in some sense a simulation is *always* wrong. After all, it's not the real thing. We didn't buy any cereal, or run a room draw. So beware of confusing what really *would* happen with what a simulation suggests *might* happen. Always be sure to indicate that future results will not match your simulated results exactly.

- *Model the outcome chances accurately.* A common mistake in constructing a simulation is to adopt a strategy that may appear to produce the right kind of results, but that does not accurately model the situation. For example, in our room draw we could have gotten 0, 1, 2, or 3 team members. Why not just see how often these digits occur in random digits from 0 to 9, ignoring the digits 4 and up?

  3 2 1 7 9 0 0 5 9 7 3 7 9 2 5 2 4 1 3 8

  3 2 1 x x 0 0 x x x 3 x x 2 x 2 x 1 3 x

DRAFT: Do not distribute or copy

Here it seems fairly likely that three team members would be chosen. But there's a big problem with this approach. Although the digits 0, 1, 2, and 3 occur with equal frequency among random digits, the outcomes of 0,1,2, or 3 team members selected are *not* equally likely. This "simulation" overlooks important details in the real situation and thus doesn't model the room draw process accurately.

- *Run enough trials*. Simulation is cheap and fairly easy to do. Don't try to draw conclusions based on 5 or 10 trials (even though we did for illustration purposes here). We'll make precise how many trials to use in later chapters. For now, err on the side of large numbers of trials.

Key Concepts

Random	An event is random if we know what outcomes could happen, but not which particular values did or will happen.
Random numbers	Random numbers are hard to generate. Nevertheless, several internet sites offer an unlimited supply of equally likely random values.
Simulation	A simulation models random events by using random numbers to specify event outcomes with relative frequencies that correspond to the true real-world relative frequencies we are trying to model.

Connections

Simulation	Simulations often generate many outcomes of a response variable, and we are often interested in the distribution of these responses. The tools we use to display and summarize the distribution of any real variable are appropriate for displaying and summarizing randomly generated responses as well.
	Make histograms, boxplots, and normal probability plots of the response variables from simulations and summarize them with measures of center and spread. Be especially careful to report the variation of your response variable.
	Don't forget to *Think* about your analyses. Simulations can hide subtle errors. A careful analysis of the responses can save you from erroneous conclusions based on a faulty simulation.
	You may be less likely to find an outlier in simulated responses, but if you find one, you should certainly find out how it happened.

Skills

Think

- Be able to recognize random outcomes in a real-world situation.
- Be able to recognize when a simulation might usefully model random behavior in the real world.

Show

- Know how to perform a simulation either by generating random numbers on a computer or by using some other source of random values such as dice, a spinner, or a table of random numbers.

Tell

- Be able to describe a simulation so that others could repeat it
- Be able to discuss the results of s simulation study and draw conclusions about the question being investigated.

Exercises

1. **Coin Toss** Is a coin flip random? Why or why not, in your opinion?

2. **Casino** A casino claims that its electronic "video roulette" machine is truly random. What should that claim mean?

3. **The Lottery** Many states run lotteries, giving away millions of dollars if you match a certain set of winning numbers. How are those numbers determined? Do you think this method guarantees randomness? Explain.

4. **Games** Many kinds of games people play rely on randomness. Cite three different methods commonly used in the attempt to achieve this randomness, and discuss the effectiveness of each.

5. **Bad Simulations** Explain why each simulation described below fails to properly model the real situation.
   a) Use a random integer 0 – 9 to represent the number of heads that appear when 9 coins are tossed.
   b) A basketball player takes a foul shot. Look at a random digit, using an odd digit to represent a good shot and an even digit to represent a miss.
   c) Use five random digits 1 – 13 to represent the denominations of the cards in a poker hand.

6. **More Bad Simulations** Explain why each simulation described below fails to properly model the real situation.
   a) Use random numbers 2 through 12 to represent the sum of the faces when two dice are rolled.
   b) Use a random integer 0 – 5 to represent the number of boys in a family of 5 children.
   c) Simulate a baseball player's time at bat by letting 0 = an out, 1 = a single, 2 = a double, 3 = a triple, and 4 = a home run.

7. **Wrong Conclusion** A statistics student properly simulated the length of the checkout lines in a grocery store, then reported "The average length of the line will be 3.2 people." What is wrong with this conclusion?

8. **Another Wrong Conclusion** After simulating the spread of a disease a researcher wrote "24% of the people contracted the disease." What should the correct conclusion be?

9. **Cereal** In the chapter's example, 20% of the cereal boxes contained a picture of Tiger Woods, 30% Lance Armstrong, and the rest Serena Williams. Suppose your Mom agrees to buy you five boxes of cereal. Estimate the probability that you end up with a complete set of the pictures. Your simulation should have at least 20 runs.

10. **Cereal, Again** Suppose you really want the Tiger Woods picture. How many boxes of cereal do you need to buy to be pretty sure of getting at least one? Your simulation should use at least 10 runs.

11. **Multiple Choice** You take a quiz with 6 multiple choice questions. After you studied, you estimated that you would have about an 80% chance of getting any individual question right. What are your chances of getting them all right? Your simulation should use at least 20 runs.

12. **Lucky Guessing?** A friend of yours who took that same multiple choice quiz got all 6 questions right, but now claims to have guessed blindly on every question. If each question offered 4 possible answers do you believe her? Explain, basing your argument on a simulation involving at least 10 runs.

13. **Driving Test** You are about to take the road test for your driver's license. You hear that only 34% of candidates pass the test the first time, but the percentage rises to 72% on retests. Estimate the average number of tests drivers take in order to get a license. Your simulation should use at least 20 runs.

14. **Still Learning?** As in Exercise 11, assume that your chance of passing the driver's test is 34% the first time, and 72% for retests. Estimate the percentage of those tested who still do not have a driver's license after two attempts.

15. **Basketball Strategy** Late in a basketball game the team that is behind often fouls someone in an attempt to get the ball back. Usually the opposing player will get to shoot foul shots "one and one", meaning he gets a shot, and then a second shot if he makes the first one. Suppose the opposing player has made 72% of his foul shots this season. Estimate the number of points he will score.

16. **Blood Donors** A person with Type O-positive blood can receive blood only from other Type O donors. About 44% of the population has type O blood. At a blood drive, how many potential donors do you expect to examine in order to get three units of Type O blood?

17. **Free Groceries** In order to attract shoppers, a supermarket runs a weekly contest that involves "scratch-off" cards. With each purchase customers get a card with a black spot obscuring a message. When the spot is scratched away most of the cards simply say "Sorry – please try again." But during the week 100 customers will get cards that make them eligible for a drawing for free groceries. 10 of the cards say they may be worth $200, 10 others $100, 20 may be worth $50, and the rest could be worth $20. To register those cards customers write their names on them and put them in a barrel at the front of the store. At the end of the week the store manager draws cards at random, awarding the lucky customers free groceries in the amount specified on their card. The

drawings continue until the store has given away over $500 of free groceries. Estimate the average number of winners each week.

18. **Find the Ace** A new electronics store holds a contest to attract shoppers. Once an hour someone in the store is chosen at random to play the Music Game. Here's how it works. An ace and four other cards are shuffled and placed face down on a table. The customer gets to turn cards over one at a time looking for the ace. The person wins $100 worth of free CDs or DVDs if the ace is the first card, $50 if it is the second card, $20, $10, or $5 if it is the third, fourth, or fifth card chosen. What is the average dollar amount of music the store will give away?

19. **The Family** Many couples want to have both a boy and a girl. If they decide to continue to have children until they have one child of each gender, what would the average family size be?

20. **A Bigger Family** Suppose a couple will continue having children until they have at least two children of each gender (two boys <u>and</u> two girls). How many children might they expect to have?

21. **Dice Game** You are playing a children's game in which the number of spaces you get to move is determined by rolling a die. You must land exactly on the final space in order to win. If you are 10 spaces away, how many turns might it take you to win?

22. **Parcheesi** You are three spaces from a win in Parcheesi. On each turn you will roll two dice. To win you must roll a total of 3, or roll a 3 on one of the dice. How many turns might you expect this to take?

23. **The Hot Hand** A basketball player with a 65% shooting percentage has just made 6 shots in a row. The announcer says this player "is hot tonight! She's in the zone!" Assume the player takes about 20 shots per game. Is it unusual for her to make 6 or more shots in a row during a game?

24. **The World Series** The World Series ends when a team wins 4 games. Suppose that sports analysts consider one team a bit stronger, with a 55% chance to win any individual game. Estimate the likelihood that the underdog wins the series.

25. **Bowling** In the tenth frame a bowler may earn a score from 0 to 30. If the first ball is a strike, the bowler gets to roll two more balls. If the first ball is not a strike, the bowler rolls a second ball and earns the right to roll a third if he gets a spare (knocks down all remaining pins with the second ball). His score is the total number of pins for all balls. How many points might a bowler be expected to score?

Find out using a simulation based on the following assumptions:
• The bowler makes a strike 40% of the time.

- If he misses a strike with the first ball, he picks up the spare with the second ball 70% of the time.
- If he makes neither a strike nor a spare he will get 6, 7, 8, or 9 pins (with equal likelihood).

26. **Teammates** Four couples at a dinner party play a board game after the meal. They decide to play as teams of two, and to select the teams randomly. All eight people write their names on slips of paper. The slips are thoroughly mixed, then drawn two at a time. How likely is it that every person will be teamed with someone other than the person they came with?

27. **Another Frame** How good a bowler are you?
    a) Make a set of assumptions (like those in Exercise 25) describing your game.
    b) Use a simulation to estimate your score in the tenth frame.
    c) Use a simulation to estimate your score for an entire game.

28. **Second Team** Suppose the couples in Exercise 26 choose the teams by having one member of each couple write their names on the cards, and the other people each pick a card at random. How likely is it that every person will be teamed with someone other than the person they came with?

29. **Job Discrimination?** A company with a large sales staff announces openings for three positions as regional managers. 22 of the current sales persons apply, 12 men and 10 women. After the interviews, when the company announces the newly appointed managers, all three positions go to women. The men complain of job discrimination. Do they have a case? Simulate a random selection of three people from the applicant pool and make a decision about the likelihood that a fair process would result in hiring all women.

30. **Deer** Freed of natural predators, deer populations are growing rapidly in many areas of the country. Let's examine this situation. About 30% of fawns survive to become adults. A female deer first breeds at the age of 8 – 10 months, giving birth just after she is a year old. About 60% of these first offspring are male, with 90% single births and 10% twins. After that, the mature doe will give birth each year, with male and female offspring equally likely and only about 20% single births. Estimate the number of offspring in the family tree of one 4 year-old doe.

31. **Tires** A tire manufacturer believes that the tread life of their snow tires can be described by a Normal model with mean 32000 mile and standard deviation 2500 miles. You buy 4 of these tires, hoping to drive them at least 30000 miles. Estimate the chances that all four last at least that long.

32. **Freshmen** A certain college estimates that SAT scores of students who apply for admission can be described by a Normal model with mean

DRAFT: Do not distribute or copy

1050 and standard deviation 120. Admissions officers search the pile of envelopes, opening them at random looking for three applicants with SAT scores over 1200. How many envelopes do you think they will need to open?

12 Sample Surveys

W E HAVE LEARNED WAYS TO DISPLAY, DESCRIBE, AND SUMMARIZE DATA. But up to now, our conclusions have been limited to the particular batch of data we are examining. That's OK as far as it goes, but it doesn't go very far. We usually aren't satisfied with conclusions based only on *this* group of customers, or the people who answered the survey on *this* particular day. To make business decisions, to do science, to choose wise investments, or to understand what voters think they'll do in the next election we need to stretch beyond the data at hand to the world at large.

To make that stretch we need three ideas. You'll find the first one natural. The second may be more surprising. The third is one of the strange but true facts that often confuse those who don't know Statistics.

Idea 1: Examine a Part of the Whole

The first idea is to draw a sample. We'd like to know about an entire **population** of individuals, but examining all of them is usually impractical if not impossible. So we settle for examining a smaller group of individuals – a **sample** – selected from the population.

You do this every day. For example, suppose you wonder how the vegetable soup you're cooking for dinner tonight is going to go over with your friends. To decide whether it meets your standards, you only need to try a small amount. You might taste just a spoonful or two. You certainly don't have to consume the whole pot. You trust that the taste will *represent* the flavor of the entire pot. The idea behind your tasting is that a small sample – if selected properly – can represent the entire population.

It's hard to go a day without hearing about the latest opinion poll. These polls are examples of **sample surveys**, designed to ask questions of a small group of people in the hope of learning something about the entire population. Most likely, you've never been selected to be part of one of these national opinion polls – that's true of most people. So how can the pollsters claim that a sample is representative of the entire population? Well, the answer is that professional pollsters work quite hard to ensure that the "taste" – the sample that they take – represents the population. If not, the sample can give misleading information about the population.

There's an important truth here: The population is determined by *what we want to know*. This is often determined by the *Why* of study. By contrast, the sample is those we can reach to obtain responses—the *Who* of the study. So it is determined by practical constraints rather than idealistic goals..

What are the basic techniques for making sure that a sample is representative? Sometimes it's instructive to see how to do something by studying a really dismal failure. Here's a

DRAFT: Do not distribute or copy

famous one. By the beginning of the 20th century it was common for newspapers to ask readers to return "straw" ballots on a variety of topics. (Today's internet surveys are the same idea gone electronic.) The earliest known example of such a straw vote in the United States dates back to 1824.

The success of these regional polls in the early 1900's inspired national magazines to try their luck. Although the *Farm Journal* was probably the first, the *Literary Digest* was at the top of the heap. During the period 1916 to 1936 it regularly surveyed public opinion and forecast election results correctly. During the 1936 presidential campaign between Alf Landon and Franklin Delano Roosevelt, the *Literary Digest* mailed more than 10 million ballots. They got back an astonishing 2.4 million. (Polls were still a relatively novel idea and many people thought it was important to send back their opinions). The results from the millions of responses were clear; Alf Landon would be the next president by a landslide: 57% to 43%. You remember President Landon, don't you? In fact, Landon carried only two states. Roosevelt won 64% to 36% and, perhaps coincidentally, the *Digest* went bankrupt soon afterward.

What went wrong? The problem was that the *Digest* sample was not representative. They made some mistakes that are now considered classics. First, let's look at how they got the list of 10,000,000 names to start with. Where would you go to get such a list? You might think of using phone numbers as a way to select people—and that's just what the *Digest* did. But in 1936, at the height of the Great Depression, telephones were real luxuries. Any list of phone owners would include far more rich than poor people. In fact, it wasn't until 1986 that enough families in the U.S. had telephones so that phoning became a reliable way of surveying people[1]. The other lists available to the *Digest* were even less representative – drivers' registrations and memberships in clubs, such as country clubs.

The main campaign issue in 1936 was the economy. Roosevelt's core supporters, who tended to be less well-off, were not well-represented in the *Digest's* sample, so the results of a survey based on that sample did not reflect the opinions of the overall population. It did not matter how well it was measured, nor how many people responded,

A sample that does not represent the population in some important way—for example, one that overlooks an important group—is said to be

A young pollster named George Gallup used a subsample of only 3000 of the 2.4 million responses that the *Literary Digest* received to reproduce the wrong prediction of Landon's victory. He then used an entirely different sample of 50,000 and predicted that Roosevelt would get 56% of the vote to Landon's 44%. His sample was apparently much more **representative** of the actual voting populace. The Gallup Organization went on to become one of the leading poll companies.

---

[1] But even today, phone numbers must be computer generated to make sure that the phone owners are representative. Using only phone book listings would miss both unlisted numbers and people who have recently moved. Leaving these groups out may make the sample unrepresentative.

DRAFT: Do not distribute or copy

biased. Bias is the bugaboo of sampling–the one thing above all to avoid. There is usually no way to fix a biased sample and no way to salvage useful information from it.

How can we avoid the *Digest's* errors? To make the sample as representative as possible you might be tempted to handpick the individuals included in the sample with care and precision. But the best strategy is to do something quite different. We should select individuals for the sample *at random*. The value of deliberately introducing randomness is one of the great insights of Statistics.

Idea 2: Randomize

Think back to the soup sample. Suppose you add some salt to the pot. If you sample it from the top before stirring, what will happen? Because the salt sits on the top, you'll get the misleading idea that the whole pot is salty. Of course, if you sample from the bottom, you'll get an equally misleading idea that the whole pot is bland. By stirring, you *randomize* the amount of salt throughout the pot, making each taste more typical in terms of the amount of salt in the whole pot.

Randomization can protect you against factors that you know are in the data. It can also help protect against factors that you aren't even aware of. Suppose, while you weren't looking, a friend added a handful of peas to the soup. They are down at the bottom of the pot, mixing with the other vegetables. If you don't randomize the soup by stirring, your test spoonful from the top won't have any peas. By stirring in the salt, you *also* randomize the peas throughout the pot, making your sample taste more typical of the overall pot *even though you did not know the peas were there*. So randomizing protects us by giving us a representative sample even over effects we were unaware of.

How would we "stir" people in our survey? We'd try to select them at random. Randomizing protects us from the influences of *all* the features of our population, even ones that we may not have thought about. It does that by making sure that *on the average* the sample looks like the rest of the population.

> **Why not match the sample to the population?**
>
> Rather than randomizing, we could try to design our sample so that the people we choose are typical in terms of every characteristic we can think of. In the 1936 vote, rich and poor voted differently as in no previous election. So, we'd like the income levels of those we sample to *match* the population. How about age? Do young and old vote alike? Political affiliation? Marital status? Having children? Living in the suburbs? Soccer Mom? We can't possibly think of all the things that might be important. Even if we could, we won't be able to *match* our sample to the population for all these characteristics.

Not only does randomizing protect us from bias, it actually makes it possible for us to draw inferences about the population when we see only a sample. Such inferences are among the most powerful things we can do with Statistics, and we'll spend much of the rest of the book discussing them. But throughout that discussion, keep in mind that it is all made possible because we deliberately choose things randomly.

Here's an example from a company's database of 3.5 million customers. We've taken two samples of size 8,000 at random from the population. Here's how the means and proportions match up on seven variables.

Age	White%	Female%	# Children	Income Bracket (1-7)	Wealth bracket (1-9)	Homeowner? (% Yes)
61.4 years	85.12%	56.2%	1.54 kids	3.91	5.29	71.36%
61.2	84.44	56.4	1.51	3.88	5.33	72.30%

Notice how well randomizing has stirred the population. We didn't look at these variables when we drew the samples, but randomizing has automatically matched them pretty closely. And we can reasonably assume that since they don't differ too much from each other, they don't differ much from the rest of the population either.

Idea 3: It's the Sample Size

How large a random sample do we need for the sample to be reasonably representative of the population? Obviously, if your sample is too small, it can't give much information. But you might think that we need a large percentage or *fraction* of the population. That's what most people think. But, it turns out that all that matters is the *number* of individuals in the sample. It doesn't depend on the size of the population at all[2]. A random sample of 100 students in a college represents the student body just about as well as a random sample of 100 voters represents the entire

---

[2] Well, that's not exactly true. If the population is small enough, and the sample becomes a large enough percentage of the whole population it can matter. But unless you're sampling more than 10% of the entire population, it's only the size of the sample that matters.

DRAFT: Do not distribute or copy

electorate of the United States. This is the *third* idea and probably the most surprising one in designing surveys.

How can it be that only the number in the sample, and not how big the population is, matters? Well, let's return one last time to that pot of soup. If you're cooking for a banquet rather than just for a few people, your pot will be bigger, but do you need a bigger spoon to decide how the soup tastes? Of course not. The same size spoonful is probably enough to make a decision about the entire pot no matter how large the pot. The *fraction* of the population that you've sampled doesn't matter. It's the *sample size* itself that's important.

This somewhat surprising idea is of key importance to the design of any sample survey, because it determines the balance between how well the survey can measure the population and how much the survey costs.

So how big a sample do we need? It all depends on what we're estimating. If you're just interested in the broth, then you can just taste a sip from as spoon. But to get an idea of what's really in the soup, you need a large enough taste to be a *representative* sample from the pot, including a selection of the vegetables as well. For a survey that tries to find the proportion of the population that fall into a category, you'll usually need a large enough sample to see several respondents in each category -- usually at least several hundred respondents -- to say anything precise enough to be useful.[3]

> A friend who knows that you are taking statistics asks your advice on her study. What can you possibly say that won't sound stupid or be wrong? Just say: "If you could just get a larger sample size it would probably improve your study." A larger sample might not be worth the cost, but it will almost always make the results more precise.

Does a Census make Sense?

It is particularly difficult to compile a complete **census** of all members of a population as large, complex, and spread out as the U.S. population. The U.S. Census is known to miss some residents. On occasion the undercount has been striking. For example, there have been blocks in inner cities in which the number of residents recorded by the Census was smaller than the number of electric meters for which bills were being paid. What makes the problem particularly important is that some groups have a higher probability of being missed than others – the homeless, the poor, the indigent. The Census Bureau proposed that they might use random sampling to estimate the number of residents missed by the ordinary census. Unfortunately, the resulting debate has become more political that statistical.

Why bother determining the right sample size? Wouldn't it be better to just include everyone and "sample" the entire population? Such a special sample is called a **census**. Although a census would appear to provide the best possible information about the population, there are a number of reasons why it might not.

First, it can be difficult to complete a census. There always seem to be some individuals who are hard to locate or hard to measure. The cost of locating the last few cases may far exceed your budget. It

---

[3] Chapter 19 gives the details behind this statement and shows how to decide on a sample size for a survey.

Copyright © 2001, Dick De Veaux and Paul Velleman

can also be just plain impractical to take a census. If you were a taste tester for the Hostess Company, you probably wouldn't want to census *all* the Twinkies on the production line. Aside from the fact that you couldn't possibly eat that many Twinkies, it would defeat the purpose of your job. You wouldn't have any left to sell. And, a wine tasting wouldn't be very practical if we needed to drink the whole bottle to get an idea of the quality. So, it's often not practical to attempt a census.

Second, populations rarely stand still. In populations of people, babies are born, and folks die or leave the country. In opinion surveys, events may cause a shift in opinion during the survey. Even if you could take a census, the population changes while you work, so it is never possible to get a perfect measure. A sample surveyed in less time may give more accurate information.

Third, taking a census can be more complex than sampling. Often a census requires a team effort or the cooperation of the population members. Because it tries to count everyone, the U.S. census records too many college students. Many are included by their families and are then also counted a second time in a report filed by their schools. Other errors of this sort can be found throughout the Census.

Populations and Parameters

Any quantity that we calculate from data could be called a "statistic." But, in practice, we usually use a statistic to estimate a population parameter.

A study found that teens were less likely to "buckle up". The National Center for Chronic Disease Prevention and Health Promotion reports that 21.7% of US teens never or rarely wear seatbelts.[4] What does this statement mean? We're sure they didn't take a census—even if they had, they must have missed some teens. So what *does* the 21.7% mean? We can't possibly know how many teenagers wear seatbelts. Reality is just too complex. But, as we've seen many times before, we can simplify the question by building a model.

When we simplify in this way, we can focus on the *parameters* of the model rather than on specifying the entire model. A parameter such as this, one that is part of a model for a population value, is called a **population parameter**.

But let's not forget about the data. We use the data to try to estimate the population parameters. As we know, any summary found from the data is a **statistic**. Those statistics that estimate population parameters are particularly interesting. Sometimes—and especially when we match statistics with the parameters they estimate—you'll see the (redundant) term **sample statistic**[5].

---

[4] http://www.cdc.gov/nccdphp/dash/MMWRFile/ss4504.ht
[5] Where else could a statistic come from?

DRAFT: Do not distribute or copy

We've already met two parameters in Chapter 6, the mean, μ, and the standard deviation, σ. We'll try to keep denoting population model parameters with Greek letters and the corresponding statistics with Latin letters. Usually, but not always, the letter used for the statistic and the parameter correspond in a natural way. So the standard deviation of the data is s, and the corresponding parameter is σ (Greek for s). We used r to denote the sample correlation. The corresponding correlation in a model for the population would be called ρ (rho). The slope of a linear regression estimated from the data is b_1. But if we think about a (linear) *model* for the population, we'd denote the slope parameter β_1 (beta).

Get the pattern? Good. Now it breaks down. We denote the mean of a population model with μ (because μ is the Greek letter for m). It might make sense to denote the sample mean with m, but longstanding convention is to put a bar over anything when we average it, so we write $\bar{y}$. What about proportions? Suppose we want to talk about the proportion of teens who don't wear seatbelts. If we use p to denote the proportion from the data, what is the corresponding model parameter? By all rights it should be π. Some books do this, but, statements like π = .25 might be confusing because π has been equal to 3.1415926… for so long, and it's worked so *well*. So, once again we violate the rule. We'll use p for the population model parameter and $\hat{p}$ for the proportion from the data. Here's a table summarizing the notation:

<table>
<tr><td rowspan="6">

Notation alert
This entire table is a notation alert.

</td></tr>
</table>

Name	Statistic	Parameter
Mean	$\bar{y}$	μ (mu pronounced meeoo, not moo)
Standard Deviation	s	σ (sigma)
Correlation	r	ρ (rho pronounced row)
Regression coefficient	b	β (beta – pronounced baytah[6])
Proportion	$\hat{p}$	p (pee)

[6] If you're American. If you're British, it's "beetah"

Simple Random Samples

We draw samples because we can't work with the entire population. But we need to be sure that the statistics we compute from the sample accurately reflect the corresponding parameters. A sample that does this is said to be **representative**.

How would you select a representative sample? Most people would say that every individual in the population should have an equal chance to be selected, and certainly that seems fair. But it is not sufficient. There are many ways to give everyone an equal chance that still wouldn't give a representative sample. Consider, for example, a school that has equal numbers of males and females. We could sample like this. Flip a coin. If it comes up heads, select 100 female students at random. If it comes up tails, select 100 males at random. Everyone has an equal chance of selection, but every sample is of only a single sex—hardly representative.

So we need to do better. Suppose we insist that every possible *sample* of the size we plan to draw has an equal chance to be selected. This ensures that situations like the one above can't occur and still guarantees that each person has an equal chance of being selected. What's different is that with this method each *combination* of people has an equal chance of being selected as well. A sample drawn in this way is called a **Simple Random Sample**, usually abbreviated **SRS**. An SRS is the standard against which we measure other sampling methods and the sampling method on which the theory of working with sampled data is based.

To select a sample at random we first need to define where the sample will come from. The **sampling frame** is a list of individuals from which the sample is drawn. For example, to draw a random sample of students at a school, we might obtain a list of all registered full-time students and sample from that list. In defining the sampling frame we must deal with the details of defining the population. Are part-time students included? Those who are attending school elsewhere and transferring credits back to the school?

Now that we have a sampling frame, the easiest way to choose an SRS is with random numbers. We have already seen good ways to obtain these. We can assign a random number to each individual in the sampling frame. We then select only those whose random numbers satisfy some rule. For example, to get 20% of the sampling frame, we might assign single random digits (0 to 9) and select only those with random digits of 5 and 6.

Other Sampling Designs

Simple Random Sampling is not the only fair way to sample. More complicated designs may save time or money or help avoid sampling

DRAFT: Do not distribute or copy

problems. But all **statistical sampling** designs have in common the idea that chance is used to select the sample rather than human choice.

Designs that are used to sample from large populations—especially those residing across large areas—are often more complicated than simple random samples. Sometimes the population is first split up into homogeneous groups, called **strata**, before the sample is selected. Then simple random sampling is used within each stratum before the results are combined. This is the essence of **stratified random sampling**.

Why would we want to complicate things? Here's an example. Suppose we want to survey how students feel about funding for the football team at a large University. The campus is 60% men and 40% women. We suspect that men and women have different views on the funding and we want to protect ourselves from getting a really bad sample, one that has too many men or women, by chance. If we select 100 people for the survey at random we might get 35 men and 65 women, which might bias our result. To avoid this, we can decide to force a representative sex balance. Then we could select 60 men at random and 40 women at random. This would guarantee that the proportions of men and women within the sample match the proportions in the population. You can imagine the importance of stratifying by race, income, age and other characteristics depending on the questions in the survey.

In addition to reducing bias, stratifying can reduce the variability of our results. When we restrict by strata, additional samples are more like one another, so statistics calculated for the sampled values will vary less from one sample to another. This reduced variability is an important added benefit of stratifying.

Here is a different challenge. Suppose you wanted to survey members of Catholic churches in New York City. It would be very difficult to obtain a list of people with their religious affiliations in order to conduct a simple random sample. But, you probably *could* find a list of all Catholic churches in New York. Then, you could select several *churches* at random and use an SRS to select individuals within each church. Sometimes selecting a group or **cluster** of individuals and then randomly sampling within each cluster is best sampling method available to us. The sampling design is called **cluster sampling**. Each church in this case is a cluster. But members of the same church may be more alike in their opinions than members of different churches. So a survey of 500 members from 5 different churches might not contain the same information as a survey of 500 members from all Catholics in the city.

Most surveys conducted by professional polling organizations use some combination of stratified and cluster sampling as well as simple random samples. Sampling schemes that combine these methods are called **multistage samples**.

Systematic Samples

Sometimes we draw a sample by selecting individuals systematically. For example, you might survey every 10th person on an alphabetical list of students. But you still must start the systematic selection from a randomly selected individual. When there is no reason to believe that the order of the list could be associated in any way with the responses sought, systematic sampling can give a representative sample. And systematic sampling can be much less expensive than true random sampling. But if you use a systematic sample, you should justify the assumption that the systematic method is not associated with any of the measured variables.

Sampling – Step by Step

The assignment says: "Conduct your own sample survey to find out how many hours per week students at your college spend watching TV during the school year." Let's see how we might do this step by step.

Think

Population & Parameter

Identify the W's of the study. The *Who* is population and the associated sampling frame, The *What* identifies the parameter of interest and the variables measured. The *How, When,* and *Where* are given by the sampling plan.

Often thinking about the *Why* will help to see whether the sampling frame and plan are adequate to learn about the population.

The population studied was students at my school. We obtained a list of all students currently enrolled and used it as the sampling frame. The parameter of interest was the number of TV hours watched per week during the school year, which we attempted to measure by asking students how much TV they watched during the previous week.

Sampling Plan

Specify sampling method and the sample size, *n*. Specify how the sample was actually drawn. What is the sampling frame?

The description should, if possible, be complete enough to

We decided against stratifying by class or sex. We selected a simple random sample of 200 students from our list. We obtained a list of random digits from an internet site, matched it to an alphabetically arranged list of students, and

DRAFT: Do not distribute or copy

possible, be complete enough to allow someone to replicate the procedure, drawing another sample from the same population in the same manner. But a good description of the procedure is essential even if it could never practically be repeated.

Show

Terms like simple random sample, cluster sample, and stratified sample often appear in this part of the discussion. You must also describe how the randomization was performed.

Sampling Practice:

Specify when, where, and how the sampling was performed. Specify any other details of your survey such as how respondents were contacted, what incentives they were offered to encourage them to respond, how non-respondents were treated, and so on.

Tell

Summary and Interpretation

This report should include a discussion of all the elements listed above. In addition, it is good practice to discuss any special circumstances. Professional polling organizations report the *When* of their samples, but will also note, for example, any important news that might have changed respondents' opinions during the sampling process. For example, in this survey a major news story or sporting event

selected all students who were assigned a "4". This method generated a sample of 212 students from the population of 2133 students.

The survey was taken over the period Oct. 15 to Oct. 25. Surveys were sent to selected students by e-mail with the request that they respond by e-mail as well.

During the period Oct.15 – Oct. 25 2003, 212 students were randomly selected using a simple random sample from a list of all students currently enrolled. The survey they received asked the question:

"How many hours did you spend watching television last week?"

Of the 212 students surveyed, 110 responded. It is possible that the nonrespondents differ in the number of TV hours watched from those who responded, but we were unable to follow them up due to

might change students' TV viewing behavior.

The report should include the statistics from the sample and the conclusions about the population that you reached.

limited time and funds. The 110 respondents reported an average 3.62 hours of TV watching per week. The median was only 2 hours/week. A histogram of the data (below) shows that the data are highly right skewed, indicating that the median might be a more appropriate summary of the typical TV watching of the students. Most of the students (90%) watch between 0 and 10 hours per week while 30% reported watching less than one hour per week. A few watch much more. About 3% reported watching more than 20 hours per week.

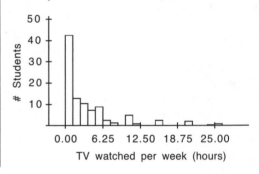

Who's Who?

The *Who* of a survey can refer to different groups, and the resulting ambiguity can tell you a lot about the success of a study. First, of course, you should think about the population of interest. Often, you'll find that this is not really a well-defined group (who, exactly, is a teenager?). Even if the population is clear, it may not be a practical group to study.[7] (For example, all those who will vote in the next election.)

Second, you must specify the sampling frame. (Do you have a list of teenagers to sample from? How about a list of registered voters?) Usually the sampling frame is not the group you *really* want to know about. (All those registered to vote are not equally likely to show up.) But the sampling frame limits what your survey can find out.

---

[7] Some disciplines differentiate the "theoretical population" of interest from the "study population" that we can practically hope to study.

Then there's the sample itself. These are the individuals for whom we *intend* to measure responses, but we may not succeed with all of them. Non-response is a problem in many surveys. ("I know it's dinner time, but I'm sure you wouldn't mind answering a few questions. It'll only take 20 minutes or so. Oh, you would?")

Finally, there are the actual respondents. These are the individuals about whom we *can* get data and draw conclusions. But they might not be representative of the sample, the sampling frame, or the population.

At each step, the group we can study is constrained further. The *Who* keeps changing. And each constraint can introduce biases. A careful study should address the question of how well each group matches the population of interest. One of the main benefits of Simple Random Sampling is that it never loses it's sense of who's *Who*. The *Who* in an SRS is the population of interest from which we've drawn a representative sample.

What Can Go Wrong – or, How to Sample Badly

Bad sample designs yield worthless data. And there is no way to correct for a bad sample. So it is wise to pay attention to sample design – and to beware of reports based on poor samples.

Sample Badly with Volunteers

Many of the most convenient forms of sampling can be seriously biased. One of the most common dangerous sampling methods is a voluntary response sample. In a voluntary response sample, a large group of individuals is invited to respond, and all who do respond are counted. This method is used by call-in shows, 900 numbers, internet polls, and letters written to Congress members. But voluntary response samples

If you had it to do over again, would you have children?

Ann Landers, the advice columnist, asked parents this question. The overwhelming majority – 70% of the more than 10,000 people who wrote in – said no, kids weren't worth it. A more carefully designed survey later showed that about 90% of parents actually are happy with their decision to have children. What accounts for the striking difference in these two results? What kind of parents do you think are most likely to respond to the original question? (On the other hand, how many parents would admit to a telephone interviewer that they were sorry to have had kids?)

are almost always biased and so conclusions drawn from them are almost always wrong.

A voluntary response sample is often biased toward those with strong opinions or those who are strongly motivated. People with very negative opinions tend to respond more often than those with equally strong positive opinions. The sample is not representative even though every individual in the population may have been offered the chance to respond, and the resulting **voluntary response bias** invalidates the survey.

How often do people write to their congressional representative when they're pretty happy about how things are going? Which survey would *you* be more likely to respond to – one that asked "Should the minimum age to drive a car be raised to 25?", or one that asked "Should shoe sizes be adjusted so women's and men's sizes correspond?"

Sample Badly, but Conveniently

> Do you use the Internet?
> Click here o for yes.
> Click here o for no.

Another sampling method that doesn't work is convenience sampling. In **convenience sampling,** as the name suggests, we simply include the individuals who are at hand. Unfortunately, this group may not be representative of the population. A recent survey of 437 potential home buyers in Orange County, California found, among other things that

" All but 2 percent of the buyers have at least one computer at home, and 62 percent have two or more. Of those with a computer, 99 percent are connected to the Internet."[8]

But a bit later in the article, we learn that the survey was conducted via the Internet! That was a convenient way to collect data and surely easier than drawing a simple random sample, but perhaps home builders shouldn't conclude from this study that *every* family has a computer and an internet connection.

Internet convenience surveys are worthless. As voluntary response surveys they have no well-defined sampling frame (all those who use the Internet and visit their site?) and thus report no useful information. Do not believe them.

Many surveys conducted at shopping malls suffer from the same problem. People in shopping malls are not necessarily representative of the population of interest. Mall shoppers tend to be more affluent, and include a larger percentage of teenagers and retirees than the population at large. To make matters worse, survey interviewers tend to select individuals who look safe, or easy to interview.

You may think that convenience sampling is only a problem for students or other beginning samplers. But, in fact, convenience sampling is a

---

[8] JENNIFER HIEGER ,"Portrait of homebuyer household: 2 kids and a PC," The Orange County Register, July 27, 2001

DRAFT: Do not distribute or copy

widespread problem in the business world. When a company wants to find out what people think about their products or services, who do they survey? The easiest people to sample are their own customers. After all, the company has a list of its own customers with addresses, phone numbers and other information—or at least a list of those customers who bothered to send it their registration cards. They can easily stratify by age, sex or other information that they have. But, no matter how they select a sample from their customers, the sample is still a convenience sample. They'll find out only how their own customers feel about their services and, unless they take the extra effort to go outside their own customer base, will never learn how those who *don't* buy their product feel about it.

Sample from a Bad Sample Frame

<design example of incentive>
You may already have won a trip to Scranton!

A simple SRS from an incomplete sampling frame introduces bias because the individuals included may differ from the ones not in the frame. People in prison, homeless people, students, long-term travelers are all likely to be missed. In telephone surveys, selecting numbers at random from the phone book misses those with unlisted numbers (who might be wealthier), so pollsters often generate phone numbers randomly from *all* possible numbers.

Undercoverage

Many of these survey designs suffer from **undercoverage** in which some portion of the population is not sampled at all or has a smaller representation in the sample than it has in the population. Undercoverage can arise for a number of reasons, but it is always a potential problem.

Telephone surveys used to be able to find someone at home in the middle of the day. But now that most people work outside the home, telephone surveys are more likely to be conducted when people are likely to be home, interrupting your dinner. Of course, those who eat out often may be less likely to be surveyed – a possible source of undercoverage.

What Else Can go Wrong?

- *Watch out for nonrespondents.* A common and serious potential source of bias for most surveys is **nonresponse bias**. No survey succeeds in getting responses from everyone. The problem is that those who don't respond may differ from those who do. And they may differ on just the variables we care about. The lack of response will then bias the results.

Rather than sending out a large number of surveys for which the response rate will be low, it may be better to design a smaller randomized survey for which you have the resources to ensure a high response rate.

One of the problems with nonresponse bias is that it is usually impossible to tell what the nonrespondents might have said.

Don't bore respondents with surveys that go on and on and on and on... Surveys that are too long are more likely to be refused, reducing the response rate and biasing *all* the results. When designing a survey, always make clear the purpose (the *Why*) of the survey, and the population to be sampled (and about whom you hope to draw conclusions.) For each question in the survey, ask "what would I do if I knew the answer to this question?" If you don't have a use for the answer, then don't ask the question.

Do people like filling out questionnaires?
A business school student wanted to study how people feel about filling out questionnaires. To do this, he designed – you guessed it – a questionnaire, and gave it to a sample of all the other students at his business school. He was surprised and happy to learn that nearly all the questionnaires he got back indicated a very positive attitude toward answering surveys. From this he concluded that people in general must not mind filling out questionnaires.

- *Work hard to avoid subtly influencing responses.* **Response bias** refers to anything in the survey design that influences the responses. Response bias is not the opposite of nonresponse bias. (We don't make these terms up, just try to explain 'em.) Response biases include the tendency of respondents to tailor their responses to try to please the interviewer, the ways in which the wording of the questions can change responses, and the natural unwillingness of respondents to reveal personal facts or admit to illegal or unapproved behavior.

People responding to the survey questions often want to please the interviewer either consciously or unconsciously. The sex, race, attire, or behavior of the interviewer can influence the answers by subtle (or not so subtle) indications that certain answers are more desirable than others.

The **wording** of the question can influence the responses. This is often the most serious problem in a survey. Asking a question with a leading statement is a good way to bias the response. Many surveys, especially those conducted by special interest groups, present one side of an issue before the question itself. For example, asking a question like:

> Given that the threat of nuclear war is higher now that it has ever been in human history, and the fact that a nuclear war poses a threat to the very existence of the human race, would you favor an all out nuclear test ban?

will probably result in a higher percentage of people in favor of the ban than the simpler:

> Are you in favor of or opposed to a nuclear test ban?

A Short Survey
Given the fact that those who understand Statistics are smarter, and better looking than those who don't, don't you think it is important to take a course in Statistics?

Remember the *Literary Digest* survey?

It turns out that they were wrong on *two* counts. First, their list of 10,000,000 people was not representative. There was a selection bias in their sampling frame. But there was also a non-response bias. We know this because the *Digest* also surveyed a *systematic* sample in Chicago, sending the same question used in the larger survey to every 3rd registered voter. But they *still* got a result in favor of Landon, even though Chicago voted overwhelmingly for Roosevelt in the election. That suggests that the Roosevelt supporters were less likely to respond to the *Digest* survey.

How to Think about Biases

Look for biases in any survey you encounter. If you design one of your own, ask someone else to help look for biases that may not be obvious to you. And do this *before* you collect your data. There is no way to recover from a biased sample or a survey that asks biased questions.

Sorry. Don't ask. Can't be done.

A bigger sample size for a biased study just gives you a bigger useless study. A really big sample gives you an even bigger useless study. (Think of the 2.4 million *Literary Digest* responses.)

Spend your time and resources reducing biases. No other use of resources is as worthwhile as reducing the biases.

If you possibly can, pre-test your survey. Administer the survey in the exact form that you intend to use it to a small sample drawn from the population you intend to sample. Look for misunderstandings, misinterpretation, confusion, or other possible biases. Then redesign your survey instrument.

Always report your sampling methods in detail. Others may be able to detect biases where you did not expect to find them.

Copyright © 2001, Dick De Veaux and Paul Velleman

Sampling and the Computer

Computer-generated pseudo-random numbers are usually quite good enough for drawing random samples. But there is little reason not to use the truly random values available on the Internet.

Here is a convenient way to draw an SRS of a specified size using a computer-based sampling frame. The sampling frame can be a list of names or of identification numbers arrayed, for example, as a column in a spreadsheet, statistics program, or database:

a) Generate random numbers of enough digits that each exceeds the size of the sampling frame list by several digits. This makes duplication unlikely.

b) Assign the random numbers arbitrarily to individuals in the sampling frame list. For example, put them in an adjacent column.

c) Sort the list of random numbers, *carrying along* the sampling frame list.

d) Now the first n values in the sorted sampling frame column are an SRS of n values from the entire sampling frame.

Key Concepts

Population	The entire group of individuals or instances about whom we hope to learn.
Sample	A representative subset of a population, examined in hope of learning about the population.
Population Parameter	A numerically valued attribute of a model for a population. We rarely expect to know the true value of a population parameter, but we do hope to estimate it from sampled data. For example, the mean income of all employed people in the country is a population parameter.
Statistic	Statistics are values calculated for sampled data. Those that correspond to, and thus estimate a population parameter are of particular interest. For example, the mean income of all employed people in a representative sample can provide a good estimate of the corresponding population parameter.
Bias	Any systematic failure of a sample to represent its population is bias. It is almost impossible to recover from a biased sample, so any efforts to avoid bias are well-spent. Common errors include: • relying on voluntary response • undercoverage of the population

DRAFT: Do not distribute or copy

	• nonresponse bias
Simple Random Sample	A simple random sample of n elements is one in which each set of n elements in the population has an equal chance of selection.
Sampling frame	A list of individuals from whom the sample is drawn is called the sampling frame. Individuals who may be the the population of interest but who are not in the sampling frame cannot be included in any sample.
Sampling Variability	The natural tendency of randomly drawn samples to differ, one from another. Sometimes, unfortunately, called *sampling error*, sampling variability is no error at all, but just the natural result of random sampling.
Stratified Random Sample	A sampling design in which the population is divided into several subpopulations, or strata, and random samples then drawn from each stratum. If the strata are homogeneous but are different from each other a stratified sample may yield more consistent results.
Cluster Sample	A sampling design in which groups or clusters are chosen at random and then samples drawn within them. Cluster sampling is usually selected as a matter of convenience, practicality, or cost.
Convenience Sample	When the individuals who are conveniently available make up the sample, it is a convenience sample. Convenience samples often fail to be representative.
Voluntary Response Bias	Bias introduced to a sample when individuals can choose on their own whether to participate in the sample. Samples based on voluntary response are always invalid and cannot be recovered, no matter how large the sample size.
Undercoverage	When we fail to sample from some part of the population or sample in a way that gives a part of the population less representation then it has in the population, the sample suffers from undercoverage.
Nonresponse Bias	Bias introduced to a sample when a large fraction of those sampled fail to respond. Those who do respond are likely to not represent the entire sample.
Randomization	The best defense against bias is randomization, in which each individual is given a fair, random, chance of selection.

Skills

When you complete this lesson you should:

> *Think*
>
> - Know the basic concepts and terminology of sampling (see the list above, for example).
>
> - Recognize population parameters in descriptions of populations and samples
>
> - Understand the value of randomization as a defense against bias.
>
> - Understand the value of sampling to estimate population parameters from statistics calculated on representative samples drawn from the population.
>
> *Show*
>
> - Know how to draw a Simple Random Sample from a master list of a population using a computer or using a table of random numbers.
>
> *Tell*
>
> - Know what to report about a sample as part of your account of a statistical analysis.
>
> - Report possible sources of bias in samples. Recognize voluntary response and nonresponse as sources of bias in a sample survey.

Exercises

1– 10. **What did they do?** For the following reports about statistical studies identify the following items (if possible). If you can't tell, then say so—this often happens when we read about a survey.
  a) the population;
  b) the population parameter of interest;
  c) the sampling frame;
  d) the sample;
  e) the sampling method, including whether or not randomization was employed;
  f) any potential sources of bias you can detect and any problems you see in generalizing to the population of interest.

1. A business magazine mailed a questionnaire to the Human Resource directors of all of the Fortune 500 companies, and received responses from 23% of them. Those responding reported that they did not find that such surveys intruded significantly on their workday.

DRAFT: Do not distribute or copy

2. A question posted on the web site www.Lycos.com on 18 June 2000 asked visitors to the site to say whether they thought that marijuana should be legally available for medicinal purposes.

3. Consumers' Union asked all subscribers whether they had used alternative medical treatments and, if so, whether they had benefited from them. For almost all of the treatments, approximately 20% of those responding reported cures or substantial improvement in their condition.

4. The Gallup Poll (www.gallup.com) interviewed 1423 randomly selected American citizens and reported that when "asked which type of content bothers them most on TV, 44% of Americans identify 'violence,' 23 choose 'lewd and profane language' while 22% say 'sexual situations.'" [September 10-14, 1999]

5. Researchers waited outside a bar they had randomly selected from a list of such establishments. They stopped every tenth person who came out of the bar and asked whether he or she thought drinking and driving was a serious problem.

6. Hoping to learn what issues may resonate with voters in the coming election, the campaign director for a mayoral candidate selects one block from each of the city's election districts. Staff members go there and interview all the residents they can find.

7. The Environmental Protection Agency took soil samples at 16 locations near a former industrial waste dump and checked each for evidence of toxic chemicals. They found no elevated levels of any harmful substances.

8. State police set up a roadblock to check cars for up-to-date registration, insurance, and safety inspections. They usually find problems with about 10% of the cars they stop.

9. A company packaging snack foods maintains quality control by randomly selecting ten cases from each day's production and weighing the bags. Then they open one bag from each case and inspect the contents.

10. Dairy inspectors visit farms unannounced and take samples of the milk to test for contamination. If the milk is found to contain dirt, antibiotics, or other foreign matter the milk will be destroyed and the farm re-inspected until purity is restored.

11. **Parent Opinion, Part 1** In a large city school system with 20 elementary schools, the school board is considering the adoption of a new policy that would require elementary students to pass a test in

order to be promoted to the next grade. The PTA wants to find out whether parents agree with this plan. Listed below are some of the ideas proposed for gathering data. For each, indicate what kind of sampling strategy is involved and what (if any) biases might result.

 a) Put a big ad in the newspaper asking people to log their opinions on the PTA website.
 b) Randomly select one of the elementary schools and contact every parent by phone.
 c) Send a survey sent home with every student, and ask parents to fill it out and return it the next day.
 d) Randomly select 20 parents from each elementary school. Send them a survey, and follow up with a phone call if they do not return the survey within a week.

12. **Parent Opinion, Part 2** Let's revisit the school system described in Exercise 11. Four new sampling strategies have been proposed to help the PTA determine whether parents favor requiring elementary students to pass a test in order to be promoted to the next grade. For each, indicate what kind of sampling strategy is involved and what (if any) biases might result.

 a) Run a poll on the local TV news asking people to dial one of two phone numbers to indicate whether they favor or oppose the plan.
 b) Hold a PTA meeting at each of the 20 elementary schools and tally the opinions expressed there.
 c) Randomly select one class at each elementary school and contact each of those parents.
 d) Go through the district's enrollment records, selecting every 40th parent. PTA volunteers will go to those homes to interview the people chosen.

13. **Wording the Survey** Two members of the PTA committee have proposed different questions to ask in seeking parents' opinions.

 Question 1: *Should elementary age children have to pass high stakes tests in order to remain with their classmates?*

 Question 2: *Should schools and students be held accountable for meeting yearly learning goals by testing students before they advance to the next grade?*

 a) Do you think responses to these two questions might differ? How? What kind of bias is this?
 b) Propose a question with more neutral wording that might better assess parental opinion.

14. **Survey Questions** Examine each of the questions below for possible bias. If you think the question is biased indicate how, and propose a better question.

a) Should companies that pollute the environment be compelled to pay the costs of cleanup?

b) Given that 18-year olds are old enough to vote and to serve in the military, is it fair to set the drinking age at 21?

c) Do you think high school students should be required to wear uniforms, or not?

d) Given mankind's great tradition of exploration, do you favor continued funding for space flights?

15. **Phone Surveys** Any time we conduct a survey we must take care to avoid undercoverage. Suppose we plan to select 500 names from the city phone book, call their homes between noon and 4pm, and interview whomever answers, anticipating contacts with at least 200 people.

a) Why is it difficult to use a simple random sample here?

b) Describe a more convenient, but still random, sampling strategy.

c) What kinds of households are likely to be included in the eventual sample of opinion? Who will be excluded?

d) Suppose instead that we continue calling each number, perhaps in the morning or evening, until an adult is contacted and interviewed. How does this improve the sampling design?

e) Random digit dialing machines can generate the phone calls for us. How would this improve our design? Is anyone still excluded?

16. **Cell Phone Survey** What about drawing a random sample only from cell phone exchanges? Discuss the advantages and disadvantages of such a sampling method as compared with surveying randomly generated telephone numbers from non-cell phone exchanges. Do you think these advantages and disadvantages have changed over time? How do you expect they'll change in the future?

17. **Arm Length** How long is your arm, compared to your hand size? Put your right thumb at your left shoulder bone, stretch your hand open wide, and extend your hand down your arm. Put your thumb at the place where your little finger is and extend down the arm again. Repeat this a third time. Now your little finger will probably have reached the back of your left hand. If the fourth hand width goes past the end of your middle finger, turn your hand sideways and count finger widths to get to there.

a) How many hand and finger widths is your arm?

b) Suppose you repeat your measurement 10 times and average your results. What parameter would this average estimate? What is the population?

c) Suppose you now collect arm lengths measured in this way from 9 friends and average these 10 measurements. What is the population now? What parameter would this average estimate?

d) Do you think these 10 arm lengths are likely to be representative of the population of arm lengths in your community? In the country? Why or why not?

18. **Fuel Economy** Occasionally when I fill my car with gas I figure out how many miles per gallon I car got. I wrote down those results after 6 fill-ups in the past few months. Overall it appears my car gets 28.8 miles per gallon.
   a) What statistic have I calculated?
   b) What is the parameter I am trying to estimate?
   c) How might my results be biased?
   d) When the EPA checks a car like mine to predict its fuel economy, what parameter are they trying to estimate?

19. **Accounting** Between quarterly audits a company likes to check on their accounting procedures to address any problems before they become serious. The accounting staff processes payments on about 120 orders each day. The next day the supervisor rechecks 10 of the transactions to be sure they were processed properly.
   a) Propose a sampling strategy for the supervisor.
   b) How would you modify that strategy if the company makes both wholesale and retail sales, requiring different bookkeeping procedures?

20. **Happy Workers**? A manufacturing company employs 14 project managers, 48 foremen, and 377 laborers. In an effort to keep informed about any possible sources of employee discontent, management wants to conduct job satisfaction interviews with a sample of employees every month.
   a) Do you see any danger of bias in the company's plan? Explain.
   b) Propose a sampling strategy that uses a simple random sample.
   c) Why do you think a simple random sample might not provide the representative opinion the company seeks?
   d) Propose a better sampling strategy.
   e) Listed below are the last names of the project managers. Use random numbers to select two people to be interviewed. Be sure to explain your method carefully.

Barrett	Bowman	Chen
DeLara	DeRoos	Grigorov
Maceli	Mulvaney	Pagliarulo
Rosica	Smithson	Tadros
Williams	Yamamoto	

DRAFT: Do not distribute or copy

21. **Quality Control** Sammy's Salsa, a small local company, produces 20 cases of salsa a day. Each case contains 12 jars, and is imprinted with a code indicating the date and batch number. To help maintain consistency, at the end of each day Sammy selects three bottles of salsa, weighs the contents, and tastes the product. Help Sammy select the sample jars. Today's cases are coded 07N61 through 07N80.
    a) Carefully explain your sampling strategy.
    b) Show how to use random numbers to pick the 3 jars for testing.
    c) Did you use a simple random sample? Explain.

22. **A Fish Story** Concerned about reports of discolored scales on fish caught downstream from a newly sited chemical plant, scientists set up a field station in a shoreline public park. For one week they asked fisherman there to bring any fish they caught to the field station for a brief inspection. At the end of the week the scientists said that 18% of the 234 fish that were submitted for inspection displayed the discoloration. From this information, can the researchers estimate what proportion of fish in the river have discolored scales? Explain.

23. **Sampling Methods** Consider each situation described below. Do you think the proposed sampling method is appropriate? Explain.
    a) We want to know what percentage of local doctors accept Medicaid patients. We call the offices of 50 doctors randomly selected from local yellow page listings.
    b) We want to know what percentage of local businesses anticipate hiring additional employees in the upcoming month. We randomly select a page in the Yellow Pages, and call every business listed there.

24. **More Sampling Methods** Consider each situation described below. Do you think the proposed sampling method is appropriate? Explain.
    a) We want to know if there is neighborhood support to turn a vacant lot into a playground. We spend a Saturday afternoon going door-to-door in the neighborhood asking people to sign a petition.
    b) We want to know if students at our college are satisfied with the selection of food available on campus. We go to the largest cafeteria and interview every tenth person in line.

13 Experiments

Who gets good grades? And more importantly, why? Is there something schools and parents could do to help weaker students improve their grades? Some people think they have an answer: music! No, not your iPod, but an instrument. In a 1981 study conducted at Mission Viejo High School, in California, researchers compared the scholastic performance of music students to non-music students. Guess what? The music students had a much higher overall grade point average than the non-music students, 3.59 to 2.91. Not only that, a whopping 16% of the music students had all A's compared with only 5% of the non-music students.

As a result of this study and others, many parent groups and educators pressed for expanded music programs in the nation's schools. They explain that the work ethic, discipline, and feeling of accomplishment fostered by learning to play an instrument also enhance a person's ability to succeed in school. They argue that involving more students in music will raise academic performance. What do you think? Does this study provide solid evidence? Or are there other possible explanations for the difference in grades? Is there any way to really prove such a conjecture?

Investigative Studies

For rare illnesses, it is not practical to draw a large enough sample to see many ill respondents, so the only option remaining is to interview those who have become ill to develop retrospective data. The likely causes of both Legionnaires' disease and HIV were initially identified from such retrospective studies of the small populations who were initially infected. But to confirm the causes, researchers needed laboratory-based experiments.

This research tried to show an association between music education and grades. But it didn't sample subjects at random. Nor did it assign students to get music education. Instead, it merely observed students "in the wild." Such studies are called **observational studies**. In addition, this was a **retrospective study**, because researchers identified subjects who studied music and then collected data on their past grades.

What's wrong with concluding that music education causes good grades? One high school during one academic year may not be representative of the whole United States. That's true, but the real problem is that studying music was not the *only* difference between the two groups of students. The claim that music study *caused* higher grades depends on there being *no other differences* between the groups that could account for the differences in grades.

But we can think of lots of other reasons why the groups might perform differently. Maybe students who study music have better work habits to start with, and this makes them successful in both music and coursework. Maybe music students have more parental support (someone had to pay for all those lessons) and that support enhanced their academic performance, too. Maybe they came from wealthier homes and had other advantages. Or maybe smarter kids just like to play musical instruments.

It should be clear that this study can't be used to prove that music lessons *cause* grades to improve. How can we do better? We might start by selecting young students who have not begun music lessons. We could then track their academic performance over several years, comparing those who later choose to study music with those who do not. Identifying subjects in advance and collecting data as events unfold would make this a **prospective study**.

But students who choose to study an instrument might still differ from the others in some important way. And it may be this difference —whether we know what it is or not—rather than music itself that leads to better grades.

Is it ever possible to prove a cause and effect relationship? Well, yes it is, but we would have to take a different approach. We could take a group of third graders, randomly assign half to take music lessons, and forbid the other half to do so. Then we could compare their grades several years later. This kind of study design is called an **experiment**.

An experiment requires a **random assignment** of subjects to treatments. Only a good experiment can justify a claim like "music lessons cause higher grades". Questions such as "Does taking vitamin C reduce the chance of getting a cold?" or "Does working with computers improve performance in Statistics class?" and, importantly, "Is this drug a safe and effective treatment for that disease?" require a designed experiment.

> No drug can be sold in the U.S. without first showing in a suitably designed experiment approved by the FDA (Federal Drug Administration) that it is safe and effective. The small print on the booklet that comes with many prescription drugs usually describes the outcomes of the experiment.

> He that leaves nothing to chance will do few things ill, but he will do very few things.
> Lord Halifax 1633-1695

Randomized, Comparative Experiments

> An experiment:
> *Manipulates* the factor levels to create treatments
> *Randomly assigns* subjects to these treatment levels
> *Compares* the responses of the subject groups across treatment levels.

Experiments study the relationship between two or more variables. An experimenter must identify at least one explanatory variable, called a **factor**, to manipulate and at least one **response** variable to measure. What distinguishes an experiment from other types of investigation is that the experimenter actively and deliberately changes the factors to control the details of the possible treatments, and assigns the subjects to those treatments *at random*. The experimenter then observes the response variable and *compares* responses for different groups of subjects who have been treated differently.

For example, we might design an experiment to see whether the amount of sleep and exercise you get affects your performance.

The individuals on whom or which we experiment are known by a variety of terms. Humans who are experimented on are commonly called **subjects** or **participants**. Other individuals (rats, days, petri dishes of bacteria) are commonly referred to by the more generic term **experimental unit**. We'll recruit subjects for our sleep deprivation experiment by advertising in statistics class. We'll probably have better luck if we invite them to be participants than if we advertise our need for experimental units.

The specific values that the experimenter chooses for a factor are called the **levels** of the factor. We might assign our participants to sleep for 4, 6, or 8 hours. Often there are several factors at a variety of levels. (Our subjects will also be assigned to a treadmill for 0, or 30 minutes.) The combination of specific levels from all the factors that an experimental unit receives is known as its **treatment**. (Our subjects could have 6 different treatments — three sleep levels by two exercise levels)

How should we assign our participants to these treatments? Some students prefer 4 hours of sleep, while others need 8. Some exercise regularly; others are couch potatoes. Should we let the students choose the treatments they'd prefer? No. That would not be a good idea. In fact, to have any hope of drawing a fair conclusion, we must assign our participant to their treatments *at random*.

Experiment design was advanced in the nineteenth century by work in psychophysics by Gustav Fechner (1801-1887)[1], the founder of experimental psychology. Fechner designed ingenious experiments that exhibit many of the features of modern designed experiments. Fechner was careful to control for the effects of factors that might affect his results. For example, he cautioned readers in his 1860 book *Elemete der Psychophysik* to group experiment trials together to minimize the possible effects of time of day and fatigue.

It may be obvious to you that we shouldn't let the students choose the treatment they'd prefer, but the need for random assignment is a lesson that has been hard for some to accept. For example, physicians might naturally prefer to assign patients to the therapy that they think best rather than have a random element such as a coin flip determine the treatment. But we've known for more than a century that for the results of an experiment to be valid, there is no way to avoid deliberate randomization.

The deep insight that experiments should use random assignment is quite an old one. It is due to the American philosopher and scientist, C.S. Peirce in his experiments with J. Jastrow published in 1885.

The Four Principles of Experimental[1] Design

1   **Control:** We control sources of variation other than the factors we are testing by making them as similar as possible for all treatment groups. For human subjects, we try to treat them alike. However, there is always a question of degree and practicality. Controlling extraneous sources of variation reduces the variability of the responses, making it easier to detect differences among the treatment groups.

But making generalizations from the experiment to other levels of the controlled factor can be risky. For example, suppose we test two laundry detergents and carefully control the water temperature to 180° F. This would reduce the variation in our results due to water temperature, but what could we say about the detergents' performance in cold water? Not much. It would be hard to justify extrapolating the results to other temperatures.

2   **Randomize:** As in sample surveys, **randomization** allows us to equalize the effects of unknown or uncontrollable sources of variation. It does not eliminate the effects of these sources, but it smears them out across the treatment levels so that we can see past them. If experimental units are not assigned to treatments at random, you do not have an experiment and will not be able to use the powerful methods of statistics to draw conclusions from your study. Assigning subjects to treatments at random reduces bias due to uncontrolled sources of variation. Randomization protects us even from effects we didn't know about. There's an adage that says "control what you can, and randomize the rest". This may be good advice, but we should be sure when we control that we don't want to generalize to other conditions.

3   **Replicate.** Two kinds of replication show up in comparative experiments. First, we should repeat the experiment, applying the treatments to a number of subjects. Only with such replication can we estimate the variability of responses. Without assessing the variation, the experiment is not complete. The outcome of an experiment on a single subject is an anecdote, not data.

---

[1] We might prefer the term "experiment design," which suggests designing experiments to the common alternative "experimental design," which suggests that the design itself is under experiment, but it is not the common phrasing, so we'll stick with the standard term. You could also say "design of experiments", but we won't.

DRAFT: Do not distribute or copy

Replicating Cold Fusion

"The origins of Cold Fusion have been loudly and widely documented in the press and popular literature. Pons and Fleischmann, fearing they were about to be scooped by a competitor named Steven Jones from nearby Brigham Young University, and with the encouragement of their own administration, held a press conference on March 23, 1989 at the University of Utah, to announce what seemed to be the scientific discovery of the century. Nuclear fusion, producing usable amounts of heat, could be induced to take place on a table-top by electrolyzing heavy water, using electrodes made of palladium and platinum, two precious metals. If so, the world's energy problems were at an end, to say nothing of the fiscal difficulties of the University of Utah. What followed was a kind of feeding frenzy, science by press conference and e-mail, confirmations and disconfirmations, claims and retractions, ugly charges and obfuscation, science gone berserk. For all practical purposes, it ended a mere 5 weeks after it began, on May 1st, 1989, at a dramatic session of The American Physical Society, in Baltimore. Although there were numerous presentations at this session, only two really counted. Steven Koonin and Nathan Lewis, speaking for himself and Charles Barnes, all three from Caltech, executed between them a perfect slam-dunk that cast Cold Fusion right out of the arena of mainstream science. ...seasoned experimentalists like Lewis and Barnes refused to believe what they couldn't reproduce in their own laboratories." –David Goodstein *http://www.its.caltech.edu/~dg/fusion.html*

A second kind of replication shows up when the experimental units are not a representative sample from the population of interest. We may believe that what is true of the students in Psych 101 who volunteered for the sleep experiment is true of all humans, but we'll feel more confident of our conclusions after the experiment is *replicated* in another part of the country, with people of different ages, and at different times of the year. **Replication** of an entire experiment with the controlled sources of variation at different levels is an essential step in science.

Blocking: The ability of randomizing to equalize variation across treatment groups works best in the long run. For example, if were allocating players to two 6-player soccer teams from a pool of 12 children, we might do so at random to equalize the talent. But what if there were 2 12-year-olds and 10 6-year-olds in the group? Randomizing may place both 12 year olds on the same team. In the long run, if we did this over and over, it would all equalize. But wouldn't it be better to assign one 12 year to each group (at random) and five 6 year olds to each team (at random)? By doing this we would improve the fairness in the short run. This approach makes the division more fair by recognizing the variation in *Age* and allocating the players *within* each age level. When we do this, we call the variable *Age* a **blocking variable.** The levels of *Age* are called blocks.

Sometimes, attributes of the experimental units that we are not studying and that we can't control may nevertheless affect the outcomes of an experiment. If we group similar individuals together and then randomize within each of these **blocks** we can remove much of the variability due to the difference among the blocks. Blocking is an important compromise between randomization and control.

Designing an Experiment, Step-by-Step

An ad for *OptiGro* plant fertilizer claims that with their product you will grow "juicier, tastier" tomatoes. You'd like to test their claim, and wonder whether you might be able to get by with half the specified dose. How can you set up an experiment to check out their claim?

Of course, you'll have to get some tomatoes, try growing some plants with the product and some without, and see what happens. But you'll need a clearer plan than that. How should you design your experiment?

A **completely randomized experiment** is the ideal simple design, just as a *simple random sample* is the ideal simple sample – and for many of the same reasons.

Let's work through the design, step-by-step. We'll design the simplest kind of experiment, a **completely randomized experiment in one factor**. Since this is a *design* for an experiment, most of the steps are part of the Think stage. The statements in the right column are the kinds of things you would need to say in *proposing* an experiment. But you'd need to include them in the "methods" section of a report once the experiment is run.

Think

Goal: State what you want to know.

> We want to know whether tomato plants grown with OptiGro yield juicier, tastier tomatoes than plants raised in otherwise similar circumstances but without the fertilizer.

Response: Specify the response variable.

> We will evaluate the juiciness and taste of the tomatoes by asking a panel of judges to rate them on a scale from 1 to 7 in juiciness and in taste.

Treatments: Specify the factor levels and the treatments.

> The factor is fertilizer, and specifically *OptiGro* fertilizer. We will grow tomatoes at three different factor levels: some with no fertilizer, some with half the specified amount of *OptiGro* and some with the full dose of *OptiGro*. These are the three treatments.

Experimental units: Specify the experimental units.

> We will obtain 24 tomato plants from a local garden store.

Control any sources of variability you know of and can control.	We will locate the farm plots together so that the plants get similar amounts of sun and rain and experience similar temperatures. We will weed the plots equally and otherwise treat the plants alike.
Randomly assign experimental units to treatments to equalize the effects of unknown or uncontrollable sources of variation. Specify how the random numbers needed for randomization were obtained	We will randomly divide the plants into three groups. We will use random numbers generated by an internet site to determine the random assignment.
Replicate results by placing more than one plant in each treatment group.	There are 8 plants in each treatment group.
Specify any other experiment details. You must give enough details so that another experimenter could exactly replicate your experiment. It is generally better to include details that might seem irrelevant than to leave out matters that could turn out make a difference.	We will grow the plants until the tomatoes are mature as judged by reaching a standard color. We will harvest the tomatoes when ripe and store them for evaluation.
Specify how to **measure the response.**	We will set up a numerical scale of juiciness and one of tastiness for our taste testers. Several people will taste slices of tomato and rate them.
Show Once you collect the data, you'll need to display it and compare the results for the three treatment groups.	We will display our results in side-by-side boxplots to compare the three treatment groups. We will compare the means of the groups.

Tell

To answer the initial question, we ask whether the differences we observe in the means of the three groups are meaningful.

Because this is a randomized experiment, we can attribute significant differences to the treatments. To do this properly, we'll need methods from what is called "statistical inference", the subject of the rest of this book.

If the differences in taste and juiciness among the groups are greater than the usual variation among tomatoes might lead us to expect, we may be able to conclude that these differences are due to treatment with the fertilizer.

Does the Difference Make a Difference?

We've said that if the differences among the treatment groups are big enough, we'll attribute the differences to the treatments. But how will we know whether the differences are big enough?

Would we expect the group means to be identical? Not really. Even if the treatment made no difference whatever, there would still be some variation. We assigned the plants to treatments at random. And a different random assignment would have led to different results. So even a repeat of the *same* treatment on a different randomly assigned set of plants would lead to a different mean. The real question is whether the differences we observed are about as big as we'd get just from the randomization alone, or whether they are bigger than that. If we decide that they're bigger, we'll attribute the differences to the treatments. In that case we say the differences are **statistically significant.**

But how will we decide if something is different enough to be considered statistically significant? We'll answer that question precisely in a later chapter, but to get some intuition, think about deciding whether a coin is fair. If we flip a fair coin 100 times, we expect, *on average* to get 50 heads. Suppose we get 54 heads out of 100. That wouldn't be very surprising because it is well within the bounds of ordinary random fluctuations. What if we'd seen 94 heads? That's clearly outside the bounds. We'd be pretty sure that the coin flips were not random. But what about 74 heads? Is that far enough from 50% to arouse our suspicions? That's the sort of question we need to ask of our experiment results.

In Statistics terminology, 94 heads would be statistically significant and 54 heads would not. Whether 74 is statistically significant or not would depend on the chance of getting 74 heads in 100 flips of a fair coin and on our tolerance for believing that rare events can happen to us. We'll make that reasoning clear in later chapters.

DRAFT: Do not distribute or copy

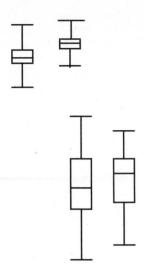

Back at the tomato stand, we ask whether the differences we see among the treatment groups are the kind of differences we'd expect from randomization. A good way to get a feeling for that is to look at how much our results vary among plants that get the same treatment. Boxplots of our results by treatment group can give us a general idea.

For example, here are two pairs of boxplots whose centers differ by exactly the same amount. In the upper set, that difference appears to be larger than we'd expect just by chance. Why? Because the variation is quite small within treatment groups, so the larger difference between the groups is unlikely to be just from the randomization. But in the bottom pair, that same difference between the centers looks less impressive. There the variation within each group swamps the difference *between* the two means. We'd say the difference is statistically significant in the upper pair and not statistically significant in the lower pair.

The boxplots in both pairs have centers the same distance apart, but when the spreads are large, the observed difference may be just from random fluctuation. Fig 13.1

Later we'll see statistical tests that quantify this intuition. But for now, the important point is that a difference is statistically significant if we don't believe that it is likely to have occurred due only to chance.

Diagrams

An experiment is carried out over time with specific actions occurring in a specified order. A diagram of the procedure can help in thinking about experiments.[2]

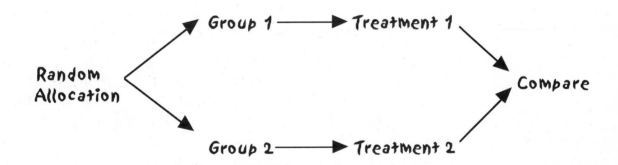

The diagram emphasizes the random allocation of subjects to treatment groups, the separate treatments applied to these groups, and the ultimate comparison of results. It is best to specify the responses that

---

[2] Diagrams of this sort were introduced by David Moore in his textbooks near the end of the 20th century, and are still widely used.

will be compared. A good way to start comparing results for the treatment groups is with boxplots.

We can diagram our tomato experiment like this:

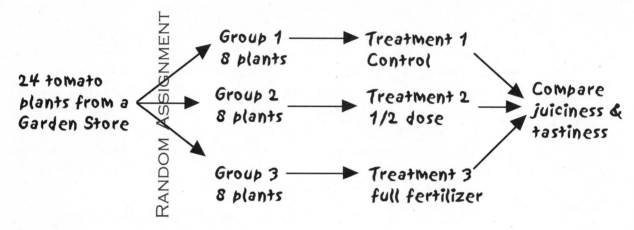

Experiments and Samples

Both experiments and sample surveys use randomization to get unbiased data. But they do so in different ways and for different purposes. Sample surveys try to estimate population parameters, so the sample needs to be as representative of the population as possible. By contrast, experiments try to assess the effects of treatments. Experiment units are not always drawn randomly from a population. For example, a medical experiment may deal only with patients who have the disease under study. The randomization is in the assignment of their therapy. This is appropriate because our focus is on differences in the effects of the treatments.

Unless the experimental units are chosen from the population at random, you cannot immediately generalize experiment results to larger populations until the experiment has been repeated under different circumstances. An experiment result that is shown also to be true in a different season, in a different country, for a different species, and so on, is much more persuasive.

Don't Tell

Experiments are rarely performed on random samples from a population. Don't describe the subjects in an experiment as a random sample unless they really are. More likely, the randomization was in assigning subjects to treatments.

But even without choosing experimental units from a population at random, experiments can draw stronger conclusions than surveys. By looking only at the differences across treatment groups, experiments cancel out many sources of bias. For example, the entire pool of subjects may be biased and not representative of the population. (College students may need more sleep on average than the general population.) When we assign subjects randomly to treatment groups, all the groups are still biased, but *in the same way*. When we consider the differences in their responses, these biases cancel out, allowing us to see the differences due to treatment effects more clearly.

Control Treatments

Suppose you wanted to test a $300 piece of software designed to speed up download times. You could just try it on several files and record the download times, but you probably want to *compare* the speed to what would happen *without* the software installed. Such a baseline measurement is called a **control** treatment and the group of subjects to whom it is applied is called a **control group**.

This is a use of the word "control" in an entirely different context. Previously we controlled extraneous sources of variation by keeping them constant. Here, we use a control treatment as another *level* of the factor in order to compare the results to a level of interest to the situation where "nothing happens".

Blinding

Human are notoriously susceptible to errors in judgment[3]. All of us. When we know what treatment was assigned, it is very difficult not to let that knowledge influence our assessment of the response, even when we try to be careful.

Suppose you were trying to advise your school on which brand of cola to stock in the school's vending machines. You set up an experiment to see which of the three competing brands students prefer (or whether they can tell the difference at all.) But people have brand loyalties. You probably prefer one brand already. So if you knew which brand you were tasting, it might influence your rating. To avoid this bias, it would be better to disguise the brands as much as possible. This strategy is called **blinding** the participants to the treatment.[4]

But it isn't just the subjects who should be blind. Experimenters themselves often subconsciously behave in ways that favor what they believe. Even technicians may treat plants or test animals differently if, for example, they expect them to die. An animal that starts doing a little better than others by showing an increased appetite may get

Blinding by Misleading

Social science experiments can sometimes blind subjects by misleading them about the purpose of a study. One of the authors participated as an undergraduate volunteer in a (now infamous) psychology experiment using such a blinding method. The subjects were told that the experiment was about three-dimensional spatial perception and were assigned to draw a model of a horse. While they were busy drawing, a loud noise and then groaning were heard coming from the room next door. The *real* purpose of the experiment was to see how people reacted to the apparent disaster. The experimenters wanted to see whether the social pressure of being in groups made people react to the disaster differently. Subjects had been randomly assigned to draw either in groups or alone. The experimenter had no interest in how well the subjects could draw the horse, but the subjects were blinded to the treatment because they were misled.

---

[3] For example, here we are in chapter 13 and you're still bothering to look at the footnotes.

[4] C.S. Peirce, in the same 1885 work in which he introduced randomization, also recommended blinding.

Copyright © 2001, Dick De Veaux and Paul Velleman

fed a bit more than the experimental protocol specifies.

People are so good at picking up subtle cues about treatments that the best (in fact, the *only*) defense against such biases in experiments on human subjects is to keep *anyone* who could affect the outcome or the measurement of the response from knowing which subjects have been assigned to which treatments. So not only should your cola-tasting subjects be blinded, *you,* as the experimenter, shouldn't know which drink is which either—at least until you are ready to analyze the results.

There are two main classes of individuals who can affect the outcome of the experiment:

- those who could *influence the results* (the subjects, treatment administrators, or technicians) and

- those who *evaluate the results* (judges, treating physicians, etc.)

When every individual in *either* of these classes is blinded, an experiment is said to be **single blind.** When everyone in *both* classes is blinded, we call the experiment **double blind.** [5] Even if several individuals in one class are blinded – for example, both the patients and the technicians who administer the treatment—the study would still be just single blind. If only some of the individuals in a class are blind – for example, if subjects are not told of their treatment, but the administering technician is not blind—there is a substantial risk that subjects can discern their treatment from subtle cues in the technician's behavior or that the technician might inadvertently treat subjects differently. Such experiments cannot be considered truly blind.

Placebos

The Placebo effect is stronger when placebo treatments are administered with authority or by a figure who appears to be an authority. "Doctors" in white coats generate a stronger effect than salespeople in polyester suits. But the placebo effect is not reduced much even when subjects know that the effect exists.

People often suspect that they've gotten the placebo if nothing at all happens. So, recently, drug manufacturers have gone so far in making placebos realistic that they sometimes even give them the same side effects as the drug being tested! When those side effects include loss of appetite or sexual dysfunction, the practice may raise ethical questions.

Often simply applying *any* treatment can induce an improvement. Every parent knows the medicinal value of a kiss to make a toddler's scrape or bump stop hurting. Some of the improvement due to a treatment – even an effective treatment—can be due to the simple act of treating. To separate these two effects, we can use a control treatment that mimics the treatment itself.

A "fake" treatment that looks just like the treatments being tested is called a **placebo.**

---

[5] A recent study found that physicians, articles in medical journals, and textbooks teaching statistics for physicians were confused and inconsistent in their understanding and use of the terminology of blinding. Unfortunately, the authors of the article were themselves confused about these terms. P. J. Devereaux, et. al.,"Physician Interpretations and Textbook Definitions of Blinding Terminology in Randomized Controlled Trials," *JAMA.* 2001;285:2000-2003

DRAFT: Do not distribute or copy

Placebos are the best way to blind subjects from knowing whether they are receiving the treatment or not. One common version of a placebo in drug testing is a "sugar pill". Especially when psychological attitude can affect the results, control group subjects treated with a placebo may show an improvement.

The fact is that subjects treated with a placebo sometimes improve. It is not unusual for 20% or more of subjects given a placebo to report reduction in pain, improved movement, or greater alertness, or even to demonstrate improved health or performance. This **placebo effect** highlights both the importance of effective blinding and the importance of comparing treatments to a control. Placebo controls are so effective that you should use them as an essential tool for blinding whenever possible.

The best experiments are usually:

- Randomized,
- Comparative,
- Double-blind, and
- Placebo controlled.

Does Ginkgo Biloba Improve Memory?

Researchers investigated the purported memory-enhancing effect of Ginkgo Biloba tree extract. ("Ginkgo for Memory Enhancement A Randomized Controlled Trial," Paul R. Solomon; Felicity Adams; Amanda Silver; Jill Zimmer; Richard DeVeaux, *JAMA. 2002;288:835-840s*) In a randomized, comparative, double-blind, placebo controlled study, they administered treatments to 230 elderly community members. One group received Ginkoba™ according the manufacturer's instructions. The other received a similar-looking placebo. Thirteen different tests of memory were administered before and after treatment. The placebo group showed greater improvement on 7 of them; the treatment group on the other 6. None showed any significant differences. Here are boxplots of one measure.

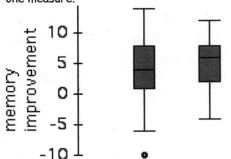

Blocking

Suppose we wanted to use 18 tomato plants for our tomato experiment, but there were only 12 tomato plants left at the garden store. So we drove down the road to the nursery and bought 6 more plants. We worry that the tomato plants from the two stores are different somehow, and, in fact, they don't really look the same to us.

How can we design the experiment so that the differences between the stores don't mess up our attempts to see differences among fertilizer levels? We can't treat the store the same way as the fertilizer because we can't assign it as we would a factor in the experiment. You can't tell a tomato what store to come from.

The plants from each store will be more like each other than like the plants from the other store. When groups of experimental units are similar, it often a good idea to gather them together into **block**s. By blocking we isolate the variability due to the differences between the blocks so that we can see the differences due to the treatments more

Copyright © 2001, Dick De Veaux and Paul Velleman

clearly. Here, we would define the plants from each store to be a block. The randomization is introduced when we randomly assign treatments within each block.

In a retrospective or prospective study, subjects are sometimes paired together because they are similar in ways *not* under study. **Matching subjects in this way can reduce variation in much the same way as blocking.** For example, a retrospective study of music education and grades might match each student who studies an instrument with one who is similar in family income and gender but didn't study an instrument. When we compare grades of music students to those of non-music students, the matching would reduce the variation due to income and gender differences.

In a completely randomized design, each of the 18 plants would have an equal chance to land in each of the three treatment groups. But we realize that the store may have an effect. To isolate the store effect, we assign the plants to treatments at random *within* each block. So we now have six treatment groups, three for each block. Within each block, we'll randomly assign the same number of plants to each of the three treatments. The experiment is still fair because each treatment is still applied (at random) to the same number of plants and to the same proportion from each store: 4 from store A and 2 from store B. Because the randomization occurs only within the blocks (plants from one store cannot be assigned to treatment groups for the other) we call it a **randomized block design**.

In effect, we conduct two parallel experiments, one for tomatoes from each store, and then combine the results. The picture tells the story:

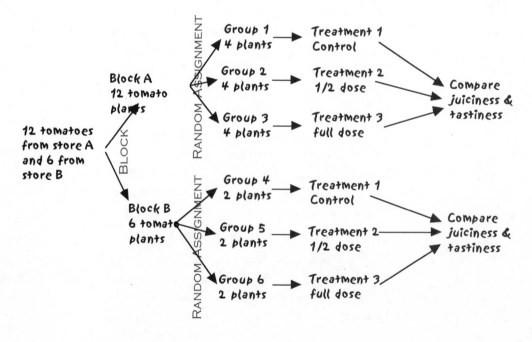

Blocking is the same idea for experiments as stratifying is for sampling. Both methods group together subjects that are similar and randomize within those groups as a way to remove unwanted variation. (But be careful with your terminology. Don't say that we "stratify" a design or "block" a sample.) We use blocks to reduce variability and allow us to see the effects of the factors, not as factors to be studied themselves.

*Adding More Factors

There are two kinds of gardeners; those who care for their plants daily, providing water and tending them lovingly, and those who stick them in the ground and let Mother Nature supply what rain she will (and the makers of *OptiGrow* want to please both kinds). Maybe we should include watering the plants (or not) as part of our experiment. Can we study a second factor at the same time and still learn as much about fertilizers?

We now have two factors (fertilizer at three levels, and irrigation at two levels). We combine them in all possible ways to yield six treatments:

	No Fertilizer	Half Fertilizer	Full Fertilizer
No added water	1	2	3
Daily watering	4	5	6

If we allocate the original 12 plants, the experiment now assigns two plants to each of these six treatments at random. This experiment is a **completely randomized two-factor experiment** because any plant could end up assigned at random to any of the six treatments (and we have two factors).

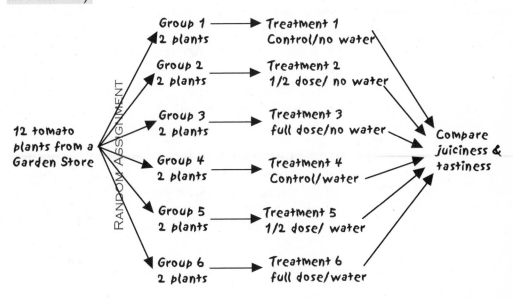

It is often important to include several factors in the same experiment in order to see what happens when the factor levels are applied in different *combinations*. A common misconception is that applying several factors at once makes it difficult to separate out the effects of the individual factors. You may hear people say that experiments should always be run "one factor at a time". In fact, just the opposite is true. Experiments with more than one factor are both more efficient and provide more information than one-at-a-time experiments. There are many ways to design efficient multi-factor experiments, and you can take a whole course on the design and analysis of such experiments[6].

Confounding

Professor Stephen Ceci of Cornell University performed an experiment to investigate the effect of a teacher's classroom style on student evaluations. He taught a class in developmental psychology during two successive terms to a total of 472 students in two very similar classes. He kept everything about his teaching identical (same text, same syllabus, same office hours, etc.) and modified only his style in class. During the Fall term he maintained a subdued demeanor. During the Spring term, he used expansive gestures and lectured with more enthusiasm, varying his vocal pitch and using more hand gestures. He administered a standard student evaluation form at the end of each term.

The students in the Fall term class rated him only an average teacher. Those in the Spring term class rated him an excellent teacher, praising his knowledge and accessibility, and even the quality of the textbook. On the question "How much did you learn in the course?" the average response changed from 2.93 to 4.05 on a 5-point scale.[7]

How much of the difference he observed was due to his difference in manner and how much might have been due to the season of the year? Fall term in Ithaca, NY (home of Cornell University) starts out colorful and pleasantly warm but ends cold and bleak. Spring term starts out bitter and snowy and ends with blooming flowers and singing birds. Might students' overall happiness have been affected by the season and reflected in their evaluations?

Unfortunately, there is no way to tell. Nothing in the data enables us to tease apart these two effects because all of the students who experience the subdued manner did so during the Fall term and all who experience the expansive manner did so during the Spring. When the levels of one

---

[6] We've included some references at the back of this chapter if you want to learn more.

[7] But the two classes performed almost identically well on the final exam.

DRAFT: Do not distribute or copy

factor are associated with the levels of another factor we say that these two factors are **confounded**.

In some experiments, such as this one, it is just not possible to avoid some confounding. Professor Ceci could have randomly assigned students to one of two classes during the same term, but then we might question whether mornings or afternoons were better, or whether he really delivered the same class the second time (after practicing on the first class). Or he could have had another professor deliver the second class, but that would have raised more serious issues about differences in the two professors and concern over more serious confounding.

---

*A two-factor example

Confounding can also arise from a badly designed multi factor experiment. Here's a classic. A credit card bank wanted to test the sensitivity of the market to two factors: the annual fee charged for a card and the annual percentage rate charged. Not wanting to scrimp on sample size, they selected 100,000 people at random from a mailing list. They sent out 50,000 offers with a low rate and no fee, and 50,000 offers out with a higher rate and a $50 annual fee. Guess what happened? That's right -- people preferred the low price, no fee card. No surprise. In fact, they signed up for that card at over twice the rate as the other offer. And because of the large sample size, the bank was able to estimate the difference precisely. But the question they really wanted to answer was: "How much of the change was due to the rate, and how much was due to the fee?" Unfortunately, there is simply no way to separate out the two effects. If they had just sent out all 4 possible different treatments: low rate, no fee, low rate $50 fee, high rate no fee and high rate with $50 fee, each to 25,000 people, they could have learned about both factors *and* they could have also seen what happens when the two factors occur in combination.

What Can Go Wrong

- *Beware of confounding.* Use randomization whenever possible to ensure that the factors not in your experiment are not confounded with your treatment levels. Be alert to confounding that cannot be avoided, and report it along with your results.

- *Bad things can happen even to good experiments.* Protect yourself by recording additional information. An experiment in which the air conditioning failed for two weeks, affecting the results, was saved by recording the temperature (although it was not originally one of the factors) and estimating the effect the higher temperature had on the response.[8]

It is generally good practice to collect as much information about your experimental units and the circumstances of the experiment as possible. For example, in the tomato experiment, it would be wise to record details of the weather (temperature, rainfall, sunlight) that might affect the plants and any facts available about their growing situation. (Is one side of the field in shade sooner than the other as the day proceeds? Is one area lower and a bit wetter?) Sometimes we can use this extra information during the analysis to reduce biases.

- *Don't spend your entire budget on the first run.* Just as it is a good idea to pre-test a survey, it is always wise to try a small pilot experiment before running the full-scale experiment. You may learn, for example how to choose factor levels more effectively, about effects you forgot to control, and about unanticipated confoundings.

Experiments and the Computer

Most experiments are analyzed with a computer statistics program. You should almost always display the results of a comparative experiment with side-by-side boxplots. You may also want to display the means and standard deviations of the treatment groups in a table.

The analyses offered by statistics packages for comparative randomized experiments fall under the general heading of Analysis of Variance, usually abbreviated ANOVA. These analyses are beyond the scope of this chapter.

Connections

The fundamental role of randomization in experiments clearly points back to our discussions of randomization, to our experiments with simulations, and to our use of randomization in sampling. And the similarities and differences between experiments and samples are important to keep in mind and can make each concept clearer.

Experiments compare groups of subjects that have been treated differently. Graphics such as boxplots, that help us compare groups, are closely related to these ideas. Think about what we look for to tell whether two groups look really different in a boxplot and you'll be thinking about the same issues as experiment designers.

Generally, we are going to consider how different the mean responses are for different treatment groups. And we're going to judge whether those differences are large by using standard deviations as rulers. (That's

---

[8] DeVeaux and Szelewski, *Journal of Chromatographic Science,* **27**:9, 1989, 513-518

DRAFT: Do not distribute or copy

why we needed to replicate results for each treatment; we need to be able to estimate those standard deviations.) The discussion of chapter 6 introduced this fundamental statistical thought, and it is going to just keep coming back over and over again. Statistics is about variation.

We will see a number of ways to analyze results from experiments in subsequent chapters.

Key Concepts

Observational Study	A study based on data where no manipulation of factors has been employed.
Retrospective Study	An observational study in which subjects are selected and then asked about their previous conditions or behaviors. Because retrospective studies are not based on random samples, they usually focus on estimating differences between groups or associations between variables.
Prospective Study	An observational study in which subjects are followed to observe future outcomes. Because no treatments are deliberately applied, a prospective study is not an experiment. Nevertheless, prospective studies typically focus on estimating differences among groups that might appear as the groups are followed during the course of the study.
Experiment	An experiment *manipulates* factor levels to create treatments, *randomly assigns* subjects to these treatment levels, and then *compares* the responses of the subject groups across treatment levels.
Random assignment	An experiment requires that experimental units be assigned to treatment groups at random. This is called random assignment.
Factor	A discrete variable whose levels are controlled by the experimenter. Experiments attempt to discover the effects that differences in factor levels may have on the responses of the experimental units.
Response	A quantitative variable whose values are measured and compared across different treatments. In a randomized experiment, large response differences can be attributed to the

	effect of differences in treatment level.
Experiment units	Individuals on whom an experiment is performed. Usually called **subjects** or **participants** when they are human.
Level	The specific values that the experimenter chooses for a factor are called the levels of the factor.
Treatment	The process, intervention, or other controlled circumstance applied to randomly assigned experiment units. Treatments are the different levels of a single factor or are made up of combinations of levels of two or more factors.
Principles of Experimental Design	• **Control** aspects of the experiment that we know may have an effect on the response, but that are not the factors being studied. • **Block** to reduce the effects of identifiable attributes of the subjects that cannot be controlled . • **Randomize** subjects to treatments to even out effects for which we cannot control. • **Replicate** over as many subjects as possible. Results for a single subject are just anecdotes. If, as often happens, the subjects of the experiment are not a representative sample from the population of interest, replicate the entire study with a different group of subjects, preferably from a different part of the population.
Control Group	The experimental units assigned to a baseline treatment level, typically either the default treatment, which is well-understood, or a null, placebo treatment. Their responses provide a basis for comparison.
Blinding	• When subjects do not know which treatment has been assigned to them, the study is said to be blind. • When others in contact with the subjects, for example to administer treatments or evaluate responses, are also unaware of which treatment the subject has received, the study is said to be double-blind.
Placebo	A null treatment known to have no effect,

DRAFT: Do not distribute or copy

	administered for comparison because many subjects respond to such a null treatment (known as a placebo effect). Only by comparing to a placebo can we be sure that the observed effect of a treatment is not due simply to the placebo effect.
Placebo effect	The tendency of many human subjects (often 20% or more of experiment subjects) to show a response even when administered a placebo.
Block	When groups of experimental units are similar, it often a good idea to gather them together into **block**s. By blocking we isolate the variability due to the differences between the blocks so that we can see the differences due to the treatments more clearly.
Matching	In a retrospective or prospective study, subjects who are similar in ways not under study may be **matched** and then compared with each other on the variables of interest. Matching, like blocking, reduces unwanted variation.
Confounding	When the levels of one factor are associated with the levels of another factor we say that these two factors are confounded.
Designs	In a **completely randomized design**, all experimental units have an equal chance of receiving any treatment.
	In a **randomized block design**, the randomization only occurs within blocks.

Skills

After completing this lesson you should:

> *Think*
>
> - Know the four basic principles of sound experiment design: Control, Randomize, Replicate, and Block, and be able to explain each.
>
> - Recognize the factors, the treatments and the response variable in a description of a designed experiment.
>
> - Understand the essential importance of randomization in assigning treatments to experimental units.

- Understand the importance of replication to move from anecdotes to general conclusions.

- Understand the value of blocking so that variability due to differences in attributes of the subjects can be removed.

- Understand the importance of a Control group and the need for a Placebo treatment in some studies.

- Understand the importance of blinding and double-blinding in studies on human subjects and be able to identify blinding and the need for blinding in experiments.

- Recognize the value of a placebo in blinding human participants.

Show

- Be able to design a completely randomized experiment to test the effect of a single factor.

- Be able to design an experiment in which blocking is used to reduce variation.

- Know how to use boxplots to compare responses for different treatment groups. Understand that you should *never* proceed with any other analysis of a designed experiment without first looking at the boxplots.

- Know how to compare the responses in different treatment groups to assess whether the differences are larger than could be reasonably expected from ordinary sampling variability.

Tell

- Know how to report the results of an experiment. Tell who the subjects are and how their assignment to treatments was determined. Report on how the response variable was measured and with what measurement units.

- Understand that your description of an experiment should be sufficient for another researcher to replicate the study with the same methods.

- Report on the statistical significance of the result in terms of whether the observed group-to-group differences are larger than could be expected from ordinary sampling variation.

DRAFT: Do not distribute or copy

Exercises

1 – 18. What's the Design? Read each brief report of statistical research, and identify:
  a) whether it was an investigative study or an experiment.

If it was an investigative study, identify (if possible):
  b) whether it was retrospective or prospective;
  c) the subjects studied, and how they were selected;
  d) the parameter of interest;
  e) the nature and scope of the conclusion the study can reach.

If it was an experiment, identify (if possible):
  b) the subjects studied;
  c) the factor(s) in the experiment, and the number of levels for each,
  d) the number of treatments;
  e) the response variable measured;
  f) the design (completely randomized, blocked, or matched);
  g) whether it was blind (or double-blind);
  h) the nature and scope of the conclusion the experiment can reach..

1. Over a four-month period, among 30 people with bipolar disorder, patients who were given a high dose (10 gm/day) of omega-3 fats from fish oil improved more than those given a placebo. *Arch. Gen. Psych. 56:407, 1999.*

2. The leg muscles of men aged 60 to 75 were 50 to 80 percent stronger after they participated in a 16-week, high-intensity resistance-training program twice a week. *J. Gerontol. 55A:B336, 2000.*

3. In a test of roughly 200 men and women, those with moderately high blood pressure (averaging 164/89) did worse on tests of memory and reaction time than those with normal blood pressure. *Hypertension 36:1079, 2000*

4. Among a group of disabled women aged 65 and older who were tracked for several years, those who had a vitamin B-12 deficiency were twice as likely to suffer severe depression as those who did not. *Amer. J. Psych, 157:715, 2000.*

5. An examination of the medical records of more than 360,000 Swedish men showed that those who were overweight or had had high blood pressure had a higher risk of kidney cancer (*New Eng. J. Med 3434: 1305, 2000*)

6. To research the effects of "dietary patterns" on blood pressure in 459 subjects, subjects were randomly assigned to three groups and had their meals prepared by dieticians. Those who were fed a diet low in fat and cholesterol and high in fruits, vegetables, and low-fat dairy

foods (known as the DASH diet) lowered their systolic blood pressure by an average of 6.7 points when compared to subjects fed a control diet. *http://dash.bwh.harvard.edu/research.html*

7. After menopause many women take supplemental estrogen. There is some concern that if these women also drink alcohol their estrogen levels will rise too high. 24 volunteers, 12 receiving supplemental estrogen and 12 who were not, were randomly divided into two groups. One group drank an alcoholic beverage, the other a non-alcoholic beverage. An hour later everyone's estrogen level was checked. Only these on supplemental estrogen who drank alcohol showed a marked increase.

8. Is diet or exercise effective in combating insomnia? Some believe that cutting out desserts can help alleviate the problem, while others recommend exercise. 40 volunteers suffering from insomnia agreed to participate in a month-long experiment. Half were randomly assigned to a special no-desserts diet; the others continue desserts as usual. Half of the people in each of these groups were randomly assigned to an exercise program while the others did not exercise. Those who ate no desserts and engaged in exercise showed the most improvement.

9. Some gardeners prefer to use non-chemical methods to control insect pests in their gardens. Researchers have designed two kinds of traps, and want to know which design will be more effective. They randomly choose ten locations in a large garden and place one of each kind of trap at each location. After a week they count the number of bugs in each trap.

10. Researchers have linked an increase in the incidence of breast cancer in Italy to dioxin released by an industrial accident in 1976. The study identified 981 women who lived near the site of the industrial explosion and were under age 40 at the time. Fifteen of the women had developed breast cancer, at an unusually young average age of 45. Medical records showed that these women had heightened concentrations of dioxin in their blood, and that each ten-fold increase in dioxin level was associated with a doubling of the risk of breast cancer. [*Science News*, Aug 3, 2002]

11. In 2002 the journal *Science* reported that a study of women in Finland indicated that having sons shortened the life spans of mothers by about 34 weeks per son, but that daughters helped to lengthen the mothers' lives. The data came from church records from the period 1640 to 1870.

12. In 2001 a report in the *Journal of the American Cancer Institute* indicated that women who work nights have a 60% greater risk of developing breast cancer. Researchers based these findings on the

work histories of 763 women with breast cancer and 741 women without the disease.

13. The May 4, 2000 issue of *Science News* reported that, contrary to popular belief, depressed individuals cry no more often in response to sad situations than non-depressed people. Researchers studied 23 men and 48 women with major depression, and 9 men and 24 women with no depression. They showed the subjects a sad film about a boy whose father has died, noting whether or not the subjects cried. Women cried more often than men, but there were no significant differences between the depressed and non-depressed groups.

14. Scientists at a major pharmaceutical firm investigated the effectiveness of an herbal compound to treat the common cold. They exposed each subject to a cold virus, then gave him or her either the herbal compound or a sugar solution known to have no effect on colds. Several days later they assessed the patient's condition using a cold severity scale ranging 0 - 5. They found no evidence of the benefits of the compound.

15. Scientists examined the glycogen content of rats' brains at their normal bedtimes, and after they had been kept awake for an extra 6, 12, or 24 hours. They found that glycogen was 38% lower among rats that had been sleep-deprived for 12 hours or more, and that the levels recovered during subsequent sleep. These researchers speculate that we may need to sleep in order to restore the brain's energy fuel. [*Science News*, July 20, 2002]

16. Some people who race greyhounds give the dogs large doses of vitamins C in the belief that the dogs will run faster. Investigators at the University of Florida tried three different diets in random order on each of 5 racing greyhounds. They were surprised to find that when the dogs ate high amounts of vitamin C they ran more slowly. [*Science News*, July 20, 2002]

17. Some people claim that they can get relief from migraine headache pain by drinking a large glass of ice water. Researchers plan to enlist several people who suffer from migraines in a test. When a participant experiences a migraine headache he or she will take a pill that may be a standard pain-reliever or a placebo. Half of each group will also drink ice water. Participants will then report the level of pain relief they experience.

18. Weight is an issue for both humans and their pets. A dog food company wants to test a new lower calorie food to see if it is effective in helping inactive dogs maintain a healthy weight. They have found several dog owners willing to participate in the trial. The dogs have

been classified as small, medium, or large breeds, and the company will supply some owners of each size dog with one of the two foods. The owners have agreed not to feed their dogs anything else for a period of 6 months, when the dogs' weights will be checked.

19. **Tomatoes** Describe a strategy to randomly split the 24 tomatoes into the three groups for the chapter's completely randomized single factor test of *OptiGro* fertilizer.

20. **Tomatoes II** The chapter also described a completely randomized 2-factor experiment testing *OptiGro* fertilizer in conjunction with two different routines for watering the plants. Describe a strategy to randomly assign the 24 tomato plants to the six treatments.

21. **Mozart** Will listening to a Mozart piano sonata make you smarter? In a 1995 study, Rauscher, Shaw, and Ky reported that when students were given a spatial reasoning section of a standard IQ test, those who listened to Mozart for 10 minutes improved their scores more than those who simply sat quietly.

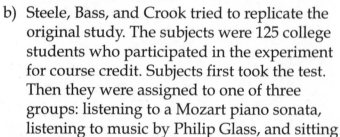

a) These researchers said the differences were statistically significant. Explain what that means in this context.

b) Steele, Bass, and Crook tried to replicate the original study. The subjects were 125 college students who participated in the experiment for course credit. Subjects first took the test. Then they were assigned to one of three groups: listening to a Mozart piano sonata, listening to music by Philip Glass, and sitting for 10 minutes in silence. After three days of treatments they were retested. Draw a diagram displaying the design of this experiment.

c) The boxplots show the difference in before and after scores for the three groups. Did the Mozart group show improvement?

d) Do you think the results prove that listening to Mozart is beneficial? Explain.

22. **More Mozart** An advertisement selling specially designed music CD's of Mozart's music specifically because they will "strengthen your mind, heal your body, and unlock your creative spirit" claims (we *swear!*) that "In Japan, a brewery reports that their best sake is made when Mozart is played near the yeast." Suppose, just for the sake (as it were) of discussion, you wished to design an experiment to test whether this is true. Assume you have the full cooperation of the sake brewery. Specify how you would design the experiment. Indicate factors and response and how they would be measured, controlled, or randomized.

23. **Frumpies** The maker of *Frumpies,* "The breakfast of rug rats", want to improve their marketing, so they consult you:
    a) They first want to know what fraction of children, ages 10–13, like their celery-flavored cereal. What kind of study should they perform?
    b) They are thinking of introducing a new flavor, *maple-marshmallow Frumpies,* and want to know whether children will prefer the new flavor to the old one. Design a completely randomized experiment to investigate this question.
    c) They suspect that children who regularly watch the Saturday-morning cartoon show staring *Frump,* the flying teenage warrior rabbit who eats *Frumpies* in every episode, may respond differently to the new flavor. How would you take that into account in your design?

24. **Full Moon** It is a common belief that people behave strangely when there is a full moon, and that as a result police and emergency rooms are busier than usual. Design a way you could find out is there is any merit to this belief. Will you use an observational study or an experiment? Why?

25. **Wine** Many researchers have concluded that wine is good for your health, citing several studies showing higher levels of "good" cholesterol and fewer heart attacks among wine drinkers. A 2001 Danish study published in the Archives of Internal Medicine raised some questions about that conventional view. Researchers have followed a group of children born at a Copenhagen hospital between 1959 and 1961 for the past forty years. These researchers now report that in this group the adults who drink wine are richer and better educated than those who do not.
    a) What kind of study was this?
    b) It is generally true that people with high levels of education and high socioeconomic status are healthier than others. How does this call into question the health benefits of wine?
    c) Do these studies prove that wine prevents heart attacks, that drinking wine makes you richer, that being rich helps prevent heart attacks, or none of these? Explain.

26. **Swimming** Recently a group of adults who swim regularly for exercise were evaluated for depression. It turned out that these swimmers were less likely to be depressed than the general population. The researchers said the difference was statistically significant.
    a) What does "statistically significant" mean in this context?
    b) Is this an experiment or an observational study? Explain.

c) News reports claimed this study proved that swimming can prevent depression. Explain why this conclusion is not justified by the study. Include an example of a possible confounding variable.

d) But perhaps it is true. We wonder if exercise can ward off depression, and whether anaerobic exercise (like weight training) is as effective as aerobic exercise (like swimming). We find 120 volunteers not currently engaged in a regular program of exercise. Design an appropriate experiment.

27. **Dowsing** A water dowser claims to be able to sense the presence of water using a forked stick. Suppose we wish to set up an experiment to test his ability. We get 20 identical containers, fill some with water, and ask the dowser to tell which ones are full and which empty.
a) How will we randomize this procedure?
b) The dowser correctly identifies the contents of 12 out of 20 containers. Do you think this level of success is statistically significant? Explain.
c) How many correct identifications (out of 20) would the dowser have to make to convince you that the forked stick trick works? Explain.

28. **Healing** A medical researcher suspects that giving post-surgical patients large doses of Vitamin E will speed their recovery time by helping their incisions heal more quickly. Design an experiment to test this conjecture. Be sure to identify the factors, levels, treatments, response variable, and the role of randomization.

29. **Reading** Some schools teach reading using phonics (the sounds made by letters) and others using whole language (word recognition). Suppose a school district wants to know which method works better. Suggest a design for an appropriate experiment.

30. **Gas Mileage** Do cars get better gas mileage with premium instead of unleaded gasoline? While it might be possible to test some engines in a laboratory setting, we'd rather use real cars and real drivers in real day-to-day driving, so we get 20 volunteers. Design the experiment.

31. **Weekend Deaths** A study published in the New England Journal of Medicine (Aug 2001) suggests that it's dangerous to enter a hospital on a weekend. During a 10-year period researchers tracked over 4 million emergency admissions to hospitals in Ontario, Canada. Their findings revealed that patients admitted on weekends had a much higher risk of death than those who went to the emergency room on weekdays.
b) The researchers said the difference in death rates was "statistically significant". Explain in this context what that means.
c) What kind of study was this?

d) If you think you are quite ill on a Saturday, should you wait until Monday to seek medical help? Explain.

e) Suggest some possible explanations for this troubling finding.

32. **Shingles** A research doctor has discovered a new ointment that she believes will be more effective than the current medication in the treatment of shingles (a painful skin rash). Eight patients have volunteered to participate in the initial trials of this ointment. You are the statistician hired as a consultant to help design a completely randomized experiment.

a) Describe how you will conduct this experiment.

b) Suppose the eight patients' last names start with the letters A - H. Using the random numbers listed below, show which patients you will assign to each treatment. Explain your randomization procedure clearly.

    41098 18329 78458 31685 55259

c) Can you make this experiment double blind? If so, explain how.

d) The initial experiment revealed that males and females may respond differently to the ointment. Further testing of the drug's effectiveness is now planned, and many patients have volunteered. What changes in your first design, if any, would you make for this second stage of testing?

33. **Beetles** Hoping to learn how to control crop damage by a certain species of beetle, a researcher plans to test two different pesticides in small plots of corn. A few days after application of the chemicals he'll check the number of beetle larvae found on each plant. The researcher wants to know if either pesticide works, and whether there is a significant difference in effectiveness between them. Design an appropriate experiment.

34. **SAT Prep** Can special study courses actually help raise SAT scores? One organization says that the 30 students they tutored achieved an average gain of 60 points when they retook the test.

a) Explain why this does not necessarily prove that the special course caused the scores to go up.

b) Propose a design for an experiment that could test the effectiveness of the tutorial course.

c) Suppose you suspect that the tutorial course might be more helpful for students whose initial scores were particularly low. How would this affect your proposed design?

35. **Safety Switch** An industrial machine requires an emergency shutoff switch that must be designed so that it can be easily operated with either hand. Design an experiment to find out whether workers will be able to deactivate the machine as quickly with their left hands as

with their right hands. Be sure to explain the role of randomization in your design.

36. **Washing Clothes** A consumers group wants to test the effectiveness of a new "organic" laundry detergent and make recommendations to customers about how to best use the product. They intentionally get grass stains on 30 white t-shirts in order to see how well the detergent will clean them. They want to try the detergent in cold, water, and hot water on both the "regular" and "delicates" wash cycles. Design an appropriate experiment, indicating the number of factors, levels, and treatments. Explain the role of randomization in your experiment.

III Gathering Data – Quick Review

Before you can make a boxplot, calculate a mean, describe a distribution, or fit a line, you must have meaningful data to work with. Getting good data is essential to any investigation. No amount of clever analysis can make up for badly collected data. Here's a brief summary of the key concepts and skills:

➤ The way you gather depends both on what you want to discover and on what is practical.

➤ To get some insight into what might happen in a real situation, model it with a **simulation** using random numbers.

➤ To answer questions about a target population, collect information from a sample with a **survey** or poll.
  - Choose the sample randomly. Random sampling designs include simple, stratified, systematic, cluster, and multistage.
  - A simple random sample draws without restriction from the entire target population.
  - When there are subgroups within the population that may respond differently, use a stratified sample.
  - Avoid bias, a systematic distortion of the results. Sample designs that allow undercoverage or response bias, and designs such as voluntary response, convenience, and judgment samples do not faithfully represent the population.
  - Samples will naturally vary one from another. This sample-to-sample variation is called sampling error. Each sample only approximates the target population.

➤ **Investigative studies** collect information from a sample drawn from a target population.
  - Retrospective studies examine existing data. Prospective studies identify subjects in advance, then follow them to collect data as it is created, perhaps over many years.
  - Investigative studies can spot associations between variables, but cannot establish cause and effect. It is impossible to eliminate the risk of lurking or confounding variables.

➤ To see how different treatments influence a response variable, design an **experiment**.
  - Assign subjects to treatments randomly. If you don't assign treatments randomly, you haven't done an experiment.
  - Control known sources of variation as much as possible. Reduce variation that cannot be controlled by using blocking or matching.
  - Replicate the experiment, assigning several subjects to each treatment level.

- If possible, replicate the entire experiment with an entirely different collection of subjects.
- A well-designed experiment can provide evidence that changes in the factors cause changes in the response variable.

Now for more opportunities to review these concepts and skills…

Exercises

1 – 18: What design? Analyze the design of each research reported. Is it a sample, study or an experiment? If a sample, what are the population, the parameter of interest , and the sampling procedure? If a study, was it retrospective or prospective? If an experiment, describe the factors, treatments, randomization, response variable, and any blocking, matching, or blinding that may be present. In each, what kind of conclusions can be reached?

1. Researchers identified 242 children in the Cleveland area who had been born prematurely (at about 29 weeks). They examined these children at age 8 and again at age 20, comparing them to another group of 233 children not born prematurely. According to their report, published in the *New England Journal of Medicine*, the "preemies" engaged in significantly less risky behavior than the others. Differences between the groups showed up in the use of alcohol and marijuana, conviction of crimes, and teenage pregnancy.

2. The journal *Circulation* reported that among 1900 people who had heart attacks, those who drank an average of 19 cups of tea a week were 44% more likely than non-drinkers to survive at least 3 years after the attack

3. Researchers at the Purina Pet Institute studied Labrador retrievers for evidence of a relationship between diet and longevity. At 8-weeks of age, two puppies of the same gender and weight were randomly assigned to one of two groups -- a total of 48 dogs in all. One group was allowed to eat all they wanted, while the other group was a low-calorie diet (about 75% as much as the others). The median lifespan of dogs fed the restricted diet was 22 months longer than other dogs. [*Science News*, Vol. 161, No. 19]

4. Radon is a radioactive gas found in some homes that poses a health risk to residents. In order to assess the level of contamination in their area, a county health department wants to test a few homes. If the risk seems high they will and publicize the results to emphasize the need for home testing. Officials plan to use the local property tax list to randomly choose 25 homes from various areas of the county.

5. Almost 90000 women participated in a 16-year study of the role of the vitamin folate in preventing colon cancer. Some of the women had family histories of colon cancer in close relatives. In this at-risk group the incidence of colon cancer was cut in half among those who maintained a

high folate intake . No such difference was observed in those with no family-based risk. [*Science News*, 2002, Vol 161, No 16]

6. In a study appearing in the journal *Science* a research team reports that plants in southern England are flowering earlier in the spring. Records of the first flowering dates for 385 species over a period of 47 years indicate that flowering has advanced an average of 15 days per decade, an indication of climate warming according to the authors.

7. Fireworks manufacturers face a dilemma. They must be sure that the rockets work properly, but test-firing a rocket essentially destroys it. On the other hand, not testing the product leaves open the danger that they sell a bunch of duds, leading to unhappy customers and loss of future sales. The solution, of course, is to test a few of the rockets produced each day, assuming that if those tested work properly the others are ready for sale.

8. Can makeup damage fetal development? Many cosmetics contain a class of chemicals called phthlates. Studies that exposed some laboratory animals to these chemicals found a heightened incidence of damage to male reproductive systems. Since traces of phthlates are found in the urine of women who use beauty products, there is growing concern that they may present a risk to male fetuses. [*Science News*, July 20, 2002]

9. Can long-term exposure to strong electromagnetic fields cause cancer? Researchers in Italy tracked down 13 years worth of medical records for people living near Vatican Radio's powerful broadcast antennas. A disproportionate share of the leukemia cases occurred among men and children who lived within 6 kilometers of the antennas. [*Science News*, July 20, 2002]

10. Some doctors have expressed concern that men who have vasectomies seemed to be more likely to develop prostate cancer. Medical researchers used a national cancer registry to identify 923 men who had had prostate cancer and 1224 men of similar ages who had not. Roughly one quarter of the men in each group had undergone a vasectomy, many over 25 years before the study. The study's authors concluded that there is strong evidence that having the operation presents no long-term risk for developing prostate cancer. [*Science News*, July 20, 2002]

11. Researchers investigating appetite control as a means of losing weight found that female rats ate less and lost weight after injections of the hormone leptin, while male rats responded better to insulin. [*Science News*, July 20, 2002]

12. An artisan wants to create pottery that has the appearance of age. He prepares several samples of clay with four different glazes and test fires them in a kiln at three different temperature settings.

13. Tests of gene therapy on laboratory rats have raised hopes of stopping the degeneration of tissue that characterizes chronic heart failure. Researchers at UC San Diego used hamsters with cardiac disease, randomly assigning 30 to get the gene therapy and leaving the other 28 untreated. Five weeks after treatment the gene therapy group's heart muscles stabilized while the untreated hamsters continued to weaken. [*Science News*, July 27, 2002]

14. Researchers at the University of Bristol (England) investigated reasons why different species of birds begin to sing at different times in the morning. They captured and examined birds of 57 species at 7 different sites. They measured the diameter of the birds' eyes and also recorded the time of day at which each species began to sing. These researchers reported a strong relationship between eye diameter and time of singing, saying that birds with bigger eyes tended to sing earlier. [*Science News*, 2002, Vol. 161, No 16]

15. An orange juice processing plant will accept a shipment of fruit only after several hundred oranges selected from various locations within the truck are carefully inspected. If too many of those checked show signs of unsuitability for juice (bruised, rotten, unripe, etc.) the whole truckload is rejected.

16. A soft drink manufacturer must be sure the bottle caps on the soda are fully sealed and will not come off easily. Inspectors pull a few bottles off the production line at regular intervals and test the caps. If they detect any problems they will stop the bottling process to adjust or repair the machine that caps the bottles.

17. Physically fit people are less likely to die of cancer. A report in the May 2002 issue of *Medicine and Science in Sport and Exercise* followed at 25892 men aged 30 to 87 for 10 years. The most physically fit men had a 55% lower risk of death from cancer than the least fit group.

18. Does the use of computer software in introductory statistics classes lead to better understanding of the concepts? A professor teaching two sections of stats decides to investigate. She teaches both sections using the same lectures and assignments, but gives one class statistics software to help them with their homework. The classes will take the same final exam, and graders will not know which students used computers during the semester. The professor is concerned that students who have had calculus may perform differently from those who have not, so she plans to compare software vs no–software scores separately for these two groups of students.

19. **Point Spread** When taking bets on sporting events bookmakers often include a "point spread" that awards the weaker team extra points. In theory this makes the outcome of the bet a tossup. Suppose a gambler places a $10 bet and picks the winners of five games. If he is right about

fewer than 3 of the games, he loses. If he gets 3, 4, or all 5 correct he is paid $10, $20, or $50 respectively. Estimate the amount such a bettor might expect to lose over many weeks of gambling.

20. **The Lottery** Many people spend a lot of money trying to win huge jackpots in state lotteries. Let's play a simplified version using only the numbers from 1 to 20. You bet on three numbers. The state picks five winning numbers. If your three are all among the winners, you are rich!
    a) Simulate repeated plays. How long did it take you to win?
    b) In real lotteries there are many more choices (often 54), and you must match all five winning numbers. Explain how these changes affect your chances of hitting the jackpot.

21. **Everyday Randomness** Aside from casinos, lotteries, and games there are other situations you encounter where something is described as "random" in some way. Give three different examples. Describe how randomness is (or is not) achieved in each.

22. **Cell Phone Risks** Researchers at the Washington University School of Medicine randomly placed 480 rats into one of 3 chambers containing radio antennas. One group was exposed to digital cell phone radio waves, the second to analog cell phone waves, and the third group to no radio waves. Two years later the rats were examined for signs of brain tumors. In June 2002 the scientists said that differences among the three groups were not statistically significant.
    a) Is this a study or an experiment? Explain.
    b) Explain in this context what "statistically significant" means.
    c) Comment on the fact that this research was supported by funding from Motorola.

23. **Tips** In restaurants, servers rely upon tips as a major source income. Does serving candy after the meal produce larger tips? To find out two waiters determined randomly whether or not to give candy to 92 dining parties. They recorded the sizes of the tips, and reported that guests getting candy tipped an average of 17.8% of the bill, compared to an average tip of only 15.1% from those who got no candy. [Sweetening the till: The use of candy to increase restaurant tipping. Journal of Applied Social Psychology, 32(2), 300-309.]
    a) Was this an experiment or an observational study? Explain.
    b) Is it reasonable to conclude that the candy caused guests to tip more? Explain.
    c) The researchers said the difference was statistically significant. Explain in this context what that means.

24. **Tips, Take 2** In another experiment to see if getting candy after a meal would induce customers to leave a bigger tip, a waitress randomly decided what to do with 80 dining parties. Some parties received no candy, some just one piece, and some two pieces. Others initially got just

one piece of candy, and then the waitress suggested that they take another piece. She recorded the tips received, finding that, in general, the more candy the higher the tip, but the highest tips (23%) came from the parties who got one piece and then were offered more. [Sweetening the till: The use of candy to increase restaurant tipping. Journal of Applied Social Psychology, 32(2), 300-309.]

a) Diagram this experiment.
b) How many factors are there? How many levels?
c) How many treatments are there?
d) What is the response variable?
e) Did this experiment involve blinding? Double blinding?
f) In what way might the waitress, perhaps unintentionally, have biased the results?

25. **Cloning** In September 1998 *USA Weekend* magazine asked "Should humans be cloned?" Readers were invited to register a "Yes" or "No" answer by calling one of two different 900 numbers. Based on 38023 responses the magazine reported "9 out of 10 readers oppose cloning."

a) Explain why you think the conclusion is not justified. Describe the types of bias that may be present.
b) Reword the question in a way that you think might create a more positive response.

26. **Laundry** An experiment to test a new laundry detergent, *SparkleKleen*, is being conducted by a consumer advocate group. They would like to compare its performance to a laboratory standard detergent that they have used in previous experiments. They can stain 16 swatches of cloth with 2 tsp. of a common staining compound and then use a well-calibrated optical scanner to detect the amount of the stain is left after washing with detergent. To save time in the experiment, several suggestions have been made. Comment on the possible merits and drawbacks of each one.

a) Since data for the laboratory standard detergent are already available from previous experiments, for this experiment wash all 16 swatches with *SparkleKleen*, and compare the results to the previous data.
b) Use both detergents with 8 separate runs each, but to save time, use only a 10 second wash time with very hot water.
c) To ease bookkeeping, run successively all of the standard detergent washes on 8 swatches, then run all of the *SparkleKleen* washes on the other 8 swatches.
d) Rather than run the experiment, use data from the company that produced *SparkleKleen*, and compare them with past data from the standard detergent.

27. **When to Stop?** You play a game that involves rolling a die. You can roll as many times as you want, and your score is the total for all the rolls. But… if you roll a 6 your score is 0 and your turn is over. What might be a good strategy for a game like this?

DRAFT: Do not distribute or copy

a) One of your opponents decides to roll 4 times, then stop (hoping not to get the dreaded 6 before then). Use a simulation to estimate his average score.

b) Another opponent decides to roll until she gets at least 12 points, then stop. Use a simulation to estimate her average score.

c) Propose another strategy that you would use to play this game. Simulate several turns using your strategy. Do you think you would beat the two opponents?

28. **Rivets** A company that manufactures rivets believes the shear strength of the rivets they manufacture follows a Normal model with a mean breaking strength of 950 pounds and a standard deviation of 40 pounds.

a) What is the probability that a rivet selected at random will break when tested under a 900 pound load?

b) You're trying to improve the rivets and want to examine some that fail. Use a simulation to estimate how many rivets you might need to test in order to find three that fail at 900 pounds (or below).

29. **Homecoming** A college statistics class conducted a survey concerning community attitudes about the college's large Homecoming celebration. That survey drew its sample in the following manner: Telephone numbers were generated at random by selecting one of the local telephone exchanges (first three digits) at random, and then generating a random 4-digit number to follow the exchange. If a person answered the phone and the call was to a residence, then that person was taken to be the subject for interview. (Undergraduate students and those under voting age were excluded, as was anyone who could not speak English.) Calls were placed until a sample of 200 eligible respondents had been reached.

a) Did every telephone number that could possibly occur in that community have an equal chance of being generated?

b) Did this method of generating telephone numbers result in a Simple Random Sample of local residences? Explain.

c) Did this method generate a Simple Random Sample of local voters? Explain.

d) Did this method generate an unbiased sample of households? Explain.

30. **Youthful Appearance** *Readers' Digest* reported results of several surveys that asked graduate students to examine photographs of men and women and try to guess their ages. Researchers compared these guesses to the number of times the people in the pictures reported having sexual intercourse. It turned out that those who had been more sexually active were judged as looking younger, and that the difference was described as "statistically significant." Psychologist David Weeks, who compiled the research, speculated that lovemaking boosts hormones that "reduce

fatty tissue and increase lean muscle, giving a more youthful appearance."

a) What does "statistically significant" mean in this context?

b) Explain in statistical terms why you laughed at Dr. Weeks' conclusion. Propose an alternative explanation for these results.

31. **Smoking and Alzheimer's** Medical studies indicate that smokers are less likely to develop Alzheimer's disease than people who never smoked.

a) Does this prove that smoking may offer some protection against Alzheimer's? Explain.

b) Offer an alternative explanation for this association.

c) How would you conduct a study to investigate this issue?

32. **Antacids** A researcher wants to compare the performance of three types of antacid in volunteers suffering from acid reflux disease. Because men and women may react differently to this medication, the subjects are split into two groups by gender. Subjects in each group are randomly assigned to take one of the antacids or to take a sugar pill made to look the same. The subjects will rate their level of discomfort 30 minutes after eating.

a) What kind of design is this?

b) The experiment uses volunteers rather than a random sample of all people suffering from acid reflux disease. Does this make the results invalid? Explain.

c) How may the use of the placebo confound this experiment? Explain.

33. **Sex and Violence** Does the content of a television program impact viewers' memory of the products advertised in commercials? Design an experiment to compare the ability of viewers to recall brand names of items featured in commercials during programs with violent content, sexual content, or neutral content.

34. **Pubs** In England, a Leeds University researcher said that the local watering hole's welcoming atmosphere helps men to get rid of the stresses of modern life and is vital for their psychological well-being. Author of the report Dr. Colin Gill said rather than complain, women should encourage men to pop out for a swift half. "Pub-time allows men to bond with friends and colleagues," he said. "Men need break-out time as much as women and are mentally healthier for it." Gill added that men might feel unfulfilled or empty if they had not been to the pub for a week. The report, commissioned by alcohol-free beer brand Kaliber, surveyed 900 men on their reasons for going to the pub. More than 40 percent said they went for the conversation, with relaxation and a friendly atmosphere being the other most common reasons. Only one in 10 listed alcohol as the overriding reason.

Let's examine this news story from a statistical perspective.

a) What are the W's: who, what , why, when, where?

b) What population does the researcher think the study applies to?

c) What is the most important thing about the selection process that the article does *not* tell us?

d) How do *you* think the 900 respondents were selected? (Name a method of drawing a sample that is likely to have been used.)

e) Do you think that the report that only 10% of respondents said that alcohol was an important reason for going to the pub might be a biased result? Why?

35. **Age and Party** The Gallup Poll conducted a representative telephone survey during the first quarter of 1999. Among their reported results was the following table concerning the preferred political party affiliation of respondents and their ages.

Age	Republican	Democratic	Independent	Total
18-29	241	351	409	1001
30-49	299	330	370	999
50-64	282	341	375	998
65+	279	382	343	1004
Total	1101	1404	1497	4002

a) What sampling strategy do you think the pollsters used? Explain.

b) What percentage of the people surveyed were Democrats?

c) Do you think this is a good estimate of the percentage of voters in the US who are registered Democrats? Why or why not?

d) In creating this sample design, what question do you think the pollsters were trying to answer?

36. **Bias?** Political analyst Michael Barone has written that "conservatives are more likely than others to refuse to respond to polls, particularly those polls taken by media outlets that conservatives consider biased." (*The Weekly Standard*, March 10, 1997.) The Pew Research Foundation tested this assertion by asking the same questions in a national survey run by standard methods and in a more rigorous survey that was a true SRS with careful follow-up to encourage participation. The response rate in the "standard survey" was 42%. The response rate in the "Rigorous survey" was 71%.

a) What kind of bias does Barone claim may exist in polls?

b) What is the population for these surveys?

c) On the question of political position, the Pew researchers report the following table:

	Standard Survey	Rigorous Survey
Conservative	37%	35%
Moderate	40%	41%
Liberal	19%	20%

What makes you think these results are incomplete?

d) The Pew Researchers report that differences between opinions expressed on the two surveys were not statistically significant. Explain what "statistically significant" means in this context.

37. **Save the Grapes** Vineyard owners have problems with birds that like to eat the ripening grapes. Grapes damaged by birds cannot be used for winemaking (or much of anything else). Some vineyards use scarecrows to try to keep birds away. Others use netting that covers the plants. Owners really would like to know if either method works, and if so which one is better. One owner has offered to let you use his vineyard this year for an experiment. Propose a design. Carefully indicate how you would set up the experiment, specifying the factor(s) and response variable.

38. **Bats** It is generally believed that baseball players can hit the ball farther with aluminum bats than with the traditional wooden ones. Is that true? And, if so, how much farther? Players on your local high school baseball team have agreed to help you find out. Design an appropriate experiment.

39. **Knees** Research reported in the spring of 2002 cast doubt on the effectiveness of arthroscopic knee surgery for patients with arthritis. Patients suffering from arthritis pain who volunteered to participate in the study were randomly divided into groups. One group received arthroscopic knee surgery. The other group underwent "placebo surgery" during which incisions were made in their knees, but no surgery was actually performed. Followup evaluations over a period of two years found that differences in the amount of pain relief experienced by the two groups were not statistically significant.
a) Why did the researchers feel it was necessary to have some of the patients undergo "placebo surgery"?
b) Because patients had to consent to participate in this experiment, the subjects were essentially self-selected – a kind of voluntary response group. Explain why that does not invalidate the findings of the experiment.
c) What does "statistically significant" mean in this context?

40. **NBA Draft Lottery** Professional basketball teams hold a "draft" each year in which they get to pick the best available college and high school players. In an effort to promote competition, teams with the worst records get to pick first, theoretically allowing them to add better players. To combat the fear that teams with no chance to make the playoffs might try to getter better draft picks by intentionally losing late-season games, the NBA's Board of Governors adopted a weighted lottery system in 1990. Under this system the 11 teams that did not make the playoffs were eligible for the lottery. The NBA prepared 55 cards, each naming one of the teams. The team with the worst won-loss record was named on 11 of the cards, the second-worst team on 10 cards, and so

on, with the team with the best record among the non-playoff clubs getting only one chance at having the first pick. The cards were mixed, then drawn randomly to determine the order in which the teams could draft players. (Since 1995 there have been 13 teams involved in the lottery, using a complicated system with 14 numbered ping-pong balls drawn in groups of four. You can read about it at www.nba.com/news/lottery02_evolution.html.) Suppose there are two exceptional players available in this year's draft, and your favorite team had the third-worst record. Use a simulation to find out how likely it is that your team gets to pick first or second. Describe your simulation carefully.

41. **Security** There are 20 first class passengers and 120 coach passengers scheduled on a flight. In addition to the usual security screening, 10% of the passengers will be subjected to a more complete search.
    a) Describe a sampling strategy to randomly select those to be searched.
    b) Here is the first class passenger list and a set of random digits. Select two passengers to be searched, carefully demonstrating your process.

    65436 71127 04879 41516 20451 02227 94769 23593

Bergman	Cox	Fontana	Perl
Bowman	DeLara	Forester	Rabkin
Burkhauser	Delli-Bovi	Frongillo	Roufaiel
Castillo	Dugan	Furnas	Swafford
Clancy	Febo	LePage	Testut

    c) Explain how you would use a random number table to select the coach passengers to be searched.

42. **Profiling?** Among the 20 first class passengers on the flight described in Exercise 27 there were four businessmen from the Middle East. Two of them were the two passengers selected to be searched. They complained of profiling, but the airline claims that the selection was random. What do you think? Support your conclusion with a simulation.

43. **Par 4** In theory a golfer playing a par 4 hole tees off, hitting the ball in the fairway, then hits an approach shot onto the green. The first putt (usually long) probably won't go in, but the second putt (usually much shorter) should. Sounds simple enough, but how many strokes might it really take? Use a simulation to estimate a pretty good golfer's score based on these assumptions:
    - The tee shot hits the fairway 70% of the time.
    - A first approach shot lands on the green 80% of the time from the fairway, but only 40% of the time otherwise.
    - Subsequent approach shots land on the green 90% of the time.
    - The first putt goes in 20% of the time, and subsequent putts go in 90% of the time.

44. **The Back Nine** Use simulations to estimate more golf scores, similar to the procedure in Exercise 24.
   a) On a par 3, where the golfer hopes the tee shot lands on the green. Assume that the tee shot behaves like the first approach shot described in Exercise 43.
   b) On a par 5, where the second shot will reach the green 10% of the time and hit the fairway 60% of the time. If it does not hit the green the golfer must play an approach shot as described in Exercise 43.
   c) Create a list of assumptions that describe your golfing ability and then simulate your score on a few holes. Explain your simulation clearly.

IV Randomness and Probability

14 From Randomness to Probability

WHAT'S THE DIFFERENCE BETWEEN RANDOMNESS AND CHAOS? At first glance they might seem to be the same. Neither of their outcomes can be anticipated with certainty. But random phenomena have another important feature. In the long run, they settle down in a way that is actually consistent and predictable. Chaotic processes don't do this. It's this property of randomness that enables us to do Statistics. We'll show what we mean in this chapter and the next as we tame randomness and turn it into something that we can use.

Dealing with Random Phenomena

Every day you drive through the intersection at College and Main. Even though it may seem that the light is always red when you get there, you know this can't really be true. In fact, if you try really hard, you can recall just sailing through the green light once in a while.

What's random here? The light itself is governed by a timer. Its pattern isn't haphazard. In fact, the light may even be red at precisely the same times each day. It's the pattern of *your driving* that is random. No, we're not insinuating that you can't keep the car on the road. But at the precision level of the 30 seconds or so that the light spends being red or green, the time you arrive at the light *is random*. So, even if you try to leave your house at exactly the same time every day, whether the light is red or green as *you* reach the intersection is a random phenomenon.

Is the color of the light completely unpredictable? When you stop to think about it (maybe while waiting for the green light), it's clear that we do expect some kind of *regularity* in your long-run experience. Some *fraction* of the time the light will be red as you get to the intersection. How can we figure out what that fraction is?

You might record what happens at the intersection each day and graph the *accumulated percentage* of red lights like this:

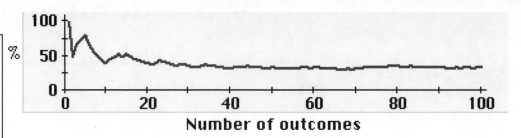

The overall percent of times the light is red settles down as we see more outcomes.
Figure 14.1

The first day you recorded the light it was red. Then on the next five days, it was green, then red again, then red, green, and green. If we plot the % red against the day, the graph would start at 100% because the first time the light was red. (1 out of 1 for 100%). Then the next time it was green, so the accumulated percentage drops to 50% (1 out of 2). The third day it was red again (2 out of 3 or 66% red), then red (3 out of 4 or 75%), then green twice in a row (3 out of 5 for 60% red and then 3 out of 6 for 50%), and so on. As you collect a new data point for each day, this new datum becomes a smaller and smaller *fraction* of the accumulated experience, so, in the long run, the graph settles down. As it settles down, we can see that, in fact, the light is red only about 35% of the time.

Probability

Now, if you were asked for the *probability* that you would be stopped at the traffic light at College and Main, you might naturally say that it was 35%. You would base that on knowing (from your data collection) that, in the long run, the fraction of the time the light is red is 35%. We could also say that the long-run *relative frequency* of red lights settles down to about 35%

Terminology Alert

A **Phenomenon** consists of **Trials**.
Each **Trial** has an **Outcome**.
Outcomes combine to make **Events**.

And that is exactly what we mean by probability. The **probability** of an event is its long-run relative frequency.

Although we may not be able to predict a *particular* individual outcome such as how a flipped coin will land, we are reasonably sure that a fair coin will fall heads about half the time *in the long run*. Of course, in the real world, we usually can't see the "true" proportions hiding behind the random outcomes. This forces us to reason backwards as we did with the traffic light.

When talking about long run behavior it helps to define our terms. For any random phenomenon, each attempt, or **trial,** generates an **outcome**. In these words, something happens on each trial, and we call whatever happens the outcome. These outcomes are *individual* possibilities such as the number we see on top when we throw a die. But often we want to talk about *combinations* of outcomes like "The number on the die is less than 4". We call such a combination an **event**.

In order to think about such combinations of outcomes, it really simplifies things if the individual trials are **independent**. Roughly

DRAFT: Do not distribute or copy

speaking, this means that the outcome of one trial doesn't influence or change the outcome of another. (In Chapter 3 we called two *variables* independent for similar reasons.) For example, if we drove to work with a friend in another car right behind us, we couldn't just add his observations to ours. Most of the time, his experience will just duplicate ours. Except for those few times when the light turns red just after we enter the intersection, the light will be the same for him as for us. His observations would not be independent of ours. Because they are almost repeats of our observations, they wouldn't give us any more information, and the graph would not settle down as quickly. In order for us to make statements about the long run behavior of random phenomenon, the trials have to be independent.

The Law of Large Numbers

Do random phenomena always behave so well? If we are going to use long-run relative frequency as our definition of probability, we should first be sure that it will, in fact, settle down to a particular value. Couldn't it be that the probability will just bounce back and forth between two values forever, never settling on just one number? Fortunately, a principle called the **Law of Large Numbers** (LLN) gives us the guarantee that we need. It says that the long run *relative frequency* of repeated independent events gets closer and closer to the *true* relative frequency as the number of trials increases.

Although the LLN wasn't proven until the 18th century, everyone expects the kind of long run regularity that the Law describes from everyday experience. If the light at College and Main is set by the traffic engineers to be red 35% of the time for the drivers on College Avenue, then none of us are surprised to find out that in the long run, if you arrive at the intersection from College Avenue, *you'll* encounter a red light 35% of the time.

But yet, the Law is often misunderstood because the idea of the *long run* is hard to grasp. Many gamblers believe that, for example, that a number that has not come up on the roulette wheel or in a lottery for a long time, is "due" to occur – and they give the Law of Large Numbers as their reason. (Well, they usually call it the "Law of Averages" or some similar term, but the LLN is what they really mean.) But the LLN doesn't apply to short-run behavior. The problem is that probabilities even out only in the long run. And (according to the LLN) the long run must be *infinitely* long to give them enough time to even out.

In fact, the so-called "Law of Averages" doesn't exist at all. The common (mis) understanding of this "Law" is that random phenomena are supposed to *compensate* somehow for whatever happened in the past. So if recent results have fallen to one side of what is expected, somehow

"For even the most stupid of men, by some instinct of nature, by himself and without any instruction (which is a remarkable thing), is convinced that the more observations have been made, the less danger there is of wandering from one's goal" – Jacob Bernoulli, 1713 (quoted by Stigler 1986 p. 67), discoverer of the LLN.
picture at http://www-groups.dcs.st-andrews.ac.uk/~history/Pict Display/Bernoulli_Jacob.html

results on the other side are "due" because the results must "average out" to the right value. Is a .300 hitter in baseball who has struck out the last 6 times *due* for a hit his next time up? If you've just flipped a fair coin 5 Heads in a row, is the next flip more likely to be Tails because the coin *owes us* a Tail?.

Don't Think

Don't let yourself think that there is a Law of Averages that promises short-term compensation for recent deviations from expected behavior. A belief in such a "Law" can lead to money lost gambling and to poor business decisions.

No. This is not the way random phenomena work. The coin can't *remember* what happened and make things come out right. In fact, if you flipped a fair coin several thousand times, you would find lots of long streaks of all Heads. And if we looked at *all* streaks of 5 (or 6, or 10…) Heads, we'd see that, on the average, the next flip is *just as likely to be Heads or Tails* even after a streak. The Law of Large Numbers promises that given a very large number of trials (a *long run*), the distribution of subsequent results will *eventually* overwhelm any recent drift away from what is expected. The long run is a long time.

> If a fair coin has landed Heads five times in a row, is the next flip more likely to be a Tail? Five Heads and no Tails looks lopsided. In flipping a fair coin shouldn't we expect about 50% heads and 50% tails? Doesn't the coin "owe" us some Tails in the next few flips? Let's flip it another 100 times. In the next 100 flips, we'd expect to get about 50 more heads and 50 more tails. So after 105 flips we'd have about 55 Heads and 50 Tails – close enough to 50/50 for comfort. The lesson of the LLN is that random processes don't need to compensate in the *short* run to get back to the right long-run probabilities.

This is an easy simulation to do for yourself on a calculator or with a statistics package.

To watch this, we ran a simulation of 100,000 flips of a fair coin. We simply collected 100,000 random numbers, and let the numbers 0-4 represent a Heads and the numbers 5-9 represent Tails. In our 100,000 "flips", there were 2981 streaks of at least 5 heads. If the "Law of Averages" were true, we'd expect the next flip to more likely be Tails to even things out. Actually the next flip was Heads 1550 times and Tails 1431 times or Heads 51.9% of the time. If the probabilities don't change and the events are independent, the probability of the next trial is *always* the same, no matter what has happened up to then. There is *no* Law of Averages for short runs.

Keno and the Law of Averages

Of course, sometimes an apparent drift from what we expect means that the probabilities are, in fact, *not* what we thought. If you get 10 heads in a row maybe the coin has heads on both sides!

DRAFT: Do not distribute or copy

The "Law of Averages" in everyday life

Dear Abby: My husband and I just had our eighth child. Another girl, and I am really one disappointed woman. I suppose I should thank God she was healthy, but, Abby, this one was supposed to have been a boy. Even the doctor told me that the law of averages was in our favor 100 to one. (Abigail Van Buren, 1974. Quoted in Karl Smith (1991), *The Nature of Mathematics*, 6th ed., Pacific Grove, CA: Brooks/Cole, p 589

The law of averages is what baseball is all about," say Kiner. ... What this means in Seaver's case is that he is now "paying" in the percentages for his 1969 season in which he had a 25-7 record... ("Baseball law of averages taking toll on Seaver," *New Haven Register*, June 2, 1974. Quoted in Gary Smith (1985) *Statistical Reasoning*, Boston: Allyn and Bacon, p. 175 both quoted in Richard L. Scheaffer, *et. al.*, *Activity-Based Statistics*, New York, Springer Verlag, p.71-72.

Keno is a simple casino game where numbers from 1 to 80 are chosen. The numbers, as in most lottery games, are supposed to be equally likely. Payoffs are made depending on how many of those numbers you match on your card. A group of graduate students from a Statistics department decided to take a field trip to Reno. They (*very* discreetly) wrote down the outcomes of the games for a couple of days, then drove back to *test* whether the numbers were, in fact, equally likely. It turned out that some numbers were *more likely* to come up than others. Rather than bet on the "law of averages" and put their money on the numbers that were "due", the students put their faith in the LLN—and all their (and their friends) money on the numbers that had come up before. After they pocketed more than $50,000, they were escorted off the premises and invited never to show their faces in that casino again.

Probability

Now that we know, thanks to the Law of Large Numbers, that relative frequencies settle down in the long run, we can officially give the name **probability** to that value. If the relative frequency of red lights settles down to 35%, we say that the *probability* of a red light is .35, and write

$$P(Red) = .35.$$

We can't record more "red lights" than the number of times we hit the intersection (or fewer than none) so our probability must be a value between 0 and 1:

$$0 \leq P \leq 1.$$

A probability of zero indicates impossibility. A probability of one indicates certainty. Remember that we said "in the long run". So we have to wait infinitely long to be sure that an event is impossible or certain.

Probability was first studied by a group of French mathematicians interested in games of chance (OK, gambling). To make things simple, they started by looking at games in which all the possible outcomes were *equally likely*. It's easy to think of situations where this is true, especially in gambling. It's equally likely to get any one of six outcomes from the toss of a fair die. Any of the 52 cards is equally likely to be picked from a well-shuffled deck. Each slot of a roulette wheel is equally likely (or at least it *should* be).

When events are equally likely, the probability of their occurrence is easy to compute – it's just 1 divided by the number of possible outcomes. So, the probability of rolling a 3 from a fair die is 1/6. The probability of picking the Ace of Spades from the top of a well-shuffled deck is 1/52.

But don't get trapped into thinking that random events are always equally likely. The chances of winning a lottery--especially lotteries with very large payoffs--is small. But people (especially poor people) continue to buy tickets. In an attempt to understand why, an interviewer asked someone who had just purchased a lottery ticket, "What do you think your chances are of winning the lottery". The reply was "Oh, about 50-50". The shocked interviewer asked, "How do you get that?" to which the response was, "Well, the way I figure it, either I win, or I don't!"

The moral of this story is that events are *not* always equally likely.

Personal Probability

What's the probability that your grade in this Statistics course will be an A? You may be able to come up with a number that seems reasonable. Of course no matter how confident or depressed you feel about your chances for success, your probability should be between 0 and 1. But how did you come up with this probability? From our discussion of probability, we've said that probability represents the relative frequency or the fraction of times that the event occurs in the long run. Is that what you meant? Probably not – even if you plan on taking the course over and over and over.

We use the language of probability in everyday speech to express a degree of uncertainty *without* basing it on long-run relative frequencies. Your personal assessment of the probability of getting an A expresses your uncertainty about the outcome. That uncertainty may be based on how comfortable you are feeling in the course, or on your midterm grade, but it can't be based on long-run behavior. We call this kind of probability a subjective or **personal probability**[1].

But while personal probabilities may be based on experience, they are not based on either long run relative frequencies or on equally likely events. So they don't display the kind of consistency that we'll need for probabilities to have. For that reason, we will stick to formally defined probabilities. You should be alert to the difference.

The line between personal probability and relative frequency probability can be a fuzzy one. When a weather forecaster predicts a probability of

---

[1] Personal probabilities are interesting and useful, but we won't be dealing with them further in this book beyond warning you to be alert for when a stated probability is a personal statement of belief rather than an assessment of long-run relative frequency.

DRAFT: Do not distribute or copy

rain of 40%, is this a personal probability or a relative frequency probability? The claim may be that 40% of the time, when the map looks like this, it has rained (over some period of time). Or the forecaster may be stating a personal opinion that is based on years of experience and reflects a sense of what has happened in the past in similar situations. When you hear a probability stated, it is good to try to ascertain what kind of probability is intended.

Formal Probability

1   If the probability is 0, the event *never* occurs, and likewise if it has probability 1, it *always* occurs. Even if you think an event is very unlikely, its probability can't be negative, and even if you're sure it will happen, its probability can't be greater than 1. So we require that

A probability is a number between 0 and 1.

For any event A, $0 \leq P(A) \leq 1$

2   If a random phenomenon has only one possible outcome, it is not very interesting (or very random). So we need to distribute the probabilities among all the outcomes a trial can have. How can we do that without getting into trouble? For example, consider what you are doing as you read this book. If the possible outcomes are:

A: you read to the end of this chapter before stopping,

B: you finish this section but stop reading before the end of the chapter, or

C: you bail out before the end of this section.

When we go to assign probabilities to these outcomes, the first thing to be sure of is that we distribute all of the available probability. Something always occurs, so the probability of *something* happening is 1.

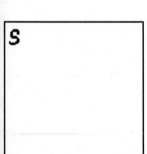

We put all the possible outcomes into a big event called S.

Making this more formal gives the

"Something's gotta happen rule":

The probability of the set of all possible outcomes of a Trial must be 1.

P(S) = 1. (S represents the set of all possible outcomes).

3   Suppose the probability of getting an A in this course is 0.4. What's the probability of not getting an A? Yes, it's 0.6. The set of outcomes that are *not* in the event **A** is called the **complement** of **A**, and is denoted **A^C**. This leads to the **Complement Rule:**

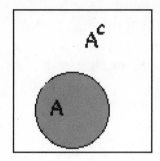

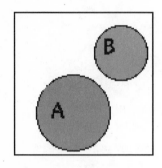

The probability of an event occurring is 1 minus the probability that it doesn't occur.

$$P(A) = 1 - P(A^C).$$

4 Suppose the probability that a randomly selected student is a Sophomore(**A**) is .20 and the probability that he or she is a Junior (**B**) is .30. What is the probability that the student is *either* a Sophomore *or* a Junior (**A** *or* **B**)? If you guessed 0.50 you've deduced the **Addition Rule**, which says that you can add the probabilities of events that have no outcomes in common. Events like this, that can't occur together, are called **disjoint**. The **Addition Rule** states:

For two disjoint events A and B the probability that one *or* the other occurs is the sum of the probabilities of the two events.

$$P(A \text{ } or \text{ } B) = P(A) + P(B) \text{ provided that A and B are disjoint.}$$

We can always add the probabilities of outcomes because they are always disjoint. A trial can't come out in two different ways at the same time. This gives us an easy way to check whether the probabilities we've assigned are **legitimate**.

By the "Something's gotta happen rule," the total of the probabilities of all possible outcomes must be exactly one. No more, no less. And because they are disjoint, we can just add them up to check. For example, suppose we're trying to select an undergraduate student at random. If we were told the probabilities of selecting at random a Freshman, Sophomore, Junior, or Senior were .25, .23, .22, and .20, respectively, and that there were no other possibilities, we would know that something was wrong. These "probabilities" sum to only .90, so this is not a legitimate probability assignment. Similarly, a claim that the probabilities were .26, .27, .29. and .30 would be wrong because these "probabilities" sum to more than 1.0.

But be careful. The Addition Rule doesn't work for events that aren't disjoint. If the probability of owning an MP3 player is 0.50 and the probability of owning a computer is 0.90, the probability of owning either an MP3 player or a computer may be pretty high, but it is *not* 1.40! Why can't you add probabilities like this? Because these events are not disjoint. You *can* own both. The events are not disjoint. In the next chapter, we'll see how to add probabilities for events like these, but we'll need another rule.

5 The color of a traffic light as you reach that intersection is a random outcome. Suppose the light spends 35% of its time red in your direction and the other 65% either green or yellow. What is the chance of finding it red two days in a row? That's the same as asking the probability of finding it red today *and* finding it red tomorrow. For independent events, the answer is very simple. And the color of the light today *is*

DRAFT: Do not distribute or copy

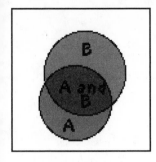

independent of the color yesterday. The **Multiplication Rule** says that for independent events, to find the probability that both events occur, we just multiply the probabilities together. Formally:

For two independent events A and B, the probability that both A and B occur is the product of the probabilities of the two events.

P(A *and* B) = P(A)P(B) provided that A and B are independent.

This rule can be extended to more than just two independent events. What's the chance of finding the light red every day this week? We can just multiply the probability of it happening each day, so it's:

$$0.35 \times 0.35 \times 0.35 \times 0.35 \times 0.35 = 0.00525$$

or, about 5 times in a thousand. Of course, to calculate this probability we have used the assumption that the events are independent.

Many statistics methods assume independence, but *assuming* independence doesn't make it true. We'll talk about conditions to check in data to help judge whether the independence assumption is reasonable.

Putting the Rules to Work

In most situations where we want to find a probability, we'll use the rule in combination.

For example, What's the chance that we'll hit a red light *at least once* during the week? Hitting at least one red light means that we hit either 1, 2,3,4 or 5 red lights during the week. So, we could calculate the probability of hitting at least one red light by first calculating the probability of hitting exactly 1 red light during the week, then exactly 2, then 3, 4 and 5. Then we just add them up.

Aarrgghh!

There must be an easier way to do this, and there is.

It can be easier to work with the *complement* of the event we're really interested in. Once we have the complement's probability, we know (from rule 3) that the probability of the event we're interested in is just 1 minus the probability of the complement. What's the complement of getting at least one red light? It's getting *no* red lights, five days in a row. We know the probability of hitting a red light is .35 each day, so by the complement rule, the probability of *not* hitting a red light is 1 – .35 or .65 each day. So, the probability of making it through five consecutive days without hitting a red light is $.65^5$. This is the probability of the complement of what we wanted. Now, taking the complement of this compound event, we find the probability that it *doesn't* happen (*not* 0 red lights) is $1 - .65^5 = 1 - .116 = 0.88$.

Probability Step-by-Step

The five rules we've seen can be used in a number of different combinations to answer a surprising number of questions. Let's try one to see how we might go about it.

In 2001 Masterfoods, the manufacturers of M&M's ® milk chocolate candies decided to add another color to the standard color lineup of brown, yellow, red, orange, blue, and green. To decide which color, they surveyed kids in nearly every country of the world and asked them to vote among Purple, Pink, and Teal. The global winner --- Purple! In the U.S. 42% of those who voted said purple, 37% said teal and only 19% said pink. But in Japan the percentages were 38% pink 36% teal and only 16% purple. Let's use Japan's percentages to ask some questions.

1. What is the probability that a Japanese M&M's survey respondent selected at random preferred either "pink" or "teal"?
2. If we pick two respondents at random what is the probability that they *both* selected "purple"?
3. If we pick three respondents at random, what it is the probability that *at least one* preferred "purple"?

Think

The probability of an event is its long term relative frequency. It can be determined in several ways: by looking at many replications of an event, by deducing it from equally likely events, or by using some other information. Here, we are told the relative frequencies of the three responses.

Make sure the probabilities are legitimate. They're not here. Either there was a mistake or the other voters must have chosen a color other than the three given. A check of other countries shows a similar deficit, so probably we are seeing those who had no preference or who wrote in another color.

The M&M's web site reports the proportions of Japanese votes by color. These give us the probability of selecting a voter who preferred each of the colors:

P(Pink) = .38

P(Teal) = .36

P(Purple) = .16

Each is between 0 and 1, but these don't add up to 1. The remaining 10% of the voters must have not expressed a preference or written in another color. We'll put them together into "No Preference" and add:

P(No Preference) = .10. With this addition, we have a legitimate assignment of probabilities.

DRAFT: Do not distribute or copy

Show /Tell	1 What is the probability that a Japanese M&M's survey respondent selected at random preferred either "pink" or "teal"?	A respondent can't choose both Pink and Teal, so these events are disjoint and we can apply the Addition Rule. It tells us that P(Pink or Teal) = P(Pink) + P(Teal) = .38 + .36 = .74 The probability that the respondent said Pink or Teal is 0.74
	2 If we pick two respondents at random what is the probability that they both said "purple"?	
Think	To use the multiplication rule, we'll need independent events. Independence seems like a reasonable assumption here. The choice of one respondent is not likely to have affected the choice of another.	We'll assume the events are independent because the outcome of one is unlikely to affect the outcome of another.
Show /Tell	For both respondents to pick purple, each one has to pick purple.	P(both purple) = P(first respondent picks purple and second respondent picks purple) = P(first respondent picks purple) x P(second respondent picks purple) = .16 x .16= .026 The probability that both respondents pick purple is .026.
	3. If we pick three respondents at random, what it is the probability that at least one preferred "purple"?	

Think	The phrase "at least…" often flags a question best answered by looking at the complement, and that's the best approach here. The complement of "at least one preferred purple" is "None of them preferred purple."	P(at least one picked Purple) = $P(\{\text{none picked purple}\}^C)$ = 1 - P(none picked purple) by Rule 3.
Show /Tell	We calculate P{None Purple} by using the multiplication rule. Then we can use the complement rule to get the probability we want.	P(none picked purple) = P(not purple and not purple and not purple) . These are independent events because they are choices by 3 independent respondents, so P(none picked purple) = P(first not purple) x P(second not purple) x P(third not purple) = $P(\text{not purple})^3$. P(not purple) = 1 – P(purple) = 1 - .16 =.84. So P(none one picked purple) = $.84^3$= .59 Finally, P(at least one picked purple) = 1 - P(none picked purple) = 1 - .59 = .41 The chance that at least one of the respondents picked purple is 41%.

What Can Go Wrong?

- *Beware of probabilities that don't add up to 1.* To be a legitimate probability distribution, the sum of the probabilities for all possible outcomes must total 1. If the sum is less than one, you may need to add another category, "other" and assign the remaining probability to that outcome. If the sum is more than one, check that the outcomes are disjoint. If they are not, then you can't assign probabilities by just counting relative frequencies.

- *Don't add probabilities of events if they're not disjoint.* Events must be disjoint to use the Addition Rule. The probability of being under 80 *or* a female is not the probability of being under 80 *plus* the probability of being female. That sum will be over 1.

- *Don't multiply probabilities of events if they're not independent.* The probability of selecting a student at random who is over 6'10"

DRAFT: Do not distribute or copy

tall *and* on the basketball team is *not* the probability the student is 6' 10" tall *times* the probability they're on the basketball team. Knowing that the student is over 6'10" changes the probability of their being on the basketball team. You can't multiply these probabilities. The multiplication of probabilities of events that are not independent is one of the most common errors in dealing with probabilities.

- ***Don't confuse disjoint and independent.*** Disjoint events *can't* be independent. If A={You get an A in this class} and B={You get a B in this class}, A and B are disjoint. Are they independent? If you find out that A is true, does that change the probability of B? You bet it does! So they can't be independent.

Key Concepts

Random Phenomenon	A phenomenon is random if we know what outcomes could happen, but not which particular values did or will happen.
Trial	A single attempt or realization of a Random Phenomenon.
Outcome	The outcome of a trial is the value measured, observed, or reported for an individual instance of that trial.
	Outcomes are considered to be either:
	Discrete if they have distinct values such as Heads or Tails, or
	Continuous if they take on numeric values in some range of possible values.
Event	A collection of outcomes. Usually, we identify events in order to attach probabilities to them. We denote events with bold capital letters such as **A**, **B**, or **C**.
Independence (informally)	Two events are *independent* if knowing whether one event occurs does not alter the probability that the other event occurs.
Law of Large Numbers	The Law of Large Numbers states that the long run *relative frequency* of repeated independent events gets closer and closer to the *true* relative frequency as the number of trials increases.

Probability	The probability of an event is a number between 0 and 1 that reports the likelihood of the event's occurrence. A probability can be derived from equally likely outcomes, from the long run proportion of the event's occurrence, or from known proportions. We write P(**A**) for the probability of the event **A**.
"Something's gotta happen rule"	The sum of the probabilities of all possible outcomes of a Trial must be 1.
Complement Rule	The probability of an event occurring is 1 minus the probability that it doesn't occur. $$P(A) = 1 - P(A^C)$$
Disjoint	Two events are disjoint if they share no outcomes in common. If **A** and **B** are disjoint, then knowing that **A** occurs tells us that **B** cannot occur.
Addition Rule	If A and B are disjoint events, then $$P(\mathbf{A}\ or\ \mathbf{B}) = P(\mathbf{A}) + P(\mathbf{B}).$$
Multiplication Rule	If **A** and **B** are independent events, then $$P(\mathbf{A}\ and\ \mathbf{B}) = P(\mathbf{A}) * P(\mathbf{B}).$$

Skills

When you complete this lesson you should:

Think

- Understand that random phenomena are unpredictable in the short term but show long-run regularity.

- Be able to recognize random outcomes in a real-world situation.

- Know that the relative frequency of an outcome of a random phenomenon settles down as we gather more random outcomes. Be able to state the Law of Large Numbers.

- Know the basic definitions and rules of probability

Show

- Use the facts about probability to determine whether an assignment of probabilities is legitimate. Each probability must be a number between 0 and 1 and the sum of the probabilities assigned to all possible outcomes must be 1.

- Know how and when to apply the Addition rule. Know that events must be disjoint for the Addition rule to apply.

- Know how and when to apply the Multiplication rule. Know that events must be independent for the Multiplication rule to apply. Be able to use the

DRAFT: Do not distribute or copy

multiplication rule to find probabilities for combinations of independent events.

- Know how to use the Complement rule to make calculating probabilities simpler. Recognize that probabilities of "at least..." are likely to be simplified in this way.

Tell

- Be able to use statements about probability in describing a random phenomenon. You will need this skill soon for making statements about statistical inference.

- Know and be able to use correctly the terms sample space, disjoint events, and independent events.

Exercises

1. **Roulette** A casino claims that its roulette wheel is truly random. What should that claim mean?

2. **Rain** The weather reporter on TV makes predictions such as that the chance of rain is 25%. What do you think is the meaning of such a phrase?

3. **Winter** Comment on the following quotation:

   "What I think is our best determination is it will be a colder than normal winter," said Pamela Naber Knox, a Wisconsin state climatologist. "I'm basing that on a couple of different things. First, in looking at the past few winters, there has been a lack of really cold weather. Even though we are not supposed to use the law of averages, we are due." (Associated Press, Fall 1992, Quoted by Schaeffer, *et. al.*)

4. **Rain** After an unusually dry autumn a radio announcer is heard to say, "Watch out! We'll pay for these sunny days later on this winter." Explain what he is trying to say, and comment on the validity of his reasoning.

5. **Cold Streak** A batter who had failed to get a hit in seven consecutive times at bat then hits a game-winning home run. When talking to reporters afterwards he says he was very confident that last time at bat because he knew he was "due for a hit". Comment on his reasoning.

6. **Crash** Commercial airplanes have an excellent safety record. Nonetheless there are crashes occasionally, with the loss of many

lives. In the weeks following a crash, airlines often report a drop in passengers, probably because people are afraid to risk flying.

a) A travel agent suggests that, since the law of averages makes it highly unlikely to have two plane crashes within a few weeks of each other, flying soon after a crash is the safest time. What do you think?

b) If the airline industry proudly announces that they have set a new record for the longest period of safe flights would you be reluctant to fly? Are they due to have crash?

7. **Fire Insurance** Insurance companies collect annual payments from homeowners in exchange for paying to rebuild houses that burn down.

a) Why should you be reluctant to accept a $300 payment from your neighbor to replace his house should it burn down during the coming year?

b) Why can the insurance company make that offer?

8. **Jackpot** On January 20, 2000 the International Gaming Technology company issued a press release:

(LAS VEGAS, Nev.) – Cynthia Jay was smiling ear to ear as she walked into the news conference at The Desert Inn Resort in Las Vegas today, and well she should. Last night, the 37-year-old cocktail waitress won the world's largest slot jackpot -- $34,959,458 – on a Megabucks machine. She said she had played $27 in the machine when the jackpot hit. Nevada Megabucks has produced 49 major winners in its 14-year history. The top jackpot builds from a base amount of $7 million and can be won with a 3-coin ($3) bet. [www.igtonline.com]

a) How can the Desert Inn afford to give away millions of dollars on a $3 bet?

b) Why did they issue a press release? Wouldn't most businesses want to keep such a huge loss quiet?

9. **Spinner** The plastic arrow on a spinner for a child's game stops rotating to point at a color that will determine what happens next. Which of the following probability assignments are possible?

Probabilities of ...

	Red	Yellow	Green	Blue
a)	0.25	0.25	0.25	0.25
b)	0.1	0.2	0.3	0.4
c)	0.2	0.3	0.4	0.5
d)	0	0	1	0
e)	0.1	0.2	1.2	-1.5

10. **Scratch Off** Many stores run "secret sales": shoppers receive cards that determine how large a discount they get, but the percentage is revealed by scratching off that black stuff (What *is* that?) only after

the purchase has been totaled at the cash register. The store is required to reveal (in the fine print) the distribution of discounts available. Which of these probability assignments are plausible?

		Probabilities of ...		
	10% off	20% off	30% off	50% off
a)	0.2	0.2	0.2	0.2
b)	0.5	0.3	0.2	0.1
c)	0.80	0.10	0.05	0.05
d)	0.75	0.25	0.25	-0.25
e)	1	0	0	0

11. **Car Repairs** A consumer organization estimates that over a one-year period 17% of cars will need to be repaired once, 7% twice, and 4% will require 3 or more repairs.
    a) What is the probability that a car chosen at random will need
        1. no repairs?
        2. no more than one repair?
        3. some repairs?
    b) If you own 2 cars, what is the probability that
        1. neither will need repair?
        2. both will need repair?

12. **Stats Projects** In a large introductory statistics lecture hall, the professor reports that 55% of the students enrolled have never taken a calculus course, 32% have taken only one semester of calculus, and the rest have taken two or more semesters of calculus. The professor randomly assigns students to groups of three to work on a project for the course.
    a) What is the probability that the first groupmate you meet has studied
        1. some calculus?
        2. no more than one semester of calculus.
    b) What is the probability that, of your other two groupmates,
        1. neither has studied calculus?
        2. both have studied at least one semester of calculus.
        3. at least one has had more than one semester of calculus?

13. **M&M's** The Mars company says that yellow candies make up 20% of their plain M&M's, red another 20%, and orange, blue, and green are each 10%. The rest are brown.
    a) If you pick an M&M at random what is the probability that
        1. it is brown?
        2. it is yellow or orange?
        3. it is not green?
        4. it is purple?

Copyright © 2001, Dick De Veaux and Paul Velleman

    b) If you pick three M&M's in a row, what is the probability that
        1. they are all brown?
        2. the third one is the first one that's red?
        3. none are yellow?
        4. at least one is green?

14. **Blood** The American Red Cross says that about 45% of the US population has Type O blood, 40 % Type A, 11% Type B, and the rest Type AB.
    a) Someone volunteers to give blood. What is the probability that this donor
        1. has Type AB blood?
        2. has Type A or Type B?
        3. is not Type O?
    b) Among four potential donors, what is the probability that
        1. all are Type O?
        2. no one is Type AB?
        3. they are not all Type A?
        4. at least one person is Type B?

15. **Disjoint or Independent?** In problem 13 you calculated probabilities of getting various M&Ms. Some of your answers depended on the assumption that the outcomes described were *disjoint*; that is, they could not both happen at the same time. Other answers depended on the assumption that the events were *independent*; that is, the occurrence of one of them doesn't affect the probability of the other. Do you understand the difference between disjoint and independent?
    a) If you draw one M&M, are the events of getting a Red one and getting an Orange one disjoint or independent or neither?
    b) If you draw two M&M's one after the other, are the events of getting a Red on the first and a Red on the second disjoint or independent or neither?
    c) Can disjoint events ever be independent? Explain.

16. **Disjoint or Independent?** In problem 14 you calculated probabilities involving various blood types. Some of your answers depended on the assumption that the outcomes described were *disjoint*; that is, they could not both happen at the same time. Other answers depended on the assumption that the events were *independent*; that is, the occurrence of one of them doesn't affect the probability of the other. Do you understand the difference between disjoint and independent?
    a) If you examine one person, are the events that person is Type A and that person is Type B disjoint or independent or neither?
    b) If you examine two people, are the events that the first is Type A and the second Type B disjoint or independent or neither?
    c) Can disjoint events ever be independent? Explain.

17. **Dice** You roll a fair die three times. What is the probability that
    a) you roll all 6's?
    b) you roll all odd numbers?
    c) none of your rolls gets a number divisible by 3?
    d) you roll at least one 5?
    e) the numbers you roll are not all 5's.

18. **Slot Machine** A slot machine has three wheels that spin independently. Each has 10 symbols: 4 bars, 3 lemons, 2 cherries, and a bell. If you play, what is the probability
    a) you get 3 lemons?
    b) you get no fruit symbols?
    c) you get 3 bells (the jackpot)?
    d) you get no bells?
    e) you get at least one bar (an automatic loser)?

19. **Champion Bowler** A certain bowler can roll a strike 70% of the time. What is the probability that she
    a) goes three consecutive frames without a strike?
    b) makes her first strike in the third frame?
    c) has at least one strike in the first three frames?
    d) rolls a perfect game (12 consecutive strikes)?

20. **The Train** To get to work a commuter must cross train tracks. The time the train arrives varies slightly from day to day, but the commuter estimates he'll get stopped on about 15% of the workdays. During a certain 5-day workweek, what is the probability that he
    a) gets stopped on Monday and again on Tuesday?
    b) gets stopped for the first time on Thursday?
    c) gets stopped every day?
    d) gets stopped at least once during the week?

21. **Voters** Suppose that in your city 37% of the voters are registered as Democrats, 29% as Republicans, and 11% as members of other parties (Liberal, Right to Life, Green, etc.). Voters not aligned with any official party are termed "Independent". You are conducting a poll by calling registered voters at random. In your first three calls, what is the probability you talk to
    a) all Republicans?
    b) no Democrats?
    c) at least one Independent?

22. **Religion** Census reports for a city indicate that 62% of residents classify themselves as Christian, 12% as Jewish, and 16% as members of other religions (Muslims, Buddhists, etc.). The remaining residents classified themselves as Non-religious. A polling organization seeking information about public opinions wants to be sure to talk

with people with a variety of religious views, and makes random phone calls. Among the first four people they call, what is the probability they reach

a) all Christians?

b) no Jews?

c) at least one person who is non-religious?

23. **Tires** You bought a new set of four tires from a manufacturer who just announced a recall because 2% of those tires are defective. What is the probability that at least one of yours is defective?

24. **Pepsi** For a sales promotion the manufacturer places winning symbols under the caps of 10% of all Pepsi bottles. You buy a 6-pack; what is the probability that you win something?

25. **9/11?** On September 11, 2002, the first anniversary of the terrorist attack on the World Trade Center, the New York State Lottery's daily number came up 9-1-1. An interesting coincidence, or a cosmic sign?

a) What is the probability that the winning three numbers match the date on any given day?

b) What is the probability that a whole year passes without this happening?

c) What is the probability that the date and winning lottery number match at least once during any year?

d) If every one of the 50 states has a 3 digit lottery, what is the probability that at least one of them will come up 911 on Sept 11?

15 Probability Rules!

Let's face it. Probabilities of simple events are just not that interesting. But when we combine events and think about conditional outcomes, things get juicier. We saw back in Chapter 3 that the chance of surviving the *Titanic* changed depending on the ticket class of the passenger. But to navigate the stormy seas of probability, we'll need some rules to steer by.

Remember, for any random phenomenon, each **trial** generates an **outcome**. An **event** is *any* set or collection of outcomes. The collection of *all possible* outcomes is called the **sample space**, and denoted S.[1]

If you flip a coin, what is the sample space? All you can get is heads or tails, (we'll ignore the possibility that it lands on the edge). So the sample space is just the set {H,T} H for heads and T for tails. It's no big deal. To make it seem more important, some books use the Greek letter Ω instead of S. But whatever the symbol, the **sample space** is just the collection of *all the possible outcomes*.

Events

Pull a bill from your wallet or pocket without looking at it. An outcome of this trial is the bill you select. The sample space, is all the bills in circulation: **S**={\$1 bill, \$2 bill, \$5 bill, \$10 bill, \$20 bill, \$50 bill, \$100 bill } These are *all* the possible outcomes. (In spite of what you may have seen in bank robbery movies, there are no \$500 or \$1000 bills.)

We can combine possible outcomes of such a trial into events. So, for example, the event **A** = {\$1, \$5, \$10} represents selecting a 1, 5, or 10 dollar bill. The event **B** = {a bill that does not have a President on it} is the collection of outcomes;… (Don't Look! Can you name them?)…{\$10 (Hamilton)} and {\$100 (Franklin)}. The event **C** = {enough money to pay for a \$12 meal with one bill} is the set of outcomes {\$20, \$50, \$100}.

---

[1] Mathematicians like to use the term space as a fancy name for a set. It's sounds more high tech, and makes a set sound like something more important. Sort of like referring to the closet they gave you as a dorm room as your "living space." So, it can be a real plus. But remember that it's really just a bunch of outcomes.

In January 2002, the 12 member nations of the European Union started using the Euro to replace all their separate currencies. The Euro was conceived to be equal in value roughly to a U.S. Dollar and is split into 100 parts called, cents. The coins are almost like U.S coins in size. There are 1, 5, 10, 20, 50 cent coins. But there's also a 2c , and 1E and 2E coins. The smallest bill is the 5E. The others are 10, 20, 50, 100, 200 and 500(!) Euros.

Notice that outcomes don't have to be equally likely. You'd probably be more surprised (and pleased) to pull out a $100 bill than a $1 bill, but it's not very likely. You probably carry many more $1 than $100 bills, but without information about the probability of each outcome, we can't calculate the probability of such events.

When outcomes *are* equally likely, probabilities for events are easy to find just by counting. 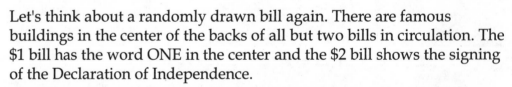When the k possible outcomes are equally likely, each has a probability of $1/k$. For example, consider the final digit of the serial number of that bill you extracted at random. Final digits are equally likely to be any digit from 0 to 9.

So, what's the probability of randomly selecting a bill whose serial number ends in an odd digit? We could simulate this event by simply assigning the digits to the random numbers 0 through 9. Because half of the digits from 0 to 9 are odd, you wouldn't be surprised to learn that the probability of finding a bill whose last digit is odd is 5/10. We can make this more formal by saying that for any event, **A**, that is made up of *equally likely* outcomes,

$$P(\mathbf{A}) = \frac{count\ of\ outcomes\ in\ \mathbf{A}}{count\ of\ all\ possible\ outcomes}.$$

Be careful! This rule won't work unless the outcomes are *equally likely*. The probability of the event **C** (getting more than $12 on your bill) is NOT 3/7. There are 7 possible outcomes, and 3 of them exceed $12, but they are NOT equally likely. And the probability that your lottery ticket will win still isn't 1/2.

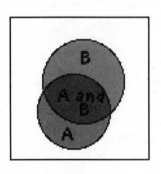

Let's think about a randomly drawn bill again. There are famous buildings in the center of the backs of all but two bills in circulation. The $1 bill has the word ONE in the center and the $2 bill shows the signing of the Declaration of Independence.

What is the probability of randomly selecting **A**= {a bill with an odd-numbered value} or B={a bill with a building on the reverse}?We know A={$1,$5} and B={$5,$10,$20,$50,$100}. But we know P(**A** or **B**) is not simply the sum P(**A**) + P(**B**), because the events **A** and **B** are not disjoint. So what can we do?

DRAFT: Do not distribute or copy

The First Three Rules for Working with Probability Rules

Make a picture.

Make a picture.

Make a picture.

We are dealing with probabilities now, not data, but the three rules don't change. The most common kind of picture to make is one like we just used, called a Venn diagram. Even experienced statisticians make Venn diagrams to help them think about probabilities of compound and overlapping events. You should too.

John Venn (1834-1923) created the Venn Diagram. His book on probability, *The Logic of Chance* was said to be "strikingly original and considerably influenced the development of the theory of statistics." By John Maynard Keynes, one of the founders of Economics.

The General Addition Rule

So, what is the probability of randomly selecting a bill with an odd-numbered value *or* a building on the reverse? As the diagram shows, we can't add the two probabilities because the events overlap. There are outcomes in the *intersection* of **A** and **B**. Let's put the actual outcomes on the Venn diagram. The box represents the sample space. Notice that the $2 bill has neither a building nor an odd denomination, so it sits outside both circles.

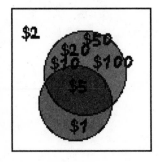

It's the $5 bill that plays a crucial role here because it is both odd *and* has a building on the reverse. It's in both **A** and **B**, which places it in the *intersection* of the two circles. The reason we can't simply add the probabilities of **A** and **B** is that we'd include the $5 bill twice.

If we did add the two probabilities, we could compensate by *subtracting* out the probability of that $5 bill. So,

P(odd number value *or* building)

= P(odd number value) + P(building) – P(odd number value *and* building)

= P($1, $5) + P($5, $10, $20, $50, $100) – P($5).

This rule works in general. We add the probabilities of two events and then subtract out the probability of their intersection. This approach gives us The **General Addition Rule,** which does not require disjoint events:

$$P(\mathbf{A} \ or \ \mathbf{B}) = P(\mathbf{A}) + P(\mathbf{B}) - P(\mathbf{A} \ and \ \mathbf{B})$$

> ## Would you like dessert or coffee?
>
> Natural language can be ambiguous. In the question above, is the answer one of the two alternatives, or simply "yes"? That kind of ambiguity can confuse our probabilities.
>
> Suppose we had been asked the different question: What is the probability that the bill we draw has *either* an odd value, or a building, but *not both*. Which bills are we talking about now? The set we're interested in would be {$1, $10, $20, $50, $100}. We don't include the $5 bill in the set because it has both characteristics.
>
> Why isn't this the same answer as before? The problem is that when we say the word *or*, we usually mean *either* one *or* both. We don't usually mean the *exclusive* version of or as in: "would you like the fish *or* the vegetarian alternative?" So, usually when we ask for the probability that **A** *or* **B** occurs, we mean **A** or **B** or both. And we know that probability is P(**A**)+ P(**B**) – P(**A** *and* **B**). The general rule subtracts the probability of the outcomes in **A** *and* **B** because we've counted those outcomes *twice*. But they're still there.
>
> But if we really mean **A** or **B**, but NOT both, then we have to get *rid* of the outcomes in {**A** and **B**}. So P(**A** or **B**, but *not* both) = P(**A** *or* **B**) – P(**A** *and* **B**) = P(**A***)* +P(**B**) –2*P(**A** *and* **B**). Now we've subtracted P(**A** *and* **B**) twice. Once because we don't want to double-count these events, and a second time because we really didn't want to count them at all. At this point it would be a good idea to draw a picture and make sure you see how this works!

DRAFT: Do not distribute or copy

It Depends...

Two psychologists surveyed 478 children in grades 4, 5, and 6 in elementary schools in Michigan. They stratified their sample, drawing roughly 1/3 from rural, suburban, and urban schools. Among their questions, they asked the students whether their primary goal was to get good grades, to be popular, or to be good at sports. One question of interest was whether boys and girls at this age had similar goals.

Here is a *contingency table* giving counts of the students by their goals and gender.

	Grades	Popular	Sports	total
boy	117	50	60	227
girl	130	91	30	251
total	247	141	90	478

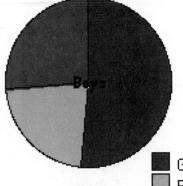

Grades
Popular
Sports

The distribution of goals for boys and girls. Table 15.1

Back in Chapter 3 we looked at contingency tables and graphed the *conditional distributions*. The graphs show the *relative frequencies* with which boys and girls named the three goals. It's only a short step from these relative frequencies to probabilities.

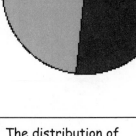

Let's focus in on this study and make the sample space just the set of these students. If we select a student at random from this study, the probability we select a girl is just the corresponding relative frequency (since we're equally likely to select any of the 478 students). There are 251 girls in the data out of a total of 478, giving a probability of

$$P(Girl) = 251/478 = .525$$

The distribution of goals for boys and girls. Figure 15.1

The same method works for more complicated events like intersections. For example, what is the probability of selecting a girl whose goal is to be popular? Well, 91 girls named popularity as their goal, so the probability is

$$P(Girl \text{ and } Popular) = 91/478 = 0.19$$

The probability of selecting a student whose goal is to excel at Sports is

$$P(Sports) = 90/478 = 0.188$$

We've done this sort of thing before in Chapter 3. But now, because we've defined the sample space as these 478 students, we can recognize the relative frequencies as probabilities.

But, what if we are given the information that the selected student is a girl? Would that change the probability that the selected student's goal would be sports? You bet it would! The pie charts show that girls are much less likely to say their goal is to excel at sports than are boys. When we restrict our focus to girls, we look only at the girls' row of the table, which gives the conditional distribution of goals given "girl". Of the 251 girls, only 30 of them said the their goal was to excel at sports.

We write the probability that a selected student wants to excel at sports *given that we have selected a girl* as:

$$P(\text{Sports} \mid \text{Girl}) = 30/251 = 0.12$$

For boys, we look at the conditional distribution of goals given "boy" shown in the top row of the table. There, of the 227 boys, 60 said their goal was to excel at sports. So, $P(\text{Sports} \mid \text{Boy}) = 60/227 = 0.26$, more than twice the girl's probability.

In general, when we want the probability of an event from a *conditional* distribution, we write $P(\textbf{B} \mid \textbf{A})$ and pronounce it "the probability of **B** *given* **A**." A probability that takes into account a given *condition* such as this is called a **conditional probability**.

Let's look at what we did. We worked with the counts, but we could work with the probabilities just as well. There were 30 students who both were girls and had sports as their goal, and there are 251 girls. So we found the probability to be: 30/251. To find the probability of the event **B** *given* the event **A**, we restrict our attention to the outcomes in **A**. We then find in what fraction of *those* outcomes **B** also occurred. Formally, we write:

$$P(\textbf{B} \mid \textbf{A}) = \frac{P(\textbf{A} \; and \; \textbf{B})}{P(\textbf{A})}$$

Thinking this through, we can see that it is just what we have been doing, but with counts. Look back at the girls for whom sports was the goal. How did we calculate $P(\text{Sports} \mid \text{Girl})$?

But the rule says to use probabilities. It says to take $P(\textbf{A} \; and \; \textbf{B})/P(\textbf{A})$. And the result is the same whether we use counts or probabilities because the total in the sample cancels out:

$$\frac{P(Sports \; and \; Girl)}{P(Girl)} = \frac{30/478}{251/478} = \frac{30}{251}$$

To use the formula for conditional probability, we're supposed to insist on one restriction. The formula doesn't work if $P(\textbf{A})$ is 0. That would mean that that we were "given" the fact that **A** was true even though the probability of **A** is zero, which would be a contradiction. So the formula only works when the event that's given has probability greater than 0. Let's take our rule out for a spin. What's the probability that we have selected a girl *given* that the selected student's goal is popularity? Applying the rule we get

$$P(\text{girl} \mid \text{popular}) = \frac{P(\text{girl } and \text{ popular})}{P(\text{popular})}$$

$$= \frac{91/478}{141/478} = \frac{91}{141}$$

The General Multiplication Rule

Remember the Multiplication Rule? It said

P(**A** and **B**) = P(**A**) P(**B**) when **A** and **B** are independent.

But now we can write a more general rule that doesn't require independence. In fact, we've *already* written it down. We just need to rearrange the equation a bit.

The equation in the definition for conditional probability contains the probability of **A** *and* **B**. Rearranging the equation gives

P(**A** *and* **B**) = P(**A**) P(**B** | **A**)

This is a multiplication rule for compound events that does not require that the events be independent.

Better than that, it even makes sense. The probability of two events **A** and **B**, *both* occurring is the probability that event **A** occurs multiplied by the probability that event **B** *also* occurs – that is, by the probability that event **B** occurs *given* that event **A** occurs.

It probably occurs to you that there's nothing special about which set we call **A** and which one we call **B**. We should be able to state this the other way around. And indeed we can. It is equally true that:

P(**A** *and* **B**) = P(**B**) P(**A** | **B**)

Independence

Let's return to the question of just what it means for events to be independent. We've said informally that what we mean by independence is that the outcome of one event does not influence the probability of the other. With our new notation for conditional probabilities, we can write a formal definition: Events **A** and **B** are independent whenever

P(**B** | **A**) = P(**B**).

Now, we can see that the multiplication rule for independent events we saw in Chapter 14 is just a special case of the general multiplication rule. The general rule says:

$$P(A \text{ and } B) = P(A)\, P(B \mid A)$$

whether the events are independent or not. But when events **A** and **B** are independent, we can write P(**B**) for P(**B** | **A**) and we get back our simple rule:

$$P(A \text{ and } B) = P(A)\, P(B).$$

Sometimes people use this statement as the definition of independent, but we find the other definition more intuitive. It doesn't really matter, but the idea is that the probabilities of independent events don't change when you find out that one of them has occurred.

Is the probability of having good grades as a goal independent of the gender of the responding student? Looks like it might be. We need to check whether

$$P(\text{grades} \mid \text{girl}) = P(\text{grades})$$

$$\frac{130}{251} = 0.52 \overset{?}{=} \frac{247}{478} = 0.52$$

To this accuracy, it looks like we can consider the events independent.

> If we had to pick one idea in this chapter that you should understand and remember, it is the definition and meaning of independence. We'll need this idea in every one of the chapters that follow this one.

Independent ≠ Disjoint

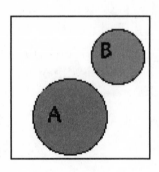

Are disjoint events independent? Both concepts seem to have similar ideas of separation and distinctness about them, but in fact disjoint events *cannot* be independent. Let's see why. Consider the two disjoint events {You get an A in this course} and {You get a B in this course}. They're disjoint because they have no outcomes in common. But now suppose you learn that you *did* get an A in the course. What now is the probability that you did get a B? You can't get both grades, so it must be 0.

But look what that means. Knowing that the first event (getting an A) occurred changed your probability for the second event (down to zero). So the events aren't independent.

Disjoint events can't be independent. They have no outcomes in common, so knowing that one occurred means the other didn't. A common error is to treat disjoint events as if they were independent, and apply the multiplication rule for independent events. Don't do that.

Depending on Independence

It is much easier to think about independent events than to deal with conditional probabilities. It seems that most people's natural intuition for probabilities breaks down when it comes to conditional probabilities.

DRAFT: Do not distribute or copy

Someone may estimate the probability of a compound event by multiplying the probabilities of its component events together without asking seriously whether those probabilities are independent.

For example, experts have assured us that the probability of a major failure of a commercial nuclear plant is so small that we should not expect such a failure to occur even in a span of hundreds of years. But after only a few decades of commercial nuclear power, the world has seen two failures (Chernobyl and Three Mile Island). How could the estimates have been so wrong?

Well, one simple part of the failure calculation is to test a valve and determine that valves such as this one fail only once in, say 100 years of normal use. For a coolant failure to occur several valves must fail. So we need the compound probability, P(valve 1 fails *and* valve 2 fails *and...*). A simple risk assessment might multiply the small probability of one valve failure together as many times as needed.

But if the valves all came from the same manufacturer, a flaw in one might be found in the others. And maybe when the first fails, it puts additional pressure on the next one in line. In either case, the events aren't independent and so we can't simply multiply the probabilities together.

Whenever you see probabilities multiplied together, stop and ask whether you think they are really independent.

Probability Rules Step-by-Step

Police report that 78% of drivers stopped on suspicion of drunk driving are given a breath test, 36% a blood test, and 22% both tests. What is the probability that a randomly selected DWI suspect is given

1. a test?
2. a blood test or a breath test, but not both?
3. neither test?

Think

Define the events we're interested in and make a picture.

Let A = {suspect is given a breath test}.
Let B = {suspect is given a blood test}.

Then determine the probabilities that are given.

We are told that P(A) = .78. We are also told that P(B) = .36. We are also told that P(A *and* B) = .22.

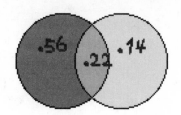

Then, figure out what you want to know in terms of the events and use the rules to solve for the probabilities. Sometimes translating the words to equations is the trickiest step.

Show/ Tell

1. What is the probability that the suspect is given a test?

2. What is the probability that the suspect gets either a blood test or a breath test but NOT both?

3. What is the probability that the suspect gets neither test?

1. The probability the suspect is given a test is P(A or B) = P(A) + P(B) – P(A and B) from the general addition rule. Putting the numbers into the equation, P(A or B) = .78 + .36 - .22 = .92.

   So 92% of all suspects get a test.

2. P(A or B but NOT both) =

   P(A) + P(B) – P(A and B) – P(A and B) = .92-.22 = .70.

   70% of the suspects get *exactly* one of the tests

3. P(neither test) = 1 – P(either test) = 1 – P(A or B) = 1 - .92 = .08. Only 8% of the suspects get no test.

Drawing without Replacement

Room Draw is a process for assigning dormitory rooms to students. Sometimes, when students have the same priority, they are assigned randomly to the currently available dorm rooms. When it's you and your friend's turn to draw, there are 12 rooms left. Three are in Gold hall, a very desirable dorm with spacious wood-paneled rooms. Four are in Silver hall, centrally located, but not quite as desirable. And five are in Wood hall, a new dorm with cramped rooms, located half a mile from the center of campus on the edge of the woods.

Naturally, you and your friend would like to both score rooms in Gold. What are your chances? In particular, what is the chance that you *both* can get rooms in Gold?

If you go first, the chance that *you* will draw one of the Gold rooms is 3/12. Now, with you clutching your prized room assignment, what

DRAFT: Do not distribute or copy

chance does your friend have? There are now only 11 rooms left and but two in Gold, so your friend's chance is now 2/11.

Using our notation, we write

P(friend draws Gold | you draw Gold) = 2/11.

The reason the denominator changes is that we draw these rooms *without replacement.* That is, once one is drawn, it doesn't go back into the pool.

We often sample without replacement. When we draw from a very large population, the change in the denominator is too small to worry about. But when there's a small population to draw from, as in this case, we need to take note and adjust the probabilities.

And the chances of *both* of you lucking out? Well, now we have the two probabilities we need for the General Multiplication rule. So we can write:

P(you = Gold AND friend = Gold)   = P(you = Gold) x P(friend = Gold | you = Gold)

$$= 3/12 * 2/11 = 1/22 = 0.045$$

Now, it doesn't matter who went first, or even if the rooms were drawn simultaneously. Even if the room draw was accomplished by shuffling cards with the names of the dormitories on them and then dealing them out to 12 applicants rather than by each drawing a room in turn, we can still *think* of the calculation as having taking place in two steps:

$$\xrightarrow{3/12} \text{Gold} \xrightarrow{2/11} \text{Gold | Gold}$$

That is, one of you has a probability of 3/12 of drawing a Gold room and the other then has a probability of 2/11 of also drawing a Gold room. It doesn't matter whose draw we think of first. But the probability changes for the second person nonetheless. The diagram shows this ordering of our thoughts.

The idea of diagramming conditional probabilities this way leads to a more general way to help our thinking with pictures – one that works for calculating conditional probabilities even when they involve different variables.

Tree Diagrams

For men, binge drinking is defined as having five or more drinks in a row, and for women as having four or more drinks in a row. (The difference is due to the difference in weight). According to a study by the Harvard School of Public Health[2], 44% of college students engage in binge drinking, 37% drink moderately, and 19% abstain entirely. Another study, published in the *American Journal of Health Behavior* finds that among binge drinkers aged 21-34, 17% have been involved in an alcohol-related automobile accident, while among non-bingers of the same age, only 9% have been involved in such accidents.

With these statistics, what is the probability that a randomly selected college student will be a binge drinker who has had an alcohol-related car accident?

Well, the probability of selecting a binge drinker is about 44%. To find the probability of selecting someone who is both a binge drinker and a driver with an alcohol-related accident we would need to pull out the General Multiplication rule and multiply the probability of one of the events by the conditional probability of the other given the first.

Or we *could* make a picture. Which would you prefer?

We thought so.

The kind of picture that helps us think through this kind of reasoning is called a **tree diagram**, because it shows sequences of events, like we had in room draw, as paths that look like branches of a tree. Because the number of different paths we can take can get large, we usually draw the tree starting from the left and growing vine-like across the page, although sometimes you'll see them drawn from the bottom up or top down.

The first branch of our tree separates students according to their drinking habits. We label each branch of the tree with a possible outcome and its corresponding probability:

'Why,' said the Dodo, 'the best way to explain it is to do it.' -- Lewis Carroll

---

[2] Binge Drinking on Campus: Results of a National Study by Henry Wechsler, Ph.D.; George W. Dowdall, Ph.D.; Andrea Davenport; and William DeJong, Ph.D

DRAFT: Do not distribute or copy

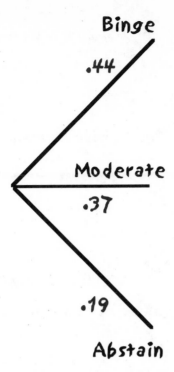

We can diagram the three outcomes of Drinking and indicate their respective probabilities with a simple tree diagram. Fig 15.2

Notice that we cover all possible outcomes with the branches. The probabilities add up to one. But we're also interested in car accidents. The probability of having an alcohol-related accident *depends* on one's drinking behavior. Because the probabilities are *conditional,* we draw the alternatives separately on each branch of the tree:

Extending the tree diagram, we can show both drinking and accident outcomes. The accident probabilities are conditional on the drinking outcomes. Figure 15.3

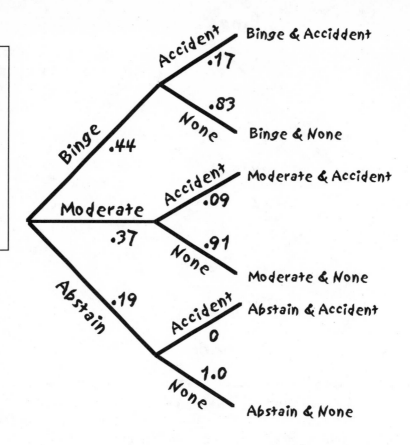

On each of the second set of branches we write the possible outcomes associated with having an alcohol-related car accident (having an accident or not) and the associated probability. These probabilities are different because they are *conditional* depending on the student's drinking behaviors. (It shouldn't be too surprising that those who binge drink have a higher probability of alcohol-related accidents.) And, they add up to one, because given the outcome on the first, branch, these outcomes cover all the possibilities. Looking back at the General Multiplication rule, it's easy to see how the tree pictures the calculation. To find the probability that a randomly selected student will be a binge drinker who has had an alcohol-related car accident, we follow the top branches. The probability of selecting a binger is 0.44. The conditional probability of an accident *given* binge drinking is 0.17. And the General Multiplication Rule tells us that to find the *joint* probability of binge drinker and having an accident, we multiply these two probabilities together:

P(Binge AND Accident) = P(Binge) x P(Accident | Binge)

= 0.44 x 0.17 = 0.075

And we can do the same for each combination of outcomes:

DRAFT: Do not distribute or copy

We can find the probabilities of compound events by multiplying the probabilities along the branch of the tree that leads to the event, just the way the General Multiplication Rule specifies. Figure 15.4

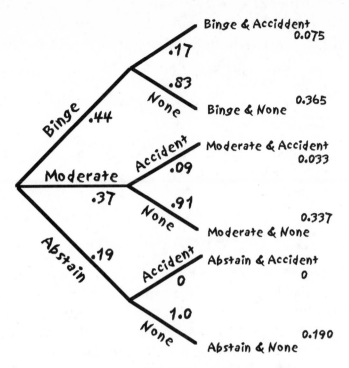

All the outcomes at the far right are disjoint because at each branch of the tree we chose between disjoint alternatives. And they are *all* the possibilities. So the probabilities on the far right must add up to one.

Because the final outcomes are disjoint, we can add up their probabilities to get probabilities for compound events. For example, what's the probability that a selected student has had an alcohol-related car accident? We simply find *all* the outcomes on the far right where an accident has happened. There are three and their probabilities add: 0.075+0.033+0 = 0.108, or 10.8%.

Reversing the Conditioning

If we know a student has had an alcohol-related accident, what's the probability that the student is a binge drinker? That's an interesting question, but we can't just read it from the tree. The tree gives us P(Accident | Binger), but we want P(Binger | Accident) – the conditioning in the other direction. And the two probabilities are definitely *not* the same. We have reversed the conditioning.

We may not have the conditional probability we want, but we do know everything we need to know to find it. To find a conditional probability, we need the probability that both events happen divided by the probability that the given event occurs. We have already found the probability of an accident: 0.075 + 0.033 + 0 = 0.108.

The joint probability that a student is both a binge drinker and someone who's had an accident is found from the top branch: 0.075. Now, we've restricted the *who* of the problem to the students with accidents, so we divide the two to find the conditional probability:

$$P(\text{Binge} \mid \text{Accident}) = P(\text{Binge } and \text{ Accident})/P(\text{Accident})$$

$$= 0.075/0.108$$

$$= 0.694.$$

So the chance that a student who has an alcohol-related car accident is a binge drinker is over 69%! As we said, reversing the conditioning is rarely intuitive. But tree diagrams help us keep track of the calculation when there aren't too many alternatives to consider.

Reversing the Conditioning Step-By Step

When the authors were in college there were only three requirements for graduation that were the same for all students: you had to be able to tread water for 2 minutes, you had to learn a foreign language, and you had to be free of tuberculosis. For the last requirement, all freshmen had to take a TB screening test that consisted of a nurse jabbing what looked like a corn cob holder into your forearm. You were then expected to report back in 48 hours to have it checked. If you were healthy and TB free, it was supposed to look as though you'd never had the test.

Sometime during the 48 hours, one of us had a reaction. When he finally saw the nurse, his arm was about 50% bigger than normal and a very unhealthy red. Did he have TB? The nurse had said that the test was very effective. So, it seemed that the chances must be pretty high that he had TB. How high do you think the chances were? Go ahead and guess. Guess low.

We'll call **A** the event of actually being sick and **B** the event of testing positive. To start a tree, we need to know $P(\mathbf{A})$, the probability of having TB. Even today TB is a fairly uncommon disease with a incidence of about 5 cases per 10,000 in the U.S, so $P(\mathbf{A}) = .0005$. We also need to know the conditional probabilities $P(\mathbf{B}\mid\mathbf{A})$ and $P(\mathbf{B}\mid\mathbf{A}^c)$. Diagnostic tests can make two kinds of errors. They can give a positive result for a healthy person (a *false positive*), or a negative result for a sick person (a *false negative*). Being 99% accurate usually means a false positive rate of 1%. That is, someone who doesn't have the disease, has a 1% chance of testing positive anyway. So we can write $P(\mathbf{B}\mid\mathbf{A}^c) = .01$.

Since a false negative is more serious (because a sick person might not get treatment) tests are usually constructed to have a lower false negative rate. We don't know exactly, but let's assume a 0.1% false negative rate. So only 0.1% of sick people test negative. We can write $P(\mathbf{B}^c\mid\mathbf{A}) = .001$.

Think

Define the events we're interested in and their probabilities.

We know that $P(B | A^c) = .01$ and $P(B^c | A) = .001$. We are also given that $P(A) = .0005$.

Figure out what you want to know in terms of the events. Use the definition of conditional probability to write the event whose probability you want to find.

We're interested in the probability that he had TB given that he tested positive: $P(A | B)$.

Show

Draw the tree diagram. When probabilities are very small like these are, be careful to keep all the significant digits.

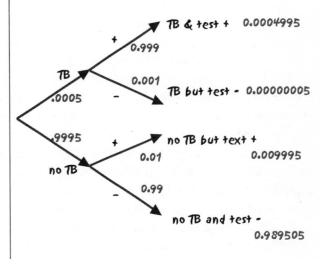

To finish the tree we need $P(A^c)$, $P(B^c | A^c)$ and $P(B | A)$. We can find each of these from the complement rule:

$P(A^c) = 1 - P(A) = .9995$

$P(B^c | A^c) = 1 - P(B | A^c)$

$\qquad = 1 - .01 \quad = .99$ and

$P(B | A) = 1 - P(B^c | A)$

$\qquad = 1 - .001. \quad = .999$

Add up the probabilities corresponding to the condition of interest—in this case, testing positive. We can add the probabilities from the tree twigs that correspond to testing positive because the tree shows disjoint events.

$P(B) = .0004995 + .009995$

$\qquad = 0.010495$

Divide the probability of the outcome of interest (here, having TB given a positive test) by the probability (or frequency) of satisfying the condition (testing positive).

$P(A | B) = P(A \text{ and } B)/P(B)$

$\qquad = 0.0004995/.010495$

$\qquad = 0.047$

Tell

The chance of having TB even after you test positive is less than 5%.

When we reverse the order of conditioning we change the "who" we are concerned with. With events of low probability, the result can be surprising. That's why patients who test positive for HIV, for example, are always told to seek medical counseling. They may have only a small chance of actually being infected. And that's why global drug or disease testing can have unexpected consequences if people interpret *testing* positive as probably *being* positive.

*Bayes's Rule

When we have P(**A** | **B**) but want the *reverse* probability P(**B** | **A**), we need to find : P(**A** and **B**) and P(**A**). A tree is often a convenient way of finding these probabilities. It can even work when we have more than two possible events, as we saw in the binge drinking example. But, instead of using the tree, we *could* write the calculation algebraically, showing exactly how we found the quantities that we needed: P(**A** and **B**) and P(**A**). The result is a formula known at Bayes's Rule after the Rev. Thomas Bayes (1702(?) – 1761), who was credited with the rule after his death, when he could no longer defend himself.[3] Bayes's Rule is quite important in statistics and is the foundation of an approach to statistical analysis known as Bayesian statistics. Although the simple rule deals with two alternative outcomes, the rule can be extended to the case where there are more that two branches to the first split of the tree. The principle remains the same (although the math gets more difficult.) Bayes's Rule is just a formula for reversing the probability from the conditional probability that you're originally given.

Who Discovered Bayes's Rule?

Stigler's "Law of Eponymy" states that discoveries that are named for someone (*eponyms*), are usually named for the wrong person. Steven Stigler, who admits he didn't originate the Law, is an expert on the history of Statistics, and he suspected that the Law might apply to Bayes's Rule. He looked at the possibility that another candidate—one Nicholas Saunderson—was the real discoverer, not the Rev. Bayes. He assembled historical evidence and compared probabilities that the historical events would have happened *given* that Bayes was the discoverer of the rule, with the corresponding probabilities *given* that Saunderson was the discoverer. But of course, what he really wanted to know were the probabilities that Bayes or Saunderson were the discoverers. How did he *reverse* the conditional probabilities? He used Bayes's rule and concluded that actually, it is more likely that Saunderson is the real originator of the rule.

But that doesn't change our tradition of naming the rule for Bayes and calling the branch of statistics arising from this approach Bayesian Statistics. The Bayesians would never stand for being called Saundersonians anyway.

---

[3] Bayes's Rule says that $P(\mathbf{B} \mid \mathbf{A}) = \dfrac{P(\mathbf{A} \mid \mathbf{B})P(\mathbf{B})}{P(\mathbf{A} \mid \mathbf{B})P(\mathbf{B}) + P(\mathbf{A} \mid \mathbf{B}^{c})P(\mathbf{B}^{c})}$. Try it with the TB testing probabilities.

DRAFT: Do not distribute or copy

What Can Go Wrong

- ***Don't use a simple probability rule where the General rule is appropriate.*** Don't assume independence without reason to believe it. Don't assume that outcomes are disjoint without checking. Remember that the general rules apply even when outcomes are in fact independent or disjoint.

- ***Don't find probabilities for samples drawn without replacement as if they had been drawn with replacement.*** Remember to adjust the denominator of your probabilities. This warning only applies when we draw from small populations or draw a large fraction of a finite population. When the population is very large compared to the sample size, the adjustments make no difference, and we ignore them.

- ***Don't reverse conditioning naively.*** As we have seen, the probability of **A** given **B** may not, and in general, does not resemble the probability of **B** given **A**. And, as we have seen, the true probability may be counter-intuitive.

Connections

This chapter shows the unintuitive side of probability. If you've been thinking "my mind doesn't work this way," you're probably right. Humans don't seem to find conditional and compound probabilities natural. These are the questions on which people often make mistakes. In fact, Statisticians make mistakes with conditional probability embarrassingly often.

But our central connection is to the guiding principle that Statistics is about understanding the world. The events discussed in this chapter are close to the kinds of real-world situations where understanding probabilities matters. The methods and concepts of this chapter are the tools you need to understand the part of the real world that deals with the outcomes of complex, uncertain, events.

Key Concepts

Event	A collection of outcomes. Usually, we identify events in order to attach probabilities to them.
Outcome	The outcome of an event is the value measured, observed, or reported for an individual instance of that event.
	Outcomes are considered to be either:
	Discrete if they have distinct values such as

	Heads or Tails, or
	Continuous if they take on numeric values in some range of possible values.
Sample Space	The collection of all possible outcome values. The sample space has a probability of one.
Disjoint events	Two events are *disjoint* if they have no outcomes in common.
Addition Rule	If A and B are disjoint events, then P(**A** *or* **B**) = P(**A**) + P(**B**).
Independence (casually)	Two events are *independent* if knowing whether one event occurs does not alter the probability that the other event occurs.
General Addition Rule	For any two events, **A** and **B**, P(**A** *or* **B**) = P(**A**) + P(**B**) – P(**A** *and* **B**)
Multiplication Rule	If **A** and **B** are independent events, then P(**A** *and* **B**) = P(**A**) * P(**B**).
Conditional probability	$$P(\mathbf{B}\,|\,\mathbf{A}) = \frac{P(\mathbf{A}\ and\ \mathbf{B})}{P(\mathbf{A})}$$ P(**B** | **A**) is read "the probability of **B** *given* **A**"
General Multiplication Rule	For any two events, **A** and **B**, P(**A** *and* **B**) = P(**A**) P(**B** | **A**)
Independence (formally)	P(**B** | **A**) = P(**B**) *when* **A** *and* **B** *are independent*
Tree Diagram	A display of conditional events or probabilities that is helpful in thinking through conditioning.

Skills

When you complete this lesson you should:

Think
• Understand that the probability of an event is the proportion of times it occurs in many repetitions of a random phenomenon.
• Understand the concept of conditional probability as redefining the "who" of concern according to the information about the event that is *given*.
• Understand the concept of Independence.
Show
• Know how and when to apply the General Addition rule.

DRAFT: Do not distribute or copy

- Know how to find probabilities for compound events as fractions of counts of occurrences in a two-way table.

- Know how and when to apply the General Multiplication rule.

- Know how to make and use a tree diagram to understand conditional probabilities and reverse conditioning.

Tell

- Be able to make a clear statement about a conditional probability that makes clear how the condition affects the probability.

- Avoid making statements that assume independence of events when there is no clear demonstration that they are in fact independent.

Exercises

1. **Sample Spaces** For each of the following, list the sample space and tell whether you think the events are equally likely.
   a) Toss 2 coins; record the order of heads and tails.
   b) A family has 3 children; record the number of boys.
   c) Flip a coin until you get a head or 3 consecutive tails.
   d) Roll two dice; record the larger number.

2. **Sample Spaces** For each of the following, list the sample space and tell whether you think the events are equally likely.
   a) Roll two dice; record the sum of the numbers.
   b) A family has 3 children; record the genders in order of birth.
   c) Toss four coins; record the number of tails.
   d) Toss a coin 10 times; record the longest run of heads.

3. **Homes** Real estate ads suggest that 64% of homes for sale have garages, 21% have swimming pools, and 17% have both features. What is the probability that a home for sale has
   a) a pool or a garage?
   b) neither a pool nor a garage?
   c) a pool but no garage?

4. **Travel** Suppose the probability that a US resident has traveled to Canada is 0.18, to Mexico is 0.09, and to both countries is 0.04. What is the probability that an American is chosen at random has
   a) traveled to Canada but not Mexico?
   b) traveled to either Canada or Mexico?
   c) not traveled to either country?

5. **Amenities** A check of dorm rooms on a large college campus revealed that 38% had refrigerators, 52% had TVs, and 21% had both a TV and refrigerator. What is the probability that a randomly selected dorm room has

a) a TV but no refrigerator?
b) a TV or a refrigerator, but not both?
c) neither a TV nor a refrigerator?

6. **Workers** Employment data at a large company reveals that 72% of the workers are married, that 44% are college graduates, and that half of the college grads are married. What is the probability that a randomly chosen worker
   a) is neither married nor a college graduate?
   b) is married but not a college graduate?
   c) is married or a college graduate?

7. **Cards** You draw a card at random from a deck of cards. Find each of the following conditional probabilities:
   a) the card is a heart, given that it is red.
   b) the card is red, given that it is a heart.
   c) the card is an ace, given that it is red.
   d) the card is a Queen, given that it is a face card.

8. **Pets** In its monthly report the local animal shelter states that they currently have 24 dogs and 18 cats available for adoption. 8 of the dogs and 6 of the cats are male. Find each of the following conditional probabilities if an animal is selected at random:
   a) the pet is male, given that it is a cat.
   b) the pet is a cat, given that is female.
   c) the pet is female, given that it is a dog.

9. **Health** The probabilities that an adult American male has high blood pressure and/or high cholesterol are shown in the table.
   a) What is the probability that a man has both conditions?
   b) What is the probability that he has high blood pressure?

	Blood Pressure	
Cholesterol	High	OK
High	0.11	0.21
OK	0.16	0.52

   c) What is the probability that a man with high blood pressure has high cholesterol?
   d) What is the probability that a man has high blood pressure if it is known that he has high cholesterol?

10. **Death Penalty** The table shows the political affiliation of American voters and their positions on the death penalty.
   a) What is the probability that a randomly chosen voter favors the death penalty?
   b) What is the probability that a Republican favors the death penalty?

	Death Penalty	
Party	Favor	Oppose
Republican	0.26	0.04
Democrat	0.12	0.24
Other	0.24	0.10

   c) What is the probability that a voter who favors the death penalty is a Democrat?

DRAFT: Do not distribute or copy

d) A candidate thinks she has a good chance of gaining the votes of anyone who is a Republican or in favor of the death penalty. What portion of the voters is that?

11. **Sick Kids** 70% of kids who visit a doctor have a fever, and 30% of kids with a fever have sore throats. What is the probability that a kid who goes to the doctor has a fever and a sore throat?

12. **Sick Cars** 20% of cars that are inspected have faulty pollution control systems. The cost if repairing a pollution control system exceeds $100 about 40% of the time. What is the probability when a driver takes her car in for inspection she will end up paying over $100 to repair the pollution control system?

13. **Cards** You are dealt a hand of three cards, one at a time. Find the probability of each of the following.
    a) The first heart you get is the third card dealt.
    b) Your cards are all red.
    c) You get no spades.
    d) You have at least one ace.

14. **Another Hand** You pick three cards at random from a deck. Find the probability of each event described below.
    a) You get no aces.
    b) You get all hearts.
    c) The third card is your first red card.
    d) You have at least one diamond.

15. **Batteries** A junk box in your room contains a dozen old batteries, five of which are totally dead. You start picking batteries one at a time and testing them. Find the probability of each outcome.
    a) The first two you choose are both good.
    b) At least one of the first three works.
    c) The first four you pick all work.
    d) You have to pick 5 batteries in order to find one that works.

16. **Shirts** The soccer team's shirts have arrived in a big box, and people just start grabbing them, looking for the right size. The box contains 4 mediums, 10 larges, and 6 extra-large shirts. You want a medium for you and one for your sister. Find the probability of each event described.
    a) The first two you grab are the wrong sizes.
    b) The first medium shirt you find is the third one you check.
    c) The first four shirts you pick are all extra-large.
    d) At least one of the first four shirts you check is a medium.

17. **Eligibility** A university requires its biology majors to take a course called BioResearch. The prerequisite for this course is that students

must have taken either a statistics course or a computer course. By the time they are juniors, 52% of the Bio majors have taken statistics, 23% have had a computer course, and 7% have done both.
a) What percent of the junior Bio majors are ineligible for BioResearch?
b) What is the probability that a junior Bio major who has taken statistics has also taken a computer course?
c) Are taking these two courses disjoint? Explain.
d) Are taking these two courses independent? Explain.

18. **Benefits** 56% of all American workers have a workplace retirement plan, 68% have health insurance, and 49% have both benefits. We select a worker at random.
a) What is the probability he has neither employer-sponsored health insurance nor a retirement plan.
b) What is the probability he has health insurance, if he has a retirement plan?
c) Are having health insurance and a retirement plan independent? Explain.
d) Are having these two benefits disjoint? Explain.

19. **For Sale** In the real estate ads described in Exercise 3, 64% of homes for sale have garages, 21% have swimming pools, and 17% have both features.
a) If a home for sale has a garage, what is the probability that it has a pool, too.
b) Are having a garage and a pool independent? Explain.
c) Are having a garage and a pool disjoint? Explain.

20. **On the Road Again** According to Exercise 4, the probability that a US resident has traveled to Canada is 0.18, to Mexico is 0.09, and to both countries is 0.04.
a) What is the probability that someone who has traveled to Mexico has visited Canada, too.
b) Are travel to Mexico and Canada disjoint events? Explain.
c) Are travel to Mexico and Canada independent? Explain.

21. **Cards** If you draw a card at random from a well-shuffled deck, is getting an ace independent of the suit? Explain.

22. **Pets Again** The local animal shelter in Exercise 8 reported that they currently have 24 dogs and 18 cats available for adoption. 8 of the dogs and 6 of the cats are male. Are the species and gender of the animals independent? Explain.

23. **Men's Health, Again** Given the table of probabilities from Exercise 9, are high blood pressure and high cholesterol

Cholesterol	Blood Pressure	
	High	OK
High	0.11	0.21
OK	0.16	0.52

independent? Explain.

24. **Politics** Given the table of probabilities from Exercise 10, are party affiliation and position on the death penalty independent? Explain?

	Death Penalty	
Party	Favor	Oppose
Republican	0.26	0.04
Democrat	0.12	0.24
Other	0.24	0.10

25. **Luggage** Leah is flying from Boston to Denver with a connection in Chicago. The probability her first flight leaves on time is 0.15. If the flight is on time, the probability that her luggage will make the connecting flight in Chicago is 0.95, but if the first flight is delayed the probability that the luggage will make it is only 0.65.
    a) Are the first flight leaving on time and the luggage making the connection independent events? Explain.
    b) What is the probability that her luggage arrives in Denver with her?

26. **Graduation** A private college report contains these statistics:
    > 70% of incoming freshmen attended public schools.
    > 75% of public school students who enroll as freshmen eventually graduate.
    > 90% of other freshmen eventually graduate.
    a) Is there any evidence that a freshman's chances to graduate may depend upon what kind of high school the student attended? Explain.
    b) What percent of freshmen eventually graduate?

27. **Late Luggage** Remember Leah (Exercise 25)? Suppose you pick her up at the Denver airport, and her luggage is not there. What is the probability that Leah's first flight was delayed?

28. **Graduation, Part II** What percent of students who graduate from the college in Exercise 26 attended a public high school?

29. **Absenteeism** A company's records indicate that on any given day about 1% of their day shift employees and 2% of the night shift employees will miss work. 60% of the employees work the day shift.
    a) Is absenteeism independent of shift worked? Explain.
    b) What percent of employees are absent on any given day?

30. **Lungs and Smoke** Suppose that 23% of adults smoke cigarettes. It is known that 57% of smokers and 13% of non-smokers develop a certain lung condition by age 60.
    a) Explain how these statistics indicate that the lung condition and smoking are not independent.

    b) What is the probability that a randomly selected 60-year old has this lung condition?

31. **Absenteeism, Part II** At the company described in Exercise 29, what percent of the absent employees are on the night shift?

32. **Lungs and Smoke, Again** Based on the statistics in Exercise 30, what is the probability that someone with the lung condition was a smoker?

33. **Drunks** Police often set up sobriety checkpoints – roadblocks where drivers are asked a few brief questions to allow the officer to judge whether or not the person may have been drinking. If the officer does not suspect a problem, drivers are released to go on their way. Otherwise, drivers are detained for a breathalyzer test that will determine whether or not they are arrested. The police say that based on the brief initial stop, trained officers can make the right decision 80% of the time. Suppose the police operate a sobriety checkpoint after 9pm on a Saturday night, a time when national traffic safety experts suspect that about 12% of drivers have been drinking.
    a) You are stopped at the checkpoint and, of course, have not been drinking. What is the probability that you are detained for further testing?
    b) What is the probability that any given driver will be detained?
    c) What is the probability that a driver who is detained has actually been drinking?
    d) What is the probability that a driver who was released had actually been drinking?

34. **Polygraphs** Lie detectors are controversial instruments, barred from use as evidence in many courts. Nonetheless, many employers use lie detector screening as part of their hiring process in the hope that they can avoid hiring people who might be dishonest. There has been some research, but no agreement, about the reliability of polygraph tests. Based on this research, suppose that a polygraph can detect 65% of lies, but incorrectly identifies 15% of true statements as lies.

A certain company believes that 95% of their job applicants are trustworthy. They give everyone a polygraph test, asking "Have you ever stolen anything from your place of work?" Naturally, all the applicants answer "No", but the polygraph identifies some of those answers as lies, making the person ineligible for a job. What is the probability that a job applicant rejected under suspicion of dishonesty was actually trustworthy?

35. **Dishwashers** Dan's Diner employs 3 dishwashers. Al washes 40% of the dishes, and breaks only 1% of those he handles. Betty and Chuck each wash 30% of the dishes, and Betty breaks only 1% of hers, but

      DRAFT: Do not distribute or copy

Chuck breaks 3% of the dishes he washes. (He, of course, will need a new job soon ...)You go to Dan's for supper one night and hear a dish break at the sink. What is the probability that Chuck is on the job?

36. **Parts** A company assembling computer keyboards and other peripherals buys electrical connectors from three suppliers. They prefer to use Supplier A because only 1% of those connectors prove to be defective. Unfortunately, Supplier A can only deliver 80% of the connectors they need. The company gets 15% of the connectors from supplier B, of which 2% are defective, and the rest from supplier C, of which 4% are defective. You buy one of this company's keyboards and find that it has a defective connector. What is the probability that it originated with supplier A?

16 Random Variables*

INSURANCE COMPANIES MAKE BETS. They bet that you're going to live a long life. You bet that you're going to die sooner. But both you and the insurance company want them to stay in business. So it is important to find a "fair price" for your bet. Of course, the right price for *you* depends on many factors, and nobody can predict exactly how long you'll live. But, when the company averages over enough customers, they can make reasonably accurate estimates of the amount they can expect to collect on a policy before they have to pay its benefit.

Here's a simple example: An insurance company offers a "Death and Disability" policy that pays $10,000 when you die or $5,000 if you are permanently disabled. They charge a premium of only $50 a year for this benefit. Is the company likely to make a profit selling such a plan? To answer this question, the company needs to know the *probability* that their clients will die or be disabled in any year. From actuarial information like this, the company can calculate the **expected value** of this policy.

What is an Actuary?

Actuaries are the daring people who put a price on risk, estimating the likelihood and costs of rare events so they can be insured. That takes financial, statistical, and business skills (and a bit of chutzpah). It also makes them invaluable to many businesses. Actuaries are rather rare themselves; only about 19,000 work in North America. Perhaps because of this, they are well paid. If you're enjoying this course, you may want to look into a career as an actuary. Contact the Society of Actuaries, or the Casualty Actuarial Society (who, despite what it might look like, did not pay for this blurb.)

Expected Value: Center

We'll want to build a probability model in order to answer the questions about the insurance companies' risk. But first we need to define a few terms. The amount the company pays out on an individual policy is called a **random variable** because its value is based on the outcome of a random event. We use a capital letter, like X, to denote a random variable. A particular value that it can have we'll denote by the corresponding lower-case letter, in this case x. For the insurance company, x can be $10,000(if you die that year), $5000 (if you are disabled) or $0 (if neither occurs). (Because we can list all the outcomes we might formally call this random variable a **discrete** random variable. Otherwise, we'd call it a **continuous** random variable). The collection of all the possible values and the probabilities that they occur is called the **probability model** for the random variable.

Suppose, for example, that the death rate in any year is 1 of every 1000 people, and that another 2 out of 1000 suffer some kind of disability. Then we can display the probability model for this insurance policy in a table like this:

Notation Alert
Are we now taking over all capital letters? Well, not really. The most common letters for random variables are X, Y, and Z. Be cautious. If you see a capital letter, it might denote a random variable.

Policyholder Outcome	Payout x	Probability $P(X=x)$
death	10,000	$\frac{1}{1000}$
disability	5000	$\frac{2}{1000}$
neither	0	$\frac{997}{1000}$

DRAFT: Do not distribute or copy

To see what the insurance company can expect, imagine that they insure exactly 1000 people. Further imagine that, in perfect accordance with the probabilities, 1 of the policyholders dies, 2 are disabled, and the remaining 997 survive the year unscathed. The company would pay $10,000 to one client and $5000 to each of 2 clients. That's a total of $20,000, or an average of 20000/1000 = $20 per policy. Since they are charging people $50 for the policy, they expect to make a profit of $30 per customer. Not bad!

We can't predict what *will* happen during any given year, but we can say what we *expect* to happen. What we (or, rather the insurance company) need is the probability model. The expected value of a policy is a parameter of this model. In fact, it's the mean. We'll signify this with the notation μ (for population mean), or $E(X)$ for expected value. But this isn't an average of some data values, so we won't estimate it. Instead, we assume that the probabilities are known and simply calculate the expected value from them.

How did we come up with $20 as the expected value of a policy? Here's the calculation:

As we've seen, it often simplifies probability calculations to think about some (convenient) number of outcomes. For example, here we could imagine that we have exactly 1000 clients. Of those, exactly 1 died and 2 were disabled corresponding to what the probabilities would say. So our total payout comes to $20,000 or $20 per policy.

$$\mu = E(X) = \frac{10000(1) + 5000(2) + 0(997)}{1000}$$

Instead of writing the expected value as one big fraction, we can rewrite it as separate terms each divided by 1000. How convenient! See the probabilities? For each policy, there's a 1/1000 chance that we'll have to pay $10,000 for a death and a 2/1000 chance that we'll have to pay $5,000 for a disability. And, of course, there's a 997/1000 chance that we won't have to pay anything.

$$\mu = E(X)$$
$$= \$10,000\left(\frac{1}{1000}\right) + \$5000\left(\frac{2}{1000}\right) + \$0\left(\frac{997}{1000}\right)$$
$$= \$20$$

Take a good look at the expression now. It 's actually easy to calculate the expected value of a random variable - just multiply each possible value by the probability that it occurs, and find the sum.

$$\mu = E(X) = \sum x \cdot P(X = x)$$

Be sure that every possible outcome is included in the sum. And verify that you have a valid probability model to start with – the probabilities should each be between 0 and 1 and should sum to one.

First center, now spread ...

Of course this expected value (or mean) is not what actually happens to any particular policyholder - no individual policy actually costs the company $20. We are dealing with random events, so some policyholders receive big payouts, others nothing. Because the insurance company must anticipate this variability, they need to know the standard deviation of the random variable.

For data, we computed the standard deviation by first computing the deviation from the mean and squaring it. We do that with random variables as well. First, we find the deviation of each payout from the mean (expected value):

Policyholder Outcome	Payout x	Probability $P(X=x)$	Deviation $(x - \mu)$
death	10,000	$\frac{1}{1000}$	(10000- 20) = 9980
disability	5000	$\frac{2}{1000}$	(5000 - 20) = 4980
neither	0	$\frac{997}{1000}$	(0 - 20) = -20

Next we square each deviation, multiply it by the appropriate probability, and sum those products. That gives us the variance of X. Here's what it looks like:

$$Var(X) = 9980^2\left(\tfrac{1}{1000}\right) + 4980^2\left(\tfrac{2}{1000}\right) + (-20)^2\left(\tfrac{997}{1000}\right) = 149600$$

Finally, we take the square root to get the standard deviation: $SD(X) = \sqrt{149600} \approx \$386.78$. The insurance company can expect an average payout of $20 per policy, with a standard deviation of $386.78.

Think about that. The company charges $50 for each policy and expects to pay out $20 per policy. Sounds like an easy way to make $30. In fact, most of the time (probability 997/1000) the company pockets the entire $50. But would you consider insuring your roommate? The problem is that occasionally the company loses big. With probability 1/1000 they'll pay out $10,000and with probability 2/1000 they'll pay out $5000. That may be more risk than you're willing to take on. The standard deviation of $386.78 gives an indication that it's no sure thing. That's a pretty big spread (and risk) for a average profit of $20.

Probability

Here are the formulas for what we just did. Because these are parameters of our probability model, the variance and standard deviation can also be written as σ^2 and σ. You should recognize both kinds of notation.

$$\sigma^2 = Var(X) = \sum (x-\mu)^2 \cdot P(X=x)$$

$$\sigma = SD(X) = \sqrt{Var(X)}$$

Expected Values and Standard Deviations for Random Variables
Step-by-Step

As the head of inventory for the Knowway computer company, you were thrilled that you had managed to ship 2 computers to your biggest client the day the order arrived. But you are horrified to find out that someone had restocked refurbished computers in with the new computers in your storeroom. The shipped computers were selected randomly from the 15 computers in stock, but 4 of those were actually refurbished.

If your client gets 2 new computers, things are fine. If they get a refurbished computer, the'll send it back at your expense—$100—and you can replace it. But both computers are refurbished, they'll cancel their monthly order and you'll lose $1000. What is the expected value and the standard deviation of your loss?

Think	Define the random variable. Make a picture: This is another job for tree diagrams. If you prefer calculation to drawing, find P(NN) and P(RR), then use the complement rul to find P(NR or RN).	

	List the possible values of the random variable, and	Outcome	x	P(X=x)
		New/New	0	P(NN) = 0.524
		One Refurb	100	P(NR or RN) = 0.21+0.21 = 0.42

	determine the probability model.	Two Refurbs	1000	P(RR) = 0.057
Show	Find the expected value.	E(X) = 0 × 0.524 +100 × 0.42 +1000 × 0.057 = $99		
	Find the variance.	$Var(X) = (0-99)^2 \times 0.524 + (100-99)^2 \times 0.42$ $+(1000-99)^2 \times 0.057 = 51,408.80$		
	Find the standard deviation.	$SD(X) = \sqrt{51,408.80} = \$226.73$		
Tell	State your conclusion.	You can expect this mistake to cost your firm $99 with a standard deviation of $226.73.		
	Reality Check	Both numbers seem reasonable. The expected value of $99 is between the extreme values of $0 and $1000. The standard deviation of $226.73 reflects the fact that there's a pretty large range of outcome values.		

More About Means and Variances

Our insurance company expected to pay out an average of $20 per policy, with a standard deviation of about $387. If we take the $50 premium into account, we see they make a profit of 50 - 20 = $30 per policy. Suppose they lower the premium by $5 to $45. It's pretty clear that their expected profit also drops an average of $5 per policy, to 45 - 20 = $25.

But what about the standard deviation? We know that adding or subtracting a constant from data shifts the mean but doesn't change the variance or standard deviation. The same is true of random variables[1].

$$E(X \pm c) = E(X) \pm c \qquad Var(X \pm c) = Var(X)$$

What if the company decides to double all the payouts--that is, pay $20,000 for deaths and $10,000 for disability? This would double their average payout per policy, and also increase the variability in payouts. We have seen that multiplying or dividing all data values by a constant

---

[1] The rules in the section are true for both discrete *and* continuous random variables.

changes both the mean and standard deviation by the same factor. Variance, being the square of standard deviation, changes by the square of the constant. The same is true of random variables. In general, multiplying each value of a random variable by a constant, multiplies the mean by that constant and the variance by the *square* of the constant:

$$E(aX) = aE(X) \qquad Var(aX) = a^2Var(X)$$

This insurance company sells policies to more than just one person. How can we figure means and variances for a collection of customers? For example, how can the company find the total expected value (and standard deviation) of policies taken over all policy holders? Consider a simple case: just 2 customers, Mr. *Ecks* and Ms. *Wye*. With an expected payout of $20 on each policy, we might expect a total of 20 + 20 = $40 to be paid out on the two policies. Nothing surprising there. The expected value of the sum is the sum of the expected values.

But the variability is another matter. Is the risk of insuring 2 people the same as the risk of insuring one person for twice as much? We wouldn't expect both clients to die or become disabled in the same year. Because we've spread the risk, the standard deviation should be smaller. Indeed, this is the fundamental principle behind insurance. By spreading the risk among many policies, a company can keep the standard deviation quite small and predict its costs more accurately.

But how much smaller is the standard deviation of the sum? It turns out that, if the random variables are independent, there is a simple addition rule for variances: *The variance of the sum of two independent random variables is the sum of their variances.*

For Mr. Ecks and Ms. Wye, the insurance company can expect their outcomes to be independent, so (using X for Mr. Ecks's payout and Y for Ms. Wye's)

$$Var(X + Y) = Var(X) + Var(Y) = 149600 + 149600 = 299200$$

If they had just insured Mr. Ecks for twice as much, there would only be one outcome rather than two *independent* outcomes, so the variance would have been

$$Var(2X) = 4Var(X) = 4*149600 = 598400,$$

twice as big as with two independent policies.

Of course, variances are in squared units. The company would prefer to know standard deviations, which are in dollars. The standard deviation of the payout for two independent policies is $\sqrt{299200}$ = $547. But the

DRAFT: Do not distribute or copy

standard deviation of the payout for a single policy of twice the size is $\sqrt{598400} = \$773.5$--about 40% more.

So, if the company has 2 customers, it will have an expected annual total payout of $40 with a standard deviation of $547.

In general:

- *The mean of the sum of two random variables is the sum of the means.*

- *The mean of the difference of two random variables is the difference of the means.*

- *If the random variables are independent, the variance of their sum or difference is always the sum of the variances.*

$$E(X \pm Y) = E(X) \pm E(Y) \qquad\qquad Var(X \pm Y) = Var(X) + Var(Y)$$

Wait a minute! Is that third part correct? Do we always *add* variances? Yes. Think about the two insurance policies. Suppose we want to know the mean and standard deviation of the *difference* in payouts to the two clients. Since each policy has an expected payout of $20, the expected difference is 20 - 20 = $0. But if we also subtract variances we get $0, too, and that surely doesn't make sense. Note that if the outcomes for the two clients are independent the difference in payouts could range from $10,000 - $0 = $10,000 to $0 - $10,000 = -$10000, a spread of $20,000. The variability in differences increases as much as the variability in sums. If the company has 2 customers, the difference in payouts has a mean of $0 and a standard deviation of $547 (again).

For Random variables $X+X+X \neq 3X$.

As we've just seen, insuring one person for $30,000 is not the same risk as insuring 3 people for $10,000 each. But when each instance is an instance of the same kind of random variable, it is easy to fall into the trap of writing them with the same symbol. Don't make this common mistake. Make sure you write each instance as a *different* random variable. Just because each random variable describes a similar situation doesn't mean that each random outcome will be the same.

These are *random* variables, not the variables you saw in algebra. Being random, they take on different values each time they are evaluated. So what you really mean is $X_1 + X_2 + X_3$. Written this way, it is clear that the sum should not necessarily equal 3 times *anything*.

Hitting the Road, Step-by-Step

You are planning to spend next year wandering through the mountains of Kyrgyzstan. You plan to sell your used Isuzu Trooper and purchase an off-road Honda motor scooter when you get there. Used Isuzus of the year and mileage of yours are selling for a mean of $6,940 with a standard deviation of $250. Your research shows that scooters in Kyrgyzstan are going for about 65,000 Kyrgyzstan Soms with a standard deviation of 500 Soms. You have to survive on your profit, so you want to estimate what you can expect in your pocket after the sale and subsequent purchase. One U.S. dollar is worth about 46 Kyrgyzstan Soms.

Think	Define your variables, and write an appropriate equation.	Let A = sale price of your Isuzu (in dollars) B = purchase of a scooter (in Soms) D = profit (in Soms) D = 46A – B The sale and purchase are independent.
Show	Find the expected value, using the appropriate rules.	E(D) = E(46A – B) = 46E(A) – E(B) = 46(6940) – (65,000) E(D) = 254,240 Soms
	Find the variance, using the appropriate rules. Be sure to check the conditions first!	Since the sale and purchase are independent, Var(D) = Var(46A – B)

		$= (46)^2 Var(A) + (Var(B)$ $= 2116(250)^2 + (500)^2$ $Var(D) = 132{,}500{,}000$
	Find the standard deviation.	$SD(D) = \sqrt{132500000} = 11{,}510$ Soms
Tell	State your conclusion.	You can expect to clear about 254,240 Soms with a standard deviation of 11,510 Soms.
	Reality check.	We'd better convert back to dollars to get some sense of whether this result is plausible. About $5529 with a standard deviation of about $250. That seems reasonable.

What Can Go Wrong?

- *Probability models are still just models.* Models can be useful, but they are not reality. Think about the assumptions behind your models. Are your dice really perfectly fair? (They are probably pretty close.) But when you hear that the probability of a nuclear accident is 1/10,000,000 per year, is that likely to be a precise value? Question probabilities as you would data.

- *If the model is wrong, so is everything else.* Before you try to find the mean or standard deviation of a random variable, check that the probability model is reasonable. As a start, the probabilities in your model should add up to 1. If not, you may have calculated a probability incorrectly, or left out a value of the random variable. For instance, in the insurance example, the description mentions only death and disability. Good health is by far the most likely outcome, not to mention the best for both you and the insurance company (who gets to keep your money). Don 't overlook that.

To find the expected value of the sum or difference of random variables, we simply add or subtract means. Center is easy; spread is trickier. Watch out for some common traps.

- *Watch out for variables that aren't independent.* You can add expected values of *any* two random variables, but not variances. Suppose a survey includes questions about the number of hours of sleep people get each night and also the number of hours they are awake each day. From their answers we find the mean and standard deviation of hours asleep and hours awake. The expected total must be 24 hours; after all, people are either asleep or awake all day. The means still add just fine. But because all the totals are exactly 24 hours, the standard deviation of the total will be 0. We can't add variances here because the number of hours you are awake depends on the number of hours you sleep. Be sure to check for independence before proceeding.

- *Variances of independent random variables add. Standard deviations don't.*
- *Variances add, even when you are looking at the difference in random variables.*
- *Don't write independent instances of a random variable with notation that looks like they are the same values.* Make sure you write each instance as a different random variable. Just because each random variable describes a similar situation doesn't mean that each random outcome will be the same. These are *random* variables, not the variables you saw in algebra. Write $X_1 + X_2 + X_3$ rather than $X + X + X$.

Connections

We've seen means, variances, and standard deviations of data. We know that they estimate parameters of models for these data. Now we are looking at the probability models directly. We only have parameters because there is no data to summarize.

It should be no surprise that expected values and standard deviations adjust to shifts and changes of units in the same way as the corresponding data summaries. The fact that we can add variances of independent random quantities is fundamental and will explain why a number of statistical methods work the way they do.

Random Variables and the Computer

Statistics packages deal with data and not with random variables. Nevertheless, the calculations needed to find means and standard deviations of random variables are little more than weighted means. Most packages can manage that, but then they are just being overblown calculators.

For technological assistance with these calculations, we recommend you pull our your calculator. If you have a TI-83, then here's the formal advice:

Package	Commands & Location	Comments
TI-83	To calculate the mean and standard deviation of a discrete random variable, enter the probability model in two lists: • In one list (say L1) enter the *x* values of the variable. • In a second list (say L2) enter the associated probabilities P(X=x). • From the STAT CALC menu enter 1-VarStats L1,L2 and you'll see the mean and standard deviation.	1) You can enter the probabilities as fractions; the calculator will change them to decimals for you. 2) Notice that the calculator knows enough to call the standard deviation σ, but mistakenly uses $\bar{x}$ where it should say μ. Make sure you don't make that mistake!

Key Concepts:

Random variable	A random variable assumes any of several different values as a result of some random event. Random variables are denoted by a capital letter such as X.
Probability model	The probability model is a function that associates a probability with each value of a random variable, denoted P(X=x).
Expected value	The expected value of a random variable is its theoretical long run average value, the center of its model. Denoted μ or E(X), it is found by summing the products of variable values and probabilities: $$\mu = E(X) = \sum x \cdot P(X = x)$$
Standard deviation	The standard deviation of a random variable describes the spread in the model, and is the square root of the variance: $$\sigma^2 = Var(X) = \sum (x - \mu)^2 \cdot P(X = x)$$ $$\sigma = SD(X) = \sqrt{Var(X)}$$
When changing a random variable by a constant:	$E(X \pm c) = E(X) \pm c$ $\qquad$ $Var(X \pm c) = Var(X)$ $E(aX) = aE(X)$ $\qquad\qquad$ $Var(aX) = a^2 Var(X)$
When adding or subtracting random variables:	$E(X \pm Y) = E(X) \pm E(Y)$ and *if they are independent* $Var(X \pm Y) = Var(X) + Var(Y)$

Skills:

Upon completing this Lesson you should:

Think

- Recognize random variables.

- Understand that random variables must be independent in order to determine variability of their sum or difference.

Show

- Be able to find the probability model for a random variable.

- Know how to find the mean (expected value) and the variance of a random variable.

- Use the proper notation for these population parameters, μ or $E(X)$ for the mean, and σ, $SD(X)$, or $Var(X)$ when discussing variability.

- Know how determine the new mean and standard deviation after adding a constant, multiplying by a constant, or combining two random variables.

Tell

- Be able to interpret the meaning of the expected value and standard deviation of a random variable in the proper context.

Exercises

1. **Expected Value** Find the expected value of each random variable:

   a)

y	10	20	30
P(Y=y)	0.3	0.5	0.2

   b)

y	2	4	6	8
P(Y=y)	0.3	0.4	0.2	0.1

2. **Expected Value** Find the expected value of each random variable:

   a)

y	0	1	2
P(Y=y)	0.2	0.4	0.4

   b)

y	100	200	300	400
P(Y=y)	0.1	0.2	0.5	0.2

3. **Pick a Card, Any Card** You draw a card from a deck. If you get a red card, you win nothing. If you get a spade, you win $5. For any club, you win $10 plus an extra $20 for the ace of clubs.
   a) Create a probability model for the amount you win at this game.
   b) Find the expected amount you will win.
   c) How much would you be willing to pay to play this game?

4. **You Bet!** You roll a die. If it comes up a 6, you win $100. If not, you get to roll again. If you get a 6 the second time, you win $50. If not, you lose.
   a) Create a probability model for the amount you win at this game.
   b) Find the expected amount you will win.
   c) How much would you be willing to pay to play this game?

5. **Kids** A couple plans to have children until they get a girl, but they agree that they will not have more than three children even if all are boys.
   a) Create a probability model for the number of children they will have.
   b) Find the expected number of children.
   c) Find the expected number of boys they will have.

6. **Carnival** A carnival game offers a $100 cash prize for anyone who can break a balloon by throwing a dart at it. It costs $5 to play, and you are willing to spend up to $20 to try to win. You estimate that you have about a 10% chance of hitting the balloon on any throw.
   a) Create a probability model for this carnival game.

b) Find the expected number of darts you will throw.

c) Find your expected winnings.

7. **Software** A small software company bids on two contracts. They anticipate a profit of $50,000 if they get the larger contract and a profit of $20,000 on the smaller contract. They estimate there's a 30% chance they will get the larger contract, a 60% chance they will get the smaller contract. Assuming the contracts will be awarded independently, what is their expected profit?

8. **Racehorse** A man buys a racehorse for $20,000, and enters it in two races. He plans to sell the horse afterwards, hoping to make a profit. If the horse wins both races its value will jump to $100,000. If it wins one of the races, its will be worth $50,000. If it loses both races it will be worth only $10,000. The man believes there is a 20% chance that the horse will win the first race and a 30% chance it will win the second one. Assuming that winning the two races are independent, find the man's expected profit.

9. **Variation 1** Find the standard deviations of the random variables in Exercise 1.

10. **Variation 2** Find the standard deviations of the random variables in Exercise 2.

11. **Pick Another Card** Find the standard deviation of the amount you might win drawing a card in Exercise 3.

12. **The Die** Find the standard deviation of the amount you might win rolling a die in Exercise 4.

13. **Kids** Find the standard deviation of the number of children the couple in Exercise 5 may have.

14. **Darts** Find the standard deviation of your winnings throwing darts in Exercise 6.

15. **Repairs** The probability model below describes the number of repair calls that an appliance repair shop may receive during an hour.

Repair calls	0	1	2	3
Probability	0.1	0.3	0.4	0.2

a) How many calls should the shop expect per hour?

b) What is the standard deviation?

16. **Red Lights** A commuter must pass through five traffic lights on her way to work, and will have to stop at each one that is red. She estimates the probability model for the number of red lights she hits, as shown below.

X = # red	0	1	2	3	4	5

DRAFT: Do not distribute or copy

P(X=x)	0.05	0.25	0.35	0.15	0.15	0.05

   a) How many red lights should she expect to hit each day?

   b) What is the standard deviation?

17. **Defects** A consumer organization inspecting new cars found that many had appearance defects (dents, scratches, paint chips, etc.). While none had more than three of these defects, 7% had 3, 11% two, and 21% one defect. Find the expected number of appearance defects in a new car, and the standard deviation.

18. **Insurance** An insurance policy costs $100, and will pay policyholders $10,000 if they suffer a major injury (resulting in hospitalization) or $3000 if they suffer a minor injury (resulting in lost time from work). The company estimates that each year one in every 2000 policyholders may have a major injury and 1 in 500 a minor injury.
   a) Create a probability model for the profit on a policy.
   b) What is the company 's expected profit on this policy?
   c) What is the standard deviation?

19. **Contest** You play two games against the same opponent. The probability you win the first game is 0.4. If you win the first game, the probability you also win the second is 0.2. If you lose the first game, the probability that you win the second is 0.3.
   a) Are the two games independent? Explain your answer.
   b) What is the probability you lose both games?
   c) What is the probability you win both games?
   d) Let random variable X be the number of games you win. Find the probability model for X
   e) What are the expected value and standard deviation of X?

20. **Contracts** Your company bids for two contracts. You believe the probability you get contract #1 is 0.8. If you get contract #1, the probability you also get contract #2 will be 0.2, and if you do not get #1, the probability you get #2 will be 0.3.
   a) Are the two contracts independent? Explain.
   b) Find the probability you get both contracts.
   c) Find the probability you get no contract.
   d) Let X be the number of contracts you get. Find the probability model for X.
   e) Find the expected value and standard deviation of X.

21. **Batteries** In a group of ten batteries, 3 are dead. You choose two batteries at random.
   a) Create a probability model for the number of good batteries you get.

Copyright © 2001, Dave Bock, Dick DeVeaux, and Paul Velleman

b) What is the expected number of good ones you get?

c) What is the standard deviation?

22. **Kittens** In a litter of seven kittens, three are female. You pick two kittens at random.

a) Create a probability model for the number of male kittens you get.

b) What is the expected number of males?

c) What is the standard deviation?

23. **Random Variables** Given independent random variables with means and standard deviations as shown, find the mean and standard deviation of each of these variables:

a) $3X$
b) $Y + 6$
c) $X + Y$
d) $X - Y$

	Mean	SD
X	10	2
Y	20	5

24. **Random Variables** Given independent random variables with means and standard deviations as shown, find the mean and standard deviation of each of these variables:

a) $X - 20$
b) $0.5Y$
c) $X + Y$
d) $X - Y$

	Mean	SD
X	80	12
Y	12	3

25. **Random Variables** Given independent random variables with means and standard deviations as shown, find the mean and standard deviation of each of these variables:

a) $0.8Y$
b) $2X - 100$
c) $X + 2Y$
d) $3X - Y$

	Mean	SD
X	120	12
Y	300	16

26. **Random Variables** Given independent random variables with means and standard deviations as shown, find the mean and standard deviation of each of these variables:

a) $2Y + 20$
b) $3X$
c) $0.25X + Y$
d) $X - 5Y$

	Mean	SD
X	80	12
Y	12	3

27. **Eggs** A grocery supplier believes that in a dozen eggs, the mean number of broken ones is 0.6 with a standard deviation of 0.5 eggs. You buy 3 dozen eggs without checking them.

a) How many broken eggs do you expect to get?

b) What is the standard deviation?

c) What assumptions did you have to make about the eggs in order to answer this question?

28. **Garden** A company selling vegetable seeds in packets of 20 estimates that the mean number of seeds that will actually grow is 18, with a standard deviation of 1.2 seeds. You buy 5 different seed packets.
    a) How many bad seeds do you expect to get?
    b) What is the standard deviation?
    c) What assumptions did you make about the seeds? Do you think that assumption is warranted? Explain.

29. **Repair Calls** Find the mean and standard deviation of the number of repair calls the appliance shop in Exercise 15 should expect during an 8-hour day.

30. **Stop!** Find the mean and standard deviation of the number of red lights the commuter in Exercise 16 should expect to hit on her way to work during a 5-day work week.

31. **Fire!** An insurance company estimates that they should make an annual profit of $150 on each homeowner's policy they write, with a standard deviation of $6,000.
    a) Why is the standard deviation so large?
    b) If they write only two of these policies, what are the mean and standard deviation of their annual profit?
    c) If they write 10,000 of these policies, what are the mean and standard deviation of their annual profit?
    d) Do you think that the company is likely to be profitable? Explain.
    e) What assumptions underlie your analysis? Can you think of circumstances under which those assumptions might be violated? Explain.

32. **Casino** A casino knows that people play the slot machines in hopes of hitting the jackpot, but that most of them lose their dollar. Suppose a certain machine pays out an average of $0.92, with a standard deviation of $120.
    a) Why is the standard deviation so large?
    b) If you play five times, what are the mean and standard deviation of the casino's profit?
    c) If gamblers play this machine 1000 times in a day, what are the mean and standard deviation of the casino's profit?
    d) Do you think that the casino is likely to be profitable? Explain.

33. **Cereal** The amount of cereal that can be poured into a small bowl varies with mean 1.5 ounces and standard deviation 0.3 ounces. A large bowl holds a mean of 2.5 ounces with standard deviation of 0.4 ounces. You open a new box of cereal and pour one large and one

small bowl.

a) How much more cereal do you expect to be in the large bowl?

b) What is the standard deviation of this difference?

c) If the difference follows a Normal model, what is the probability the small bowl contains more cereal than the large one?

d) What are the mean and standard deviation of the total amount of cereal in the two bowls?

e) If the total follows a Normal model, what is the probability you poured out more than 4.5 ounces of cereal in the two bowls together?

f) The amount of cereal the manufacturer puts in the boxes is a random variable with mean 16.3 ounces, and standard deviation 0.2 ounces. Find the expected amount of cereal left in the box, and the standard deviation.

34. **Pets** The American Veterinary Association claims that the annual cost of medical care for dogs averages $100 with a standard deviation of $30, and for cats averages $120 with a standard deviation of $35.

a) What is the expected difference in the cost of medical care for dogs and cats?

b) What is the standard deviation of that difference?

c) If the difference in costs can be described by a Normal model, what is the probability that medical expenses for someone's dog are higher than for their cat.

35. **More Cereal** In Exercise 33 we poured a large and a small bowl of cereal from a box. Suppose the amount of cereal that the manufacturer puts in the boxes is a random variable with mean 16.2 ounces, and standard deviation 0.1 ounces.

a) Find the expected amount of cereal left in the box.

b) What is the standard deviation?

c) If the weight of the remaining cereal can be described by a Normal model, what is the probability that the box still contains more than 13 ounces?

36. **More Pets** You are thinking about getting two dogs and a cat. The means and standard deviations of veterinary bills. Assume that veterinary expenses are independent and have a Normal model with the means and standard deviations described in Exercise 34.

a) Define appropriate variables and express the total costs you may have.

b) Describe the model for this total cost. Be sure to specify its name, expected value, and standard deviation.

c) What is the probability that your total expenses will exceed $400?

37. **Medley** In the 4x100 medley relay event four swimmers swim 100 yards, each using a different stroke. A college team preparing for

their conference championships looks at the times they have posted and creates a model based on the following assumptions:

- the swimmers' performances are independent;
- each swimmer's times follow a Normal model;
- the means and standard deviations of the times (in seconds) are:

Swimmer	Mean	St. Dev.
1 (backstroke)	50.72	0.24
2 (breaststroke)	55.51	0.22
3 (butterfly)	49.43	0.25
4 (freestyle)	44.91	0.21

a) What are the mean and standard deviation for the relay team's total time in this event?

b) Their best time so far this season was 3:19.48. (That's 199.48 seconds.) Do you think they are likely to swim faster than this at the conference championships? Explain.

38. **Bikes** Bicycles arrive at a bike shop in boxes. Before they can be sold they must be unpacked, assembled, and tuned (lubricated, adjusted, etc.). Based on past experience, the shop manager makes the following assumptions about how long this may take:

- the times for each setup phase are independent;
- the times for each phase follow a Normal model;
- the means and standard deviations of the times (in minutes) are:

Phase	Mean	St. Dev.
Unpacking	3.5	0.7
Assembly	21.8	2.4
Tuning	12.3	2.7

a) What are the mean and standard deviation for the total bicycle setup time??

b) A customer decides to buy a bike like one of the display models, but wants a different color. The shop has one, still in the box. The manager says they can have it ready in half an hour. Do you think that the bike will be set up and ready to go as promised? Explain.

39. **Farmers' Market** A farmer has 100 lbs of apples and 50 lbs of potatoes for sale. The market price for apples (per lb) is a random variable with mean 0.5 dollars and standard deviation 0.2 dollars. Similarly, for a pound of potatoes, the mean price is 0.3 dollars and standard deviation 0.1 dollars. It also costs him 2 dollars to bring all the apples and potatoes to the market. The market is busy with eager shoppers, so we can assume that he will be able to sell all of his produce.

a) Define your random variables, and use them to express the farmer's net income.
b) Find the mean.
c) Find the standard deviation of the net income.
d) Do you need to make any assumptions in calculating the mean? How about the standard deviation?

40. **Bike Sale** The Exercise 38 bicycle shop will be offering 2 specially priced children's models at a sidewalk sale. The basic model will sell for $120, and the deluxe model for $150. Past experience indicates that sales of the basic model will have a mean of 5.4 bikes with standard deviation 1.2, and sales of the deluxe model will have mean 3.2 bikes with standard deviation 0.8 bikes. The cost of setting up for the sidewalk sale is $200.
a) Define random variables and use them to express the bicycle shop's net income.
b) What is the mean of the net income?
c) What is the standard deviation of the net income?
d) Do you need to make any assumptions in calculating the mean? How about the standard deviation?

17 Probability Models*

When we last saw our heroine, she was…

Oops! Wrong book. What we mean to say is that several chapters ago we simulated buying cereal boxes to get sports cards. You remember the setup:

"Suppose a cereal manufacturer starts putting pictures of famous athletes in boxes of their cereal, a common marketing ploy. They announce that 20% of the boxes will contain a picture of Tiger Woods, 30% a picture of Lance Armstrong, and the rest a picture of Serena Williams."

Now, instead of simulation, we can use probability.

Searching for Tiger

You've *got* to have the Tiger Woods picture, so you start madly opening boxes of cereal hoping to find one. Assuming that the pictures are randomly distributed, there's a 20% chance you succeed on any box you open. We call the act of opening a box a "trial", and note that:

- There are only two possible outcomes (called success and failure) on each trial. Either you get Tiger's picture or you don't.

- The probability of success, denoted p, is the same on every trial. Here $p = 0.20$.

- The trials are independent. Finding Tiger in the first box does not change what might happen when you reach for the next box.

Situations like this occur often, and are called **Bernoulli trials**. Common examples of Bernoulli trials include tossing a coin, looking for defective products rolling off an assembly line, or even shooting free throws in a basketball game.

Back to Tiger. What's the probability you find his picture in the first box of cereal? 20%, of course. We could write P(#boxes = 1) = 0.20.

How about the probability that you don't find Tiger until the second box? Well, that means you fail on the first trial and

Tiger Woods on the 14th tee during the practice round for the 131st British Open Championships figure 17.1

http://picsrv.altdc3.va.twimm.net/fif=/spsce/16225.fpx &obj=iip,1.0&wid=195&c

Daniel Bernoulli (1700-1782) was the nephew of Jakob, whom you saw in chapter 14. He was the first to work out the mathematics for what we now call Bernoulli trials. Figure 17.2
http://www-groups.dcs.st-and.ac.uk/~history/Mathematicians/Bernoulli_Daniel.html

then succeed on the second. With the probability of success 20%, the probability of failure, denoted q, is $1 - 0.2 = 80\%$. Since the trials are independent the probability of getting your first success on the second trial is $P(\#boxes = 2) = (0.8)(0.2) = 0.16$.

Of course, you could have a run of bad luck. Maybe you won't find Tiger until the 5th box of cereal. What are the chances of that? You'd have to fail 4 straight times and then succeed, so $P(\#boxes = 5) = (0.8)^4(0.2) = 0.08192$.

How many boxes might you expect to have to open? We could reason that since Tiger's picture is in 20% of the boxes, or 1 in 5, we expect to find his picture, on average, in the fifth box; that is $\mu = \dfrac{1}{0.2} = 5$ boxes.

That's correct, but not easy to prove.

The Geometric Model

A single Bernoulli trial is usually not all that interesting. We might not care about a particular cereal box. We are more likely to want to know how long it will take us to achieve a success. The model that tells us this probability is called the **geometric probability model**. Geometric models are completely specified by one parameter: p, the probability of success, and are denoted $Geom(p)$. Since achieving the first success on trial number X requires first experiencing $X - 1$ failures, the probabilities are easily expressed by a formula.

> **Geometric Probability Model for Bernoulli Trials: Geom(p)**
>
> p = probability of success (and $q = 1 - p$ = probability of failure)
>
> X = number of trials until the first success occurs
>
> $$P(X) = q^{x-1}p$$
>
> Expected value: $\mu = \dfrac{1}{p}$

DRAFT: Do not distribute or copy

$$\text{Standard deviation: } \sigma = \sqrt{\frac{q}{p^2}}$$

Independence

One of the important requirements for Bernoulli trials is that the trials are independent. Sometimes that's a reasonable assumption. Is it true for our example? We said that whether we find a Tiger Woods card in one box has no effect on the probabilities in other boxes. This is almost true. If exactly 20% of the boxes have Tiger Woods cards then when you find one, you've reduced the number of remaining Tiger Woods cards. With a few million boxes of cereal, the difference is hardly worth mentioning.

But if you knew there were 2 Tiger Woods cards hiding in the 10 boxes of cereal on the market shelf, then finding one in the first box you try would clearly change your chances of finding Tiger in the next box.

If we had an infinite number of boxes, there wouldn't be a problem. It is selecting from a finite population that causes the probabilities to change, making the trials not independent. Obviously, taking 2 out of 10 boxes changes the probability. And taking even a few hundred out of millions makes little difference. But fortunately, we have a rule of thumb for the in-between cases to help us decide whether we can behave as if Bernoulli trials are independent. The rule of thumb is that if we've looked at less than 10% of the population, we can pretend that the trials are still independent.

The 10% Condition

Bernoulli trials must be independent. If that assumption is violated, it is still okay to proceed when the sample is smaller than 10% of the population.

Working with the Geometric, Step-by-Step

People with O-negative blood are called "universal donors" because O-negative blood can be given to anyone else, regardless of the recipient's blood type. Only about 6% of people have O-negative blood. If donors line up at random for a blood drive, how many do you expect to examine before you find someone who is O-negative? What is the probability that the first O-negative donor found is one of the first 4 people in line?

Think	Check to see that these are Bernoulli trials.	• There are 2 outcomes; 　success = O-neg, 　failure = other blood types • The probability of success, $p = 0.06$, because people have lined up at random. • Trials are *not* independent, because the population is finite, *but* the donors lined up are fewer than 10% of all possible donors.
	Define the random variable and specify the model.	Let X = number of donors until O-neg is found. We can model X with a *Geom*(0.06)
Show	Find the mean.	$E(X) = \dfrac{1}{0.06} \approx 16.7$
	Calculate the requested probability.	$P(X = 1) + P(X = 2) + P(X = 3) + P(X = 4)$ $= (0.06) + (0.94)(0.06) + (0.94)^2(0.06)$ $+ (0.94)^3(0.06)$ ≈ 0.2193
Tell	State your conclusion.	In blood drives such as this one, we expect to examine an average of 16.7 people to find a universal donor. About 22% of the time we'll find one among the first 4 people in line.

The Binomial Model

Same situation; different question. You buy 5 boxes of cereal. What is the probability you get *exactly two* pictures of Tiger Woods? Before, we asked how long it would take until our first success. Now we want to find the probability of getting 2 successes among the 5 trials. We are still talking about Bernoulli trials, but now we're asking a different question.

This time we are interested in the number of successes in the 5 trials. We want to find $P(\#successes = 2)$. This is an example of a **binomial** probability. It takes two parameters to define this binomial model: the number of trials, n, and the probability of success, p. We denote this Binom(n,p). Here, $n = 5$ trials, and $p = 0.2$, the probability finding a Tiger Woods card in any trial.

DRAFT: Do not distribute or copy

Exactly 2 successes in 5 trials means 2 successes and 3 failures. It seems logical that the probability should be $(0.2)^2(0.8)^3$. Too bad! It's not that easy. That calculation would give you the probability of finding Tiger in the first 2 boxes and not in the next 3. But you could find Tiger in the third and fifth boxes and still have 2 successes. The probability of those outcomes in that particular order is $(0.8)(0.8)(0.2)(0.8)(0.2)$. That's also $(0.2)^2(0.8)^3$. In fact, the probability will always be the same no matter what order the successes and failures occur in. Any time we get 2 successes in 5 trials, no matter what the order, the probability will be $(0.2)^2(0.8)^3$. But we need to take account of all the possible orders in which the outcomes can occur.

And these orders are *disjoint*. (For example, if your successes came on the first 2 trials, they couldn't come on the last two.) So we can use the Addition Rule and add up the probabilities for all the possible orderings. And since the probabilities are all the same, we just need to know how many orders are possible. For small numbers, we can just make a tree diagram and count the branches. For larger numbers this isn't practical, so we let the computer or calculator do the work.

The number of different orders in which we can have k successes in n trials is written $_nC_k$ and pronounced "n choose k". (The "C" actually stands for "combinations".) There's a formula, but you won't be calculating it by hand.

Math Box

$$_nC_k = \frac{n!}{k!(n-k)!} \text{ where } n! = n\times(n-1)\times\ldots\times1$$

For 2 successes in 5 trials, $_5C_2 = \dfrac{5!}{2!(5-2)!} = \dfrac{5\times4\times3\times2\times1}{2\times1\times3\times2\times1} = \dfrac{5\times4}{2\times1} = 10$. So there are 10 ways to get 2 Tiger pictures in 5 boxes, and the probability of each is $(0.2)^2(0.8)^3$. Now we can find $P(\# \text{ successes} = 2) = 10(0.2)^2(0.8)^3 = 0.2048$.

In general, the probability of exactly k successes in n trials is $_nC_k\ p^kq^{n-k}$.

Using this formula, we could find the expected value by adding up $x\,P(X = x)$ for all values, but it would be a long, hard way to get an answer that you already know intuitively.

What *is* the expected value? If we had 100 trials with probability of success .2, how many successes would you expect? Can you think of any reason not to say 20? It seems so simple that most people wouldn't even think about it. You just multiply the probability of success by n. In other words, $E(X) = np$.[1]

But for the standard deviation, you can't just rely on your intuition. Fortunately, the formula for the standard deviation also boils down to something simple: $SD(X) = \sqrt{npq}$.

In 100 boxes of cereal, we expect to find 20 Tiger Woods cards, with a standard deviation of $\sqrt{100 \cdot .8 \cdot .2} = .4$ pictures.

Time to summarize. A binomial probability model describes the number of successes in a specified number of trials. It takes two parameters to specify this model: the number of trials n, and the probability of success p.

Binomial Probability Model for Bernoulli Trials: Binom(n,p)

n = number of trials

p = probability of success (and $q = 1 - p$ = probability of failure)

X = number of successes in n trials

$$P(X = x) = {}_nC_x\, p^x q^{n-x}, \text{ where } {}_nC_x = \frac{n!}{x!(n-x)!}$$

Mean: $\mu = np$ Standard deviation: $\sigma = \sqrt{npq}$

Working with the Binomial, Step-by-Step

Suppose 20 donors come to the blood drive. What are the mean and standard deviation of the number of number of universal donors among them? What is the probability that there are 2 or 3 universal donors?

Think	Check to see that these are Bernoulli trials.	We have 2 outcomes: O-neg or not, and 20 trials
		Probability of success p = 0.06; Trials are independent.
	Define the random variable and specify the model:	Let X = number of O-neg donors among n = 20.
		We can model X with
		Binom(20, 0.06)

---

[1] It's an amazing fact that this does work out that long way. That is,

$$\sum_{x=0}^{n} x\ {}_nC_x\, p^x q^{n-x} = np, \text{ something that is not obvious.}$$

Show	Find the expected value and standard deviation.	$E(X) = 20(0.06) = 1.2$ $SD(X) = \sqrt{20(0.06)(0.94)} \approx 1.06$
	Calculate the requested probability.	$P(X = 2 \text{ or } 3) = P(X = 2) + P(X = 3)$ $=_{20}C_2(0.06)^2(0.94)^{18} +_{20}C_3(0.06)^3(0.94)$ $\approx 0.2246 + 0.0860 = 0.3106$
Tell	State your conclusion.	In groups of 20 randomly selected blood donors, we expect to find an average of 1.2 universal donors, with standard deviation 1.06. About 31% of the time we'll find 2 or 3 universal donors among the 20 people.

The Normal to the Rescue!

Suppose the Tennessee Red Cross anticipates the need for at least 1850 units of O-negative blood this year. They estimate that they will collect blood from 32,000 donors. How great is the risk that they will fall short of meeting their need? We've just learned how to calculate such probabilities. We can use the binomial model with $n = 32,000$ and $p = 0.06$. The probability of getting *exactly* 1850 units of O- blood from 32,000 donors is $_{32000}C_{1850} \times .06^{1850} \times .94^{30150}$. No calculator on earth can calculate that first term (it has more than 100,000 digits).[2] And that's just the beginning. The problem said *at least* 1850. So we have to do it again for 1851, for 1852, and all the way up to 32,000.

When we are dealing with a large number of trials like this, making direct calculations of the probabilities becomes tedious (or outright impossible). But here an old friend--the Normal model--comes to the rescue.

The binomial model has mean $np = 1920$ and standard deviation $\sqrt{npq} \approx 42.48$. We could try approximating its distribution with a Normal model using the same mean and standard deviation. Remarkably enough, that turns out to be a very good approximation. (We'll see why in the next chapter.) With that approximation, we can find the probability:

---

[2] If your calculator can do this, then it's smart enough to use an approximation. Read on to see how you can too.

$$P(X < 1850) = P\left(z < \frac{1850 - 1920}{42.48}\right) \approx P(z < -1.65) \approx 0.05$$

There seems to be about a 5% chance that this Red Cross will run short of O-negative blood.

Can we always use a Normal model to make estimates of binomial probabilities? No. It works only for a large enough number of trials. And what we mean by "large enough" depends on the probability of success. Specifically, we need to expect to see at least 10 successes and 10 failures. That is, we check

---

The Success/Failure Condition

A binomial model is approximately Normal if
we expect at least 10 successes and 10 failures.

$$np \geq 10 \text{ and } nq \geq 10$$

Why 10? (well, actually 9)*

Cartoon sketch
of 3 blind mice
goes here.

It is easy to see where we found the magic number 10. You just need to remember how Normal models work. The problem is that a Normal model extends infinitely in both directions. But a binomial model must have between 0 and n successes. So if we use a Normal to approximate a Binomial, we have to cut off its tails. Those tails are negligible as long as 0 and n are far enough from the mean. More than three standard deviations should do it because the Normal has little probability past that. So the mean needs to be at least three standard deviations big.

We require:	$np > 3\sqrt{npq}$
Squaring yields:	$n^2 p^2 > 9npq$
Simplify:	$np > 9q$
Since $q \leq 1$ we can require	$np > 9$

For simplicity we usually demand that np (and nq for the other tail) be at least 10 to use the Normal approximation. We call this the **Success/Failure Condition.**

Continuous Random Variables

There's a problem with the Normal model; it can take on *any value*. That means we can no longer list all the possible outcomes and their probabilities, as we could for discrete random variables. Such random variables are called **continuous random variables**.

When we use the Normal model, we no longer calculate the probability that the random variable equals a *particular* value, but only that it lies *between* two values. We won't calculate the probability of getting exactly

DRAFT: Do not distribute or copy

1850 units of blood, but have no problem approximating the probability of getting 1850 *or more,* which was, after all, what we really wanted.[3]

What Can Go Wrong?

- *Be sure you have Bernoulli trials.* Be sure to check the requirements first: 2 outcomes per trial, a constant probability of success, and independence. Remember that the 10% Condition provides a reasonable substitute for independence.

- *Don't confuse Geometric and Binomial models.* Both involve Bernoulli trials, but the issues are different. If you are repeating trials until your first success that's a geometric probability. You don't know in advance how many trials you'll need - theoretically it could take forever. If you are counting the number of successes in a specified number of trials, that's a binomial probability.

- *Don't use the Normal approximation with small n.* To use a Normal approximation in place of a binomial model, there must be at least 10 expected successes and failures.

Connections

This chapter builds on what we know about random variables. We now have two more probability models to join the Normal model.

There are a number of "forward' connections from this chapter. We'll see the 10% condition and the success/failure condition often. And the facts about the Binomial distribution can help explain how proportions behave, as we'll see in the next chapter.

The Binomial, the Geometric, and the Computer

Most statistics packages offer functions that compute Binomial probabilities and many offer functions for Geometric probabilities as well. The only important differences among these functions is in what they are named and the order of their arguments.

Generically, the four functions are[4]:

---

[3] If we really had been interested in a single value, we might have found the probability of being between 1849.5 and 1850.5.

[4] In case you were curious, pdf stands for "probability density function", the technical term for what we've been calling a probability model. The letters cdf stand for "cumulative distribution function", the technical term when we want to accumulate probabilities over a range of values. These technical terms show up in many of the function names. The term "cumulative" in a function name says that it corresponds to a cdf.

Geometric pdf (prob, x)	Finds the individual geometric probability of getting the first success on trial x when the probability of success is *prob*,	For example, the probability of finding the first Tiger Woods picture in the fifth cereal box is geometric pdf(0.2, 5)
Geometric cdf (prob, x)	Finds the cumulative probability of getting the first success on or before trial x, when the probability of success is *prob*.	For example, the total probability of finding Tiger's picture in one of the first 4 boxes is Geometric cdf(0.2, 4)
Binomial pdf (n, prob, x)	Finds the probability of getting x successes in n trials when the probability of success is *prob*.	For example, binomial pdf(5, 0.2, 2) is the probability of finding Tiger's picture exactly twice among 5 boxes of cereal.
Binomial cdf (n, prob, x)	Finds the total probability of getting x or fewer successes among n trials when the probability of success is *prob*.	For example, binomial cdf(10, 0.2, 3) is the probability of finding Tiger's picture in 0, 1, 2, or 3 of 10 boxes checked.

Technology solutions automatically use the Normal approximation for the Binomial when the exact calculations become unmanageable.

Most packages provide the probability computing functions as part of a more general capability of calculating functions of variables and numbers. Look in that part of the package documentation to learn how to access the functions. The relationship between each of these functions and the generic forms is straightforward, but be careful; the term "binomial distribution" (and abbreviations of it) can be used for pdf or cdf functions or even for both by different packages.

Package	Commands & Location	Comments
Data Desk	**BinomDistr(*x, n, prob*)** (pdf) **CumBinomDistr(*x, n, prob*)** (cdf)	Data Desk does not compute geometric probabilities. These functions work in derived variables or in scratchpads.
Excel	**Binomdist(*x, n, prob, cumulative*)**	Set cumulative = true for cdf, false for pdf. Excel's function fails when x or n is large. Possibly it does not use the Normal approximation. Excel does not compute geometric probabilities
JMP	**Binomial Probability (*prob, n, x*)** (pdf) **Binomial Distribution (*prob, n, x*)** (cdf)	JMP does not compute geometric probabilities.
Minitab	Choose **Probability Distributions** from the **Calc** menu. Choose **Binomial** from the Probability Distributions submenu. To calculate the probability of getting *x* success in *n* trials, choose **Probability** To calculate the probability of getting *x* or fewer successes among *n* trials choose **Cumulative Probability**	Minitab does not compute geometric probabilities.
SPSS	**PDF.GEOM(*x, prob*)** **CDF.GEOM(*x, prob*)** **PDF.BINOM(*x, n, prob*)** **CDF.BINOM(*x, n, prob*)**	
TI-83	**geometpdf(*prob, x*)** **geometcdf(*prob, x*)** **binompdf(*n, prob, x*)** **binomcdf(*n, prob, x*)**	Find these commands in the 2nd DISTR menu (the calculator refers to models as "distributions")

Key Concepts

Bernoulli Trials, if…	1. there are two possible outcomes; 2. the probability of success is constant; 3. the trials are independent.
Geometric Model	A geometric model is appropriate for a random variable that counts the number of Bernoulli trials until the first success.
Binomial Model	A binomial model is appropriate for a random variable that counts the number of successes in a fixed number of Bernoulli trials.

Skills:

Upon completing this Lesson you should:

> *Think*
>
> - Know how to tell if a situation involves Bernoulli trials.
> - Know whether to use a geometric or a binomial model for a random variable involving Bernoulli trials.
>
> *Show*
>
> - Test the appropriate conditions before using a geometric, binomial, or Normal model.
> - Know how to find the expected value of a geometric model.
> - Be able to calculate geometric probabilities.
> - Know how to find the mean and standard deviation of a binomial model.
> - Be able to calculate binomial probabilities, perhaps with a Normal model.
>
> *Tell*
>
> - Be able to interpret means, standard deviations, and probabilities in the Bernoulli trial context.

Exercises

1. **Bernoulli** Can we use probability models based on Bernoulli trials to investigate the following situations? Explain.
   a) We roll 50 dice to find the distribution of the number of spots on the faces.
   b) How likely is it that in a group of 120 the majority may have Type A blood, given that Type A is found in 43% of the population?
   c) We deal 5 cards from a deck, and get all hearts. How likely is that?
   d) We wish to predict the outcome of a vote on the school budget, and poll 500 of the 3000 likely voters to see how many favor the proposed budget.
   e) A company realizes that about 10% of its packages are not being sealed properly. In a case of 24, is it likely that more than three are unsealed?

2. **Bernoulli 2** Can we use probability models based on Bernoulli trials to investigate the following situations? Explain.
   a) You are rolling five dice and need to get at least two 6's to win the game.

DRAFT: Do not distribute or copy

b) We record the eye colors found in a group of 500 people.

c) A manufacturer recalls a doll because about 3% have buttons that are not properly attached. Customers return 37 of these dolls to your local toy store. Are they likely to find any dangerous buttons?

d) A city council of 11 Republicans and 8 Democrats picks a committee of four at random. What is the probability they chose all Democrats?

e) A 2002 Rutgers University study found that 74% of high school students have cheated on a test at least once. Your local high school principal conducts a survey in homerooms and gets responses from 322 of the 481 students.

3. **Hoops** A basketball player has made 80% of his foul shots during the season. Find the probability that in tonight's game he ...
   a) misses for the first time on his fifth attempt.
   b) makes his first basket on his 4th shot.
   c) makes his first basket on one of his first 3 shots.

4. **Chips** Suppose a computer chip manufacturer rejects 2% of the chips produced because they fail pre-sale testing.
   a) What is the probability that the 5th chip you test is the first bad one you find?
   b) What is the probability you find a bad one within the first 10 you examine?

5. **More Hoops** For the basketball player in Exercise 3, what is the expected number of shots until he misses?

6. **Chips Ahoy** For the computer chips described in Exercise 4, How many do you expect to test before finding a bad one?

7. **Blood** Only 4% of people have Type AB blood.
   a) On average, how many donors must be checked to find someone with Type AB blood?
   b) What is the probability that there is a type AB donor among the first five people checked?
   c) What is the probability the first Type AB donor will be found among the first 6 people?
   d) What is the probability we won't a Type AB donor before the tenth person?

8. **Colorblindness** About 8% of males are colorblind. A researcher needs some colorblind subjects for an experiment, and begins checking potential subjects.
   a) On average, how many men should the researcher expect to check to find one who is colorblind?
   b) What is the probability that she won't anyone colorblind among

the first four men she checks?

c) What is the probability the first colorblind man found will be the sixth person checked?

d) What is the probability she finds someone who is colorblind before checking the tenth man?

9. **Lefties** Assume that 13% of people are left-handed. If we select five people at random, find the probability of each outcome described below?

a) The first lefty is the fifth person chosen.

b) There are some lefties among the 5 people.

c) The first lefty is the second or third person.

d) There are exactly 3 lefties in the group.

e) There are at least 3 lefties in the group.

f) There are no more than 3 lefties in the group.

10. **Arrows** An Olympic archer is able to hit the bulls-eye 80% of the time. Assume each shot is independent of the others. If she shoots 6 arrows, what is the probability of each result described below?

a) Her first bulls-eye comes on the third arrow.

b) She misses the bulls-eye at least once.

c) Her first bulls-eye comes on the fourth or fifth arrow.

d) She gets at least 4 bulls-eyes.

e) She gets exactly 4 bulls-eyes.

f) She gets at most 4 bulls-eyes

11. **Lefties Redux** Consider our group of 5 people from Exercise 9.

a) How many lefties do you expect?

b) With what standard deviation?

c) If we keep picking people until we find a lefty, how long do you expect it will take?

12. **More Arrows** Consider our archer from Exercise 10.

a) How many bulls-eyes do you expect her to get?

b) With what standard deviation?

c) If she keeps shooting arrows until she hits the bulls-eye, how long do you expect it will take?

13. **Still More Lefties** Suppose we choose 12 people instead of 5.

a) Find the mean and standard deviation of the number of right-handers in the group.

b) What is the probability that they are not all right-handed?

c) What is the probability that there are no more than 10 righties?

d) What is the probability that there are exactly 6 of each?

e) What is the probability that a majority is right-handed?

14. **Still More Arrows** Suppose our archer shoots ten arrows.

a) Find the mean and standard deviation of the number of bulls-eyes she may get.

DRAFT: Do not distribute or copy

b) What is the probability that she never misses?
c) What is the probability that there are no more than 8 bulls-eyes?
d) What is the probability that there are exactly 8 bulls-eyes?
e) What is the probability that she hits the bulls-eye more often than she misses?

15. **Tennis, Anyone?** A certain tennis player makes a successful first serve 70% of the time. Assume that each serve is independent of the others. If she serves 6 times, what is the probability she gets
a) all 6 serves in?
b) exactly 4 serves in?
c) at least 4 serves in?
d) no more than 4 serves in?

16. **Frogs** A wildlife biologist examines frogs for a genetic trait he suspects may be linked to industrial toxins in the environment. Previous research had established that this trait is usually found in one of every eight frogs. He collects and examines a dozen frogs. If the frequency of the trait has not changed, what is the probability he finds the trait in
a) none of the 12 frogs?
b) at least two frogs?
c) 3 or 4 frogs?
d) no more than 4 frogs?

17. **And More Tennis** Suppose the tennis player in Exercise 15 serves 80 times in a match.
a) What is the mean and standard deviation of the number of good serves expected?
b) Verify that you can use a Normal model to approximate the distribution of the number of good serves.
c) Use the 68-95-99.7 Rule to describe this distribution.
d) What is the probability she makes at least 65 first serves?

18. **More Arrows** The archer in Exercise 10 will be shooting 200 arrows at a large competition.
a) What are the mean and standard deviation of the number of bulls-eyes she might get?
b) Is a Normal model appropriate here? Explain.
c) Use the 68-95-99.7 Rule to describe the distribution of the number of bulls-eyes she may get.
d) Would you be surprised if she made only 140 bulls-eyes? Explain.

19. **Frogs, Part II** Based on concerns raised by his preliminary research, the biologist in Exercise 16 decides to collect and examine 150 frogs.
a) Assuming the frequency of the trait is still 1 in 8, what is the mean and standard deviation of the number of frogs with the trait he

should expect to find in his sample?

b) Verify that he can use a Normal model to approximate the distribution of the number of frogs with the trait.

c) He found the trait in 22 of his frogs. Do you think this proves that the trait has become more common? Explain.

20. **Apples** An orchard owner knows that he'll have to use about 6% of the apples he harvests for cider because they will have bruises or blemishes. He expects a tree to produce about 300 apples.

a) Describe an appropriate model for the number of cider apples that may come from that tree. Justify your model.

b) Find the probability there will be no more than a dozen cider apples.

c) Is it likely there will be over 50 cider apples? Explain.

21. **Lefties Again** A lecture hall has 200 seats with folding arm tablets, 30 of which are designed for left-handers. The average size of classes that meet there is 188, and we can assume that about 13% of students are left-handed. What is the probability that a right-handed student in one of these classes is forced to use a lefty arm tablet?

22. **No-Shows** An airline believes that 5% of passengers fail to show up for flights, and therefore they overbook (sell more tickets than there are seats). Suppose a plane will hold 265 passengers, and they sell 275 seats. What is the probability someone gets bumped?

23. **Annoying Phone Calls** A newly hired telemarketer is told he will probably make a sale on about 12% of his phone calls. The first week he called 200 people, but only made 10 sales. Should he suspect he was misled about the true success rate? Explain.

24. **The Euro** Shortly after the introduction of the Euro coin in Belgium, newspapers around the world published articles claiming the coin is biased. The stories were based on reports that someone had spun the coin 250 times and gotten 140 heads – that's 56% heads. Do you think this is evidence that spinning a Euro is unfair? Explain.

25. **Seatbelts** Police estimate that 80% of drivers now wear their seatbelts. They set up a safety roadblock, stopping cars to check for seatbelt use.

a) How many cars do they expect to stop before finding a driver whose seatbelt is not buckled?

b) What is the probability that the first unbelted driver is in the 6th car stopped?

c) What is the probability that they find the first 10 drivers are all wearing their seatbelts?

d) If they stop 30 cars during the first hour, find the mean and standard deviation of the number of drivers expected to be wearing seatbelts.

e) If they stop 120 cars during this safety check, what is the probability they find at least 20 drivers not wearing their seatbelts?

26. **Rickets** Vitamin D is essential for strong healthy bones. Our bodies produce Vitamin D naturally when sunlight falls upon the skin or it can be taken as a dietary supplement. Although the bone disease rickets was largely eliminated in England during the 1950s, some people there are concerned that this generation of children is is at increased risk because they are more likely to watch TV or play computer games than spend time outdoors. Recent research indicated that about 20% of British children are deficient in Vitamin D. Suppose doctors test a group of elementary school children.
    a) What is the probability that the first Vitamin D-deficient child is the eighth one tested?
    b) What is the probability that the first ten children tested are all okay?
    c) How many kids do they expect to test before finding one who has this vitamin deficiency?
    d) They will test 50 students in the third grade level. What is the mean and standard deviation of the number who may be deficient in Vitamin D?
    e) If they test 320 children at this school, what is the probability that no more than 50 of them have the vitamin deficiency?

27. **ESP** Scientists wish to test the mind-reading ability of a person who claims to "have ESP". They use five cards with different and distinctive symbols (square, circle, triangle, line, squiggle). Someone picks a card at random and thinks about the symbol. The "mind reader" must correctly identify which symbol was on the card. If the test consists of 100 trials, how many would this person need to get right in order to convince you that ESP may actually exist? Explain.

28. **True-False** A true-false test consists of 50 questions. How many does a student have to get right to convince you that he is not merely guessing? Explain.

Unit IV Review

Here's a brief summary of the key concepts and skills in probability and probability modeling:

➢ The Law of Large Numbers says that the more times we try something the closer the results will come to theoretical perfection.
- Don't mistakenly misinterpret the Law of Large Numbers as the "Law of Averages". There's no such thing.

➢ Basic rules of probability can handle most situations:
- To find the probability that an event OR another event happens, add their probabilities, but don't count any overlap twice.
- To find the probability that event AND another event both happen, multiply probabilities.
- Conditional probabilities tell you how likely one event is to happen, knowing that another event has happened.
- Mutually exclusive events cannot both happen at the same time.
- Two events are independent if knowing that one happens doesn't change the probability that the other happens.

➢ A probability model for a random variable describes the theoretical distribution of outcomes.
- The mean of a random variable is its expected value.
- For independent random variables, variances add.
- To estimate probabilities involving quantitative variables you may be able to use a Normal model – but only if the distribution of the variable is mound-shaped and symmetric.
- To estimate the probability you'll get your first success on a certain trial use a geometric model.
- To estimate the probability you'll get a certain number of successes in a specified number of independent trials use a Binomial model.

Ready? Just turn the page for some opportunities to check your understanding of these ideas.

Exercises

1. **Quality Control** A consumer's organization estimates that 29% of new cars have a cosmetic defect such as a scratch or a dent when they are delivered to car dealers. This same organization believes that 7% have a functional defect – something that does not work properly – and that 2% of new cars have both kinds of problems.
   a) If you buy a new car, what's the probability that it has some kind of defect?
   b) What's the probability it has a cosmetic defect but no functional defect?
   c) If you notice a dent on a new car, what's the probability it has a functional defect?
   d) Are the two kinds of defects disjoint events? Explain.
   e) Do you think the two kinds of defects are independent? Explain.

2. **Workers** A company's human resources officer reports a breakdown of employees by job type and gender shown in the table.
   a) What is the probability that a worker selected at random is
      i) female?
      ii) female or a production worker?
      iii) female, if the person works in production?
      iv) a production worker, if the person is female?

Job Type	Male	Female
Management	7	6
Supervision	8	12
Production	45	72

   b) Do these data suggest that holding a supervisory position is independent of gender? Explain.

3. **Airfares** Each year a company must send 3 officials to a meeting in China and 5 officials to a meeting in France. Airline ticket prices vary from time to time. Past experience has shown that tickets to China have a mean price of $1000 with standard deviation $150, while the mean airfare to France is $500 with standard deviation $100.
   a) Define random variables and use them to express the total amount the company will have to spend to send these delegations to the two meetings.
   b) Find the mean and standard deviation of this total cost.
   c) Find the mean and standard deviation of the difference in price of a ticket to China and a ticket to France.
   d) Do you need to make any assumptions in calculating these means? How about the standard deviations?

4. **Bipolar** Psychiatrists estimate that about 1 in 100 adults suffer from bipolar disorder. What is the probability that in a city of 10,000 there are over 200 people with this condition? Be sure to verify that a Normal model can be used here.

5. **A Game** To play a game you must pay $5 for each play. There is a 10% chance you will win $5, a 40% chance you will win $7, and a 50% chance you will win only $3.
   a) What are the mean and standard deviation of your net winnings?
   b) You play twice. Assuming the plays are independent, what are the mean and standard deviation of your total winnings?

6. **Emergency Switch** Safety engineers must determine whether industrial workers can operate a machine's emergency shutoff device. Among a group of test subjects, 66% were successful with their left hands, 82% with their right hands, and 51% with both hands.
   a) What percent of these workers could not operate the switch with either hand?
   b) Are success with right and left hands independent? Explain.
   c) Are success with right and left hands disjoint? Explain.

7. **Twins** In the US the probability of having twins (usually about 1 in 90 births) rises to about 1 in 10 for women who have been taking the fertility drug Clomid. (www.babymed.com) Among a group of 10 pregnant women, what is the probability that
   a) at least one will have twins if none were taking a fertility drug?
   b) at least one will have twins if all were taking Clomid?
   c) at least one will have twins if half were taking Clomid?

8. **Deductible** A car owner may buy insurance that will pay the full price of repairing the car after an accident, or save $12 a year by getting a policy with a $500 deductible. Her insurance company says that about 0.5% of drivers in her area have an at-fault auto accident during any given year. Based upon this information, should she buy the policy with the deductible or not? How does the value of her car influence this decision?

9. **More Twins** In a group of 5 women who became pregnant while undergoing fertility treatments with the drug Clomid, discussed in Exercise 7. What is the probability that
   a) none will have twins.
   b) exactly one will have twins?
   c) at least 3 will have twins?

10. **At Fault** The car insurance company in Exercise 8 believes that about 0.5% of drivers have an at-fault accident during a given year. Suppose they insure 1355 drivers in that city.
    a) What are the mean and standard deviation of the number who may have at-fault accidents?
    b) Can you describe the distribution of these accidents with a Normal model? Explain.

11. **Twins, Part III** At a large fertility clinic there are 152 women who became pregnant while taking Clomid. (See Exercise 7.)
    a) What are the mean and standard deviation of the number of twin births we might expect?
    b) Can we use a Normal model in this situation? Explain.
    c) What is the probability that no more than 10 of the women have twins?

12. **Child's Play** In a board game you determine the number of spaces you may move by spinning a spinner and rolling a die. The spinner has three regions: half of the spinner is marked "5" and the other half is equally divided between "10" and "20". The six faces of the die show 0, 0, 1, 2, 3, and 4 spots. When it's your turn you spin and roll, adding the numbers together to determine how far you may move.
    a) Create a probability model for the outcome on the spinner.
    b) Find the mean and standard deviation of the spinner results.
    c) Create a probability model for the outcome on the die.
    d) Find the mean and standard deviation of the die results.
    e) Find the mean and standard deviation of the number of spaces you get to move.

13. **Language** Neurological research has shown that in about 80% of people language abilities reside in the brain's left side. Another 10% display right-brain language centers, and the remaining 10% have 2-sided language control. (The latter two groups are mainly left-handers.) [*Science News*, 2002, Vol 161 No 24]
    a) Assume that a freshman composition class contains 25 randomly selected people. What is the probability no more than 15 of them have left-brain language control?
    b) In a randomly assigned group of 5 of these students, what is the probability that no one has 2-sided language control?
    c) In the entire freshman class of 1200 students, how many would you expect to find of each type?
    d) What are the mean and standard deviation of the number of these freshmen who might be right-brained in language abilities?
    e) If an assumption of normality is justified, use the 68-95-99.7 Rule to describe how many students in the freshman class might have right-brain language control.

14. **Play Again** If you land in a "Penalty Zone" on the game board described Exercise 12, your move will be determined by subtracting the roll of the die from the result on the spinner. Now what are the mean and standard deviation of the number of spots you may move?

15. **Beanstalks** In cities tall people who want to meet and socialize with other tall people can join Beanstalk Clubs. To qualify a man must be over 6'2" tall, and a woman over 5'10". According to the National Health Survey, heights of adults may have a Normal model with means heights

of 65.6″ for men and 60.9″ for women. The respective standard deviations are 2.5″ and 2.8″.

a) You are probably not surprised to learn that men are generally taller than women, but what does the greater standard deviation for women's heights indicate?

b) Who is more likely to qualify for Beanstalk membership, men or women?

c) Beanstalk members believe that height is an important factor when people select their spouses. To investigate we select at random a married man and, independently, a married woman. Define two random variables, and use them to express how many inches taller the man is than the woman.

d) What is the mean of this difference?

e) What is the standard deviation of this difference?

f) What is the probability that the man is taller than the woman (that the difference in heights is greater than 0)?

g) Suppose that a survey of married couples reveals that 92% of the husbands were taller than their wives. Based on your answer to part f), do you believe that people chose spouses independent of height? Explain.

16. **Stocks** Since the stock market began in 1872, stock prices have risen in about 73% of the years. Assuming that market performance is independent from year to year, what is the probability that
a) the market will rise for 3 consecutive years?
b) the market will rise 3 years out of the next five?
c) the market will fall during at least one of the next 5 years?
d) the market will rise during a majority of years over the next decade?

17. **Multiple Choice** A multiple-choice test has 50 questions, 4 choices each. You must get at least 30 correct to pass the test, and the questions are very difficult.
a) Are you likely to be able to pass by guessing on every question? Explain.
b) Suppose after studying for a while you believe you have raised your chances of getting each question right to 70%. How likely are you to pass now?
c) Assuming you are operating at the 70% level and the instructor arranges questions randomly, what is the probability that the third question is the first one you get right?

18. **Stock Strategy** Many investment advisors argue that after stocks have declined in value for two consecutive years, people should invest heavily because the market rarely declines 3 years in a row.

a) Since the stock market began in 1872 there have been two consecutive losing years eight times. In six of those cases the market rose during the following year. Does this confirm the advice?

b) Overall stocks have risen in value during 95 of the 130 years since the market began in 1872. How is this fact relevant in assessing the statistical reasoning of the advisors?

19. **Insurance** A 65 year-old woman takes out a $100,000 term life insurance policy. The company charges an annual premium of $520. Estimate the company's expected profit on such policies if mortality tables indicate that only 2.6% of women aged 65 die within a year.

20. **Teen Smoking** The Centers for Disease Control say that about 30% of high school students smoke tobacco (down from a high of 38% in 1997). Suppose you randomly select high school students to survey them on their attitudes toward scenes of smoking in the movies. What is the probability that
a) none of the first 4 students you interview is a smoker?
b) the first smoker is the sixth person you choose?
c) there are no more than 2 smokers among 10 people you choose.

21. **Passing Stats** Molly's college offers two sections of Stat 101. From what she has heard about the two professors listed, Molly estimates that her chances of passing the course are 0.80 if she gets Professor Scedastic and 0.60 if she gets Professor Kurtosis. The registrar uses a lottery randomly assigning the 120 enrolled students based on the number of available seats in each class. There are 70 seats in Professor Scedastic's class and 50 in Professor Kurtosis's class.
a) What is the probability that Molly will pass Statistics?
b) At the end of the semester we find out that Molly failed. What is the probability that she got professor Kurtosis?

22. **Teen Smoking II** Suppose that, as reported by the Centers for Disease Control, about 30% of high school students smoke tobacco. You randomly select 120 high school students to survey them on their attitudes toward scenes of smoking in the movies.
a) What is the expected number of smokers?
b) What is the standard deviation of the number of smokers?
c) The number of smokers among 120 randomly selected students will vary from group to group. Explain why that number can be described with a Normal model.
d) Create and interpret a model for the number of smokers among your group of 120 students using the 68-95-99.7 Rule.

23. **Random Variables** Given independent random variables with means and standard deviations as shown, find the mean and standard deviation of each of these variables:

	Mean	SD
X	50	8
Y	100	6

a) $X + 50$
b) $10Y$
c) $X + 0.5Y$
d) $X - Y$

24. **Merger** Explain why the Law of Large Numbers and facts you know about variances of independent random variables might encourage two small insurance companies to merge. (Hint: think about the expected amount and potential variability in payouts for the separate and the merged companies.)

25. **Youth Survey** According to a recent Gallup survey 93% of teens use the Internet, but there are differences in how teen boys and girls say they use computers. The telephone poll found that 77% of boys had played computer games in the past week compared to 65% of girls. On the other hand, 76% of girls said they had emailed friends in the past week, compared to only 65% of boys.
   a) For boys, the cited percentages are 77% playing computer games and 65% using email. That total is 142%, so there is obviously a mistake in the report. No? Explain.
   b) Based on these results, do you think playing games and using email are disjoint? Explain.
   c) Do you think emailing friends and gender are independent? Explain.
   d) Suppose that in fact 93% of the teens in your area do use the Internet. You want to interview a few who do not, so you start contacting teenagers at random. What is the probability that you do not find someone who does not use the Internet until the 5th person you ask?

26. **Meals** A Dartmouth college student on a meal plan reports that the amount of money he spends daily on food varies with mean $13.50 and standard deviation $7.
   a) What are the mean and standard deviation of the amount he might spend in two consecutive days?
   b) What assumption did you make in order to find that standard deviation? Are there any reasons you might question that assumption?
   c) Estimate his average weekly food costs, and the standard deviation.
   d) Do you think it likely he might spend less than $50 in a week? Explain, including any assumptions you make in your analysis.

27. **Travel to Kyrgyzstan** Your pocket copy of *Kyrgyzstan on 4237±360 Soms a Day* claims that you can expect to spend about 4237 Soms each day with a standard deviation of 360 Soms. How well can you estimate your expenses for the trip?
   a) Your budget allows you to spend 90,000 Soms. About how long can you afford to stay in Kyrgyzstan?

b) What is the standard deviation for your expenses for a trip of that duration?

c) You doubt that your total expenses will exceed your expectations by more than two standard deviations. How much extra money should you bring? On average, how much of a "cushion" will you have per day?

28. **Picking Melons** Two stores sell watermelons. At the first store the melons weigh an average of 22 pounds, with a standard deviation of 2.5 pounds. At the second store the melons are smaller, with mean 18 pounds and standard deviation 2 pounds. You select a melon at random at each store.
a) What is the mean difference in weights of the melons?
b) What is the standard deviation of the difference in weights?
c) If a Normal model can be used to describe the difference in weights, what is the probability that the melon you got at the first store is heavier?

29. **Home Sweet Home** According to the 2000 census, 66% of US households own the home they live in. A mayoral candidate conducts a survey of 820 randomly selected homes in your city and finds only 523 owned by the current residents. The candidate then attacks the incumbent mayor, saying that there is an unusually low level of home ownership there. Do you agree? Explain.

30. **Buying Melons** The first store in Exercise 28 sells watermelons for 32 cents a pound. The second store is having a sale on watermelons – only 25 cents a pound. Find the mean and standard deviation of the difference in the price you may pay for melons randomly selected at each store.

31. **Who's the Boss?** The 2000 census revealed that 26% of all firms in the United States are owned by women. You call some firms doing business locally, assuming that the national percentage is true in your area.
a) What is the probability that the first three you call are all owned by women?
b) What is the probability that none of your first four calls finds a firm that is owned by a woman?
c) Suppose none of your first five calls found a firm owned by a woman. What is the probability that your next call does?

32. **Jerseys** A Statistics professor comes home to find that all four of his children got white team shirts from soccer camp this year. He concludes that this year, unlike other years, the camp must not be using a variety of colors. But then he finds out that in each child's age group there are 4

teams, only one of which wears white shirts. Each child just happened to get on the white team at random.

a) Why was he so surprised? If each age group uses the same 4 colors, what is the probability that all four kids would get the same color shirt?

b) What is the probability that all four would get white shirts?

c) We lied. Actually, in the oldest child's group there are 6 teams instead of the 4 teams in each of the other three groups. How does this change the probabilities you calculated above?

33. **When to Stop?** In the Review Exercises for the last Unit we posed this question:

> *You play a game that involves rolling a die. You can roll as many times as you want, and your score is the total for all the rolls. But… if you roll a 6 your score is 0 and your turn is over. What might be a good strategy for a game like this?*

You attempted to devise a good strategy by simulating several plays to see what might happen. Let's try calculating a strategy.

a) On what roll would you expect to get a 6 for the first time?

b) So, roll *one time less* than that. Assuming all those rolls were not 6's, what is your expected score?

c) What is the probability that you can roll that many times without getting a 6?

34. **Plan B** Here's another attempt at developing a good strategy for the dice game in Exercise 33. Instead of stopping after a certain number of rolls, you could decide to stop when your score reaches a certain number of points.

a) How many points would you expect a roll to *add* to your score?

b) In terms of your current score, how many points would you expect a roll to *subtract* from your score?

c) Based on your answers above, at what score will another roll "break even"?

d) Describe the strategy this result suggests.

35. **Technology on Campus** Every five years the Conference Board of the Mathematical Sciences surveys college math departments. In 2000 they reported that 51% of all undergraduates taking Calculus I were in classes that used graphing calculators and 31% were in classes that used computer assignments. Suppose that 16% used both calculators and computers.

a) What percent used neither kind of technology?

b) What percent used calculators but not computers?

c) What percent of the calculator users had computer assignments?

d) Based on this survey, do calculator and computer use appear to be independent? Explain.

36. **Dogs** A census by the county dog control officer found that 18% of homes kept one dog as a pet, 4% had two dogs, and 1% had three or more. If a salesman visits two homes selected at random, what is the probability he encounters
a) no dogs.
b) some dogs.
c) dogs in each home.
d) more than one dog in each home.

37. **Socks** In your sock drawer you have 4 blue socks, 5 grey socks, and 3 black ones. Half asleep one morning, you grab two socks at random and put them on. Find the probability you end up wearing
a) two blue socks.
b) no grey socks.
c) at least one black sock.
d) a green sock.
e) matching socks.

38. **Coins** A coin is to be tossed 36 times.
a) What are the mean and standard deviation of the number of heads?
b) Suppose the resulting number of heads is unusual, two standard deviations above the mean. How many "extra" heads were observed?
c) If the coin were tossed 100 times would you still consider the same number of extra heads unusual? Explain.
d) In the 100 tosses, how many extra heads would you need to observe in order to say the results were unusual?
e) Explain how these results refute the "Law of Averages" but confirm the Law of Large Numbers.

39. **The Drake Equation** In 1961 astronomer Frank Drake developed an equation to try to estimate the number of extraterrestrial civilizations in our galaxy that might be able to communicate with us via radio transmissions. Now largely accepted by the scientific community, the Drake equation has helped spur efforts by radio astronomers to search for extraterrestrial intelligence.

So here is the equation: $N_c = N \cdot f_p \cdot n_e \cdot f_l \cdot f_i \cdot f_c \cdot f_L$.

Okay, it looks a little messy, but here's what it means:

Factor	What it represents:	Possible value
N	number of stars in the Milky Way Galaxy	200-400 billion
f_p	probability that a star has planets	20 - 50%

n_e	number of planets in a solar system capable of sustaining earth-type life	1? 2?
f_l	probability that life develops on a planet with a suitable environment	1 – 100%
f_i	probability that life evolves intelligence	50%?
f_c	probability that intelligent life develops radio communication	10 – 20%
f_L	fraction of the planet's life for which the civilization survives	$\frac{1}{1,000,000}$?
N_c	number of extraterrestrial civilization in our galaxy with which we could communicate	?

So, how many ETs are out there? That depends; values chosen for the many factors in the equation depend on ever-evolving scientific knowledge and one's personal guesses. If you would like to play with the equation yourself, see www.planetarysystems.org/drake_equation.html). But now, some questions.

a) What quantity is calculated by the first product $N \cdot f_p$?
b) What quantity is calculated by the product $N \cdot f_p \cdot n_e \cdot f_l$?
c) What probability is calculated by the product $f_l \cdot f_i$?
d) Which of the factors in the formula are conditional probabilities? Restate each in a way that makes the condition clear.

40. **Recalls** In a car rental company's fleet 70% of the cars are American brands, 20% Japanese, and the rest German. The company notes that manufacturers' recalls seem to effect 2% of the American cars, but only 1% of the others.
a) What is the probability that a randomly chosen car is recalled?
b) What is the probability that a recalled car is American?

41. **Pregnant?** Suppose that 70% of the women who, suspecting they may be pregnant and purchase an in-home pregnancy test, are actually pregnant. Further suppose that the test is 98% accurate. What is the probability that a woman whose test indicates that she is pregnant actually is?

42. **Door Prize** You are among 100 people attending a charity fundraiser at which a large screen TV will be given away as a door prize. To determine who wins, 99 white balls and 1 red one have been placed in a box and thoroughly mixed. The guests will line up, and, one at a time, pick a ball from the box. Whoever gets the red ball wins the TV, but if the ball is white it is returned to the box. If none of the 100 guests gets the red ball, the TV will be auctioned off for additional benefit of the charity.

a) What is the probability that the first person in line wins the TV?
b) You are the third person in line. What is the probability that you win the TV?
c) What is the probability that the charity gets to sell the TV because no one wins?
d) Suppose you get to pick your spot in line. Where would you want to be in order to maximize your chances of winning?
e) After hearing some protest about the plan, the organizers decide to award the prize by not returning the white balls to the box, thus insuring that one of the 100 people will draw the red ball and win the TV. Now what position in line would you choose in order to maximize your chances?

18 Sampling Distribution Models

$\mathcal{O}$N OCTOBER 27, 2000, LESS THAN TWO WEEKS before the election, an NBC news poll asked 1000 randomly selected registered voters whom they would likely vote for if the election were held that day. Forty five percent said they'd choose Al Gore and 43% expressed a similar preference for George W. Bush. A CNN poll taken at the same time found 46% for Bush and only 42% for Gore. Was one poll "wrong"? Pundits claimed that the race was "too close to call." What's going on? Should we be surprised to find that we could get proportions this different from properly selected random samples from the same population? You're probably used to seeing that observations vary, but how much variability among polls should we expect to see?

Why do sample proportions vary at all? How can surveys conducted at essentially the same time by the same organization asking the same questions get different results? The answer is at the essence of statistics. It's because each survey is based on a *different* sample of 1000 people. The proportions vary from sample to sample because the samples are composed of different people.

Who: U.S. voters
What: Presidential preference
When: Oct 27, 2000
Where: U.S.
Why: Election prediction.

It's actually pretty easy to predict how much a proportion will vary under circumstances like this. When we can understand and predict the variability of our estimates we've taken the essential step toward seeing past that variability so that we can understanding the world.

Modeling the Distribution of Sample Proportions

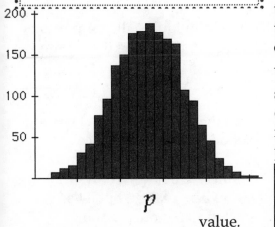

Imagine

Rather than showing real repeated samples, we can imagine what would happen if we were to actually draw many samples.

We've talked about think, show and tell. Now, we have to add *imagine*. We want to imagine the results from all the random samples of size 1000 that we didn't take. What would the histogram of all the sample proportions look like?

For Gore vs. Bush in October of 2000, where do you expect the center of the histogram to be? Of course, we don't *know* the answer to that (and probably never will). But we know that it will be at the true proportion in the population, and we can call that p. How about the *shape* of the histogram?

We don't have to just imagine. We can simulate. We want to simulate a bunch of those random samples of 1000 that we didn't really take. To do that, we'll simulate many independent random samples of size 1000 keeping the same probability of success. We chose .46 for p as a reasonable value.

> The distribution of observed proportions of voters supporting Bush in samples of 1000 simulated with $p=.46$. The histogram shows the proportions for 2000 simulated samples. Figure 18.1

Here's a histogram of the proportion saying they would vote for Bush for 2000 independent samples of 1000 voters when the true proportion is p. It should be no surprise that we don't get the same proportion for each sample we draw even though the underlying true value is the same for the population from which we've drawn the samples.

Does it surprise you that the histogram is unimodal? Symmetric? That it is centered at p? You probably don't find any of this shocking. Does the shape remind you of any model that we've discussed? It's an amazing and fortunate fact that a Normal model is just the right one for the histogram of sample proportions.

To use a Normal model we need to specify its mean and standard deviation. But which Normal model is the right one? The center of the histogram is naturally at p, so we'll put μ, the mean of the normal, at p.

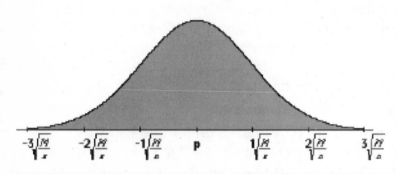

A Normal model centered a p with a standard deviation of $\sqrt{\dfrac{pq}{n}}$ is a good model for a collection of proportions found for many random samples of size n. Fig 18.2

What about the standard deviation? Usually the mean gives us no information about the standard deviation. Suppose we told you that a batch of bike helmets had a mean diameter of 26 centimeters, and asked what the standard deviation was. If you said "I have no idea," you'd be exactly right. There's no information about σ from knowing the value of μ.

But there's a special fact about proportions. With proportions we get something for free. Once we know p we automatically also know the standard deviation. The standard deviation of the histogram of sample proportions is always $\sigma(\hat{p}) = \sqrt{\dfrac{p(1-p)}{n}}$. Often we define $q = 1 - p$ to make the equation simpler and write the standard deviation as $\sqrt{\dfrac{pq}{n}}$.

When we draw simple random samples of n individuals, the proportions we find will vary from sample to sample. We can model the distribution of these sample proportions with a probability model that is $N\left(p, \sqrt{\dfrac{pq}{n}}\right)$.

For the Presidential election, we know what the true proportion favoring Bush was a week later, when the 2000 election actually took place. President Bush received 47.9% of the vote. But on October 27, the true proportion very well may have been different. We'll never know what that true percentage was while the polls were being taken, but let's suppose it was 46%. Here's a picture of the Normal model for our simulation histogram:

DRAFT: Do not distribute or copy

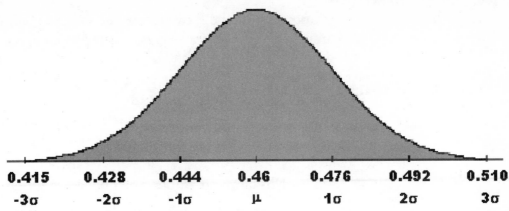

Using the observed proportion of 0.46 for *p*, gives this Normal model for the proportion of voters supporting Bush. Fig 18.3

0.415	0.428	0.444	0.46	0.476	0.492	0.510
-3σ	-2σ	-1σ	μ	1σ	2σ	3σ

We put the center at p=.46 and the standard deviation is

$$\sqrt{\frac{.46 \times .54}{1000}} = 0.016, \text{ or } 1.6\%.$$

Because we have a Normal model, we can use the 68-95-99.7 rule. For example, we know that 95% of normally distributed values are within two standard deviations of the mean, so we should not be surprised that 95% of different polls would give results that were near to 46% (.46) but varied above and below that by 3.2%. (0.032) So, the proportions supporting Bush found in the two polls of 43% and 46% are both *consistent* with a true proportion of 46%.

How good is the Normal Model?

Stop and think for a minute about what we've just said. It is a remarkable claim. We've said that if we draw repeated random samples of the same size, *n*, from some population and measure the proportion we get for each sample, then the collection of these proportions will pile up around the underlying population proportion, *p*, in such a way that a histogram of the sample proportions can be modeled well by a Normal model.

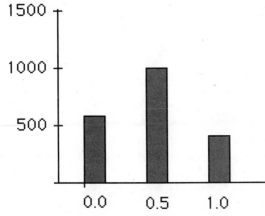

But there must be a catch. Suppose the samples were of size 2, for example. Then the only possible proportion values would be 0, .5, and 1. There's no way the histogram could ever look like a Normal model with only three possible values for the variable.

Well, there *is* a catch. The claim is only approximately true. (But, that's OK. After all, models are only supposed to be approximately true.) And the model becomes a better and better representation of the distribution of the sample

Proportions from samples of size 2 can take on only three possible values. A Normal model may not work well. Fig 18.4

Copyright © 2001, Dick De Veaux and Paul Velleman

proportions as the sample size gets bigger.[1] Samples of size 1 or 2 just aren't going to work very well. But proportions of many larger samples do have histograms that are remarkably close to a Normal model.

Assumptions and Conditions

Most models are useful only when specific **assumptions** are true. In the case of the model for the distribution of sample proportions there are two assumptions:

1) The sampled values must be independent of each other.

2) The sample size, n, must be large enough.

Of course, assumptions are hard – often impossible – to check. That's why we *assume* them. But we should check to see that the assumptions are reasonable. Fortunately, we can often check **conditions** that provide information about the assumptions. The corresponding conditions to check before using the Normal to model the distribution of sample proportions are:

> Don't forget that assumptions are never true just because we *assume* them. We really ought to say we "pretend" that these things are true.
> To help us see if these assumptions are reasonable, we'll usually have *conditions* to check.

1) **10% Condition:** If sampling has not been made with replacement (that is, returning each sampled individual to the population before drawing the next individual), then the sample size, n, must be no larger than 10% of the population. For the polls, the total population is very large, so the 1000 that were sampled is a small *fraction* of the population. There are other ways in which samples can fail to be independent, but the only good protection from such failures is to think carefully about possible reasons for the data to fail to be independent. There are no simple conditions to check that guarantee independence.

> The terms "success" and "failure" for the outcomes that have probability p and q are common in statistics. But they are arbitrary. When we say that a disease occurs with probability p, we certainly don't mean that this is a "success" in the normal sense of the word.

2) **Success/Failure Condition:** The sample size has to be big enough so that both $n\hat{p}$ and $n\hat{q}$ are greater than 10. If we label the outcome that has probability p a "success" and the outcome with probability $(1-p) = q$ a failure, then this condition says that we need to observe at least 10 successes and at least 10 failures to have enough data for sound conclusions. For the polls, a "success" might be voting for Bush. With $p = .479$, we expect $1000 \times .479 = 479$ successes and $1000 \times .521 = 521$ failures. Both are greater than 10, so there are certainly enough successes and enough failures for the condition to be satisfied.

These two conditions seem to contradict each other. Condition (2) wants a big sample size. How big depends on p. If p is near 0.5, we need a sample of only 20 or so. But if p is only .01, we'd need 1000. But

---

[1] For those of you who have had calculus and know the term, the claim is true in the limit as n grows.

DRAFT: Do not distribute or copy

condition (1) says that the sample size can be no larger than 10% of the population. Fortunately, this isn't usually a problem in practice. Often, as in polls that sample from all U.S. adults, or industrial samples from a day's production, the populations are much larger than 10 times the sample size.

A Sampling Distribution Model for a Proportion

We simulated repeated samples and looked at the histogram of sample proportions. Then we modeled this with a Normal model. This let us make statements about how much proportions vary from sample to sample. We are going to want to talk about such variation for almost every statistic we come across. So we'll want to build models like this.

These **Sampling Distribution Models** are strange because even though we depend on them, we never actually get to see them. We never actually take repeated samples from the same population and make a histogram. We only *imagine* or *simulate* them. But they're important because they act as a bridge from the real world of data to the imaginary model of the statistic and enable us to saying something about the population when all we have is data from the real world.

Once we think of the idea of a sampling distribution model, it should be clear that we can find a sampling distribution model for any statistic we can compute on sampled data. Because we are sampling at random, we can imagine drawing random samples over and over and computing the statistic for each sample. The sampling distribution model models the shape of a histogram of these values. Not surprisingly, the model works better and better as the sample size grows.

> **Notation Alert**
> Remember that we are using the "Greek Letter pee", p, for the parameter value in our model and the "hatted" value $\hat{p}$, for the observed proportion in the data.

We have now answered the question raised at the start of the chapter. To know how variable a proportion is, we need to know the proportion and the size of the sample. That's all.

> The sampling distribution model for a proportion:
> Provided that the sampled values are independent and the sample size is large enough, the sampling distribution of $\hat{p}$ is modeled by a Normal model with mean $\mu_{\hat{p}} = p$, and standard deviation $\sigma(\hat{p}) = \sqrt{\dfrac{pq}{n}}$

What isn't at all clear is whether these sampling distribution models will always be simple probability models like the Normal model. But, fortunately, many of the statistics we work with do have simple sampling distribution models. Usually they need only a parameter or two to describe them.

But why do we really care about these distributions that we can never see? Because, once we have estimates for those parameters, we can use the model to help us understand how the statistic would have been distributed if we had drawn all those samples—but without the work and expense of actually drawing them. This will help us generalize from

Copyright © 2001, Dick De Veaux and Paul Velleman

our data to the world at large. That's just the sort of thing models are good for.

Working with Sampling Distribution Models for Proportions Step-by-Step

About 13% of the population is left-handed.[2] A 200-seat school auditorium has been built with 15 "leftie seats", seats that have the built-in desk on in the left rather than the right arm of the chair. (For the right-handed readers among you, have you ever tried to take notes in a chair with the desk on the left side?) In a class of 90 students, what is the probability that there will not be enough seats for the left-handed students?

State what we want to know	We want to find the probability that in a group of 90 students, more than 15 will be left handed. Since 15 out of 90 is 16.7%, the question is equivalent to asking the probability of finding more than 16.7% left handed students out of a sample of 90.
Think Check the conditions	**10% Condition:** The 90 students in the class can be taken to be a random sample of students and are surely less than 10% of the population of all students. (Even if the school itself is small, we're imagining the population of all *possible* students that could have gone to the school).
	Success/Failure condition: $90 \times .13 = 11.7 > 10.$
Show State the parameters and the sampling distribution model	The population proportion is $p = .13$. The conditions allow us to use the Normal probability model to model the sampling distribution. The mean of this Normal model is .13 and the standard deviation is $\sqrt{\dfrac{.13 \times .87}{90}} = 0.035$.

---

[2]Actually, it is quite difficult to get an accurate estimate of the proportion of lefties in the population. Estimates range from 8 to 15%.

     DRAFT: Do not distribute or copy

Use the standard deviation as a ruler and find the z-score of the observed proportion. Find the resulting probability from a table of Normal probabilities, a computer program, or a calculator.

The proportion in question, .167 can be modeled as coming from a Normal with mean .13 and sd 0.035. So it is $z = \dfrac{.167 - .13}{.035} = 1.05$ standard deviations above the mean.

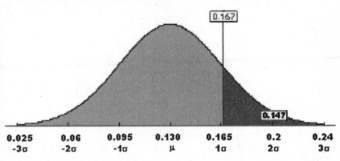

We know (from the 68-95-99.7 rule) that the probability of a value more than 1 standard deviation above the mean is about 16% (because the upper half of the 100-68% that is beyond one standard deviation from the mean is half of 32%.) For a more accurate value, we could look it up in a table or consult a calculator or computer program.

The probability that a z score is greater than 1.05 is 0.147 or 14.7%.

Tell

Discuss the probability in the context of the question.

There is a probability of about 15% that there will not be enough seats for the left handed students in the class.

Means

Like any statistic computed from a random sample, a sample mean also has a sampling distribution. Let's use simulation to get a sense of what that sampling distribution might be[3].

Here's a simple simulation. Let's start with one fair die. If we toss this die 10,000 times, what should the histogram of the numbers on the face of the die look like? Here are the results of a simulated 10,000 tosses:

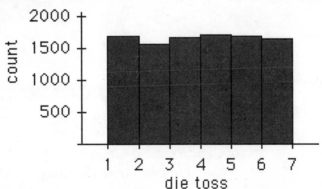

---

[3] Can you stand the tension?

Now, what would happen if we toss a *pair* of dice 10,000 times, take the *average* and plot the histogram of the average? Before you look, think a minute. Is getting an average of 1 on *two* dice as likely as getting an average of 3, or 3.5?

Let's see:

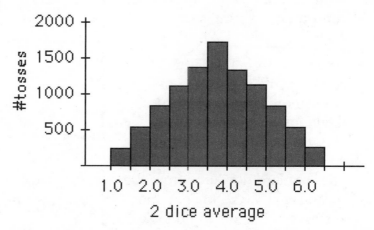

You're much more likely to get an average near 3.5 than you are to get one near 1 or 6. Without calculating those probabilities exactly, it's fairly easy to see that the *only* way to get an average of 1 is to get two 1's. But to get a total of 7 (for an average of 3.5) there are many more possibilities. This distribution even has a name – the *triangular* distribution.

What if we average 3 dice? We'll simulate 10,000 tosses of 3 dice and take their average:

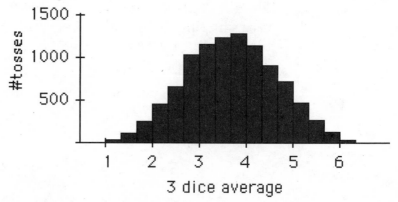

What's happening? First notice that it's getting harder to have averages near the ends. Getting an average of 1 or 6 with 3 dice requires all three to come up 1 or 6. That's less likely than for 2 dice to come up both 1 or both 6. So, the distribution is getting pushed toward the middle. But, what's happening to the shape? (This distribution doesn't have a name as far as we know.)

Let's continue this to see what happens with larger samples. Here's a histogram of 10,000 tosses of 5 dice:

DRAFT: Do not distribute or copy

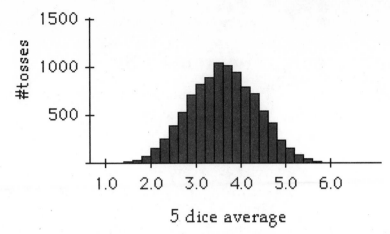

5 dice average

Now the pattern is becoming clearer. Two things continue to happen. The first fact we knew already from the Law of Large Numbers. It says that as the sample size (number of dice) gets larger, each sample average is more likely to be closer to the population mean. So, we see the shape continuing to tighten around 3.5. But the shape of the distribution is the surprising part. It is becoming bell-shaped. And not just bell-shaped; it is approaching the Normal model.

Are you convinced? Let's skip ahead and try 20 dice. The histogram of averages for throws of 20 dice looks like this:

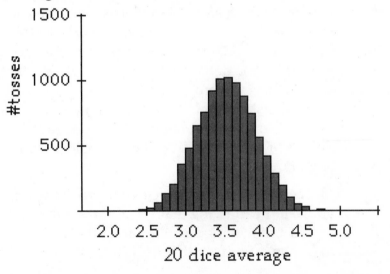

20 dice average

Now we can see the Normal shape very clearly. (And notice how much smaller the spread is). But can we count on this happening for situations other than dice throws? What kinds of sample means have sampling distributions that we can model with a Normal model? It turns out that Normal models work well amazingly often.

The Fundamental Theorem of Statistics

The dice simulation looks like a special situation. But what we saw with dice turns out to be true for means of *any* repeated random samples. The sampling distribution of *any* mean becomes Normal as the sample size grows. All we need is for the observations to be independent. We don't even care about the shape of the population distribution. This surprising fact was proved in a fairly general form in 1810 by Pierre-Simon Laplace, and caused quite a stir (at least in Mathematics circles) because it is so unintuitive. It is called the **Central Limit Theorem**[4] (CLT).

Why should the Normal model be so special as to pop up like this, seemingly out of nowhere? For once in this text, we're not going to try to persuade you that it is obvious, clear, simple, or straightforward. In fact, the CLT is surprising and a bit weird. Not only does the histogram of the sample means get closer and closer to the Normal model as the sample size grows, but *this is true regardless of the shape of the population distribution!*[5] Even if we sample from a skewed or bimodal population, the Central Limit Theorem tells us that means of repeated samples will tend to follow a Normal model as the sample size grows. Of course, you won't be surprised to learn that it works *better* (and faster) the closer the population model is to a Normal itself. And it works better for larger samples. If the data come from a population that's exactly Normal to start with, you'll only need a sample of size 1 to get the mean to have a Normal distribution. But if the population distribution is very skewed (the CEO data from Chapter 2(?) for example), it may take a mean of dozens or even hundreds of observations for the Normal approximation to work well.

The best and most convincing way to see this is to do a simulation yourself. By drawing many random samples repeatedly, finding their means and making a histogram of the means. We know of no better way to convince yourself that the Central Limit Theorem is true[6].

Pierre-Simon Laplace 1749-1827 figure 18.5
http://www-groups.dcs.st-andrews.ac.uk/~history/Mathematicians/Laplace.html

---

[4] The word "Central" in the name of the theorem means "fundamental." It does not refer to the center of a distribution.

[5] There is one technical condition. The variance of the population distribution must be finite. But that is true for almost all real populations, so we won't bother to check it.

[6] In fact, the mathematical proof of the CLT, although quite straightforward, is not intuitively convincing. One doesn't think "Oh that's obvious; I should have seen it myself." Instead, one generally just thinks "Oh". Simulation is much more convincing.

DRAFT: Do not distribute or copy

But Which Normal?

So the CLT says that the sampling distribution of any mean is Normal. But which Normal model? We know that Normals are specified by their mean and standard deviation. We'd be shocked if the histogram of those means wasn't centered at the population mean. And, in fact, it is.

We also noticed in our dice simulation that the histograms got narrower as we averaged more and more dice together. This shouldn't be surprising. Means vary less than the individual observations. Think about it for a minute. Which would be more surprising, having *one* person in your Intro Stats class who is over 6′ 9″ tall, or having the *mean* of 100 students in your Intro Stats class be over 6′ 9″? The first event is fairly rare[7]. You may have seen somebody this tall in one of your classes sometime. But finding a class of 100 whose mean height is over 6′ 9″ tall just won't happen. Why? Because means have *smaller standard deviations than the individuals*.

How much smaller? Well, we have good news and bad news. The good news is that the standard deviation falls as the sample size grows. The bad news is that it doesn't drop as fast as we might like. It only goes down by the *square root* of the sample size.

That is, the Normal model for the sampling distribution of means has a standard deviation equal to:

$$\frac{\sigma}{\sqrt{n}}$$

The n's justify the means
-- apocryphal statistical saying

where σ is the standard deviation of the population. We want to emphasize that it's a standard deviation parameter of the sampling distribution model for the mean, $\bar{y}$, so we write it as $\sigma(\bar{y})$ (pronounced "sigma of y bar"), and $\sigma(\bar{y}) = \frac{\sigma}{\sqrt{n}}$.

---

[7] If students are a random sample of adults, fewer than 1 out of 10,000 should be taller than 6′ 9″. Why might college students not really be a random sample with respect to height? But, even if they're not a perfectly random sample, a college student over 6′ 9″ tall is still rare.

> The Central Limit Theorem
> As the sample size, n, increases, the mean of n independent values has a sampling distribution that tends toward a Normal model with mean $\mu_{\bar{y}}$ equal to the population mean, μ, and standard deviation $\sigma(\bar{y}) = \dfrac{\sigma}{\sqrt{n}}$.

The CLT statement looks an awful lot like the sampling distribution model for a proportion. That's no coincidence. Proportions are really a special case of means[8]. but a very special one in which the standard deviation is linked to the mean. So the CLT covers proportions as well.

Assumptions and Conditions

The CLT requires remarkably few assumptions, so there are few conditions to check:

Random Sampling Condition: The values must be sampled randomly or the concept of a sampling distribution makes no sense.

Independence Assumption: The sampled values must be mutually independent. There is no way to check in general that the observations are independent. However, when the sample is drawn without replacement (as is usually the case) you should check the

10% Condition: The sample size, n, is no more than 10% of the population.

Diminishing Returns

The standard deviation of the sampling distribution declines *only* with the square root of the sample size and not, for example, with $1/n$. The mean of a random sample of 4 has half ($\dfrac{1}{\sqrt{4}} = \dfrac{1}{2}$) the standard deviation of an individual data values. To cut it in half again we'd need a sample of 16, and a sample of 64 to halve it once more. In practice, random sampling works well and means have smaller standard deviations than the individual data values that were averaged. This is the power of averaging.

But it always seems that if only we could afford a much larger sample, we could get the standard deviation of the sampling distribution *really* under control so that the sample mean told us still more about the unknown population mean. As we shall see, that nasty square root limits how much we can make a sample tell about the population. This is an example of something that's known as the Law of Diminishing Returns.

---

[8] Let every success get the value "1" and every failure a "0", then the proportion of 1's is just the mean of all the 0's and 1's. It turns out that $\sigma = \sqrt{pq}$.

DRAFT: Do not distribute or copy

Working with the Sampling Distribution Model for the Mean Step-by-Step

Suppose (or assume) that mean adult weight is 175 pounds with a standard deviation of 25 pounds. An elevator in our building has a weight limit of 10 persons or 2000 pounds. What is the probability that the 10 people who get on an elevator overload its weight limit?

Think	**State what we want to know.**	Asking the probability that the total weight of a sample of 10 people exceeds 2000 pounds is equivalent to asking the probability that their *mean* weight is greater than 200 pounds.
	Check the conditions	**Random Sampling Condition:** We will assume that the 10 people getting on the elevator are a random sample from the population.
		Independence Assumption: It is reasonable to think that the weights of 10 randomly sampled people will be mutually independent (but there could be exceptions – for example if they were all from the same family or if the elevator were in a building with a diet clinic!).
		10% Condition: 10 people is surely less than 10% of the population of possible elevator riders.
Show	**State the parameters and the sampling distribution model**	We've assumed that the model for weights has a mean $\mu = 175$ and standard deviation, $\sigma = 25$. The CLT tells us that we can model the sampling distribution of $\bar{y}$ with a Normal distribution with mean 175 and standard deviation $\sigma(\bar{y}) = \dfrac{25}{\sqrt{10}} = 7.9$.
		A mean weight of 200 is $z = \dfrac{200 - 175}{7.9} = 3.16$ standard deviations above the mean.
	Find the requested probability from a table for the Normal	

distribution, a computer program or a calculator.

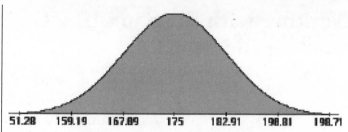

51.28   159.19   167.09   175   182.91   190.81   198.71

The probability under a standard Normal model above 3.16 is 0.0008.

The chance that a random collection of 10 adults will exceed the elevator's weight limit is 0.0008. So, given a random sample, it is quite unlikely that 10 people will exceed the total weight allowed.

Tell

Standard Error

Both of the sampling distributions we've looked at are Normal. We know for proportions, $\sigma(\hat{p}) = \sqrt{\dfrac{pq}{n}}$ and for means $\sigma(\bar{y}) = \dfrac{\sigma}{\sqrt{n}}$. These are great if we know, or can pretend that we know, p or σ, and sometimes we'll do that.

But, often we only know the observed proportion, $\hat{p}$ or the sample standard deviation, s. So of course we just use what we know and we estimate. That may not seem like a big deal, but it gets a special name. Whenever we estimate the standard deviation of a sampling distribution, we call it a **standard error**[9].

We say: "square root p-hat, q-hat over n". But "phat" looks like "fat" and "qhat" like "cat", so we might call it "square root fat cat over n"

For a proportion the standard error of $\hat{p}$ is

$$SE(\hat{p}) = \sqrt{\frac{\hat{p}\hat{q}}{n}}.$$

For the sample mean, the standard error is

$$SE(\bar{y}) = \frac{s}{\sqrt{n}}$$

You may see a "standard error" reported by a computer program in a summary or offered by a calculator. It is safe to assume that if no statistic is specified, what was meant is $SE(\bar{y})$, the standard error of the mean.

---

[9] This isn't such a great name because it isn't standard and nobody made an error. But it is much shorter and more convenient than saying "the estimated standard deviation of the sampling distribution of the sample statistic".

Sampling Distribution Models

Let's summarize what we've learned about sampling distributions. At the heart is the idea that *the statistic itself is a random quantity*. We can't know what our statistic will be because it comes from a random sample. It's just one instance of something that happened for our particular random sample. A different random sample would have given a different result. But we can think about the distribution of possible values that the statistic could have had.

We could simulate that distribution by pretending to take lots of samples. But, for the mean and the proportion, the CLT tells us that we can model their sampling distribution directly with a Normal model.

The two basic truths about sampling distributions are:

1) Sampling distributions arise because samples vary. Each random sample will have different cases and so, a different value of the statistic.

2) Although we can always simulate a sampling distribution, the Central Limit Theorem saves us the trouble for means and proportions.

Here's a picture showing the process going into the sampling distribution model:

We start with population model, which can have any shape. It can even be bimodal, or skewed (as this one is.) We label the mean of this model μ and its standard deviation, σ.

We draw one real sample (solid line) of size *n* and show its histogram and summary statistics. We *imagine* (or simulate) drawing many other samples (dotted lines), which have their own histograms and summary statistics.

We gather all the means into a histogram.

The CLT tells us we can model the shape of the histogram with a Normal model. The mean of this Normal is μ and the standard deviation is $\dfrac{\sigma}{\sqrt{n}}$. When we don't know σ, we estimate it with the standard deviation of the one real sample. That gives us the standard error, $\dfrac{s}{\sqrt{n}}$. Figure 18.6

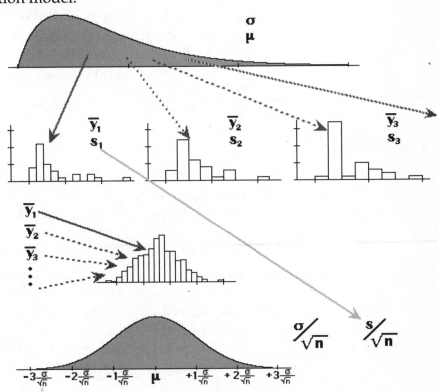

© 2001, Dick De Veaux and Paul Velleman

18-15

What can go Wrong

- *Beware of observations that are not independent.* The CLT depends crucially on the assumption of independence. If our elevator riders are related, are all from the same school (for example an elementary school) or in some other way aren't a random sample, then the statements we try to make about the mean are going to be wrong. Unfortunately, this isn't something you can check in your data. You have to think about how the data were gathered. Good sampling practice and well-designed randomized experiments assure independence.

- *Watch out for small samples from skewed populations.* The CLT assures us that the sampling distribution is normal if n is large enough. If the population is nearly Normal, even small samples work. But if the population is very skewed, then n will have to be large before the Normal model will work well. If we sampled 15 or even 20 CEO's and tried to make a statement about the mean of all CEOs' compensation, we'd likely get into trouble because the underlying distribution model is so skewed. Unfortunately, there's no good rule of thumb.[10] It just depends on how skewed the population's distribution is. Always plot the data to check.

- *Don't confuse the sampling distribution with the distribution of the sample.* When you take a sample, you always look at the distribution of the values, usually with a histogram, and you may calculate summary statistics. Examining the distribution of the sample like this is wise. But that's not the sampling distribution. The sampling distribution models an imaginary collection of the values that a statistic might have taken from all the random samples that you didn't get. We use the sampling distribution model to make statements about how the statistic varies.

Connections

The concept of a sampling distribution connects to almost everything we have done. The fundamental connection is to the deliberate application of randomness in random sampling and randomized comparative experiments. If we didn't employ randomness to generate unbiased data, then repeating the data collection would just get the same data values again (with perhaps a few new measurement or recording errors.) The *distribution* of statistic values arises directly because different *random* samples and randomized experiments would generate different statistic values.

---

[10] For proportions, of course, there is a rule: the Success/Failure condition. It works for proportions because the standard deviation of a proportion is linked to the mean.

DRAFT: Do not distribute or copy

Of course, the connection to the Normal distribution is obvious. We first introduced the Normal model before because it was "nice". As a unimodal, symmetric, distribution with 99.7% of its area within 3 standard deviations of the mean, the Normal model is easy to work with. But now we see that the Normal holds a special place among distributions because we can use it to model the sampling distribution of the mean and the proportion.

We use simulation to understand sampling distributions. In fact, some important sampling distributions were discovered first by simulation.

Key Concepts

Sampling Distribution Model	Different random samples give different values for a statistic. The sampling distribution model shows the behavior of the statistic over all the possible samples.
Central Limit Theorem	The Central Limit Theorem (CLT) states that the sampling distribution model of the sample mean (and proportion) is approximately Normal for large *n, regardless of the distribution of the population as long as the observations are independent.*
Sampling distribution model for a proportion	If assumptions of independence and random sampling are met, and we expect at least 10 successes and 10 failures, then the sampling distribution of a proportion is modeled by a Normal model with a mean equal to the true proportion value, p, and a standard deviation equal to $\sqrt{\dfrac{p(1-p)}{n}}$
Sampling distribution model for a mean	If assumptions of independence and random sampling are met, and the sample size is large enough, the sampling distribution of the sample mean is modeled by a Normal model with a mean equal to the population mean, μ, and a standard deviation equal to $\dfrac{\sigma}{\sqrt{n}}$
Standard Error	When we estimate the standard deviation of a sampling distribution using statistics found from the data, it is called a standard error.

Skills

At the end of this chapter you should:

> ### Think
>
> - Understand that the variability of a statistic (as measured by the standard deviation of its sampling distribution) depends on the size of the sample. Statistics based on larger samples are less variable.
>
> - Understand that the Central Limit Theorem gives the sampling distribution model of the mean for sufficiently large samples regardless of the underlying population.
>
> ### Show
>
> - Be able to demonstrate a sampling distribution by simulation.
>
> - Be able to use a sampling distribution model to make simple statements about the distribution of a proportion or mean under repeated sampling.
>
> ### Tell
>
> - Be able to interpret a sampling distribution model as describing the values taken by a statistic in all possible realizations of a sample or randomized experiment under the same conditions.

Exercises

1. **Coin Tosses** In a large class of introductory statistics students the professor has each person toss a coin 16 times and calculate the proportion of his or her tosses that were heads. The students then report their results, and the professor plots a histogram of these several proportions.
   a) What shape would you expect this histogram to be? Why?
   b) Where do you expect the histogram to center?
   c) How much variability would you expect among these proportions?
   d) Explain why a Normal model should not be used here.

2. **M&Ms** The candy company claims that 10% of the M&Ms they produce are green. Suppose that the candies are packaged at random in small bags containing about 50 M&Ms. A class of elementary school students learning about percents opens several bags, counts the various colors of candies, and calculates the proportion that are green.
   a) If we plot a histogram showing the proportions of green candies in the various bags, what shape would you expect it to have?
   b) Can that histogram be approximated by a Normal model? Explain.

DRAFT: Do not distribute or copy

c) Where should the center of the histogram be?

d) What should the standard deviation of the proportions be?

3. **More Coins** Suppose the class in Exercise 1 repeats the coin tossing experiment.

a) They toss the coins 25 times each. Use the 68-95-99.7 Rule to describe the sampling distribution model

b) Confirm that you can use a Normal model here.

c) They increase the number of tosses to 64 each. Draw and label the appropriate sampling distribution model. Check the appropriate conditions to justify your model.

d) Explain how the sampling distribution model changes as the number of tosses increases.

4. **Bigger Bag** Suppose the class in Exercise 2 buys bigger bags of candy, with 200 M&Ms each. Again they calculate the proportion of green candies they find.

a) Explain why it is appropriate to use a Normal model to describe the distribution of the proportion of green M&Ms they might expect.

b) Use the 68-95-99.7 Rule to describe how this proportion might vary from bag to bag.

c) How would this model change if the bags contained even more candies?

5. **Just (Un)lucky?** One of the students in the intro stats class in Exercise 3 claims to have tossed her coin 200 times and found only 42% heads. What do you think of this claim? Explain.

6. **Too Many Green Ones?** In a really large bag of M&Ms the kids in Exercise 4 found 500 candies, and 12% of them were green. Is this an unusually large proportion of green M&Ms? Explain.

7. **Speeding** State Police believe that 70% of the drivers traveling on a major interstate highway exceed the speed limit. They plan to set up a radar trap and check the speeds of 80 cars.

a) Using the 68-95-99.7 Rule, draw and label the distribution of the proportion of these cars the police will observe speeding.

b) Do you think the appropriate conditions are met? Explain.

8. **Smoking** Public health statistics indicate that 26.4% of American adults smoke cigarettes. Using the 68-95-99.7 Rule, describe the sampling distribution model for the proportion of smokers among a randomly selected group of 50 adults. Be sure to discuss your assumptions and conditions.

9. **Loans** Based on past experience a bank believes that 7% of the people who receive loans will not make payments on time. They have

recently approved 200 loans.
a) What are the mean and standard deviation of the proportion of clients in this group who may not make timely payments?
b) What assumptions underlie your model? Are the conditions met? Explain.
c) What is the probability that over 10% of these clients will not make timely payments?

10. **Contacts** Assume that 30% of students at a University wear contact lenses.
a) We randomly pick 100 students. Let $\hat{p}$ represent the proportion of students in this sample who wear contacts. What is the appropriate model for the distribution of $\hat{p}$? Specify the name of the distribution, the mean, and the standard deviation. Be sure to verify that the conditions are met.
b) What is the approximate probability that over one third of this sample wear contacts?

11. **Polling** Just before a referendum on a school budget a local newspaper polls 400 voters in an attempt to predict whether the budget will pass. Suppose that the budget actually has the support of 52% of the voters. What is the probability the newspaper's sample will lead them to predict defeat? Be sure to verify that the assumptions and conditions necessary for your analysis are met.

12. **Seeds** Information on a packet of seeds claims that the germination rate is 92%. What is the probability that over 95% of the 160 seeds in the packet will germinate? Be sure to discuss your assumptions and check the conditions that support your model.

13. **Apples** When a truckload of apples arrives at a packing plant, a random sample of 150 is selected and examined for bruises, discoloration, and other defects. The whole truckload will be rejected if over 5% of the sample is unsatisfactory. Suppose that in fact 8% of the apples on the truck do not meet the desired standard. What is the probability that the shipment will be accepted anyway?

14. **Genetic Defect** It is believed that 4% of children have a gene that may be linked to juvenile diabetes. Researchers hoping to track 20 of these children for several years test 732 newborns for presence of this gene. What is the probability that they find enough subjects for their study?

15. **Non-Smokers** While some non-smokers do not mind being seated in a smoking section of a restaurant, about 60% of the customers demand a smoke-free area. A new restaurant is being planned to have 120 seats. How many seats should be in the non-smoking area in order to be very sure of having enough seating there? Comment on the assumptions and conditions that support your model, and

explain what "very sure" meant to you.

16. **Meals** A restaurateur anticipates serving about 180 people on a Friday evening, and believes that about 20% of the patrons will order the chef's steak special. How many of those meals should he plan on serving in order to be pretty sure of having enough steaks on hand to meet customer demand? Justify your answer, including an explanation of what "pretty sure" meant to you.

17. **Sampling** A sample is chosen randomly from a population that can be described by a Normal model.
    a) What is the sampling distribution model for the sample mean? Describe shape, center, and spread.
    b) If we choose a larger sample, what is the effect on this sampling distribution model?

18. **Sampling, Part II** A sample is chosen randomly from a population that was strongly skewed to the left.
    a) Describe the sampling distribution model for the sample mean if the sample size is small.
    b) If we make the sample larger, what happens to the sampling distribution model's shape, center, and spread?
    c) As we make the sample larger, what happens to the expected distribution of the data in the sample?

19. **GPAs** A college's data about the incoming freshmen indicates that the mean of their high school GPAs was 3.4 with a standard deviation of 0.35; the distribution was roughly mound-shaped and only slightly skewed. The students are randomly assigned to freshman writing seminars in groups of 25. What might the mean GPA of one of these seminar groups be? Describe the appropriate sampling distribution model – shape, center, and spread – with attention to assumptions and conditions. Make a sketch using the 68-95-99.7 Rule.

20. **Home Values** Assessment records indicate that the value of homes in a small city is skewed high, with a mean of $140,000 and standard deviation of $60,000. To check the accuracy of the assessment data, officials plan to conduct a detailed appraisal of 100 homes selected at random. Using the 68-95-99.7 Rule, draw and label an appropriate sampling model for the mean value of the homes selected.

21. **Pregnancy** Assume that the duration of human pregnancies can be described by a Normal model with mean 266 days and standard deviation 16 days.
    a) What percentage of pregnancies should last between 270 and 280 days?
    b) At least how many days should the longest 25% of all pregnancies

last?

c) Suppose a certain obstetrician is currently providing prenatal care to 60 pregnant women. Let $\bar{y}$ represent the mean length of their pregnancies. According to the Central Limit Theorem, what is the distribution of this sample mean, $\bar{y}$? Specify the model, mean, and standard deviation.

d) What is the probability that the mean duration of these patients' pregnancies will be less than 260 days?

22. **Rainfall** Statistics from Cornell's Northeast Regional Climate Center indicate that Ithaca, NY gets an average of 35.4" of rain each year, with standard deviation 4.2". Assume that a Normal model applies.
a) During what percentage of years does Ithaca get over 40 inches of rain?
b) Less than how much rain falls in the driest 20% of all years?
c) A Cornell student is in Ithaca for 4 years. Let $\bar{y}$ represent the mean amount of rain for those 4 years. Describe the sampling distribution model of this sample mean, $\bar{y}$.
d) What is the probability that those four years average less than 30 inches of rain?

23. **Pregnant Again** The duration of human pregnancies may not actually follow a Normal model, as described in Exercise 21.
a) Explain why it may be somewhat skewed to the left.
b) If the correct model is in fact skewed, does that change your answers to parts a, b, and c of Exercise 21? Explain why or why not for each.

24. **At Work** Some business analysts estimate that the length of time people work at a job has a mean of 6.2 years and standard deviation 4.5 years.
a) Explain why you suspect this distribution may be skewed to the right.
b) Explain why you could estimate the probability that 100 people selected at random had worked for their employers an average of 10 years or more, but you could not estimate the probability that an individual had done so.

25. **Dice and Dollars** You roll a die, winning nothing if the number of spots is odd, $1 for a 2 or a 4, and $10 for a 6.
a) Find the expected value and standard deviation of your prospective winnings.
b) You play twice. Find the mean and expected value of your total winnings.
c) You play 40 times. What is the probability that you win at least $100?

26. **New Game** You pay $10 and roll a die. If you get a 6, you win $50. If not, you get to roll again. If you get a 6 this time you get your $10

DRAFT: Do not distribute or copy

back.
a) Create a probability model for this game.
b) Find the expected value and standard deviation of your prospective winnings.
c) You play this game five times. Find the expected value and standard deviation of your average winnings.
d) 100 people play this game. What is the probability the person running the game makes a profit?

27. **Pollution** Carbon monoxide (CO) emissions for a certain kind of car varies with mean 2.9 gm/mi and standard deviation 0.4 gm/mi. A company has 80 of these cars in its fleet. Let $\bar{y}$ represent the mean CO level for the company's fleet.
a) What is the approximate model for the distribution of $\bar{y}$? Explain.
b) Estimate the probability that $\bar{y}$ is between 3.0 and 3.1 gm/mi.
c) There is only a 5% chance that the fleet's mean CO level is greater than what value?

28. **Potato Chips** The weight of potato chips in a medium size bag is stated to be 10 ounces. The amount that the packaging machine puts in these bags is believed to have a Normal model with mean 10.2 ounces and standard deviation 0.12 ounces.
a) What fraction of all bags sold are underweight?
b) Some of the chips are sold in "bargain packs" of 3 bags. What is the probability that none of the 3 is underweight?
c) What is the probability that the mean weight of the three bags is below the stated amount?
d) What is the probability that the mean weight of a 24-bag case of potato chips is below 10 ounces?

29. **Tips** A waiter believes the distribution of his tips has a model that is slightly skewed to the right, with a mean of $9.60 and standard deviation of $5.40.
a) Explain why you cannot determine the probability that a given party will tip him at least $20.
b) Can you estimate the probability that the next 4 parties will tip an average of at least $15? Explain.
c) Is it likely that his 10 parties today will tip an average of at least $15? Explain.

30. **Groceries** Grocery store receipts show that customer purchases have a skewed distribution with a mean of $32 and standard deviation $20.
a) Explain why you cannot determine the probability that the next customer will spend at least $40.
b) Can you estimate the probability that the next 10 customers will spend an average of at least $40? Explain.

c) Is it likely that the next 50 customers will spend an average of at least $40? Explain.

31. **More Tips** The waiter in Exercise 29 usually waits on about 40 parties over a weekend of work.
    a) Estimate the probability that he will earn at least $500 in tips.
    b) How much does he earn on the best 10% of such weekends?

32. **More Groceries** Suppose the store in Exercise 30 had 312 customers today.
    a) Estimate the probability that the store's revenues were at least $10,000.
    b) If in a typical day, the store serves 312 customers, how much does the store take in on the worst 10% of such days?

33. **IQs** Suppose that IQ's of a East State University's students can be described by a Normal model with mean 130 and standard deviation 8 points. Also suppose that IQ's of students from West State U. can be described by a Normal model with mean 120 and standard deviation 10.
    a) We select one student at random from East State. Find the probability that this student's IQ is at least 125 points.
    b) We select one student at random from each school. Find the probability that the East State student's IQ is at least 5 points higher than the West State student's IQ.
    c) We select 3 W State students at random. Find the probability that this group's average IQ is at least 125 points.
    d) We also select 3 E State students at random. What is the probability that their average IQ is at least 5 points higher than the average for the three W-Staters?

34. **Milk** Although most of us buy milk by the quart or gallon, farmers measure daily production in pounds. Ayrshire cows average 47 pounds of milk a day, with a standard deviation of 6 pounds. For Jersey cows the mean daily production is 43 pounds, with a standard deviation of 5 pounds. Assume that Normal models describe milk production for these breeds.
    a) We select an Ayrshire at random. What is the probability that she averages over 50 pounds of milk a day?
    b) What is the probability that a randomly selected Ayrshire gives more milk than a randomly selected Jersey?
    c) A farmer has 20 Jerseys. What is the probability the average production for this small herd exceeds 45 pounds of milk a day?
    d) A neighboring farmer has 10 Ayrshires. What is the probability that his herd average is at least 5 pounds higher than the average for the Jersey herd?

Chapter 19

Confidence Intervals for Proportions

WHO	Sea fans
WHAT	Percent infected
WHEN	June 2000
WHERE	Las Redes Reef, Akumal, Mexico, 40 feet deep

Coral are in decline worldwide, possibly because of pollution or changes in sea temperature. The consequences of this decline are far-reaching. The death of coral reefs will be an early warning of climate changes.

One spectacular kind of coral, the sea fan, looks like a plant growing from the sea floor, but it is actually an animal.[1] A sea fan of the size in the photo above may have taken 40 years to grow, but it can be killed quickly by pollution or disease. Sea fans in the Caribbean Sea have been under attack by the disease *aspergillosis*. In June of 2000, the sea fan disease team from Dr. Drew Harvell's lab sampled sea fans at the Las Redes Reef in Akumal, Mexico, at a depth of 40 feet. They found that 54 of the 104 sea fans they sampled were infected with the disease. What might this say about the prevalence of this disease among sea fans in general?

We have a sample proportion, which we write as $\hat{p}$, of 54/104, or 51.9%. Our first guess might be that this observed proportion is close to the population proportion, p. But we also know that if the researchers had drawn a second sample of 104 sea fans at roughly the same time, the proportion infected from that sample would probably not have been exactly 51.9%. We hope it would have been close.

What *can* we say about the population proportion, p? To start to answer this question, think about how different the sample proportion might have been if we'd taken another random sample from the same population. But wait. Remember that we aren't actually going to take more samples. We just want to *imagine* how the sample proportions might vary from sample to sample. In other words, we want to know about the *sampling distribution* of the sample proportion of infected sea fans.

---

[1]For purists, sea fans are actually colonies of genetically identical animals.

A Confidence Interval

So let's look at our model for the sampling distribution. What do we know about it? We know it's approximately Normal (under certain assumptions, which we should be careful to check) and that its mean is the proportion of all infected sea fans on the Las Redes Reef. Is the infected proportion of *all* sea fans 51.9%? No, that's just $\hat{p}$, our estimate. We don't know the proportion, p, of all the infected sea fans; that's what we're trying to find out. But we do know that the sampling distribution model of $\hat{p}$ is centered at p. And we know that the standard deviation of the sampling distribution is $\sqrt{\dfrac{pq}{n}}$.

NOTATION ALERT:

Remember that q is just shorthand for $1 - p$, and $\hat{q} = 1 - \hat{p}$.

Since we don't know p, we can't find the true standard deviation of the sampling distribution model, so instead we'll use the standard error (SE),

$$SE\,(\hat{p}) = \sqrt{\frac{\hat{p}\hat{q}}{n}} = \sqrt{\frac{(.519)(.481)}{104}} = .049 = 4.9\%$$

So, now we know that the sampling model for $\hat{p}$ should look like this:

Figure 19.1

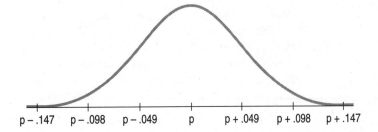

| p − .147 | p − .098 | p − .049 | p | p + .049 | p + .098 | p + .147 |

Great. What does that tell us? Well, because it's Normal it says that, about 68% of all samples will have $\hat{p}$'s within 1 SE (0.049) of p. And about 95% of all samples will be within $p \pm 2$ SE. But where is *our* sample proportion in this picture? We still don't know!

We do know that for 95% of random samples, $\hat{p}$ will be no more than 2 SE away from p. So let's look at this from $\hat{p}$'s point of view. If I'm $\hat{p}$, there's a 95% chance that p is no more than 2 SE away from me. If I reach out 2 SE, or 2 × 0.049, away from me on both sides, I'm 95% sure that p will be within my grasp. Now, I've got him. Probably.

Figure 19.2

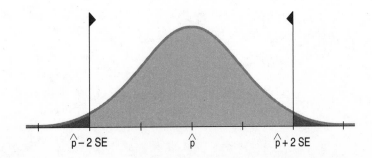

$\hat{p} - 2\,SE \qquad\qquad \hat{p} \qquad\qquad \hat{p} + 2\,SE$

So what can we really say about p? Here's a list of things we'd like to be able to say, in order of strongest to weakest and the reasons we can't say most of them:

1. **"51.9% of *all* sea fans on the Las Redes Reef are infected."** It would be nice to be able to make absolute statements about population values with certainty, but we just don't have enough information to do that. There is no way to be sure that the population proportion is the same as the sample proportion; in fact, it almost certainly isn't. Observations vary. Another sample would yield a different sample proportion.

2. **"It is *probably* true that 51.9% of all sea fans on the Las Redes Reef are infected."** Wrong. In fact we can be pretty sure that whatever the true proportion is, it is not exactly 51.900%. So the statement is not true.

3. **"We don't know exactly what proportion of sea fans on the Las Redes Reef are infected but we *know* that it's within the interval 51.9% ± 2 × 4.9%— that is, between 42.1% and 61.7%."** This is getting closer, but we still can't be certain. We can't know for sure that the true proportion is in this range.

4. **"We don't know exactly what proportion of sea fans on the Las Redes Reef are infected, but the interval from 42.1% and 61.7% *probably* contains the true proportion."** We've now fudged twice—first by giving an interval and second by admitting that we only think the interval "probably" contains the true value.

That last statement may seem a bit wishy-washy. But we can do a little better by quantifying what we mean by "probably." We saw that 95% of the time when we reach out 2 *SE* from $\hat{p}$ we'll capture p, so we can be 95% confident that this is one of those times. After putting a number on the probability that this interval covers the true proportion, we've given our best guess of where the parameter is and how certain we are that it's within some range.

5. **"We are 95% confident that between 42.1% and 61.7% of Las Redes sea fans are infected."** Statements like these are called **confidence intervals**. They're the best we can do.

In fact, this confidence interval is so standard for a single proportion that you may see it simply called a "confidence interval for the proportion." You may safely assume that unless a writer declares otherwise, the one-proportion z-interval is the one that was used.

Each confidence interval we discuss in the book has a name. We'll see many different kinds of confidence intervals in the following chapters. Some will be about more than *one* sample, some will be about statistics other than *proportions*, some will use models other than the Normal (and so will not use z-scores). The interval we have calculated and interpreted is sometimes called a **one-proportion z-interval.**

Margin of Error: Certainty vs. Precision

We've just claimed that with a certain confidence we've captured the true proportion of all infected sea fans. Our confidence interval had the form

$$\hat{p} \pm 2\,SE(\hat{p})$$

The extent of the interval on either side of $\hat{p}$ is called the **margin of error** (m.o.e.). We'll want to use the same approach for many other situations besides estimating proportions. In general, confidence intervals look like this:

Estimate ± margin of error

The margin of error for our 95% confidence interval was 2 *SE*. What if we wanted to be more confident? To be more confident, we'll need to capture *p* more often, and to do that we'll need to make the interval wider. For example, if we want to be 99.7% confident, the margin of error will have to be 3 *SE*.

Figure 19.3

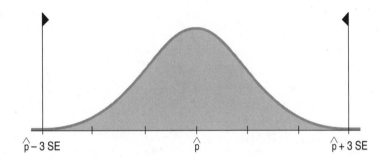

$\hat{p} - 3\,SE$ $\hat{p}$ $\hat{p} + 3\,SE$

The more confident we want to be, the larger the margin of error must be. We could be 100% confident that the proportion of infected sea fans is between 0% and 100%, but this isn't likely to be very useful. On the other hand, we could give a confidence interval from 51.8% to 52.0%, but we can't be very confident about a precise statement like this. Every confidence interval is a balance between certainty and precision.

The tension between certainty and precision is always there. Fortunately, in most cases we can be both sufficiently certain and sufficiently precise to make useful statements. There is no simple answer to the conflict. You must choose a confidence level yourself. The data can't do it for you. The choice of confidence level is somewhat arbitrary. The most commonly chosen confidence levels are 90%, 95%, and 99%, but any probability can be used. (In practice, using something like 92.9% or 97.2% is likely to make people think you're up to something.)

Critical Values

In our sea fans example we used 2 *SE* to give us a 95% confidence interval. We got the 2 from the informal 68–95–99.7% rule. But we could also look up a more exact value from a table or a computer and find that we really should use 1.96 instead of 2. We call 1.96 the **critical value** and denote it z.* For any confidence level, we can find the corresponding critical value from a computer, a calculator, or a Normal probability table.

For a 90% confidence interval, the critical value is 1.645. Here's the Normal Model Tool from ActivStats showing the critical value for a 90 percent confidence level.

Figure 19.4

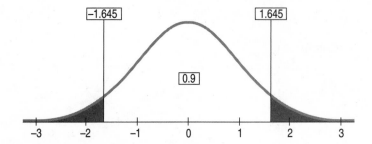

Assumptions and Conditions

We've just made some pretty sweeping statements about sea fans. Those statements were possible because we used a Normal model for the sampling distribution. But is that model appropriate?

All statistical models depend upon **assumptions.** Different models depend upon different assumptions. If those assumptions are not true, not only might the model be inappropriate, but the conclusions based on it may be wrong.

You can never be certain that an assumption is true. However, you can often decide whether it is plausible by checking a related **condition.** Here are the assumptions and the corresponding conditions you must check before creating a confidence interval about a proportion.

Independence Assumption

The data values are assumed to be independent from each other. Independence is a fundamental property, but not one we can check in the data. Instead, we think about whether independence is reasonable and we check three conditions.

Plausible Independence Condition. Is there any reason to believe that the data values somehow affect each other? (For example, might the disease in sea fans be contagious?) This condition depends on your knowledge of the situation. It's not one you can check by looking at the data.

Random Condition. Were the data sampled at random or generated from a properly randomized experiment? Proper randomization can help ensure independence.

10% Condition. Samples are almost always drawn without replacement. If the sample exceeds 10% of the population, the probability of success changes so much during the sampling that our Normal model may no longer be appropriate.

Sample Size Assumption

The model we use for inference is based on the Central Limit Theorem. The sample must be large enough to make the sampling model for the sample proportions approximately Normal. It turns out that we need more data as the proportion gets closer and closer to either edge (0 or 1). This requirement is easy to check as the following condition.

Success/Failure Condition. We must expect at least 10 "successes" and at least 10 "failures." Recall that by tradition we arbitrarily label one alternative (usually the outcome being counted) as a "success" even if it's something bad (like a sick sea fan). The other alternative is, of course, then a "failure."

A Confidence Interval for a Proportion   STEP-BY-STEP

WHO	Adults in the United States
WHAT	Response to a question about marijuana
WHEN	August 2000
WHERE	United States
HOW	507 adults were randomly sampled and asked by the Gallup Poll.
WHY	Public opinion research

In August 2000, the Gallup Poll asked 507 randomly sampled adults the question "Do you think the possession of small amounts of marijuana should be treated as a criminal offense?" Of these, 47% responded "No." What can we conclude from this survey?

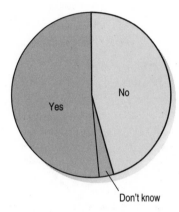

To answer this question we'll build a confidence interval for the proportion of all U.S. adults who would respond "No." There are four steps to building a confidence interval for proportions:

Parameter Identify the *parameter* you wish to estimate. This is the value we hope to catch within our confidence interval.

Choose and state a confidence level.

We wish to find an interval that is likely with 95% confidence to contain the true proportion, p, of U.S. adults who think possession of small amounts of marijuana should not be treated as a criminal offense.

Plan Check the conditions. We often cannot check assumptions. The conditions are the practical aspects of the data that we *can* check to be assured that the null model can be applied.

✓ **Plausible independence condition:** Gallup phoned a random sample of U.S. adults. It is very unlikely that any of the respondents influenced each other.

✓ **Random condition:** Gallup drew a random sample from all U.S. adults. We do not have details of the randomization, but we assume that we can trust it.

✓ **10% condition:** Although sampling was necessarily without replacement, there are many more U.S. adults than were sampled. The sample is certainly less than 10% of the population.

✓ **Success/failure condition:**

$n\hat{p} = 507 \times 47.0\% = 238.3 > 10$ and

$n\hat{q} = 507 \times 53.0\% = 268.7 > 10$
so our sample is large enough.

State the sampling distribution model for the statistic.

Under these conditions the sampling distribution of the proportion can be modeled by a Normal model.

Choose your method.

We will find a **one-proportion z-interval**.

Show **Mechanics** Construct the confidence interval.

We know: $n = 507$, $\hat{p} = .47$

$$\text{So } SE(\hat{p}) = \sqrt{\frac{\hat{p}\hat{q}}{n}} = \sqrt{\frac{.47 \times .53}{507}} = 0.022$$

We could informally use 2 for our critical value, but 1.96 is more accurate.

Because the sampling model is Normal, for a 95% confidence interval, the critical value $z^* = 1.96$.

From these, we find the margin of error as

$$\text{m.o.e.} = z^* \times SE(\hat{p}) = 1.96 \times 0.022 = 0.43$$

Reality Check The confidence interval is centered at the sample proportion and about as wide as we might expect for a sample of 500.

So the 95% confidence interval is:

$$.47 \pm 0.043 \text{ or } (0.427, 0.513)$$

Tell **Interpretation** Tell what the confidence interval means, in the proper context.

We can be 95% confident that between 42.7% and 51.3% of all U.S. adults think possession of small amounts of marijuana should not be treated as a criminal offense.

What Can Go Wrong? Confidence intervals are powerful tools. Not only do they tell what we know about the parameter value, but—more important—they also tell what we *don't* know. But in order to use them effectively, you must be clear about what you say about them.

Don't Misstate What the Interval Means

- *Don't suggest that the parameter varies.* A statement like "There is a 95% chance that the true proportion is between 42.7% and 51.3%" sounds as though you think the population proportion wanders around and sometimes happens to fall between 42.7% and 51.3%. When you interpret a confidence interval, make it clear that *you* know that the population parameter is fixed and that it is the *interval* that varies from sample to sample.
- *Don't claim that other samples will agree with yours.* Keep in mind that the confidence interval makes a statement about the true population proportion. An interpretation such as "In 95% of samples of U.S. adults the proportion who think marijuana should be decriminalized will be between 42.7% and 51.3%" is just wrong. The interval isn't about sample proportions, but about the population proportion.

- *Don't be certain about the parameter.* Saying "Between 42.1% and 61.7% of sea fans are infected" asserts that the population proportion cannot be outside that interval. Of course, we can't be absolutely certain of that. (Just pretty sure.)
- *Don't forget: It's the parameter.* Don't say, "I'm 95% confident that $\hat{p}$ is between 42.1% and 61.7%." Of course you are—in fact, we calculated that $\hat{p} = 51.8\%$ of the fans in our sample were infected. So we already *know* the sample proportion. The confidence interval is about the (unknown) population parameter, p.
- *Don't claim to know too much.* Don't say, "I'm 95% confident that between 42.1% and 61.7% of all the sea fans in the world are infected." You didn't sample from all the sea fans in the world. Just those of this type on the Las Redes Reef.
- *Do take responsibility.* Confidence intervals are about uncertainty. *You* are the one who is uncertain, not the parameter. You have to accept the responsibility and consequences of the fact that not all the intervals you compute will capture the true value. In fact, about 5% of the 95% confidence intervals you find will fail to capture the true value of the parameter.

> There are about 500 species of sea fans found on coral reefs throughout the world.

You *can* say, "I am 95% confident that between 42.1% and 61.7% of the sea fans on the Las Redes Reef are infected."[2]

Margin of Error Too Large to Be Useful

We know we can't be exact, but how precise do we need to be? A confidence interval that says that the percentage of infected sea fans is between 10% and 90% wouldn't be of much use. Most likely, you have some sense of how large a margin of error you can tolerate. What can you do?

One way to make the margin of error smaller is to reduce your level of confidence. But that may not be a useful solution. It is a rare study that reports confidence levels lower than 80%. Levels of 95% or 99% are more common.

If you are in this predicament, we're sorry for you; it's too late to help. The time to deal with this problem is when you design your study. To get a narrower interval without giving up confidence, you need to have less variability in your sample proportion. How can you do that? Choose a larger sample.

Suppose a candidate is planning a poll and wants to estimate voter support within 3% with 95% confidence. How large a sample does she need?

Let's look at the margin of error:

$$m.o.e. = z^* \sqrt{\frac{\hat{p}\hat{q}}{n}}$$

$$0.03 = 1.96 \sqrt{\frac{\hat{p}\hat{q}}{n}}$$

We want to find n, the sample size. But to find n we need a value for p. The worst case—the one that needs the largest sample size—is when p is .50, so if we use that value, we'll certainly be safe. Our candidate probably expects to be near 50%

---

[2]When we are being very careful we say, "95% of samples of this size will produce confidence intervals that capture the true proportion of infected sea fans on the Las Redes Reef."

In general the sample size needed to produce a confidence interval with a given margin of error at a given confidence level is:

$$n = \frac{z^{*\,2}\hat{p}\hat{q}}{m.o.e.^2}$$

where z^* is the critical value for the confidence level you specified.

anyway. To extract n from inside the square root, we square both sides of the equation:

$$.03^2 = 1.96^2 \left(\frac{0.5 \times 0.5}{n} \right)$$

And solve for n:

$$n = \frac{1.96^2 \times 0.50 \times 0.50}{0.03^2} = 1068$$

So we estimate that we need at least 1068 respondents to keep the margin of error as small as 3% with a confidence level of 95%.

Unfortunately, bigger samples cost more money and more effort. And because the standard error only declines with the *square root* of the sample size, to cut the standard error (and thus the m.o.e.) in half, we must *quadruple* the sample size.

Here is a table showing sample sizes and the 95% margin of error for an estimated proportion of 0.5.

n	SE_p	95% m.o.e
100	.050	±10%
200	.035	±7%
400	.025	±5%
600	.020	±4%
1,100	.015	±3%
2,400	.010	±2%
10,000	.005	±1%

Public opinion polls often use a sample size of 1000, which gives an m.o.e. of 3% when p = .5. But businesses and nonprofit organizations often use much larger samples to estimate the response to a direct mailing campaign. Why? Because the proportion of people who respond to these mailings is very small, often below 5%. So a margin of error of 3% isn't going to be of much use.

Generally a margin of error of 5% or less is acceptable, but different circumstances call for different standards. For a pilot study, a margin of error of 10% may be fine, so a sample of 100 will do quite well. In a close election, a polling organization might want to get the margin of error down to 2%. But drawing a large sample to get a smaller m.o.e. can run into trouble. It takes time to survey 2,400 people, and a survey that extends over a week or more may be trying to hit a target that moves during the time of the survey. An important event can change public opinion in the middle of the survey process.

Keep in mind that the sample size for a survey is the number of respondents, not the number of people to whom questionnaires were sent. And keep in mind that a low response rate makes any study essentially a voluntary response study, and thus of little value for inferring population values. It is almost always better to spend resources on increasing the response rate than on surveying a larger group. A full or nearly full response by a modest size sample can yield useful results.

Of course, surveys are not the only place where proportions pop up. Credit card banks sample huge mailing lists to find out what kind of response rate they're likely to get on a new type of credit card. Even pilot studies are likely to be mailed to 50,000 customers or more. In cases like these, the proportions are likely to be quite small, as will the margins of error needed to say anything useful. When p is small, very large samples will be used. Don't rely on the table, which assumes p is 50%. You will be better off finding the sample size by going back to the formula and substituting an educated guess for p.

Violations of Assumptions

Confidence intervals and margins of error are often reported along with poll results and other analyses. But it is easy to misuse them, and wise to be aware of the ways things can go wrong.

- *Watch out for biased samples.* Don't forget about the potential sources of bias in surveys that we discussed in Chapter 12. Just because we have more statistical machinery now doesn't mean we can forget what we've already learned. A questionnaire that finds that 85% of people enjoy filling out surveys still suffers from nonresponse bias even though now we're able to put confidence intervals around this (biased) estimate.
- *Think about independence.* The assumption that the values in our sample are mutually independent is one that we usually cannot check. But it always pays to think about it. For example, the disease affecting the sea fans might be contagious, so that fans growing near a diseased fan are more likely themselves to be diseased. Such contagion would violate the independence assumption and could severely affect our sample proportion. It could be that the proportion of infected sea fans on the entire reef is actually quite small and the researchers just happened to find an infected area. To avoid this, the researchers should be careful to sample sites far enough apart to make contagion unlikely.

Confidence Intervals for Proportions and the Computer

Confidence intervals for proportions are so easy and natural that you can't really do them on the computer. The problem is that most statistics programs want the "raw data" to compute with. For proportions, the raw data are the "success" and "failure" status for each case. Usually these are given as 1 or 0, but they might be category names like "yes" and "no." But often we just know the proportion of successes, $\hat{p}$, and the total count, n. Computer packages don't usually deal with summary data like these easily. In some programs you can reconstruct the original values.

But even when you have (or can reconstruct) the raw data values, you won't get *exactly* the same margin of error from a computer package as you would find working by hand. The reason is that when the packages treat the proportion as a mean they make some approximations. The result is very close, but not exactly the same.[3] But statistics means never having to say you're certain, so the approximate result is good enough.

Connections

Now we can see the practical application of sampling distributions. To find a confidence interval, we lay out an interval measured in standard deviations. We're using the standard deviation as a ruler again. But now the standard deviation we need is the standard deviation of the sampling distribution. That's the one that tells how much the proportion varies. (And when we estimate it from the data, we call it a standard error.)

---

[3]The packages treat the proportion as a mean and, as we will see, confidence intervals for means use a slightly different sampling distribution model.

Key Concepts

Confidence Interval

A level C confidence interval for a model parameter is an interval of values usually of the form

Estimate ± margin of error

found from data in such a way that C% of intervals found in this way will capture the true parameter value.

One-proportion *z*-interval

A confidence interval for a proportion based on the Normal model.

Margin of Error

In a confidence interval, the extent of the interval on either side of the observed statistic value is called the margin of error. A margin of error is typically the product of a critical value from the sampling distribution and a standard error from the data. A small margin of error corresponds to a confidence interval that pins down the parameter precisely. A large margin of error corresponds to a confidence interval that gives relatively little information about the estimated parameter.

Critical Value

The number of standard errors to move away from the mean of the sampling distribution to correspond to the specified level of confidence.

Assumptions

Every model depends on assumptions. Although we may be able to think about whether an assumption is plausible, it remains something that we *assume* and cannot verify.

Conditions

Although we cannot verify assumptions, often there are conditions about the data that we can check to see whether an assumption is at least reasonable.

Skills

When you complete this lesson you should:

- Understand confidence intervals as a balance between the precision and the certainty of a statement about a model parameter.

- Understand that the margin of error of a confidence interval for a proportion changes with the sample size and the level of confidence.

- Know how to examine your data for violations of conditions that would make inference about a population proportion unwise or invalid.

- Be able to construct a one-proportion *z*-interval.

- Be able to interpret a one-proportion *z*-interval in a simple sentence or two. Write such an interpretation so that it does not state or suggest that the parameter of interest is itself random, but rather that the bounds of the confidence interval are the random quantities about which we state our degree of confidence.

Exercises

Exercises

1. **Margin of error** A TV newsman reports the results of a poll of voters, and then says "the margin of error is plus or minus 4%". Explain carefully what that means.

2. **Margin of Error** A medical researcher estimates the percentage of children that are exposed to lead-base paint, adding that he believes his estimate has a margin of error of about 3%. Explain what the margin of error means.

3. **Conditions** Consider each situation described below. Identify the population and the sample, explain what p and $\hat{p}$ represent, and tell whether the methods of this chapter can be used to create a confidence interval.
   a) Police set up an auto checkpoint at which drivers are stopped and their cars inspected for safety problems. They find that 14 of the 134 cars stopped have at least one safety violation. They want to estimate the percentage of all cars that may be unsafe.
   b) A TV talk show asks viewers to register their opinions on prayer in schools by logging on to a website. Of the 602 people who voted, 488 favored prayer in schools. We want to estimate the level of support among the general public.
   c) A school is considering requiring students to wear uniforms. The PTA surveys parent opinion by sending a questionnaire home with all 1245 students. 380 surveys are returned, with 228 families on favor of the change.
   d) A college admits 1632 freshmen one year, and four years later 1388 of them graduate on time. The college wants to estimate the percentage of all their freshman enrollees who graduate on time.

4. **More conditions** Consider each situation described below. Identify the population and the sample, explain what p and $\hat{p}$ represent, and tell whether the methods of this chapter can be used to create a confidence interval.
   a) A consumer group hoping to assess customer experiences with auto dealers surveys 167 people who recently bought new cars. 3% of them expressed dissatisfaction with the salesperson.
   b) What percent of college students have cell phones? 2883 students were asked as they entered a football stadium, and 243 indicated they had phones with them.
   c) 240 potato plants in a field in Maine are randomly checked and only 7 showed signs of blight. How severe is the blight problem for the US potato industry?
   d) 12 of the 309 employees of a small company suffered an injury on the job last year. What can the company expect in future years?

5. **Conclusions** A catalog sales company promises to deliver orders placed on the internet within 3 days. Followup calls to a few randomly selected

customers show that a 95% confidence interval for the proportion of all orders that arrive on time is 88% ± 6%. What does this mean? Are these conclusions correct? Explain.

a) Between 82% and 94% of all orders arrive on time.

b) 95% of all random samples of customers will show that 88% of orders arrive on time.

c) 95% of all random samples of customers will show that 82%-94% of orders arrive on time.

d) We are 95% sure that between 82% and 94% of the orders placed by the customers in this sample arrived on time.

e) On 95% of the days, between 82% and 94% of the orders will arrive on time.

6. **More Conclusions** In January 2002, two students made worldwide headlines by spinning a Belgian Euro 250 times and getting 140 heads – that's 56%. That makes the 90% confidence interval <51%, 61%>. What does this mean? Are these conclusions correct? Explain.

a) Between 51% and 61% of all Euros are unfair.

b) We are 90% sure that in this experiment this Euro landed heads on between 51% and 61% of the spins.

c) We are 90% sure that spun Euros will land heads between 51% and 61% of the time.

d) If you flip a Euro many times, you can be 90% sure of getting between 51% and 61% heads.

e) 90% of all Euros will land heads between 51% and 61% of the time.

7. **Confidence intervals** Several factors are involved in the creation of a confidence interval. Among them are the sample size, the level of confidence, and the margin of error. Which statements are true?

a) For a given sample size, higher confidence means a smaller margin of error.

b) For a specified confidence level, larger samples provide smaller margins of error.

c) For a fixed margin of error, larger samples provide greater confidence.

d) For a given confidence level, halving the margin of error requires a sample twice as large.

8. **Confidence intervals, again** Several factors are involved in the creation of a confidence interval. Among them are the sample size, the level of confidence, and the margin of error. Which statements are true?

a) For a given sample size, reducing the margin of error will mean lower confidence.

b) For a certain confidence level, you can get a smaller margin of error by selecting a bigger sample.

c) For a fixed margin of error, smaller samples will mean lower confidence.

d) For a given confidence level, a sample 9 times as large will make a margin of error one third as big.

9. **Cars** What fraction of cars are made in Japan? The computer output below summarizes the results of a random sample of 50 autos. Explain carefully what it tells you.

> z-Interval for proportion
> With 90.00% Confidence, 0.29938661 < p(japan) < 0.46984416

10. **Parole** A study of 902 decisions made by the Nebraska Board of Parole produced the following computer output. Assuming these cases are representative of all cases that may come before the Board, what can you conclude?

> z-Interval for Proportion
> With 95.00% Confidence, 0.56100658 < p(parole) < 0.62524619

11. **Ghosts** A May 2000 Gallup poll found that 38% of a random sample of 1012 adults said that they believe in ghosts.
    a) Find the margin of error for this poll if we want 90% confidence in our estimate of the percent of American adults who believe in ghosts.
    b) Explain what that margin of error means.
    c) If we want to be 99% confident, will the margin of error be larger or smaller? Explain.
    d) Find that margin of error.
    e) In general, if all other aspects of the situation remain the same, will smaller margins of error involve greater or less confidence in the interval?

12. **Cloning** A May 2002 Gallup poll found that only 8% of a random sample of 1012 adults approved of attempts to clone a human.
    a) Find the margin of error for this poll if we want 95% confidence in our estimate of the percent of American adults who approve of cloning humans.
    b) Explain what that margin of error means.
    c) If we only need to be 90% confident, will the margin of error be larger or smaller? Explain.
    d) Find that margin of error.
    e) In general, if all other aspects of the situation remain the same, would smaller samples produce smaller or larger margins of error?

13. **Teenage Drivers** An insurance company checks police records on 582 accidents selected at random and notes that teenagers were at the wheel in 91 of them.
    a) Create a 95% confidence interval for the percentage of all auto accidents that involve teenage drivers.
    b) Explain what your interval means.
    c) Explain what "95% confidence" means.

    d) A politician urging tighter restrictions on teens' drivers' licenses says "In one of every 5 auto accidents a teenager is behind the wheel." Does your confidence interval support or contradict this statement? Explain.

14. **Junk mail** Direct mail advertisers send solicitations (aka "junk mail") to thousands of potential customers hoping that some will buy the company's product. The response rate is usually quite low. Suppose a company wants to test the response to a new flyer, and sends it to 1000 people randomly selected from their mailing list of over 200000 people. They get orders from 123 of the recipients.
    a) Create a 90% confidence interval for the percentage of people they contact who may buy something.
    b) Explain what this interval means.
    c) Explain what "90% confidence" means.
    d) They must decide whether to now do a mass mailing. The mailing won't be cost-effective unless it produces at least a 5% return. What does your confidence interval suggest? Explain.

15. **Safe food** Some food retailers propose subjecting food to a low level of radiation in order to improve safety, but sale of such "irradiated" food is opposed by many people. Suppose a grocer wants to find out what his customers think. He has cashiers distribute surveys at checkout and ask customers to fill them out and drop them in a box near the front door. He gets responses from 122 customers, of whom 78 oppose the radiation treatments. What can the grocer conclude about the opinions of all his customers?

16. **Local News** The mayor of a small city has suggested that the state locate a new prison there, arguing that the construction project and resulting jobs will be good for the local economy. 183 residents show up for a public hearing on the proposal, and a show of hands finds only 31 in favor of the prison project. What can the city council conclude about public support for the mayor's initiative?

17. **Marijuana, again** In the survey on drugs you read about in the chapter, the Gallup Poll actually split their sample at random, asking 505 respondents the question quoted earlier, *"Do you think the possession of small amounts of marijuana should be treated as a criminal offense?"* The other half were asked *"Do you think the use of marijuana should be made legal, or not?"* Seems like the same question, but for this way of phrasing it, only 31% said they thought marijuana should be legalized.
    a) Construct a 95% confidence interval for the true proportion of adults who think that "the use of marijuana should be made legal" according to the responses for this question.
    b) Recall that 47% of the respondents in the other random half of the study said that possession of marijuana should not be a crime. Does a proportion of 0.47 fall inside the confidence interval you just found?

    DRAFT: Do not distribute or copy

18. **Drinking** A national health organization warns that 30% of middle school students nationwide have been drunk. Concerned, a local health agency randomly and anonymously surveys 110 of the 1212 middle school students in their city. Only 21 of them report having been drunk.
    a) What proportion of the sample reported having been drunk?
    b) Does this mean that this city's youth are not drinking as much as the national data would indicate? Explain.
    c) Create a 95% confidence interval for the proportion of the city's middle school students who have been drunk.
    d) Is there any reason to believe that the national level of 30% is not true of the middle school students in this city?

19. **Marijuana Poll** In the chapter's example and again in Exercise 15 we have looked at a Gallup poll investigating the public's attitude toward legalizing marijuana. In response to one question 47% favored decriminalization, but when the question was phrased differently the proportion in favor dropped to 31%.
    a) What kind of bias may be present here?
    b) Each group consisted of 505 respondents. If we combine them, considering the overall group to be one larger random sample, what is a 95% confidence interval for the proportion of the general public that favors legalization?
    c) How does the margin of error based on this pooled sample compare to the margins of error from the separate groups? Why?

20. **Gambling** A city ballot includes a local initiative that would legalize gambling. The issue is hotly contested, and two groups decide to conduct polls to predict the outcome. The local newspaper finds 53% of 1200 randomly selected voters plan to vote "yes", while a college statistics class finds 54% of 450 randomly selected voters in support. Both groups will create 95% confidence intervals.
    a) Without finding the confidence intervals, explain which one will have the largest margin of error.
    b) Find both confidence intervals.
    c) Which group concludes that the outcome is too close to call? Why?

21. **Rickets** Vitamin D, produced naturally when sunlight falls upon the skin or ingested as a dietary supplement, is essential for strong healthy bones. The bone disease rickets was largely eliminated in England during the 1950s, but now there is concern that a generation of children more likely to watch TV or play computer games than spend time outdoors is at increased risk. A recent study of 2700 children randomly selected from all parts of England found 20% of them deficient in Vitamin D.
    a) Find a 98% confidence interval.
    b) Explain carefully what your interval means.

Copyright © 2001, Dave Bock, Paul Velleman, and Dick De Veaux

    c) Explain what "98% confidence" means.

22. **Pregnancy** In 1998 a San Diego reproductive clinic reported 49 births to 207 women under the age of 40 who had previously been unable to conceive.
    a) Write a 90% confidence interval for the success rate at this clinic.
    b) Interpret your interval in this context.
    c) Explain what "90%" confidence" means.
    d) Would it be misleading for the clinic to advertise a 25% success rate? Explain.

23. **Deer ticks** Wildlife biologists inspect 153 deer taken by hunters and find 32 of them carrying ticks that test positive for Lyme disease.
    a) Create a 90% confidence interval for the percentage of deer that may carry such ticks.
    b) If the scientists want to cut the margin of error in half, how many deer must they inspect?
    c) What concerns do you have about this sample?

24. **Pregnancy** The San Diego reproductive clinic in Exercise 22 wants to publish more definitive information on their success rate.
    a) They want to cut the stated margin of error in half. How many patients' results must they use?
    b) Do you have any concerns about this sample? Explain.

25. **Graduation** It is believed that as many as 25% of adults over 50 never graduated from high school. We wish to see if this percentage is the same among the 25-30 age group.
    a) How many of this younger age group must we survey in order to estimate the proportion of non-grads to within 6% with 90% confidence?
    b) Suppose we want to cut the margin of error to 4%. What is the necessary sample size?
    c) What sample size would produce a margin of error of 3%?

26. **Hiring** In preparing a report on the economy we need to estimate the percentage of businesses that plan to hire additional employees in the next 60 days.
    a) How many randomly selected employers must we contact in order to create an estimate in which we are 98% confident with a margin of error of 5%?
    b) Suppose we want to reduce the margin of error to 3%. What sample size will suffice?
    c) Why might it not be worth the effort to try to get an interval with a margin of error of only 1%?

27. **Graduation, Again** As in Exercise 25, we hope to estimate the percentage of adults aged 25-30 who never graduated from high school.

What sample size would allow us to increase our confidence level to 95% while reducing the margin of error to only 2%?

28. **Better Hiring Info** Editors of the business report in Exercise 26 are willing to accept a margin of error of 4%, but want 99% confidence. How many randomly selected employers will they need to contact?

29. **Pilot Study** A state's environmental agency worries that many cars may be exceeding clean air emissions standards. They hope to check a sample of vehicles in order to estimate that percentage with a margin of error of 3% and 90% confidence. To gauge the size of the problem they first pick 60 cars and find 9 with faulty emissions systems. How many should they sample for their full investigation?

30. **Pilot Study** During routine screening a doctor notices that 22% of her adult patients show higher than normal levels of glucose in their blood – a possible warning signal for diabetes. Hearing this, some medical researchers decide to conduct a large-scale study, hoping to estimate the proportion to within 4% with 98% confidence. How many randomly selected adults must they test?

31. **Approval** A newspaper reports that the governor's approval rating stands at 65%. The article adds that the poll is based on a random sample of 972 adults and has a margin of error of 2.5%. What level of confidence did the pollsters use?

32. **Amendment** A TV news reporter says that a proposed constitutional amendment is likely to win approval in the upcoming election because a poll of 1505 likely voters indicated that 52% would vote in favor. The reporter goes on to say that the margin of error for this poll was 3%.
    a) Explain why the poll is actually inconclusive.
    b) What confidence level did the pollsters use?

20 Testing Hypotheses about Proportions

INGOTS ARE HUGE PIECES OF METAL, often weighing in excess of 20,000 pounds made in a giant mold. They must be cast in one large piece to use in fabricating large structural parts for cars and planes. If they crack while being made, the crack may propagate into the zone required for the part, compromising its integrity. Airplane manufacturers insist that metal for their planes be defect free, so the ingot must be made over if any cracking is detected.

Even though the metal from the cracked ingot is recycled, the scrap cost runs into the tens of thousands of dollars. Metal manufacturer would like to avoid cracking if at all possible. But the casting process is complicated and not everything is completely under control. In one plant, only about 80% of the ingots have been free of cracks. In an attempt to reduce the cracking proportion the plant engineers and chemists recently tried out some changes in the casting process. Since then, 400 ingots have been cast and only 17% of them have cracked. Should management declare victory? Has the cracking rate really decreased or was 17% just due to luck?

We can treat the 400 ingots cast since the changes were implemented as a random sample. We know that each random sample will have a somewhat different proportion of cracked ingots. Is the 17% we observe just due to natural sampling variability, or can we assure management that the lower cracking rate is strong enough evidence to say that the true cracking rate now is really below 20%?

> "Half the money I spend on advertising is wasted; the trouble is I don't know which half."
> John Wanamaker, (attributed)

People want answers to questions like these all the time. Has the president's approval rating changed since last month? Has teenage smoking decreased in the past five years? Is the global temperature increasing? To answer such questions we'll test *hypotheses* about models.

Hypotheses

Hypothesis n.; pl. {Hypotheses}.
A supposition; a proposition or principle which is supposed or taken for granted, in order to draw a conclusion or inference for proof of the point in question; something not proved, but assumed for the purpose of argument.
Webster's Unabridged Dictionary, 1913
http://work.ucsd.edu:5141/cgi-bin/http_webster?hypothesis

In Statistics, a hypothesis proposes a model for the world. Then we look at the data. If the data are consistent with that model, we have no reason to disbelieve the hypothesis. But if the facts are inconsistent with the model, what then? It depends. If the data are only slightly out of step with the model, we might stick with the model. But if the data dramatically contradict the model, that's strong evidence that the model is incorrect.

Notice the difference between the two possibilities. If the facts are consistent with the model, they *lend support* to the hypothesis. Does this *prove* the hypothesis is true? No. Lending support is not the same as proving something. Many other models may also be consistent with the same set of facts. So, even if a hypothesis is true, we can never really prove it.

But when a hypothesis is false, we might be able to recognize that. When data are glaringly *inconsistent* with the hypothesis, it becomes clear that the hypothesis can't be right. Then we can reject it. This is the logic of traditional scientific thinking and one of the principal differences between scientific thinking and other kinds of reasoning[1].

This is also the logic of jury trials. To prove someone is guilty, we start by *assuming* they are innocent. We retain that hypothesis until the facts make it unlikely beyond a reasonable doubt. Then, and only then, we reject the hypothesis of innocence and declare the person is guilty.

In statistical tests of hypotheses, we use the same logic. We start by assuming that a hypothesis is true. Then we consider whether the data are consistent with the hypothesis. If they are, all we can do is retain the hypothesis we started with. But, if they are not, then like a jury, we ask whether they are unlikely beyond a reasonable doubt. The statistical twist is that we can quantify our level of doubt.

> For hundreds of years it was assumed that the Sun revolved around the Earth. The fact that the sun appears to rise in the East every morning and set in the West every evening is *consistent* with this hypothesis, and *seems* to lend support to it, but it certainly doesn't prove it. It may explain, however, why Copernicus, who believed that the Earth revolves around the Sun had such a hard time convincing the world of his (correct) model.

If the data are surprising, but we believe they're trustworthy, then we start to doubt the hypothesis. What do we mean by "surprising"? We can find the probability that data like these could occur based on our hypothesized model. If the results seem consistent with what we would expect from natural sampling variability, then we'll **retain** the hypothesis. But, if the probability of seeing results like our data is really low, we **reject** the hypothesis.

Of course, when we reject the hypothesis it may be that the hypothesis is actually true and we just witnessed something extremely unlikely. But, when it comes to data, statisticians don't believe in miracles. Instead, they say that if the data are unlikely *enough,* they'll reject the hypothesis.

Testing Hypotheses

How can we state and test a hypothesis about ingot cracking? Remember that we start by *assuming* a hypothesis is true. What should we assume here? The cracking rate has been at 20% for years. To test

---

[1] Throughout the book, when we talk about Science and Scientific thinking, we include most of the Social Sciences as well. Indeed, other disciplines, such as History, include works of scientific thinking. But the paradigm is considered to be a "scientific" way of thinking, so we will speak of "the scientist" but ask you to understand us to mean any person thinking scientifically.

DRAFT: Do not distribute or copy

whether the changes made by the engineers have improved the cracking rate we assume that they have in fact made no difference. So our starting hypothesis, called the null hypothesis, is that the proportion of cracks is still 20%.

The **null hypothesis**, which we denote H_0, specifies a population model parameter of interest and proposes a value for that parameter. Which value to take is often obvious from the context of the problem itself, from the Who and What of the data. But sometimes it takes a bit of thinking to translate the question we hope to answer into a hypothesis about a parameter of a particular model. Here we can write H_0: $p = .20$.

What would convince you that the cracking rate had actually gone down? Probably only if you observed a cracking rate *much lower* than 20% in your sample. If only 3 out of the next 400 ingots crack, (0.75%) you'll probably be convinced the changes helped. But. if the sample cracking rate is only slightly lower than 20%, you might be skeptical. After all, observations do vary, so we should not be surprised that natural sampling variability will result in small differences. How big must the difference be before we are convinced that the cracking rate has changed?

Whenever we ask how big a difference is we think of the standard deviation. (You *did* think of the standard deviation, didn't you?) So let's start by finding the standard deviation of the sample cracking rate. The sample cracking rate is a proportion, so we already know how to find its standard deviation.

Since the change, 400 new ingots have been cast. The sample size of 400 is big enough to satisfy the success/failure condition. (We expect 0.20*400 = 80 ingots to crack.) and we have no reason to think the ingots are not independent, so the Normal sampling distribution model should work well. The standard deviation of the sampling model is

To remind us that the parameter value comes from the null hypothesis, it is sometimes written as p_0 and the standard deviation as

$$SD(\hat{p}) = \sqrt{\frac{p_0 q_0}{n}}$$

$$SD(\hat{p}) = \sqrt{\frac{pq}{n}} = \sqrt{\frac{.20 \times .80}{400}} = 0.02 .$$

Why is this a standard deviation and not a standard error? Well, we haven't estimated anything. Once we assume the null hypothesis, it gives us a value for the model parameter p. With proportions, if we know p then we also automatically know its standard deviation. And because we find the standard deviation from the model parameter, this is a standard deviation and not a standard error. When we found a confidence interval for p we could not assume that we knew its value, so we estimated the standard deviation from the sample value, $\hat{p}$. An estimated standard deviation is a standard error.

Now we know both parameters of the Normal sampling distribution model: $p = 20\%$ and $SD(\hat{p}) = 0.02$. So, we can find out how likely it would be to see the observed value of $\hat{p} = 17\%$. Since we are using a Normal model, we find the z-score:

$$z = \frac{.17 - .20}{.02} = -1.5$$

and we ask "how likely is it to observe a value at least 1.5 standard deviations below the mean of a Normal model?" The answer (from a calculator, computer program, or the Normal tables) is about 0.067. This is probability of observing a cracking rate or 17% or less if the null model is true. Management now must decide whether an event that would happen 6.7% of the time by chance is strong enough evidence to decide that the true cracking proportion has decreased.

Beyond a reasonable doubt

We ask whether the data were unlikely beyond a reasonable doubt. We've just calculated that probability. The probability that the observed statistic value (or an even more extreme value) could occur if the null model were true – in this case 0.067 – is called the P-value.

A Trial as a Hypothesis Test

We've said that hypothesis testing is very much like a court trial. In order to understand the logic better, let's push the analogy a little further. In our imagined trial suppose the defendant has been accused of robbery. We wonder whether he is guilty or not. In British common law and those systems derived from it (including U.S. law), the null hypothesis is that the defendant is innocent. Instructions to juries are quite explicit about this.

We then marshal the evidence. For us, this means collecting data. In the trial the Prosecutor then presents evidence. This evidence takes the form of facts that seem to contradict the presumption of innocence. ("If the defendant were innocent, wouldn't it be remarkable that the police found him at the scene of the crime with a bag full of money in his hand, a mask on his face and a getaway car parked outside"?)

The next step is to judge the evidence. Evaluating the evidence is the responsibility of the jury in a trial, but it falls on your shoulders in hypothesis testing. The jury considers the evidence in the light of the *presumption* of innocence and judges whether the evidence against him would be plausible *if the defendant were in fact innocent.*

Like the jury, we ask "could these data plausibly have happened by chance if the null hypothesis were true?" If they were very unlikely to have occurred, then the evidence raises reasonable doubts in our minds about the null hypothesis.

Ultimately, we must make a decision. The standard of "beyond a reasonable doubt" is wonderfully ambiguous because it leaves the decision of to what degree the evidence contradicts the presumption of innocence in the hands of the jury. We have to ask the same question.

DRAFT: Do not distribute or copy

How unlikely is unlikely? Some people advocate setting rigid standards, like 1 time out of 20 (.05) or 1 time out of 100. But, if you have to make the decision, you must decide for yourself in any particular situation whether the probability is small enough to constitute "reasonable doubt".

What To Do with an "Innocent" Defendant

"If the People fail to satisfy their burden of proof, you must find the defendant not guilty "
--NY State Jury instructions

If the evidence is not strong enough to reject the defendant's presumption of innocence, what verdict does the jury return? They say "not guilty". Notice that they do not say that the defendant is innocent. Nor do they employ a standard of "reasonable certainty" in place of the standard of "reasonable doubt." All they say is that they have not seen sufficient evidence to convict; to reject innocence. The defendant may, in fact, be innocent, but the jury has no way to be sure.

Said statistically, the jury's null hypothesis is H_0: innocent defendant. If the evidence is too unlikely given this assumption, the jury rejects the null hypothesis and finds the defendant guilty. But – and this is an important distinction—if there is *insufficient evidence* to convict the defendant, the jury does not decide that H_0 is true and declare him innocent. Juries can only *fail to reject* the null hypothesis and declare the defendant "not guilty".

In the same way, if the data are not particularly unlikely under the assumption that the null hypothesis is true, then the most we can do is to "fail to reject" the null hypothesis. We never declare the null hypothesis to be true, because we simply do not know whether it is true or not. (After all, more evidence may come along later.) Sometimes in this case we say that the *null hypothesis has been retained*.

In the trial the burden of proof is on the prosecution. In a hypothesis test the burden of proof is on the unusual claim. The null hypothesis is the ordinary state of affairs, so it is the alternative that we consider unusual and for which we must marshal evidence.

Imagine a clinical trial testing the effectiveness of a new headache remedy. We will most likely test it against a placebo, and the null hypothesis will be that the new drug is no more effective than the placebo. But if we use only 6 people to test the drug what are we likely to conclude? The results are likely *not to be clear* with only 6 people in the trial. We will be unable to reject the hypothesis. Does this mean the drug doesn't work? Of course not. It simply means that we don't have enough evidence to reject our assumption. That's why we don't start by assuming that the drug *is more effective*. If we were to do that, then we could just test just a few people, find that the results aren't clear, and claim that we've been unable to reject our original assumption. The FDA is unlikely to be impressed by such an argument.

The Reasoning of Hypothesis Testing

Hypothesis tests follow a carefully structured path. But in order to avoid getting lost as you navigate down it, we divide that path into four distinct sections.

Hypotheses: We've already talked about the null hypothesis. But what should we believe if we reject the null? To perform a hypothesis test we must specify an alternative hypothesis. Remember that we can never prove a null hypothesis, only reject it or retain it. If we reject it, we then accept the alternative. Often, the null hypothesis is the established belief, the *status quo*. If we have a new method that we think may work better, the null hypothesis will assume that it doesn't. The alternative hypothesis would then be that it does.

In statistical hypothesis testing hypotheses are almost always about model parameters.[2] To assess how unlikely our data may be we need a null model. The null hypothesis gives a particular parameter value to use in our model. The alternative hypothesis usually gives a range of other possible values.

> **The Null hypothesis.** To perform a hypothesis test we must first translate our question of interest into a statement about model parameters. Suppose we want to see if people prefer Coke or Pepsi. How do we translate this into a null hypothesis *we can test*? We need to specify a parameter and a value for it. If we let p be the proportion of people who prefer Coke to Pepsi, we could let the null hypothesis be "$H_0: p = 50\%$". Now we can collect data and test this hypothesis.
>
> The key step is to take your question and translate it into a statement about the parameter of a model so that we can test it. In the usual shorthand, write "$H_0: parameter = value$".
>
> **The Alternative hypothesis.** The **alternative hypothesis** contains the values of the parameter we accept if we reject the null. If we reject the null hypothesis, then we accept the alternative hypothesis. In the Coke vs. Pepsi example, our null hypothesis is that $p = 0.50$. What's the alternative? We would be interested in learning that either cola was preferred. In terms of the parameter, we can write $H_A: p \neq 0.50$. If the data convince us that we should reject the null hypothesis we would accept the alternative.

Some folks just pronounce the hypothesis labels "Ho!" and "Ha!" (but it makes them seem overexcitable). Others, pronounce H_0 "H naught" as in "all is for naught"[1]). Nobody, it seems, says "H zero" or "H-Oh" so you probably shouldn't either.

---

[2] In this book they are *always* about model parameters.

DRAFT: Do not distribute or copy

Plan: To plan a statistical hypothesis test, specify the *model* you plan to use to test the null hypothesis and the parameter of interest. Of course, all models require assumptions, so you will need to state them and check any corresponding conditions. Your plan step should end with a statement such as

> "Because the conditions are satisfied, it is appropriate to model the sampling distribution of the proportion with a $N(p_0, SD(p_0))$ model."

... They make things
admirably plain,
But one hard question will
remain:
If one hypothesis you lose,
Another in its place you
choose...
-- James Russell Lowell.
Credidimus Jovem Regnare

Each test we discuss in the book has a name. You should also include the name of the test you plan to perform. We'll see many tests in the following chapters. Some will be about more than *one* sample, some about statistics other than *proportions,* some will use models other than the Normal (and so will not use z-scores). We call this test about the value of a proportion a **One proportion z-test**[3].

Mechanics: Under "Mechanics" we place the actual calculation of a test statistic from the data. Different tests we encounter will have different formulas. Usually, the mechanics are handled by a statistics program or calculator, but it is good to have the formulas recorded for reference and to know what is being computed. The ultimate goal of the calculation is to obtain a **P-value** – the probability that the observed statistic value (or an even more extreme value) could occur if the null model were correct. If the P-value is small enough, we'll reject the null hypothesis.

Conclusion: The conclusion in a hypothesis test is always a statement about the null hypothesis. The conclusion must state either that we reject or that we fail to reject the null hypothesis.

Formal tests of the null hypothesis leave the decision to reject or accept the null hypothesis solely on the size of the P-value. But in real life, we want to evaluate the costs of our decisions as well. How much would you be willing to pay for a faster computer? Shouldn't your decision depend on *how* much faster? And on how much more it costs? And costs are not just monetary. Would you use the same standard of proof for testing the safety of an airplane as for the speed of your new computer?

Your conclusion about the null hypothesis should never be the end of a testing procedure. Often there are actions to take or policies to change. In our ingot example, management must decide whether to continue the changes proposed by the engineers. The decision always includes the practical consideration of whether the new method is *worth* the cost. Suppose management decides to reject the null hypothesis of 20% cracking in favor of the alternative that it has been reduced. They must still evaluate *how much* the cracking rate has been reduced and how much it cost to accomplish it. The *size of the effect* is always a concern when we test hypotheses. A good way to look at the effect size is to examine a confidence interval as well.

---

[3] It is also called just the "one sample test for a proportion".

Alternative Alternatives

In the Coke vs. Pepsi example, we were equally interested in proportions that deviate from 50% in *either* direction. So we wrote our alternative hypothesis as H_A: $p \neq 0.50$.

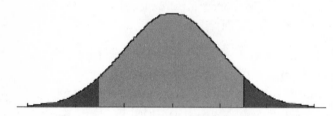

Such an alternative hypothesis is known as a **two-sided alternative** because we are equally interested in deviations either side of the null hypothesis value. For two-sided alternatives, the P-value is the probability of deviating in *either* direction from the null hypothesis value.

But in the ingot example, management is particularly interested in *lowering* the cracking rate below 20%. They probably don't want to pursue changes in the process that make the cracking rate worse. The only alternative of interest is that the cracking rate *decreases*. So we would write our alternative hypothesis as H_A: $p < 0.20$. An alternative hypothesis that focuses on deviations from the null hypothesis value in only one direction is called a **one-sided alternative**.

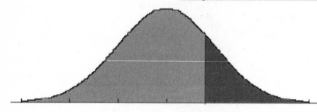

For one-sided alternatives, the P-value is the probability of deviating *only in the direction of the alternative* away from the null hypothesis value.

How do we know whether we want a one or two-sided alternative? To answer this we return to the W's, specifically the "Why" of the study. In the ingot example, the data were collected to see whether the changes improved the cracking rate. When we test a hypothesis we must specify both the null and the alternative. But the alternative is often the hypothesis that motivated the study.

In some social sciences alternative hypotheses are called "research hypotheses" and are stated clearly at the beginning of research reports. Ask "why was this study done?" and you are likely to hear about the alternative hypothesis. But keep in mind that you can't assume that the alternative is true. To be able to do the test, you must specify and assume the null. And the burden of proof is on the claim made by the research hypothesis. Without sufficient evidence otherwise, we retain the null.

Testing a Hypothesis Step-by-Step

In some cultures, male children are valued more highly than female children. Advances in medical care such as prenatal ultrasound examination now make it possible to determine the child's sex early in a pregnancy. There is a fear that some parents may not carry pregnancies

DRAFT: Do not distribute or copy

of girls to term. A study in Punjab, India[4] reports that in 1993 in one hospital 56.9% of the 550 live births that year were boys. It is a medical fact that male babies are slightly more common than female babies. The authors report a baseline for this region of 51.7% male live births. Is the sample proportion of 56.9% evidence of a change in the percentage of male births?

There are four main steps to performing a hypothesis test:

Think

Hypotheses State what we want to know.

The **Null Hypothesis** makes the claim of no difference from the baseline

We are interested only in an increase in male births, so the **Alternative Hypothesis** is one-sided.

We want to know whether the proportion of male births has increased from the established baseline of 51.7%. The parameter of interest is the proportion of male births.

H_0: $p = .517$

H_A: $p > .517$

Plan

a) Check the **conditions**

For testing proportions, the conditions are the same ones we had for making confidence intervals except that we check the success/failure condition with the *hypothesized* proportions rather than with the *observed* proportions.

✓ **Independence Assumption** There is no reason to think that the sex of one birth can affect the sex of other babies, so births can reasonably be assumed to be independent with regard to the sex of the child.

✓ **Random sampling condition:** The 550 live births are not a random sample. This may influence our ability to extend our conclusions beyond the births studied.

✓ **10% Condition:** We would like to be able to make statements about births at this hospital or at similar hospitals in India. These 550 births are less than 10% of all of those births.

---

[4] "Fetal sex determination in infants in Punjnab, India: correlations and implications", E.E. Booth, M. Verma, R.S. Beri, *BMJ* 1994;309:1259-1261 (12 November)

✓ **Success/Failure Condition:** Both $np_0 = 550(.517) = 284.35$ and $nq_0 = 550(.483) = 265.65$ are greater than 10; we expect the births of more than 10 boys and more than 10 girls, so the sample is large enough.

b) Specify the sampling distribution.

Because the conditions are satisfied, it is appropriate to model the sampling distribution of the proportion with a $N(p_0, SD(p_0))$ model.

c) Tell what test you plan to use.

We can perform a **one proportion z-test**.

Show   Mechanics:

The null model gives us the mean and (because we are working with proportions) the mean gives us the standard deviation.

The null model is a normal distribution with a mean of .517 and a standard deviation of

$$\sqrt{\frac{0.517 \times (1 - 0.517)}{550}} = 0.021.$$

We next find the z-score for the observed proportion to find out how many standard deviations it is from the hypothesized proportion.

The observed proportion, $\hat{p}$, is 0.569.

So the z-value is :

$$z = \frac{0.569 - 0.517}{0.021} = 2.44$$

From the z-score we can find the P-value, which tells us the probability of observing a value that extreme (or more).

so the sample proportion lies 2.44 standard deviations above the mean.

The probability of observing a value 2.44 standard deviations above the mean of a Normal model or higher can be found by computer, calculator, or table (see the table below), to be .0073.

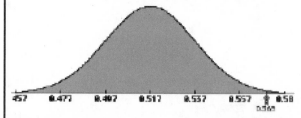

The corresponding P-value is 0073.

Tell   Conclusion: State the conclusion.

The P-value of .0073 says that if the true proportion of male babies were still at 51.7%, then an observed proportion of 56.9% male babies would

We should be careful here not to jump to any conclusions. Our P-

DRAFT: Do not distribute or copy

value is roughly at the level of 1 time in 150. We can't be sure how this deviation came about, whether this hospital is typical, or whether the time period studied was selected randomly.

occur at random only about 7 times in 1000. This suggests that the birth ratio of boys to girls is not equal to its natural level, but rather has increased.

Here is a portion of a Normal table that includes the part that gives the probability we needed for the test.

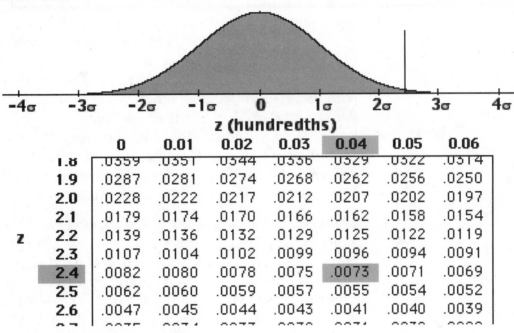

z (hundredths)	0	0.01	0.02	0.03	0.04	0.05	0.06
1.8	.0359	.0351	.0344	.0336	.0329	.0322	.0314
1.9	.0287	.0281	.0274	.0268	.0262	.0256	.0250
2.0	.0228	.0222	.0217	.0212	.0207	.0202	.0197
2.1	.0179	.0174	.0170	.0166	.0162	.0158	.0154
2.2	.0139	.0136	.0132	.0129	.0125	.0122	.0119
2.3	.0107	.0104	.0102	.0099	.0096	.0094	.0091
2.4	.0082	.0080	.0078	.0075	.0073	.0071	.0069
2.5	.0062	.0060	.0059	.0057	.0055	.0054	.0052
2.6	.0047	.0045	.0044	.0043	.0041	.0040	.0039

P-Values and Decisions: What to Tell About a Hypothesis Test

Tell More

Hypothesis tests are particularly useful when we must make a decision. Is the defendant to be considered guilty or not? Should we choose print advertising or television? Questions like these cannot always be answered with the margins of error of confidence intervals. But the absolute nature of the hypothesis test decision makes some people (including the authors) uneasy. If possible, it is often a good idea to report the confidence interval for the parameter of interest as well.

"Extraordinary claims require extraordinary proof"
-- Carl Sagan

How small should the P-value be in order for you to reject the null hypothesis? A jury needs enough evidence to show the defendant guilty "beyond a reasonable doubt". How does that translate to P-values? The answer is that it is highly context dependent. When we are screening for a disease and want to be sure we treat all those who are sick, we may be willing to reject the null hypothesis of no disease with a fairly large P-value. But a long-standing hypothesis, believed by many to be true, needs stronger evidence (and a correspondingly small P-value) to reject it.

See if you require the same P-value to reject each of the following null hypotheses:

- A renowned musicologist claims that she can distinguish between the works of Mozart and Haydn simply by hearing a randomly selected 20 seconds of music from any work by either composer. What's the null hypothesis? If she's just guessing, she'll get 50% of the pieces correct on average. So our null hypothesis is that p is 50%. If she's for real, she'll get more than 50% correct. Now, we present her with 10 pieces of Mozart or Haydn chosen at random. She gets 9 out of 10 correct. It turns out that the P-value associated with that result is 0.01. (In other words, if you tried to just guess, you'd get at least 9 out of 10 correct only about 1% of the time). What would *you* conclude? Most people would probably reject the null hypothesis and be convinced that she has some ability to do as she claims. Why? Because the P-value is small, and we don't have any particular reason to doubt the alternative.

- On the other hand, imagine a student who bets that he can make a flipped coin land the way he wants just by thinking hard. To test him we flip a fair coin 10 times. He gets 9 out of 10 right. This also has a P-value of .01. Are you willing now to reject the null hypothesis? Are you convinced that he's not just lucky? What amount of evidence *would* convince you? We require more evidence when rejecting the null hypotheses would contradict longstanding beliefs or other scientific results. Of course, with sufficient evidence we would revise our opinions (and scientific theories). That's how science makes progress.

Another reason to consider in choosing a P-value is the importance of the issue being tested. Consider the following two tests:

- A researcher claims that the proportion of college students who hold part-time jobs now is higher than the proportion known to hold such jobs a decade ago. You might be willing to believe the claim (and reject the null hypothesis of no change) with a P-value of 10%.

- An engineer claims that the proportion of rivets holding the wing on an airplane that are likely to fail is below the proportion at which the wing would fall off. What P-value would be small enough to get you to fly on that plane?

Your conclusion about any null hypothesis should be accompanied by the P-value of the test. And if possible, it should include a confidence interval for the parameter of interest. Don't just declare the null hypothesis rejected or not rejected. Report the P-value to show the

DRAFT: Do not distribute or copy

strength of the evidence against the hypothesis. This will let each reader decide whether or not to reject the null hypothesis.

Tests and Intervals Step by Step: Root, Root, Root for the Home Team?

Nelly Kelly loved baseball games,
Knew the players, knew all their names,
You could see her there ev'ry day,
Shout "Hurray" when they'd play.
Her boy friend by the name of Joe
Said, "To Coney Isle, dear, let's go,"
Then Nelly started to fret and pout,
And to him I heard her shout...

Anyone who plays or watches sports has heard of the "home field advantage". Teams tend to win more often when they play at home. Or do they? In the 2002 Major League Baseball season, there were 2425 regular season games.

Let's consider two related questions. First, we wonder whether there actually is a home field advantage. Every team plays roughly half of their games at home, half away. We'd expect, on average, that the home team should win half the games if there was no home field advantage. . In the 2002 Major League Baseball season, there were 2425 regular season games. It turns out that the home team won in 1314 of the 2425 games, or 54.2% of the time. Could this deviation from 50% be explained just from natural sampling variability, or is this evidence to suggest that there really is a home field advantage, at least in professional baseball?

But we might also want to know how large the advantage might be. We might be able to discern a statistically significant difference from 50% for the entire league, but it might nevertheless amount to less than a one game difference for any particular team—no big deal. So we'll also want a confidence interval.

"Take me out to the ball game,
Take me out with the crowd.
Buy me some peanuts and Cracker Jack,
I don't care if I never get back,
Let me root, root, **root for the home team,**
If they don't win it's a shame.
For it's one, two, three strikes, you're out,
At the old ball game."

Tests and intervals are closely related. But for proportions, they are not quite identical calculations. Seeing them together step-by-step helps to show their similarities and differences.

Think		
	Hypotheses State what we want to know.	We want to know whether the home team in professional baseball is more likely to win. The parameter of interest is the proportion of home team wins. With no advantage, we'd expect that proportion to be .50.
	The **Null Hypothesis** makes the claim of no difference from the baseline	
	We are interested only in a home field *advantage,* so the **Alternative Hypothesis** is one-sided.	Ho: $p = .50$ H_A: $p > .50$
Plan		✓ **Independence Assumption**

Check the **conditions**

Generally, the outcome of one game has no effect on the outcome of another game. But this may not always be strictly true. For example, if a key player is injured, the probability that the team will win in the next couple of games may decrease slightly, but independence is still roughly true.

✓ **Random sampling condition:** We have results for all 2425 games of the 2002 season. But we aren't just interested in 2002, and those games, while not randomly selected, are a reasonable representative sample of all recent professional baseball games.

✓ **10% Condition:** These 2425 games are less than 10% of all games.

✓ **Success/Failure Condition:** All of $np_0 = 2425(.50) = 1212.5$,

✓ $nq_0 = 2425(.50) = 1212.5$,

Specify the sampling distribution.

Because the conditions are satisfied, it is appropriate to model the sampling distribution of the proportion with a $N(p_0, SD(p_0))$ model.

Tell what test you plan to use.

We can perform a **one proportion z-test.**

Show **Mechanics:**

The null model gives us the mean and (because we are working with proportions) the mean gives us the standard deviation.

The null model is a normal distribution with a mean of .50 and a standard deviation of $\sqrt{\dfrac{0.5 \times (1 - 0.5)}{2425}} = 0.010$.

The observed proportion, $\hat{p}$, is 0.542.

So the z-value is :

We next find the z-score for the observed proportion to find out how many standard deviations it

$z = \dfrac{0.542 - 0.5}{0.01} = 4.2$.

DRAFT: Do not distribute or copy

is from the hypothesized proportion.

From the z-score we can find the P-value, which tells us the probability of observing a value that extreme (or more).

The probability of observing a value 4.2 standard deviations above the mean of a Normal model or higher can be found by computer, calculator, or table, to be < .0001.

The sample proportion lies 4.2 standard deviations above the mean.

The corresponding P-value is < .0001.

Tell

The P-value of <.0001 says that if the true proportion home teams wins were .50, then the observed value of .542 or larger would occur less than 1 out of 10,000 times. This suggests that the true proportion of home team wins is not 50%, and that there is a home field advantage.

Think Again

How big a difference are we talking about? Let's find a confidence interval for the home field advantage.

Plan

Check the **conditions**

The conditions are identical to those for the hypothesis test, with one difference. Now we are not given a hypothesized proportion, p_0, so we must instead work with the observed proportion $\hat{p}$.

Specify the sampling distribution. Notice that now the parameters are based on the observed proportion and its *standard error.*

Tell what method you plan to use.

✓ **Success/Failure Condition:** $n\hat{p} = 1314$ and

✓ $n\hat{q} = 1111$ are greater than 10.

Because the conditions are satisfied, it is appropriate to model the sampling distribution of the proportion with a $N(\hat{p},\ SE(\hat{p}))$ model.

We can find a **one-porportion z-interval.**

Show
More

Mechanics:

We can't find the sampling model standard deviation from the null model proportion (In fact we've just rejected it.) Instead, we find the standard error of $\hat{p}$ from the *observed* proportions. Other than that substitution, the calculation looks the same as for the hypothesis test.

With this large a sample size, the difference is negligible, but in smaller samples, it could make a bigger difference.

$$SE(\hat{p}) = \sqrt{\frac{0.542 \times (1 - 0.542)}{2425}} = 0.010:$$

The sampling model is Normal, so for a 95% Confidence interval, the critical value $z* = 1.96$.

The margin of error is
m.o.e. $= z* \times SE(\hat{p}) = 1.96 \times 0.010 = .0196$

So the 95% confidence interval is:
$.542 \pm 0.0196$ or $(0.522, 0.562)$

Tell All

Conclusion:

Confidence intervals help us think about the size of the effect. Here we can see that the home field advantage probably affects enough games to make a real difference.

We are 95% confident that in professional baseball the true proportion of home team wins is between 52.2 and 56.2%.

In a season of 162 games, even the low end of this interval represents about 7 games more won at home than away.

What Can Go Wrong

Hypothesis tests are so widely used — and so widely misused — that we've devoted the next chapter to discussing the issues involved.

Hypothesis Tests for Proportions and the Computer

Hypothesis tests for proportions are as easy and natural as the corresponding confidence intervals. So you really can't do them on the computer either. Chapter 19 discusses more of the details.

Connections

Hypothesis tests and confidence intervals share many of the same concepts. Both rely on sampling distribution models and because the models are the same and require the same assumptions both check the same conditions. They also calculate many of the same statistics. Tests, like confidence intervals, use the standard deviation (of the sampling distribution) as a ruler.

For testing, we find ourselves looking once again at z-scores, and we compute the P-value based on the distance of our test statistic from the

DRAFT: Do not distribute or copy

center of the null model. P-values are conditional probabilities. They give the probability of observing the result we have seen (or one even more extreme) *given* that the null hypothesis is true.

The Normal model is here again as our connection between z-score values and probabilities.

Key Concepts

Null Hypothesis	The claim being assessed in a hypothesis test is called the null hypothesis. Usually the null hypothesis is a statement of "no change from the traditional value", "no effect", "no difference", or "no relationship." For a claim to be a testable null hypothesis it must specify a value for some population parameter that can form the basis for assuming a sampling distribution for a test statistic.
Alternative Hypothesis	The alternative hypothesis proposes what we should conclude if we find the null hypothesis to be unlikely.
Two-sided Alternative	An alternative hypothesis is two-sided when we are interested in deviations in *either* direction away from the hypothesize parameter value.
One-sided Alternative	An alternative hypothesis is one-sided when we are interested in deviations in *only one* direction away from the hypothesize parameter value.
P-value	The probability of observing a value for a test statistic at least as far from the hypothesized value as the statistic value actually observed. A small P-value indicates either that the observation is improbable or that the probability calculation was based on incorrect assumptions. The assumed truth of the null hypothesis is the assumption under suspicion.
One proportion z-test	A test of the null hypothesis that the proportion of a single sample equals a specified value (H_0: $p = p_0$). The alternative may be one-sided (H_A: $p > p_0$ or H_A: $p < p_0$) or two-sided (H_A: $p \neq p_0$).

Skills:

Upon completing this Lesson you should:

> *Think*
>
> - Be able to state the null and alternative hypotheses for a one-proportion z-test.
>
> - Know the conditions that must be true for a one-proportion z-test to be appropriate and how to examine your data for violations of those conditions.
>
> - Be able to identify and use the Alternative Hypothesis when testing hypotheses. Understand how to choose between a one-sided and two-sided alternative hypothesis and know how to defend the choice of a one-sided alternative.
>
> *Show*
>
> - Perform a one-proportion z-test.
>
> *Tell*
>
> - Be able to write a sentence interpreting the results of a one-proportion z-test.
>
> - Interpret the meaning of a P-value in non-technical language, making clear that the probability claim is made about computed values and not about the population parameter of interest.

Exercises

1. **Hypotheses** Write the null and alternative hypotheses you would use to test each of the following situations.
   a) A governor is concerned about his "negatives" – the percentage of state residents who express disapproval of his job performance. His political committee pays for a series of TV ads, hoping that they can keep the negatives below 30%. They will use follow-up polling to assess the ads' effectiveness.
   b) Is a coin fair?
   c) Only about 20% of the people who try to quit smoking succeed. Sellers of a motivational tape claim that listening to the recorded messages can help people quit.

2. **More Hypotheses** Write the null and alternative hypotheses you would use to test each of the following situations.
   a) In the 1950s only about 40% of high school graduates went on to college. Has the percentage changed?
   b) 20% of cars of a certain model have needed costly transmission work after being driven between 50,000 and 100,000 miles. The

DRAFT: Do not distribute or copy

manufacturer hopes that redesign of a transmission component has solved this problem.

c) We fieldtest a new flavor soft drink, planning to market it only if we are sure that at least 60% of the people like the flavor.

3. **Negatives** After the political ad campaign described in Exercise 1a, pollsters check the governor's negatives. They test the hypothesis that the ads produced no change against the alternative that the negatives are now below 30%, and find a P-value of 0.22. Which conclusion is appropriate?
a) There is a 22% chance that the ads worked.
b) There is a 78% chance the ads worked.
c) There is a 22% chance that the poll they conducted is correct.
d) There is a 22% chance that poll results could be just natural sampling variation rather than a real change in public opinion.

4. **Dice** The seller of a loaded die claims that it will favor the outcome 6. We don't believe that claim, and roll the die 200 times to test an appropriate hypothesis. Our P-value turns out to be 0.03. Which conclusion is appropriate?
a) There is a 3% chance the die is fair.
b) There is a 97% chance the die is fair.
c) There is a 3% chance that a loaded die could randomly produce the results we observed so it is reasonable to conclude that the die is fair.
d) There is a 3% chance that a fair die could randomly produce the results we observed so it is reasonable to conclude the die is loaded.

5. **Relief** A company's old antacid formula provided relief for 70% of the people who used it. They test a new formula to see if it is better, and get a P-value of 0.27. Is it reasonable to conclude that the new formula and the old one are equally effective? Explain.

6. **Cars** A survey investigating whether the proportion of today's high school seniors that own their own cars is higher than it was decade ago finds a P-value of 0.017. Is it reasonable to conclude that more high-schoolers have cars? Explain.

7. **Blinking Timers** Many people have trouble programming their VCR's, so a company has developed what they hope will be easier instructions. Their goal is to have at least 96% of their customers succeed. They test the new system on 200 people, of whom 188 were successful. Is this strong evidence that the new system fails to meet the company's goal? A student's test of this hypothesis is shown below. How many mistakes can you find?

$$H_0: \hat{p} = 0.96$$

$$H_a: \hat{p} \neq 0.96$$

SRS, .96(200) >10

$$\frac{188}{200} = 0.94 \qquad SD(\hat{p}) = \sqrt{\frac{(.94)(.06)}{200}} = 0.017$$

$$z = \frac{0.96 - 0.94}{0.017} = 1.18$$

$$P = P(z > 1.18) = 12\%$$

There is strong evidence that the new system does not work.

8. **Got milk?** In November 2001 The Ag Globe Trotter newsletter reported that 90% of adults drink milk. A regional farmers' organization planning a new marketing campaign across their multi-county area polls a random sample of 750 adults living there. In this sample, 657 people said that they drink milk. Do these responses provide strong evidence that the 90% figure is not accurate for this region? Correct the mistakes you find in a student's attempt to test an appropriate hypothesis.

$H_0: \hat{p} = 0.9$

$H_a: \hat{p} < 0.9$

SRS, 750 >10

$$\frac{657}{750} = 0.876; \quad SD(\hat{p}) = \sqrt{\frac{(.88)(.12)}{750}} = 0.012$$

$$z = \frac{0.876 - 0.94}{0.012} = -2$$

$$P = P(z > -2) = 0.977$$

There is over a 97% chance that the stated percentage is correct for this region.

9. **Dowsing** In a rural area only about 30% of the wells that are drilled find adequate water at a depth of 100 feet or less. A local man claims to be able to find water by "dowsing" – using a forked stick to indicate where the well should be drilled. You check with 80 of his customers and find that 27 have wells less than 100 feet deep. What do you conclude about his claim? (We consider a P-value of around 5% to represent strong evidence.)
   a) Write appropriate hypotheses.
   b) Check the necessary assumptions.
   c) Perform the mechanics of the test. What is the P-value?
   d) Explain carefully what the P-value means in this context.
   e) What is your conclusion?

10. **Autism** In the 1980s it was generally believed that autism affected about 5% of the nation's children. Some people believe that the increase in the number of chemicals in the environment has led to an increase in the incidence of autism. A recent study examined 384 children and found that 46 of them showed signs of some form of autism. Is this strong evidence that the level of autism has increased? (We consider a P-value of around 5% to represent strong evidence.)
    a) Write appropriate hypotheses.
    b) Check the necessary assumptions.
    c) Perform the mechanics of the test. What is the P-value?
    d) Explain carefully what the P-value means in this context.
    e) What is your conclusion?
    f) Do environmental chemicals cause autism?

11. **Smoking** National data in the 1960s showed that about 44% of the adult population had never smoked cigarettes. In 1995 a national health survey interviewed a random sample of 881 adults and found that 52% had never been smokers.
    a) Create a 95% confidence interval for the proportion of adults (in 1995) who had never been smokers.
    b) Does this provide evidence of a change in behavior among Americans? Using your confidence interval, test an appropriate hypothesis and state your conclusion.

12. **Satisfaction** A company hopes to improve customer satisfaction, setting as a goal no more than 5% negative comments. A random survey of 350 customers found only 10 with complaints.
    a) Create a 95% confidence interval for the true level of dissatisfaction among customers.
    b) Does this provide evidence that the company has reached their goal? Using your confidence interval, test an appropriate hypothesis and state your conclusion.

13. **Pollution** A company with a fleet of 150 cars found that the emissions systems of 7 out of the 22 they tested failed to meet pollution control guidelines. Is this strong evidence that over 20% of the fleet might be out of compliance? Test an appropriate hypothesis and state your conclusion. Be sure the appropriate assumptions and conditions are satisfied before you proceed.

14. **Scratch and Dent** An appliance manufacturer stockpiles washers and dryers in a large warehouse for shipment to retail stores. Sometimes in handling them the appliances get damaged. Even though the damage may be minor the company must sell those machines at drastically reduced prices. The company goal is to keep the level of damaged machines below 2%. One day an inspector randomly checks 60 washers and finds that 5 of them have scratches or dents. Is this strong evidence

that the warehouse is failing to meet the company goal? Test an appropriate hypothesis and state your conclusion. Be sure the appropriate assumptions and conditions are satisfied before you proceed.

15. **Twins** In 2001 a national vital statistics report indicated that about 3% of all births produced twins. Data from a large city hospital found only 7 sets of twins were born to 469 teenage girls. Does that suggest that mothers under age 20 may be less likely to have twins? Test an appropriate hypothesis and state your conclusion. Be sure the appropriate assumptions and conditions are satisfied before you proceed.

16. **Football** During the 2000 season, the home team won 138 of the 240 regular season National Football League games. Is this strong evidence of a home team advantage in professional football? Test an appropriate hypothesis and state your conclusion. Be sure the appropriate assumptions and conditions are satisfied before you proceed.

17. **WebZine** A magazine is considering launching an online edition. They plan to go ahead only if they are convinced that at least 25% of their current readers would subscribe. They contact a simple random sample of 500 current subscribers, and 137 of those surveyed expressed interest. What should the company do? Test an appropriate hypothesis and state your conclusion. Be sure the appropriate assumptions and conditions are satisfied before you proceed.

18. **Seeds** A garden store wants to store leftover packets of vegetable seeds for sale the following spring, but they are concerned that the seeds may not germinate at the same rate a year later. They find a packet of last year's green bean seeds and plant them as a test. Although the packet claims a germination rate of 92%, only 171 of 200 test seeds sprout. Is this evidence that the seeds have lost viability during a year in storage? Test an appropriate hypothesis and state your conclusion. Be sure the appropriate assumptions and conditions are satisfied before you proceed.

19. **Women Executives** A company is criticized because only 13 of 43 people in executive level positions are women. The company explains that although this proportion is lower than they might wish, it is not surprising given that only 40% of all their employees are women. What do you think? Test an appropriate hypothesis and state your conclusion. Be sure the appropriate assumptions and conditions are satisfied before you proceed.

20. **Jury** Census data for a certain county shows that 19% of the adult residents are Hispanic. Suppose 72 people are called for jury duty, and only 9 of them are Hispanic. Does this call into question the fairness of the jury selection system? Explain.

DRAFT: Do not distribute or copy

21. **Dropouts** Some people are concerned that new tougher standards and high stakes tests adopted in many states may drive up the high school dropout rate. The National Center for Education Statistics reported that the high school dropout rate for the year 2000 was 10.9%. One school district, whose dropout rate has always been very close to the national average, reports that 21 of their 1782 students dropped out last year. Is their experience evidence that the dropout rate may be increasing? Explain.

22. **Acid Rain** A study of the effects of acid rain on trees in the Hopkins forest shows that of 100 trees sampled, 25 of them showed some sort of damage from acid rain. This seemed to be higher than the 15% quoted in a recent *Environmetrics* article on the average proportion of damaged trees in the Northeast. Does the sample suggest that trees in the Hopkins forest are more susceptible than the rest of the region? Comment, and write up your own conclusions based on an appropriate confidence interval as well as a test of a hypothesis. Include any assumptions you made about the data.

23. **Lost Luggage** An airline's public relations department says that they rarely lose passengers' luggage. They further claim that on those occasions when luggage is lost, 90% is recovered and delivered to its owner within 24 hours. A consumer group who surveyed a large number of air travelers found that only 103 of 122 people who lost luggage on that airline were reunited with the missing items by the next day. Does this cast doubt on the airline's claim? Explain.

24. **TV Ads** A startup company is about to market a new computer printer. They decide to gamble by running commercials during the Super Bowl. They hope that the name recognition will be worth the high cost of the ads. Their goal is that at least 40% of the public recognize their brand name and associate it with computer equipment. The day after the game, a pollster contacts 420 randomly chosen adults, and finds that 181 of them know that this company manufactures printers. Would you recommend that the company continue to advertise during Super Bowls? Explain.

21 More About Tests

Who: Trials of TT
practitioners
attempting to detect a
HEF.
What: success/failure
When: 1998 pub date
Why?: test claim of
HEF/debunk TT?

HERAPEUTIC TOUCH (TT) IS A THERAPY, TAUGHT IN MANY SCHOOLS OF NURSING, in which the practitioner moves her hands near to, but not touching, a patient in an attempt to manipulate a "human energy field."(HEF). Therapeutic Touch practitioners believe that by adjusting this field they can promote healing. However, no instrument has ever detected a "human energy field" and no experiment has ever shown that TT practitioners can detect such a field.

In 1998 the *Journal of the American Medical Association* published a paper reporting work by a then 9-year-old girl[1]. She had performed a simple experiment in which she challenged 15 TT practitioners to detect whether her unseen hand was hovering over their left or right hand (selected by a coin flip.) Each practitioner "warmed up" with a period during which they could see the experimenter's hand and each said that they could detect her human energy field. Then a screen was placed so that they could not see her hand, and they attempted 10 trials each. Overall, of 150 trials, the TT practitioners were successful 70 times, for a success proportion of 46.7%. Is there evidence from this experiment that TT practitioners can successfully detect a "human energy field"?

Zero In on the Null

Null hypotheses have special requirements. In order to perform a statistical test of the hypothesis, the null must be a statement about the value of a parameter from a model. We use this value to compute the probability that the observed sample statistic--or something even farther from the null value--would occur.

How do we choose the null hypothesis? The appropriate null arises directly from the context of the problem. It is not dictated by the data, but instead by the situation.

One good way to identify both the null and alternative hypotheses is to think about the "Why?" of the situation. A pharmaceutical company wanting to develop and market a new drug needs to show that the new drug is effective. The Federal Drug Administration (FDA) will not allow a new drug to be sold in the United States that has not been proven to be

---

[1]Rosa L, Rosa E, Sarner L, Barrett S, "A close look at therapeutic touch" *JAMA* 1998 Apr 1;279(13):1005-10

In the 1930's a series of experiments was performed at Duke University in an attempt to see whether humans were capable of extra sensory perception or ESP. To do this, a set of cards with 5 symbols, made famous in the movie *Ghostbusters*, were used.

In the experiment the "sender" selects one of the 5 cards at random from a deck and then concentrates on it. The "receiver" tries to determine which card it is. If we let p be the proportion of correct responses, what is the null hypothesis? Since there are 5 possible responses, H_0 would be $p=0.20$. What is the alternative? It seems that it should be $p > .20$, a one-sided alternative. But some ESP researchers have expressed the claim that if the proportion guessed were much *lower*

effective in a double blind, randomized clinical trial. (Most countries have similar restrictions on the introduction of new medications). The typical null hypothesis in this case is that the proportion of patients recovering after receiving the new drug is the same as we would expect of patients receiving a placebo. The alternative hypothesis is that the new drug cures a higher proportion. But a physician seeking the best treatment for her patients would probably prefer to see the new drug tested against a currently available treatment.

To write a null hypothesis you can't just choose any parameter value you like. The null must relate to the question at hand. Nor can you automatically interpret "null" to mean zero. A claim that the TT practitioners should guess correctly *none of the time* would be absurd. The null hypothesis in this case is that the proportion of correct responses is 0.5, what you'd expect from random guessing. You need to find the value for the parameter in the null hypothesis from the context of the problem.

There is a temptation to state your claim as the null hypothesis. But, as we have seen, you cannot prove a null hypothesis to be true any more than you can prove a defendant innocent. So, it makes more sense to use what you want to show as the *alternative*. This way, when you reject the null, you are left with what you want to show.

Another One-Proportion z-Test Step-by-Step

Let's look at the Therapeutic Touch experiment with a one-proportion z-test.

Think

Hypotheses:

The null hypothesis is that the TT practitioners are just guessing. Because there are two choices, if the practitioners are just guessing, they'll succeed about half the time.

A one-sided alternative hypothesis seems the natural one to test here. We wouldn't be interested in below chance performance.

We want to know whether the TT practitioners could detect a "human energy field" at better than chance levels. The parameter of interest is the proportion of successful identifications.

H_0: $p = .50$

H_A: $p > .50$

DRAFT: Do not distribute or copy

Plan

Check the **conditions**

✓ **Random sampling condition:** The experiment was randomized by flipping a coin.

✓ **10% Condition:** The experiment observes some of what could be an infinite number of trials.

✓ **Success/Failure condition:** Both $np_0 = 150(.5) = 75$ and $nq_0 = 150(.5)$ are greater than 10, showing that we expect more than 10 successes and more than 10 failures.

State the **Null Model.**

Because the conditions are satisfied, it is appropriate to model the sampling distribution of the proportion with a $N(p_0, SD(p_0))$ model.

Name the test.

We can perform a **one proportion z-test.**

Show   **Mechanics**

We use the null model to find the **P-value**.

The null model has a mean of .5 and a standard deviation of

$$\sqrt{\frac{0.5 \times 0.5}{150}} = 0.04.$$

The observed proportion, $\hat{p}$, is 0.467.

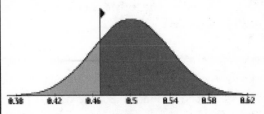

The P-value is the probability of observing a sample proportion as large as 0.467 (or larger) if the true proportion were 0.5.

The probability of observing a value .825 standard deviations below the mean of a Normal model or higher can be found by computer, calculator, or table (see

The observed value has a z-score of $z = \dfrac{.467 - .5}{.4} = -0.825$, so it is .825 standard deviations below the hypothesized mean.

the table below), to be .795.

Tell   **Conclusion:** State the conclusion.

If possible, propose a course of action.

In the case of this study, the editor of the *Journal* of the American Medical Association suggested that insurance companies reconsider paying for Therapeutic Touch treatments. This, of course, raised a storm of protest letters from those who practice TT.

The corresponding P-value is 0.795.

The P-value of 0.795 says that if the true proportion of successful detections of a human energy field is 50%, then an observed proportion of 46.7% successes or more would occur at random about 8 times in 10 — hardly a rare event. Therefore, we fail to reject the null hypothesis. There is insufficient evidence to conclude that the practitioners are performing better than they would if they were just guessing.

How to Think about P-values

A P-value is a conditional probability. It is the probability of the observed statistic *given* that the null hypothesis is true. To show this more clearly, we can write P-value = P[observed statistic value (or more extreme) | H_0].

Suppose that as a political science major you are offered the chance to be a White House intern. There would be a very high probability that next summer you'll be in Washington D.C. But if we find a student in Washington D.C. next summer, it is likely that they are a White House intern? Almost surely not. You can't switch around conditional probabilities. The P-value is P(data | H_0). What we might like to report is P(H_0 | data). But these two quantities are NOT the same.

Writing the P-value this way helps to make clear that the P-value is *not* the probability that the null hypothesis is true. It is a probability about the data. Let's say that again:

The P-value is not the probability that the null hypothesis is true.

The P-value is not even the probability that the null hypothesis is true *given* the data. We would write that probability as P[H_0 | observed statistic value]. This is the conditional probability in reverse. It would be nice to know this, but it is impossible to calculate without making additional assumptions. As we saw in TB test example of Chapter 15, reversing the order in a conditional probability is

Intuitively, smaller and smaller P-values lead us to doubt the null hypothesis more and more. But we cannot put a number on that doubt. We've agreed that extraordinary claims require stronger evidence. We've seen that we may not be willing to reject all claims with the same P-value. (recall the example of the musicologist and the student claiming mental control over a coin flip). Why was this? Because P(H0 | data) depends on our initial beliefs about P(H0). But we have no way to quantify P(H0).

difficult and the results can be counter-intuitive.

We can find the P-value, $P[\text{data} \mid H_0]$, because H_0 gives the parameter values that we need to find the required probability. But there is no direct way to find $P[H_0 \mid \text{data}]$.[2] As tempting as it may be to say that a P-value of .03 means that there is a 3% chance that the null hypothesis is true, that just isn't right. All we can say is that given the null hypothesis there is a 3% chance of observing what we have actually observed.

Alpha Levels

Where did the value 0.05 come from? In 1931 in a famous book called *The Design of Experiments*, Sir Ronald Fisher discussed the amount of evidence needed to reject a null hypothesis. He said that it was *situation dependent*, but remarked, somewhat casually, that for many scientific applications, 1 out of 20 *might be* a reasonable value. Since then, some people, indeed some entire disciplines, have acted as if the number 0.05 is sacrosanct.

A jury must decide whether the evidence reaches the level of "beyond a reasonable doubt". A business must which web design to use. Sometimes we just need to make a decision about whether or not to reject the null hypothesis.

When the P-value is small it tells us that our data are rare given the null hypothesis. But we are suspicious of rare events. If the data are "rare enough" we just don't think that could have happened. Since the data *did* happen, something must be wrong. All we can do now is to reject the null hypothesis.

But how rare is "rare"?

We can define "rare event" arbitrarily by setting a threshold for our P-value. If our P-value falls below that point we'll reject the null hypothesis. We call such results **statistically significant**. The threshold is called an **alpha level**. Not surprisingly, it is labeled with the Greek letter α. Common alpha levels are .10, .05, and .01. You have the option – almost the *obligation* — to consider your alpha level carefully and choose an appropriate one for the situation. If you're assessing the safety of airbags, you'll want a low alpha level; even .01 might not be low enough. If you're just wondering whether folks prefer their pizza with or without pepperoni, you might be happy with $\alpha = .10$. But it can be hard to justify your choice, so often we arbitrarily choose .05.

The alpha level is also called the *significance level*. When we reject the null hypothesis, we say that the test is "significant at that alpha level". We might claim to reject the null hypothesis "at the 5% level of significance."

You must select the alpha level *before* you look at the data. Otherwise you can be accused of cheating by tuning your alpha level to suit the data.

But what if the P-value does not fall below α?

---

[2] The approach to statistical inference known as Bayesian statistics addresses the question in just this way. But it requires more advanced methods.

When you have not found sufficient evidence to reject the null according to the standard you have established, and you should say that "The data have failed to provide sufficient evidence to reject the null hypothesis." Don't say that you "accept the null hypothesis." You certainly haven't proven or established it; it was assumed to begin with. In this case you *can* say that you have *retained* the null hypothesis, or simply that you've failed to reject it.

Look again at the Step-by-Step example for Therapeutic Touch. The P-value was .795. This is so much larger than any reasonable α-level that we can't reject H_0. We concluded that "we fail to reject the null hypothesis. There is insufficient evidence to conclude that the practitioners are performing better than they would if they were just guessing."

The wise man proportions his belief to the evidence. -- David Hume *Enquiry Concerning Human Understanding, 1748.*

The absolute nature of the reject/fail-to-reject decision when we use an alpha level may make you uncomfortable. If your P-value falls just slightly above your alpha level you may not reject the null. Yet a P-value just barely below the alpha level leads to rejection. If this bothers you, you're in good company. Many statisticians think it better to report the P-value than to choose an alpha level and carry the decision through to a final reject/fail-to-reject verdict. So when you decide to declare a verdict, it is a good idea to report the P-value as an indication of the strength of the evidence.

Of course, if the null hypothesis *is* true, no matter what alpha level you choose, you still have a probability α of rejecting the null hypothesis by mistake. This is the rare event we want to protect ourselves against. When we do reject the null hypothesis, no one ever thinks that *this* is one of those rare times. As statistician Stuart Hunter, notes: *The statistician says "rare events do happen — but not to me!"*

It's in the stars

Some disciplines carry this idea further and code P-values by their size. In this scheme, a P-value between 0.05 and 0.01 gets highlighted by a *. One between 0.01 and 0.001 gets two **, and a P-value less than 0.001 gets ***. This can be a convenient summary of the weight of evidence against the null hypothesis if it's not taken too literally. But we warn you against taking the distinctions too seriously and against making a black and white decision near the boundaries. The boundaries are a matter of tradition, not science; there is nothing special about .05. A P-value of 0.051 should be looked at very seriously and not casually thrown away just because it's larger than 0.05 and one that's 0.009 is not very different from one that's 0.011.

Sometimes it is best to report that the conclusion is not yet very clear and to suggest that more data be gathered. (In a trial, a jury may "hang" and be unable to return a verdict.) In these cases, it is still a good idea to report the P-value since it is the best summary we have of what the data says or fails to say about the null hypothesis.

What Not to Say about Significance

DRAFT: Do not distribute or copy

A large insurance company mines its data and finds a statistically significant (P = .04) difference between the mean value of policies sold in 2001 and 2002. The difference in the mean values was $9.83. Management did not see this as an important difference.

What do we mean when we say that a test is statistically significant? All we mean is that the test statistic had a P-value lower than our a-level. Don't be lulled into thinking that statistical significance carries with it any of the sense of practical importance or impact.

For large samples, even small, unimportant, ("insignificant") deviations from the null hypothesis can be statistically significant. On the other hand, if the sample is not large enough, even large, financially or scientifically "significant" differences may not be statistically significant.

It is good practice to report the magnitude of the difference between the observed statistic value and the null hypothesis value (in the data units) along with the P-value on which we base statistical significance.

Critical Values Again

If you just need to make a decision on the fly with no technology, remember "2". That's our old friend from the 68-95-99.7 rule corresponding to a 2-sided test at α = .05. The exact value is 1.96, but 2 is close enough for most decisions.

Before computers and calculators were common, P-values were hard to find. It was easier to select a few common alpha levels (.05, .01, .001, for example) and learn the corresponding critical values for the Normal model. You could just check your z-score against these values and decide whether to reject the null hypothesis. But with technology, P-values are easy to find. And since they give more information, there's no reason not to report them.

Here are the traditional critical values from the Normal model:

α	1-sided	2-sided
.05	1.64	1.96
.01	2.33	2.58
.001	3.09	3.29

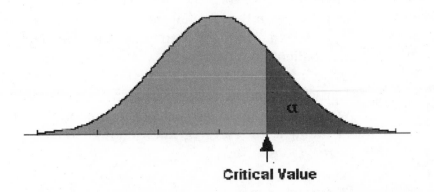

Critical Value

When the alternative is one-sided. the critical value puts all of α on one side.

Copyright © 2001, Dick De Veaux and Paul Velleman

21-7

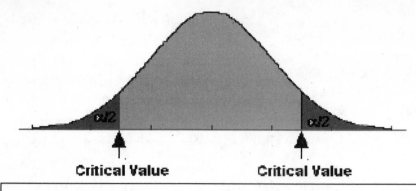

Critical Value **Critical Value**

When the alternative is two-sided, the critical value splits α equally into the two tails.

Making Errors

Nobody's perfect. Even with lots of evidence, we can still reach the wrong decision. In fact, when we perform a hypothesis test, we can make mistakes in *two* ways:

I.   The null hypothesis is true, but we mistakenly reject it.

II. The null hypothesis is false, but we fail to reject it.

These two types of errors are known as Type I and Type II errors. One way to keep the names straight is to remember that we start by assuming the null hypothesis is true, so a Type I error is the first kind of error we could make.

In medical disease testing, the null hypothesis is usually the assumption that a person is healthy. The alternative is that they have the disease we're testing for. So a Type I error is a **false positive.** A healthy person is diagnosed with the disease. A Type II error, in which an infected person is diagnosed as disease-free is a **false negative**. These errors have other names, depending on the particular discipline and context.

A false positive could mean no more than an unnecessary chest X-ray. But for a drug test or a disease like AIDS, a false positive result that is not kept confidential could have serious consequences.

Which error is more serious depends on the situation. In the jury trial, a Type I error occurs if the jury convicts an innocent person. A Type II error occurs if the jury fails to convict a guilty person. Which seems more serious? In medical diagnosis, a false negative could mean that a sick patient goes untreated. A false positive means that the person must undergo further tests. In a statistics final exam (with H_0: the student has learned 60% of the material), a Type I error would be passing a student who in fact learned only 60% of the material, while a Type II error would be failing a student, who knew enough to pass. Which of these errors seems more serious?

Here is an illustration of the situations:

		The Truth	
		H_0 **True**	H_0 **False**
My Decision	**Reject H_0**	Type I error	OK
	Retain H_0	OK	Type II error

How often will a Type I error occur? It happens when the null hypothesis is true, but we've had the bad luck to draw an unusual sample. To reject H_0, the P-value must fall below α –and (since H_0 is true) that happens *exactly* with probability α. So when you choose level α, you are setting the probability of a Type I error to α.

What if H_0 is not true? Then we can't possibly make a Type I error. You can't get a false positive from a sick person. A Type I error can happen only when H_0 is true.

When H_0 is false and we fail to reject it, we have made a Type II error. We assign the letter β to the probability of this mistake. What is the value of β? That's harder to assess than α because we don't know *how false* H_0 is. When H_0 is true, we have one parameter value. But when H_0 false, we don't have one; we have many. We can compute the probability β for any parameter value in H_A. But which one should we choose?

There is no single value for β. In fact, β is a whole collection of values, and it often displayed as a curve, plotting β against each value in H_A. Often we can focus our attention by thinking about the *effect size*. That is, ask yourself *"how big a difference would matter?"* Suppose we want to test whether placing personalized address labels in the envelope along with a request for a donation increases the response rate above the baseline of 5%. If the minimum response that would pay for the address labels is 6%, we would calculate β for $p = .06$.

Of course, we can reduce β for all values in the alternative by increasing α. Making it easier to reject the null means that we're more likely to

Notation Note
This use of α and β can be confusing. In statistics, α is almost always saved for the alpha level. But β's are sometimes used for model regression coefficients. Fortunately, it's usually quite clear which we mean.

reject it whether it is true or not. So we'd reduce β, but we'll make more Type I errors. This tension between Type I and Type II errors is inevitable. In the political arena, think of the ongoing debate between those who favor provisions to reduce Type I errors in the courts (Miranda rights, warrants required for wire taps, legal representation paid by the State if needed, etc.) and those who are concerned that Type II errors have become too common (admitting into evidence confessions made with no lawyer is present, eavesdropping on conferences with lawyers, restricting paths of appeal, etc.)

The only way to reduce *both* types of error is to collect more evidence, or in statistical terms, to collect more data. Otherwise, we just wind up trading off one kind of error against the other. Whenever you design a survey or experiment, it is a good idea to calculate β (for a reasonable α - level). Use a parameter value in the alternative that corresponds to an effect size that you would like to be able to detect. Too often studies fail because their sample sizes are too small to detect the change they are looking for.

> We have seen ways to find a sample size by specifying the margin of error. Estimating β is sometimes more appropriate, but the calculation is more complex and lies beyond the scope of this book.

Power

When the null hypothesis is false, we hope our test is able to reject it. Because this is our main concern, we refer to the probability of rejecting a false null hypothesis as the **Power** of the test. We know that β is the probability that a test fails to reject a false null hypothesis, so the power of the test is just 1 – β. We also know that a larger sample will decrease β (as long as we don't change α), so increasing the sample size will also increase the power.

When a study fails to reject the null hypothesis, the power of the test comes into question. Was the sample size big enough to detect an effect had there been one? That is, might we have missed an effect of an interesting size just because we failed to gather sufficient data?

The Therapeutic Touch experiment failed to reject the null hypothesis that the TT practitioners were just guessing. What if the experiment simply lacked adequate power to detect their ability? Suppose, as an extreme example, that the experimenter had run only 4 trials. Even getting the hand correct 3 out of 4 times would not have provided enough evidence to reject the null. With 10 trials, the practitioners would need to get at least 9 correct to reject the null at α = 0.05.

Suppose you were a health insurance company. Would you pay for Therapeutic Touch if practitioners could detect a Human Energy Field 75% of the time? Let's take that as the effect size (keeping in mind that 50% is the level of guessing). With 150 trials the TT experiment test would have been able to detect such an ability with a power of 99.99%.

DRAFT: Do not distribute or copy

So power was not an issue in this study. There is a very small chance that the study's would have failed to detect a practitioners' ability had it existed. The sample size was clearly big enough.

A Picture Worth $\dfrac{1}{P(z>3.7)}$ Words*3

It makes intuitive sense that the larger the size of the effect we seek, the easier it should be to see it. It also makes sense that the more we're willing to accept a Type I error, the less likely we will be to make a Type II error.

Here is a good way to visualize the relationships among these concepts. Suppose we are testing $H_0: p = p_0$ against the alternative that $H_A: p > p_0.$ We'll reject the null if $\hat{p}$ is big enough. By big enough, we mean $\hat{p} > C$ for some critical value, C. This is what the first picture below shows. Since, in this picture we've assumed the null is true, we make a Type I error whenever $\hat{p} > C$.

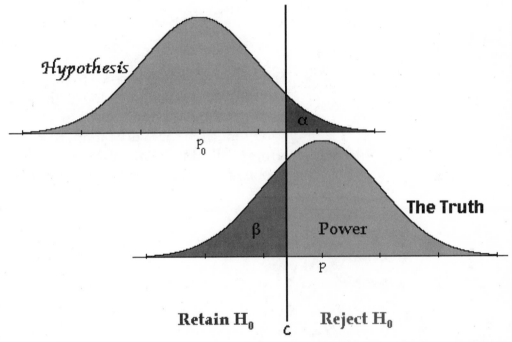

The lower picture supposes that H_0 is not true. In particular, it supposes that p is equal to p_a not $p_0.$ Now when $\hat{p} > C$, we reject H_0 as before. But now (because H_0 isn't true) this is the *right* decision. Looking at the

---

[3] Although you don't need this material to read the rest of the book, if you understand the concept of power, you'll find it much easier to think about choosing a suitable sample size for a study. We encourage you to read this section, but you needn't obsess about it.

bottom distribution, we see how often this happens. That region to the right of C is the power.

Notice that the critical value C doesn't move. We find out where it should be just from the null model and the α–level. There is only one version of the top picture. But we can draw a different bottom picture for each value of p_a. But for all of these, C does not change. We reject H_0 whenever $\hat{p} > C$. How often this happens when H_0 is *false* depends on p_a. We can see the effect on the power from the picture. If p_a were even larger, the power would be larger as well.

If p_a is the true proportion, then we should reject the null hypothesis. The *power* of the test is the probability that we do just that. What's left over in the bottom picture is the probability that we *don't* reject. That would be a Type II error. The chance of that is β.

We can see several important relationships from this figure:

- *Power = 1 - β*

- Reducing α to lower Type I error will have the effect of increasing β, the probability of a Type II error

- The larger the real difference between the hypothesized value, p_0, and the true population value, p, the smaller the chance of making a Type II error and the greater the power of the test. If the two proportions are very far apart, we are unlikely to make any errors at all – but then, we are unlikely to really need a formal hypothesis testing procedure to see such an obvious difference.

Reducing Both Type I and Type II Error*

The figure seems to show that if we reduce Type I error, we automatically must increase Type II error. But there is a way to reduce both. Can you think of it?

If we can make both curves skinnier, as shown in this second figure, then both the probability of Type I

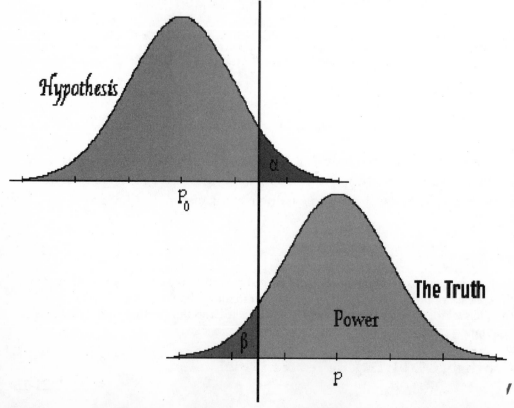

errors and the probability of Type II errors will decrease, and the power of the test will increase.

How can we accomplish that? The only way is to reduce the standard deviations by increasing the sample size. Increasing the sample size works regardless of the true population parameters. But remember the curse of diminishing returns. The standard deviation of the sampling distribution model decreases only as the *square root* of the sample size, so to halve the standard deviations we must *quadruple* the sample size.

Confidence Intervals and Hypothesis Tests

You may have noticed that confidence intervals and hypothesis tests are built from the same calculations. In fact, they are closely related. Both require the same assumptions and conditions. Because confidence intervals are naturally two-sided they correspond to two-sided tests. For example, a 95% confidence interval corresponds to a two-sided hypothesis test at $\alpha = 5\%$. In general, a confidence interval with a confidence level of $C\%$ corresponds to a two-sided hypothesis test with an α-level of $100 - C\%$.

We can ask whether the null hypothesis value is consistent with a confidence interval for the parameter at the corresponding confidence level. A hypothesized parameter value that falls within the interval is consistent with the null. One that is outside the interval would make a null hypothesis that we would reject.[4]

What Can Go Wrong?

- ***Don't change your null hypothesis after you look at the data.*** You may not look at the data first and then adjust your null hypothesis so that it will be rejected. When your sample value $\hat{p}$ turns out to be 51.8% with a standard error of 2%, don't form a null hypothesis of the form $H_0: p = .498$ knowing that you can reject it. Use your understanding of the situation to form the null hypothesis before you look at the data.[5]

---

[4] This is not exactly true for proportions. For a confidence interval, we estimate the standard error from $\hat{p}$. For the corresponding hypothesis test, we use the null hypothesis value p_0. When $\hat{p}$ and p_0 are close, they give very similar results. When they differ, you are likely to reject H_0 (because the observed proportion is far you're your hypothesized value) so you are better off basing your confidence interval on the observed proportion.

[5] It would be even better to form the hypotheses before collecting the data, but that isn't always practical if you are not collecting your own data.

Copyright © 2001, Dick De Veaux and Paul Velleman

- *Don't make what you want to show into your null hypothesis.* Remember, you can reject the null, but you can never "accept" or "prove" the null hypothesis.

- *Don't interpret the P-value as the probability that H_0 is true.* The P-value is about the data, not the hypothesis. It's the probability of the data *given* that H_0 is true, not the other way around.

- *Don't believe too strongly in arbitrary α-levels.* There's not really much difference between a P-value of 0.051 and a P-value of 0.049, but sometimes it's regarded as the difference between night (having to retain H_0) and day (being able to shout to the world that your results are "statistically significant".) It may just be better to report the P-value and a confidence interval and let the world decide along with you.

- *Don't confuse practical and statistical significance.* A large sample size can make it easy to discern even a trivial change from the null hypothesis value. On the other hand, an important difference can be missed if your test lacks sufficient power.

- *In spite of all your care, you might make a wrong decision.* We can never reduce the probability of a Type I error (α) or of a Type II error (β) to zero (but increasing the sample size helps.)

- *Always check the conditions.* The reasoning of inference depends on randomization. No amount of care in calculating a test can recover from a biased sample. The probabilities we compute depend on the independence assumption.

Connections

All of the hypothesis tests we'll see boil down to the same question: "Is the difference between two quantities large?" And our definition of "large" always depends on the standard error. The sample size is important too because it impacts the standard error (but only by its square root.)

We've discussed the close relationship between hypothesis tests and confidence intervals. They are two sides of the same coin.

The chapter also has natural links to the discussion of probability, to the Normal model, and to the two previous chapters on inference.

Key Concepts

Alpha Level	The threshold P-value that determines when we reject a null hypothesis. If we observe a statistic whose P-value based on the null hypothesis is less than α, we reject that null hypothesis.
	(The alpha level is also called the significance level.)

DRAFT: Do not distribute or copy

Statistically Significant	When the P-value falls below the α-level, we say that the test is "statistically significant" at that α-level.
Critical Value	The value in the sampling distribution whose P-value is equal to the α-level. Any statistic value farther from the null hypothesis value than the critical value will have a smaller P-value than α and will lead to rejecting the null hypothesis. The critical value is often denoted with an asterisk, as z^*, for example.
Type I Error	The error of rejecting a null hypothesis when in fact it is true (also called a "false positive"). The probability of a Type I error is α.
Type II Error	The error of failing to reject a null hypothesis when in fact it is false (also called a "false negative"). The probability of a Type II error is commonly denoted β.
Power	The probability that a hypothesis test will correctly reject a false null hypothesis is the Power of the test. To find power, we must specify a particular alternative parameter value as the "false" value. For a specific value in the alternative, the power is $1 - \beta$.

Skills:

Upon completing this Lesson you should:

Think

- Understand that statistical significance does not measure the importance or magnitude of an effect. Recognize when others misinterpret statistical significance as proof of practical importance.

- Understand the close relationship between hypothesis tests and confidence intervals.

- Be able to identify and use the Alternative Hypothesis when testing hypotheses. Understand how to choose between a one-sided and two-sided alternative hypothesis and know how to defend the choice of a one-sided alternative.

- Understand how the critical value for a test is related to the specified α–level.

- Understand that the power of a test gives the probability that it correctly rejects a false null hypothesis when a specified alternative is true.

- Understand that the power of a test depends upon the sample size. Large sample sizes lead to greater power (and thus fewer Type II errors).

Show

- Know how to complete a hypothesis test for a population proportion.

Tell

- Interpret the meaning of a P-value in non-technical language.

- Understand that P-value of a test does not give the probability that the null hypothesis is correct.

- Know that we do not "accept" a null hypothesis if we cannot reject it, but rather that we can only "fail to reject" the hypothesis for lack of evidence against it.

Exercises

1. **P-value** A medical researcher has tested a new treatment for poison ivy against the traditional ointment. With a P-value of 0.047, he concludes the new treatment is more effective. Explain what the P-value means in this context.

2. **Another P-value** Have harsher penalties and ad campaigns increased seatbelt use among drivers and passengers? Observations of commuter traffic failed to find evidence of a significant change compared to three years ago. Explain what the study's P-value of 0.17 means in this context.

3. **Alpha** A researcher developing scanners to search for hidden weapons at airports has concluded that a new device is significantly better than the current scanner. He made this decision based upon a test using $\alpha = 0.05$. Would he have made the same decision at $\alpha = 0.10$? How about $\alpha = 0.01$? Explain.

4. **Alpha Again** Environmentalists concerned about the impact of high frequency radio transmissions on birds found that there was no evidence of a higher rate of mortality rate among hatchlings in nests near cell towers. They based this conclusion on a test using $\alpha = 0.05$. Would they have made the same decision at $\alpha = 0.10$? How about $\alpha = 0.01$? Explain.

DRAFT: Do not distribute or copy

5. **Significant?** Public health officials believe that 90% of children have been vaccinated against measles. A random survey of medical records at many schools across the country found that among over 13,000 children only 89.4% had been vaccinated. A statistician would reject the 90% hypothesis with a P-value of $P = 0.011$.

   a) Explain what the P-value means in this context.

   b) The result is statistically significant, but is it important? Comment.

6. **Significant?** A new reading program may reduce the number of elementary students who read below grade level. The company that developed this program supplied materials and teacher training for a large scale test involving nearly 8500 children in several different school districts. Statistical analysis of the results showed that the percentage of students who did not attain the grade level standard was reduced from 15.9% to 15.1%. The hypothesis that the new reading program produced no improvement was rejected with a P-value of 0.023.

   a) Explain what the P-value means in this context.

   b) Even though this reading method has been shown to be significantly better, why might you not recommend that your local school adopt it?

7. **Testing Cars** A Clean Air Standard requires that vehicle exhaust emissions not exceed specified limits for various pollutants. Many states require that cars be tested annually to be sure that they meet these standards. Suppose state regulators double check a random sample of cars that a suspect repair shop has certified as okay. They will revoke the shop's license if they find significant evidence that the shop is certifying vehicles that do not meet standards.

   a) In this context, what is a Type I error?

   b) In this context, what is a Type II error?

   c) Which type of error would the shop's owner consider to be more serious?

   d) Which type of error might environmentalists consider to be more serious?

8. **Quality Control** Production managers on an assembly line must monitor the output to be sure that the level of defective products remains small. They periodically inspect a random sample of the items produced. If they find a significant increase in the proportion of items that must be rejected they will halt the assembly process until the problem can be identified and repaired.

   a) In this context, what is a Type I error?

   b) In this context, what is a Type II error?

    c)   Which type of error would the factory owner consider to be more serious?

    d)   Which type of error might customers consider to be more serious?

9.   **Cars Again** As in Exercise 7, state regulators are checking up on repair shops to see if they are certifying vehicles that do not meet pollution standards.

    a)   In this context, what is meant by the power of the test the regulators are conducting?

    b)   Will the power be greater if they test 20 or 40 cars? Why?

    c)   Will the power be greater if they use a 5% or a 10% level of significance? Why?

    d)   Will the power be greater if the repair shop's inspectors are only a little out of compliance or a lot? Why?

10.   **Production** Consider again the task of the quality control inspectors in Exercise 8.

    a)   In this context, what is meant by the power of the test the inspectors conduct?

    b)   They are currently testing 5 items each hour. Someone has proposed they test 10 each hour instead. What are the advantages and disadvantages of such a change?

    c)   Their test currently uses a 5% level of significance. What are the advantages and disadvantages of changing to an alpha level of 1%?

    d)   Suppose that as a day passes one of the machines on the assembly line produces more and more items that are defective. How will this affect the power of the test?

11.   **Equal Opportunity?** A company is sued for job discrimination because only 19% of the newly hired candidates were minorities when 27% of all applicants were minorities. Is this strong evidence that the company's hiring practices are discriminatory?

    a)   Is this a 1-tailed or a 2-tailed test? Why?

    b)   In this context, what would a Type I error be?

    c)   In this context, what would a Type II error be?

    d)   In this context, describe what is meant by the power of the test.

    e)   If the hypothesis is tested at the 5% level of significance instead of 1%, how will this affect the power of the test?

    f)   The lawsuit is based on the hiring of 37 employees. Is the power of the test higher than, lower than, or the same as it would be if it were based on 87 hires?

12.   **Stop Signs** Highway safety engineers test new road signs, hoping that increased reflectivity will make them more visible to drivers. Volunteers drive through a test course with several of the new and old style signs and rate which kind shows up the best.

    a)   Is this a 1-tailed or a 2-tailed test? Why?

    b)   In this context, what would a Type I error be?

    DRAFT: Do not distribute or copy

c) In this context, what would a Type II error be?

d) In this context, describe what is meant by the power of the test.

e) If the hypothesis is tested at the 1% level of significance instead of 5%, how will this affect the power of the test?

f) The engineers hoped to base their decision on the reactions of 50 drivers but time and budget constraints may force them to cut back to 20. How would this affect the power of the test? Explain.

13. **Dropouts** A statistics professor has observed that for several years about 13% of the students who initially enroll in his introductory statistics course withdraw before the end of the semester. A salesman suggests that he try a statistics software package that gets students more involved with computers, predicting that it will cut the dropout rate. The software is expensive, and the salesman offers to let the professor use it for a semester to see if the dropout rate goes down significantly. The professor will have to pay for the software only if he chooses to continue using it.

a) Is this a one-tail or two-tail test? Explain.

b) Write the null and alternative hypotheses.

c) In this context, explain what would happen if the professor makes a Type I error.

d) In this context, explain what would happen if the professor makes a Type II error.

e) What is meant by the power of this test?

14. **Ads** A company is willing to renew its advertising contract with a local radio station only if the station can prove that over 20% of the residents of the city have heard the ad and recognize the company's product. The radio station conducts a random phone survey of 400 people.

a) What are the hypotheses?

b) The station plans to conduct this test using a 10% level of significance, but the company wants the significance level lowered to 5%. Why?

c) What is meant by the power of this test?

d) For which level of significance will the power of this test be higher? Why?

e) They finally agree to use $\alpha = 0.05$, but the company proposes that the station call 600 people instead of the 400 initially proposed. Will that make the risk of Type II error higher or lower? Explain.

15. **Dropouts, Part II** Initially 203 students signed up for the stats course in Exercise 13. They used the software suggested by the salesman, and only 11 dropped out of the course.

a) Should the professor spend the money for this software? Support your recommendation with an appropriate test.

b) Explain carefully what your P-value means in this context.

16. **Testing the Ads** The company in Exercise 14 contacts 600 people selected at random, and only 133 remember the ad.

a) Should the company renew the contract? Support your recommendation with an appropriate test.

b) Explain carefully what your P-value means in this context.

17. **Hoops** A basketball player with a poor foul shooting record practices intensively during the off-season. He tells the coach that he has raised his proficiency from 60% to 80%. Dubious, the coach asks him to take 10 shots, and is surprised when the player hits 9 out of 10. Did the player prove that he has improved?

a) Suppose the player really is no better than before – still a 60% shooter. What is the probability he could hit at least 9 of 10 shots anyway? (Hint: Use a Binomial model.)

b) If that is what happened, now the coach thinks the player has improved when he has not. Which type of error is that?

c) If the player really can hit 80% now, and it takes at least 9 out of 10 successful shots to convince the coach, what is the power of the test?

d) List two ways the coach and player could increase the power to detect any improvement.

18. **Pottery** An artist experimenting with clay to create pottery with a special texture has been experiencing difficulty with these special pieces. About 40% break in the kiln during firing. Hoping to solve this problem she buys some more expensive clay from another supplier. She plans to make and fire 10 pieces, and will decide to use the new clay if at most one of them breaks.

a) Suppose the new expensive clay really is no better than her usual clay. What is the probability that this test convinces her to use it anyway? (Hint: Use a Binomial model.)

b) If she decides to switch to the new clay and it is no better, what kind of error did she commit?

c) If the new clay really could reduce breakage to only 20%, what is the probability that her test will not detect the improvement?

d) How can she improve the power of her test? Offer at least two suggestions.

19. **Survey** A company has surveyed a stratified sample of its employees to find out how many might take advantage of a program to help people stop smoking. You may assume that the sampling strategy was properly random and that the data gathering methodology avoided biases. The table below shows the results. For which of the groups could we use our methods of inference to determine a 95% confidence interval for the proportion of employees who would participate in the stop smoking program?

DRAFT: Do not distribute or copy

Group	Number of employees	Number surveyed	Percent to participate
Laborers	6235	300	9%
Clerical	1520	200	7%
Management	342	25	8%

20. **Fire Safety** A city law requires all buildings to have a fire safety inspection at least once every three years. Concerned that some of these inspections are not being done, the mayor orders a survey to see what fraction of the city's buildings may be out of compliance. Results for the sample appear in the table below. For which of the building classifications could you use our methods of inference to create 95% confidence intervals for the proportion of buildings lacking the required inspection?

Class	Number of buildings	Number surveyed	Percent not inspected
Single-FamilyHome	7742	200	7%
Apartment Building	205	20	10%
Commercial	407	70	16%

21. **Little League** In a 1999-2000 longitudinal study of youth baseball, researchers found that 26% of 298 young pitchers complained of elbow pain after pitching.

a) Create a 90% confidence interval for the percentage of young players who may develop elbow pain after pitching.

b) A coach claims that only about 1 kid in 5 is at risk of arm injury from pitching. Is this claim consistent with your confidence interval?

22. **News Sources** In May of 2000 the Pew Research Foundation sampled 1,593 respondents and asked how they obtain news. They report that 33% now say that they obtain news from the internet at least once a week. Pew reports a margin of error of ±3% for this result. It had generally been assumed, based on earlier polls, that only 25% got news from the internet. Does the Pew result provide strong evidence that the percentage has increased? Use the confidence interval to test an appropriate hypothesis, and state your conclusion.

22 Comparing Two Proportions

Who:	1026 U.S. adults
What:	Opinions on traits
Why:	Polling by Gallup Poll (for sale?)
When:	2001
Where:	U.S.

WHO ARE TYPICALLY MORE INTELLIGENT, MEN OR WOMEN? To find out what people think, the Gallup Poll selected a random sample of 520 women and 506 men. They showed them a list of personal attributes and asked them to indicate whether each attribute was "generally more true of men or of women."[1] When asked about intelligence, 28% of the men thought men were generally more intelligent. But only 14% of the women agreed. Is there a gender gap in opinions about which sex is smarter? This is only a random sample. What would we estimate the true size of that gap to be?

Comparisons between two percentages are much more common than questions about isolated percentages. And they are more interesting. We often want to know how two groups differ, whether a treatment is better than a placebo control, or whether this year's results are better than last year's.

Y.A.S.D.

We know the *difference* between the proportions of our two random samples. It's 14%. That sounds like a lot, but is it the sort of difference that might just be due to random sampling? To decide about that, we need a ruler. And for that we need Yet Another Standard Deviation (Y.A.S.D.)—the standard deviation of the sampling distribution. But what's the standard deviation of a difference?

The answer is simple, but not obvious. You might expect two random quantities to vary more than just one. But we can't add the standard deviations. The secret is to add their *variances:*

> *The variance of the sum or difference of two independent random quantities is the sum of their individual variances.*

For independent random quantities, **variances add.**

Why does this make sense? Grab a full box of cereal. The box claims to contain 16 ounces of cereal. We know that's not exact: there's some small variation from box to box. Now pour a bowl of cereal. Of course, your 2 ounce serving will not be exactly 2 ounces. There'll be some variation there too. How much cereal would you guess was left in the box? Do you think your guess will be as close as for the full box? *After* you pour your bowl, the amount of cereal in the box is still a random quantity (with a smaller mean than before), but it is *more variable* because of the additional variation in the amount you poured.

According to our rule, the variance of the amount of cereal left in the box would now be the *sum* of the two *variances.*

---

[1] http://www.gallup.com/poll/releases/pr010221.asp

DRAFT: Do not distribute or copy

Of course, we want a standard deviation, not a variance, but that's just a square root away. In the standard deviation form, we can write symbolically what we've just said (because it's too much bother to say it in words.)

$$SD(x - y) = \sqrt{Var(x) + Var(y)}$$

In fact, this simple formula applies only when x and y are independent.

The Standard Deviation of the Difference between two Proportions

Fortunately, proportions of independent random samples are independent. So we can put the two proportions in for x and y. And we know that the variance of a sample proportion is $\dfrac{pq}{n}$.

When we have two samples, each can have a different size and proportion value, so we need to keep them straight with subscripts. Often we choose subscripts that remind us of the groups. For our example, we might use "$_M$" and "$_F$", but generically we'll just use "$_1$" and "$_2$". The standard deviation of the difference between two sample proportions, p_1 and p_2 is:

$$SD(\hat{p}_1 - \hat{p}_2) = \sqrt{\frac{p_1 q_1}{n_1} + \frac{p_2 q_2}{n_2}}.$$

When we have the proportions in hand, we use them to estimate the variances. So the standard error is

$$SE(\hat{p}_1 - \hat{p}_2) = \sqrt{\frac{\hat{p}_1 \hat{q}_1}{n_1} + \frac{\hat{p}_2 \hat{q}_2}{n_2}}.$$

Before we look at our example, we need to check assumptions and conditions.

Assumptions and Conditions

Independence Assumptions

Within each group the data should be based on results for independent individuals. We can't check that for certain, but we *can* check:

Random Sample Condition: The data in each group should be drawn independently and at random from a homogeneous population or generated by a randomized comparative experiment.

10% Condition: When the data are sampled without replacement, the sample should not exceed 10% of the population.

When we compare two groups in this way we need an additional independence assumption. In fact, this is the most important of these

DRAFT: Do not distribute or copy

assumptions. If it is violated these methods just won't work. We check it as the

Independent Samples Condition: The two groups we are comparing must also be independent *of each other*. Usually, the independence of the groups from each other is evident from the way the data were collected.

Why is this condition so important? If we compared husbands with their wives, or a group of subjects before and after some treatment we can't just add the variances. Subjects' performance before a treatment might very well be *related* to their performance after the treatment. So the proportions are not independent and the formula does not hold. We'll see a way to compare non-independent samples in a later chapter.

Sample Size Condition

Each of the samples must be big enough. As with individual proportions, we need larger samples to estimate proportions that are near to 0% or 100%. We usually check the

Success/Failure Condition for both samples: Both samples are big enough that at least 10 successes and at least 10 failures have been observed.

The Sampling Distribution

We're almost there. We just need one more fact about proportions. We know already that for large enough samples, each of our proportions has an approximately Normal sampling distribution. The same is true of their difference.

The sampling distribution model for a difference between two independent proportions:

Provided that the sampled values are independent, the samples are independent and the sample sizes are large enough, the sampling distribution of $\hat{p}_1 - \hat{p}_2$ is modeled by a Normal model with mean

$\mu = p_1 - p_2$, and standard deviation $\sigma(\hat{p}_1 - \hat{p}_2) = \sqrt{\dfrac{p_1 q_1}{n_1} + \dfrac{p_2 q_2}{n_2}}$.

The sampling distribution model and the standard deviation give us all we need to find a margin of error for the difference in proportions.

A Two-Proportion z-Interval, Step-by-Step

Now we are ready to answer the question of how big a gap there is between the sexes in their opinions of whether men are intelligent. The question clearly calls for a confidence interval, so let's follow the four confidence interval steps. The method is called the **two-proportion z-Interval**.

Think

Parameter: Identify the parameter you wish to estimate.

(It usually doesn't matter in which direction we subtract, so for convenience we often choose the direction with a positive difference.)

Choose and state a confidence level

Plan:

Check the conditions.

We want to know the true difference in the population proportion, p_M, of American men who think that men can be described as "intelligent" and the proportion, p_F, of American women who think so. The parameter of interest is the *difference*, $p_M - p_F$.

We will find a 95% confidence interval for this parameter.

✓   **Random Sample Condition:** Gallup drew a random sample of U.S. adults.

✓   **10% condition:** Although sampling was necessarily without replacement, there are many more U.S. women and U.S. men than were sampled in each of the samples.

✓   **Independent Samples Condition** The sample of women and the sample of men are independent of each other.

The Success/failure condition must hold for each group.

✓   **Success/failure condition:**

$n\hat{p}(men) = 506 \times 27.0\% = 137 > 10$

$n\hat{q}(men) = 506 \times 73.0\% = 369 > 10$

$n\hat{p}(women) = 520 \times 14.0\% = 73 > 10$

$n\hat{q}(women) = 520 \times 86.0\% = 447 > 10$

so both samples exceed the minimum size.

State the sampling distribution model for the statistic.

Under these conditions, the sampling distribution of the difference between the sample proportions is approximately Normal with a mean of $p_M - p_F$, the true

DRAFT: Do not distribute or copy

Show

Choose your method.

Mechanics: Construct the confidence interval.

As often happens, the key step in finding the confidence interval is estimating the standard deviation of the sampling distribution model of the statistic. Here the statistic is the difference in the proportions of men and women who think that men are intelligent.

As with single proportions, an estimate of the proportions themselves, along with the sample sizes, is sufficient to give an estimate of this standard deviation.

difference between the population proportions.

We will find a **two proportion z-interval**

We know:

$$n_M = 506, n_F = 520$$

The observed sample proportions,

$$\hat{p}_M = 0.27, \hat{p}_F = 0.14$$

Because the conditions are satisfied, we can say that the sampling distribution is Normal with a mean of $p_M - p_F$ and a standard deviation of

$$\sigma(\hat{p}_M - \hat{p}_F).$$

We estimate this standard deviation from the data as

$$SE(\hat{p}_M - \hat{p}_F) = \sqrt{\frac{\hat{p}_M \hat{q}_M}{n_M} + \frac{\hat{p}_F \hat{q}_F}{n_F}}$$

Substituting the data values, this comes out to

$$\sqrt{\frac{.28(1-.28)}{506} + \frac{.14(1-.14)}{520}} = 0.025$$

Because the sampling distribution is Normal, we know that for a 95% Confidence interval, the critical value, z* is 1.96

The margin of error is the critical value (from the Normal model) times the standard error.

From these, we find the margin of error as

$$ME = 1.96 \times 0.025 = 0.049$$

So the 95% confidence interval for the true difference in the proportion of men and the proportion of women who think that the attribute "intelligent" describes

The confidence interval is the statistic ± margin of error.

men is 0.14 ± 0.049, an interval from 9% to 19%.

Tell

Interpretation: Tell what the confidence interval means.

We are 95% confident that the proportion of American men who think that the attribute "intelligent" applies more to men than to women is between 9% and 19% more than the proportion of American women who think that.

Will I Snore when I'm 64?

Who: Randomly selected U.S. adults over age 18.

What: Proportion who snore by age (less than 30, greater than 30).

When: 2001

Where: U.S.

Why: To study sleep behaviors of U.S. adults.

The National Sleep Foundation asked a random sample of 1,010 U.S. adults questions about their sleep habits. The sample was selected In the fall of 2001 from random telephone numbers, stratified by region and sex, guaranteeing that an equal number of men and women were interviewed.[2]

One of the questions asked about snoring. Of the 995 respondents, 37% percent of adults report that they snored at least a few nights a week during the past year. Would you expect that percentage to be the same for all age groups? When broken down by age, 26% of the 184 people under 30 snored, compared with 39% of the 811 in the older group. Is this difference of 13% real, or due only to the sample we've chosen?

The question calls for a hypothesis test. But now the parameter of interest is the true *difference* between the snoring rates of the two age groups.

What's the appropriate null hypothesis? That's easy here. We hypothesize that there is no difference in the proportions. This is such a natural null hypothesis, that we rarely consider any other. But we usually express it in a slightly different way. To make it relate directly to the *difference*, we hypothesize that the difference in proportions is zero:

$$H_0: p_1 - p_2 = 0$$

Everyone into the Pool

Our hypothesis is about a new parameter — the *difference* in proportions. So we'll need a standard error for that. We know that the standard error of the difference in the proportions is

$$SE(\hat{p}_1 - \hat{p}_2) = \sqrt{\frac{\hat{p}_1\hat{q}_1}{n_1} + \frac{\hat{p}_2\hat{q}_2}{n_2}}$$

and we could just plug in the numbers.

---

[2] 2002 *Sleep in America Poll*, National Sleep Foundation, Washington D.C.

DRAFT: Do not distribute or copy

But we can do better. The secret is that, as we've seen before, proportions and their standard deviations are linked.

There are two proportions in the standard error formula, but look at the null hypothesis. It says that these proportions are equal. And to do a hypothesis test, we must *assume* that the null hypothesis is true. So there should be just a single value of $\hat{p}$ in the SE formula.

How would we do this for the snoring example? If the null hypothesis is true, the two groups have the same proportion. Overall, for all adults, we see 48 + 318 = 366 snorers out of a total of 184 + 811 = 995 adults who responded to this question. So the overall proportion of snorers is $\frac{366}{995} = 0.3678$.

Combining the counts like this to get an overall proportion is called **pooling**. (In fact, whenever we combine data from different sources or different groups because be believe that they really came from the same underlying population it is called *pooling*.)

We can then put this pooled value into the formula, substituting it for *both* sample proportions in the standard error formula:

$$SE_{pooled}(\hat{p}_1 - \hat{p}_2) = \sqrt{\frac{\hat{p}_{pooled}\hat{q}_{pooled}}{n_1} + \frac{\hat{p}_{pooled}\hat{q}_{pooled}}{n_2}}$$

$$= \sqrt{\frac{.3678 \times (1 - .3678)}{184} + \frac{3678 \times (1 - .3678)}{811}}$$

which comes out to .039.

Compared to What?

Naturally, we'll reject our null hypothesis if we see a large enough difference in the two proportions. But how can we decide whether the difference we see, $\hat{p}_1 - \hat{p}_2$, is large? The answer is simple. We just compare it to its standard error.

Since the sampling distribution is Normal, we can just divide the observed difference by its standard error to get a z-score. The z-score will tell us how many standard errors the observed difference is away from 0. We can then use the 68-95-99.7 rule to decide whether this is large, or some technology to get an exact P-value. The result is a **two-proportion z-test**.

A Two Proportion z-Test, Step-by-Step

Let's look at the snoring rates of the two groups.

Think

Hypotheses: State what we want to know.

We want to know whether snoring rates differ for those under and over 30 years old.

The study simply broke down the responses by age, so there is no sense that either alternative was of interest. A two-sided alternative hypothesis is appropriate.

Ho: There is *no* difference in snoring rates between those who are 18-29 years old and those who are 30 years or over: $p_1 - p_2 = 0$.

HA: The rates are different: $p_1 - p_2 \neq 0$

Reality Check

The observed difference is 13%. That seems like a big difference from 0 with sample sizes this large.

DRAFT: Do not distribute or copy

Plan:

Check the **conditions**

✓ **Random sampling condition:** The patients were randomly selected by telephone number and stratified by sex and region.

✓ **10% Condition:** The number of adults surveyed is certainly far less than 10% of the populations.

✓ **Independent Samples Condition:** The two age groups are independent of each other because the sample was selected at random.

✓ **Success/Failure condition**[3]:

Among the younger age group, 48 snored and 136 didn't. Among the older groups, 318 snored and 493 didn't. Both the observed number of successes and failures are much more than 10 for both groups.[4]

State the **Null Model.**

Because the conditions are satisfied, it is appropriate to model the sampling distribution of the proportion with a $N(0, \sigma(p_1 - p_2))$ model.

Choose your method.

We can perform a **two proportion z-test.**

Show　　**Mechanics**

We know:

$$n_{young} = 184, \ n_{old} = 811$$

The observed sample proportions,

---

[3] Technically, this is the first time the observed counts of successes and failures can be different from those we'd expect because we expect $n\,\hat{p}_{pooled}$, but observe $n\hat{p}$. Just checking the observed counts is easy. But if your data just barely miss (say, you see 9 successes), check $n\,\hat{p}_{pooled}$ as well.

[4] This is one of those places where the traditional term "success" seems a bit weird. A success here could be that a person snores. We're just using the terms "success" and "failure" as arbitrary labels left over from studies of gambling games.

We use the null model to find the **P-value**.

$$\hat{p}_{young} = 0.261, \; \hat{p}_{old} = 0.392$$

Because the conditions are satisfied, we can say that, under the null model, the sampling distribution is Normal with a mean of 0 and a standard deviation of

$$\sigma\left(p_{old} - p_{young}\right).$$

We estimate this standard deviation from the data as

$$SE_{pooled}\left(\hat{p}_{old} - \hat{p}_{young}\right) = \sqrt{\frac{\hat{p}_{pooled}\hat{q}_{pooled}}{n_{old}} + \frac{\hat{p}_{pooled}\hat{q}_{pooled}}{n_{young}}}$$

Substituting the data values, this comes out to

$$\sqrt{\frac{.3678 \times (1 - .3678)}{811} + \frac{.3678 \times (1 - .3678)}{184}} = 0.039.$$

The probability of observing a value 3.36 standard deviations away from the mean of a Normal model or higher can be found by computer, calculator, or table (see the table below), to be 0.0008.

The observed difference between the proportions, is .392 - .261 = .131.

The P-value is the probability of observing a difference in proportion as large as 0.131 (or larger);

$$P = P\left(\left|\hat{p}_{old} - \hat{p}_{young}\right|\right) \geq 0.131$$

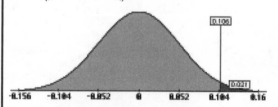

This value has a z-score of

$$z = \frac{.131 - 0}{.039} = 3.36, \text{ so the observed}$$

difference is 3.36 standard deviations larger than the hypothesized value of 0.

The two sided P-value is 0.0008.

Tell

Conclusion:

State the conclusion.

The P-value of 0.0008 says that if there really were no difference in snoring rates between the two age groups then the difference observed in this study would

DRAFT: Do not distribute or copy

happen only 8 times in 10,000. This is rare enough for us to reject the null hypothesis of no difference and conclude that older adults are more likely to snore than younger adults.

Finding Inferences for Differences Between Proportions with the Computer

It is so common to test against the null hypothesis of no difference between the two true proportions, that most statistics programs simply assume this null hypothesis. And most will automatically used the pooled standard deviation. If you wish to test a different null (say that the true difference is 0.3), you may have to search for a way to do that.

Much statistics software expects to see the raw data rather than already computed proportions. That is, they look for data for each individual in the study that names the group to which the individual belongs. They then find the n's and $\hat{p}$'s from the data and complete the test or interval calculation. Sometimes all you know are the proportions and counts. Some packages can work with those. Some can regenerate data that would have led to just those proportions, and others can only work with the raw data.

What can go wrong

Don't use two-sample proportion methods when the samples aren't independent. These methods give wrong answers when this assumption of independence is violated. Good random sampling is usually the best insurance of independent groups. Make sure that there is no relationship between the two groups. For example, you can't compare the proportion of respondents who own SUV's with the proportion of those same respondents who think the tax on gas should be eliminated. The responses are not independent because you've asked the same people. To use these methods to estimate or test the difference, you'd need to survey two different groups of people.

Alternatively, if you have a random sample, you can split your respondents according to their answers to one question and treat the two resulting groups as independent samples. So, you could estimate or test the difference in the proportions of respondents who favor eliminating the gas tax between SUV owners and non-SUV owners.

Don't apply inference methods when you don't have random samples. If the data do not come from representative random samples, then the inference about the difference in proportions will be wrong.

Don't interpret a significant difference in proportions causally. It turns out that people with higher incomes are more likely to snore. Does money affect sleep patterns? Probably not. We have seen that older people are more likely to snore, and they are also likely to earn more. In a prospective or retrospective study, there is always the danger that other lurking variables not accounted for are the real reason for an observed difference. Be careful not to jump to conclusions about causality.

Connections

- In Chapter 3 we looked at contingency tables for two categorical variables. Differences in proportions are just 2 x 2 contingency tables. You'll often see data presented in this way. For example, the snoring data could be presented as

	18-29	30 and over	Total
Snore	48	318	366
Don't snore	136	493	629
Total	184	811	995

We tested whether the column percentages of snorers were the same for the two age groups.

- This chapter gives the first examples we've seen of inference methods for a parameter other than a simple proportion. Although we have a different standard error, the step-by-step procedures are almost identical. In particular, once again we divide the statistic we see (the difference in proportions) by its standard error and get a z-score. You should feel right at home.

Key Concepts

Variances of Independent Random Variables Add	The variance of a sum or difference of random variables is the sum of the variances of those variables.
Sampling Distribution of the difference between two proportions	The sampling distribution of $\hat{p}_1 - \hat{p}_2$ is, under appropriate assumptions, modeled by a Normal model with mean $\mu = p_1 - p_2$, and standard deviation $\sigma(\hat{p}_1 - \hat{p}_2) = \sqrt{\dfrac{p_1 q_1}{n_1} + \dfrac{p_2 q_2}{n_2}}$.
Pooling	When we data from different sources that we believe are homogeneous, we can combine, or pool, the data in these groups. When we test whether two proportions are equal, we pool the data to estimate a common proportion. The

| | resulting pooled standard error is based on more data and is thus more reliable (if the null hypothesis is true). |

Skills:

Upon completing this Lesson you should:

Think

- Be able to state the null and alternative hypotheses for testing the difference between two population proportions.

- Know how to examine your data for violations of conditions that would make inference about the difference between two population proportions unwise or invalid.

- Recognize that the formula for the standard error of the difference between two independent sample proportions is based on the principle that when finding the sum or difference of two independent random variables, their variances add.

Show

- Find a confidence interval for the difference between two proportions.

- Perform a significance test of the natural null hypothesis that two population proportions are equal.

Tell

- Write a sentence describing what is said about the difference between two population proportions by a confidence interval.

- Write a sentence interpreting the results of a significance test of the null hypothesis that two population proportions are equal.

- Interpret the meaning of a P-value in non-technical language, making clear that the probability claim is made about computed values and not about the population parameter of interest.

- Know that we do not "accept" a null hypothesis if we fail to reject it.

Exercises

1. **Arthritis** The Centers for Disease Control report a survey of randomly selected Americans age 65 and older, which found that 411 of 1012 men and 535 of 1062 women suffered from some form of arthritis.

a) Are the assumptions and conditions necessary for inference satisfied? Explain.

b) Create a 95% confidence interval for the difference in the proportions of senior men and women who have this disease.

c) Interpret your interval in this context.

d) Does this confidence interval suggest that arthritis is more likely to afflict women than men? Explain.

2. **Graduation** In October 2000 the US Department of Commerce reported the results of a large scale survey on high school graduation. Researchers contacted over 25000 Americans aged 24 years to see if they had finished high school. 84.9% of the 12460 males and 88.1% of the 12678 females indicated that they had high school diplomas.

a) Are the assumptions and conditions necessary for inference satisfied? Explain.

b) Create a 95% confidence interval for the difference in graduation rates among males and females.

c) Interpret your confidence interval.

d) Does this provide strong evidence that girls are more likely than boys to complete high school? Explain.

3. **Pets** In 1991, researchers at the National Cancer Institute released the results of a study that investigated the effect of weed-killing herbicides on house pets. They examined 827 dogs from homes where an herbicide was used on a regular basis, diagnosing malignant lymphoma in 473 of them. Of the 130 dogs from homes where no herbicides were used, only 19 were found to have lymphoma.

a) What is the standard error of the difference in the two proportions?

b) Construct a 95% confidence interval for this difference.

c) State an appropriate conclusion.

4. **Carpal Tunnel** The painful wrist condition called carpal tunnel syndrome can be treated with surgery or less-invasive wrist splints. In September 2002 *TIME Magazine* reported on a study of 176 patients. Among the half that had surgery 80% showed improvement after three months, but only 54% of those who used the wrist splints improved.

a) What is the standard error of the difference in the two proportions?

b) Construct a 95% confidence interval for this difference.

c) State an appropriate conclusion.

5. **Prostate Cancer** There has been debate among doctors over whether surgery can prolong life among men suffering from prostate cancer, a type of cancer that typically develops and spreads very slowly. In the summer of 2003 *The New England Journal of Medicine* published results of some Scandanavian research. Men diagnosed with prostate cancer were randomly assigned to either undergo surgery or not. Among the 347 men who had surgery 16 eventually died of prostate cancer, compared to 31 of the 348 men who did not have surgery.

a) Was this an experiment or an observational study? Explain.

b)   Create a 95% confidence interval for the difference in rates of death for the two groups of men.

c)   Based on your confidence interval, is there evidence that surgery may be effective in preventing death from prostate cancer? Explain.

6.   **Race and Smoking** In 1995 24.8% of 550 white adults surveyed reported that they smoked cigarettes, while 25.7% of the 550 black adults surveyed were smokers.

a)   Create a 90% confidence interval for the difference in the percentages of smokers among black and white American adults.

b)   Does this survey indicate a race-based difference in smoking among American adults? Explain, using your confidence interval to test an appropriate hypothesis.

7.   **Politics** A poll checking on the level of public support for proposed antiterrorist legislation reported that 68% of the respondents were in favor. The pollsters reported a sampling error of ±3%. When the responses were broken down by party affiliation support was 2% higher among Republican respondents than Democrats. The pollsters said the margin of error for this difference was ±4%.

a)   Why is the margin of error larger for the difference in support between the parties than for the overall level of support?

b)   Based on these results, can we conclude that support is significantly higher among Republicans? Explain.

8.   **War** In September 2002 a Gallup poll found major differences of opinion based on political affiliation over whether Congress should give President Bush authority to take military action in Iraq. Overall about 50% of the 1010 respondents were in favor, with a reported margin of error of ±3%. Opinion differed greatly between Republicans, Democrats, and Independents, as seen in the bar graph.

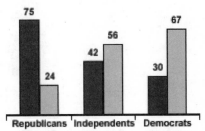

Should Congress Give
President Bush
Authority to Take Military Action?

■ % Yes, should
□ % No, should not

a)   How large did this poll estimate the difference in support between Republicans and Democrats to be?

b)   Was the margin of error for that difference equal to, greater than, or less than 3%? Explain.

9.   **Teen Smoking, Part I** A Vermont study published in December 2001 by the American Academy of Pediatrics examined parental influence on teenagers' decisions to smoke. A group of students who had never smoked were questioned about their parents' attitudes about smoking. These students were then questioned again two years later to see if

they had started smoking. The researchers found that among the 284 students who indicated that their parents disapproved of kids smoking, 54 had become established smokers. Among the 41 students who initially said their parents were lenient about smoking, 11 became smokers. Do these data provide strong evidence that parental attitude influences teenagers' decisions about smoking?

a) What kind of design did the researchers use?

b) Write appropriate hypotheses.

c) Are the assumptions and conditions necessary for inference satisfied?

d) Test the hypothesis and state your conclusion.

e) Explain in this context what your P-value means.

f) If that conclusion is actually wrong, which type of error did you commit?

10. **Depression** A study published in the Archives of General Psychiatry in March 2001 examined the impact of depression on a patient's ability to survive cardiac disease. Researchers identified 450 people with cardiac disease, evaluated them for depression, and followed the group for 4 years. Of the 361 patients with no depression, 67 died. Of the 89 patients with minor or major depression, 26 died. Among people who suffer from cardiac disease, are depressed patients more likely to die than the non-depressed?

a) What kind of design was used to collect these data?

b) Write appropriate hypotheses.

c) Are the assumptions and conditions necessary for inference satisfied?

d) Test the hypothesis and state your conclusion.

e) Explain in this context what your P-value means.

f) If your conclusion is actually incorrect, which type of error did you commit?

11. **Teen Smoking, Part II** Consider again the Vermont study discussed in Exercise 9.

a) Create a 95% confidence interval for the difference in proportion of children of approving and disapproving parents who may smoke.

b) Interpret your interval in this context.

c) Carefully explain what "95% confidence" means.

12. **Depression Revisited** Consider again the study of the association between depression and cardiac disease survivability in Exercise 10.

a) Create a 95% confidence interval for the difference in survival rates.

b) Interpret your interval in this context.

c) Carefully explain what "95% confidence" means.

13. **Pregnancy** In 1998 a San Diego reproductive clinic reported 42 live births to 157 women under the age of 38, but only 7 successes for 89 clients aged 38 and older. Is this strong evidence of a difference in the effectiveness of the clinic's methods for older women?

a) Test an appropriate hypothesis and state your conclusion.

b) If you concluded there was a difference, estimate that difference with a confidence interval and interpret your interval in context.

14. **Suicide** The August 2001 issue of *Pediatrics* reported on a study of adolescent suicide attempts. Questionnaires were given to 6577 middle and high school students, 214 of whom were adopted. 213 youngsters said they had attempted suicide within the last year – 16 of those who were adopted, and 197 who were not. Does this indicate a significantly different rate of suicide among adopted teens?

a) Test an appropriate hypothesis and state your conclusion.
b) If you concluded there was a difference, estimate that difference with a confidence interval and interpret your interval in context.

15. **Politics and Sex** One month before the election, a poll of 630 randomly selected voters showed 54% planning to vote for a certain candidate. A week later it became known that he had had an extramarital affair, and a new poll showed only 51% of 1010 voters supporting him. Do these results indicate that there was a decrease in voter support for his candidacy?

a) Test an appropriate hypothesis and state your conclusion.
b) If you concluded there was a difference, estimate that difference with a confidence interval and interpret your interval in context.

16. **Retirement** The Employee Benefit Research Institute reports that 27% of males anticipate having enough money to live comfortably in retirement, but only 18% of females express that confidence. If these results were based upon samples of 250 people of each gender, would you consider this to be strong evidence that men and women have different outlooks?

a) Test an appropriate hypothesis and state your conclusion.
b) If you concluded there was a difference, estimate that difference with a confidence interval and interpret your interval in context.

17. **Twins** In 2001 one county reported that among 3132 white women who had babies, 94 were multiple births. There were also 20 multiple births to 606 black women. Does this indicate any racial differences in the likelihood of multiple births?

a) Test an appropriate hypothesis and state your conclusion.
b) If your conclusion is incorrect, which type of error did you commit?

18. **Shopping** A survey of 430 randomly chosen adults found that 21% of the 222 men and 18% of the 208 women had purchased books online.

a) Is there evidence that men are more likely than women to make online purchases of books? Test an appropriate hypothesis and state your conclusion in context.
b) If your conclusion in fact proves to be wrong, did you make a Type I or Type II error?

19. **Mammograms** It is widely believed that regular mammogram screening may detect breast cancer early, resulting in fewer deaths from that disease. One study that investigated this issue over a period of 18 years was published during the 1970's. Among 30,565 women who had never had mammograms, 196 died of breast cancer while only 153 of 30,131 who had undergone screening died of breast cancer.

a) Do these results suggest that mammograms may be an effective screening tool to reduce breast cancer deaths?

b) If your conclusion is incorrect, what type of error have you committed?

20. **Mammograms Redux** In 2001 the conclusion of the study outlined in Exercise 19 was questioned. A new 9-year study was conducted in Sweden, comparing 21,088 women who had mammograms to 21,195 who did not. 63 of the women who underwent screening died of breast cancer, compared with 66 deaths among the control group. (NY *Times*, Dec 9,2001)

a) Do these results support the effectiveness of regular mammograms in preventing deaths from breast cancer?

b) If your conclusion is incorrect, what kind of error have you committed?

21. **Pain** Researchers comparing the effectiveness of two pain medications randomly selected a group of patients who had been complaining of a certain kind of joint pain. They randomly divided these people into two groups, then administered the painkillers. 112 people were in the group who received medication A; 84 of them said this pain reliever was effective. 66 of 108 people in the other group reported that pain reliever B was effective.

a) Write a 95% confidence interval for the percent of people who may get relief from this kind of joint pain by using medication A. Interpret your interval.

b) Write a 95% confidence interval for the percent of people who may get relief by using medication B. Interpret your interval.

c) Do the intervals for A and B overlap? What do you think this means about the comparative effectiveness of these medications?

d) Find a 95% confidence interval for the difference in the proportions of people who may find these medications effective. Interpret your interval.

e) Does this interval contain zero? What does that mean?

f) Why do the results in c) and e) seem contradictory? If we want to compare the effectiveness of these two pain relievers, which is the correct approach? Why?

22. **Gender Gap** Candidates for political office realize that different levels of support among men and women may be a crucial factor in determining the outcome of the election. One candidate finds that 52% of 473 men polled say they will vote for him, but only 45% of the 522 women in the poll express support.

DRAFT: Do not distribute or copy

a) Write a 90% confidence interval for the percent of male voters who may vote for our candidate. Interpret your interval.

b) Write a 95% confidence interval for the percent of female voters who may vote for him. Interpret your interval.

c) Do the intervals for males and females overlap? What do you think this means about the gender gap?

d) Find a 95% confidence interval for the difference in the proportions of males and females who will vote for this candidate. Interpret your interval.

e) Does this interval contain zero? What does that mean?

f) Why do the results in c) and e) seem contradictory? If we want to see if there is a gender gap among voters with respect to this candidate, which is the correct approach? Why?

23 Inferences About Means

$\mathcal{M}$OTOR VEHICLE CRASHES are the leading cause of death for people of

every age from 4 to 33 years old. In the year 2000, 41,821 people in the U.S. lost their lives due to motor vehicle accidents, up from 41,717 the year before. That means that, on average, motor vehicle crashes resulted in 115 deaths each day, or one death every 13 minutes.

Speeding is a contributing factor in 29% of all fatal accidents. Not only were 12,350 lives lost in speeding-related crashes, but the economic cost of speeding related crashes is estimated to be about $27.4 billion per year[1].

Triphammer Road is a busy road that passes through a residential neighborhood. Residents there are concerned that vehicles traveling on the road often exceed the posted speed limit of 30 miles per hour. The local police sometimes place a radar speed detector by the side of the road that displays the speed of oncoming vehicles to the drivers. They hope that, being reminded of their speed, drivers will become more aware and slow down.

The local residents are not convinced that such a passive method is helping to control the problem. They hope to make a case to the Village for additional police patrols to encourage vehicles to observe the speed limit. To help their case, a resident stood where he could see this device and recorded the speed of vehicles passing it during a 15 minute period one day. When clusters of vehicles passed by, he recorded only the speed of the front vehicle. Here are the data:

[1] National Highway Traffic Safety Administration

DRAFT: Do not distribute or copy

Who: vehicles on
    Triphammer road
What: Speed
    Units: Miles per hour
When: April 11, 2000, 1pm
Where: A small town in the
    Northeast US.
Why: Concern over impact
    on residential
    neiahborhood

speed
29
34
34
28
30
29
38
31
29
34
32
31
27
37
29
26
24
34
36
31
34
36
21

We are interested both in estimating the true mean speed and in testing whether it exceeds the posted speed limit. Although the sample of vehicles is a convenience sample, not a truly random sample, there is no compelling reason to believe that vehicles at one time of day are driving faster or slower than vehicles at another time of day[2], so we can take the sample to be representative.

These data differ from data on proportions in one important way. Proportions are usually reported as summaries. After all, individual responses are just "success" and "failure" or "1" and "0." But quantitative data are usually reported for each individual. When you have a value for each individual, you should remember the three rules of data analysis and plot the data, as we have done here.

Because we have quantitative data, we summarize it with means and standard deviations. Because we want to do inference, we'll think about sampling distributions, but we already know most of the facts we need.

---

[2] Except, perhaps, at rush hour. But at that time, traffic is slowed. Our concern is with ordinary traffic during the day.

Getting started

You know how to create confidence intervals and test hypotheses about proportions (if you don't, this would be a good time for a quick review.) Now we want to do the same thing for means. Just as we did before, we will base both our confidence interval and our hypothesis test on the sampling model. And we know from the Central Limit Theorem that the sampling model we need is still the Normal. This is true for means no matter what shape population the data come from.

We also know that the standard deviation of the model is $\sigma(\bar{y}) = \dfrac{\sigma}{\sqrt{n}}$.

When we estimate the standard deviation of the sampling model from the data, it is called the *standard error*. We'll use that term and the $SE(\bar{y})$ notation. But remember, it's just the standard deviation of the sampling model.

For proportions we knew that $\sigma(\hat{p}) = \sqrt{\dfrac{pq}{n}}$, so we used $SE(\hat{p}) = \sqrt{\dfrac{\hat{p}\hat{q}}{n}}$ to estimate the standard deviation. Because they are linked, knowing $\hat{p}$, gave us its standard deviation. For means, knowing $\bar{y}$ doesn't tell us *anything* about $\sigma(\bar{y})$. So what should we do? We do what any sensible person would do: we estimate σ with s, the sample standard deviation.

The resulting standard error is $SE(\bar{y}) = \dfrac{s}{\sqrt{n}}$.

A century ago, people used the Normal model with this standard error, assuming it would work. After all, a similar estimate worked fine for proportions. And, for large sample sizes it *did* work reasonably well.

But they began to notice problems for smaller samples. The trouble is that $SE(\bar{y})$ is based on the sample statistic, s, which varies from sample to sample. This extra variation can mess up the margin of error and P-value, especially for a small sample. Somehow, we have to allow for the extra variation.

The plot is even thicker than that. Not only is there extra variation in $SE(\bar{y})$, but even the *shape* of its sampling model changes. The model is no longer Normal. And the shape changes more for small samples than for larger ones.

William S. Gosset, the man who first realized that fact, transformed Statistics, but most people who use his work don't know his name.

Gosset's *t*

Gosset had a job that made him the envy of many. He was the quality control engineer for the Guinness Brewery in Dublin, Ireland. His job was to make sure that the stout (a thick, dark beer) leaving the brewery was of high enough quality to meet the demands of the brewery's many discerning customers. It is easy to imagine, when testing stout, why a large sample with many observations might be undesirable, not to mention dangerous to one's health. So Gosset often used small samples of size 3 or 4. But he noticed that with samples of this size, his tests for quality weren't quite right. He knew this because when the batches that he rejected were sent back to the laboratory for more extensive testing, too often they turned out to be OK.

To find the sampling distribution of the mean, Gosset simulated it *by hand*. He drew paper slips of small samples from a hat *hundreds of times* and computed the means and standard deviations with a mechanically cranked calculator. Now you could repeat in seconds on a computer the experiment that took him over a year. Gosset's work was so meticulous that not only did he get the shape of the new histogram approximately right, but he was even to figure out the exact *formula* for it from his sample. This fact was not proven mathematically until years later by Sir R.A. Fisher.

Gosset checked the stout's quality by performing hypothesis tests. He knew that the test would make some Type I errors and reject about 5% of the *good* batches of stout. But the lab told him that he was in fact rejecting about 15% of the good batches. Gosset knew that something was wrong, and it bugged him.

Gosset took time off to study the problem (and earn a graduate degree in the emerging field of Statistics). He figured out that when he used the estimated standard error, $\frac{s}{\sqrt{n}}$, the shape of the sampling model changed. He even figured out what the new model should be and called it a *t*-distribution.

The Guinness Company didn't give Gosset a lot of support for his work. In fact, they had a policy against publishing results. Gosset had to convince them that he was not publishing an industrial secret, and (as part of getting permission to publish) had to use a pseudonym. The pseudonym he chose was "Student," and ever since, the model he found has been known as **Student's *t***.

The shape of Gosset's model is different for different sample sizes. So, the Student's *t* models form a whole *family* of related distributions that depend on a parameter known as **degrees of freedom**. We often denote degrees of freedom as *df*, and the model as t_{df} with the degrees of freedom as a subscript.

What does this Mean for Means?

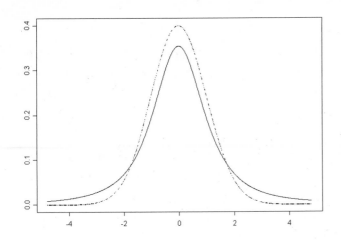

To make confidence intervals or test hypotheses for means we need to use Gosset's model. Which one? Well, for means, it turns out the right degrees of freedom is $df = n-1$.

When Gosset corrected the model for the extra uncertainty, the margin of error got bigger, as you might have guessed. So when you use Gosset's model instead of the Normal model, your confidence intervals will be just a bit wider and your P-values just a bit larger. But that's just the correcting you need. By using the t model you've compensated for the extra variability in just the right way.

The t model on 2 degrees of freedom has fatter tails than the Normal model. So the 68-95-99.7 rule doesn't work for t models with only a few degrees of freedom.

Student's t- models are unimodal, symmetric, and bell-shaped just like the Normal. But t models with only a few degrees of freedom have much fatter tails than the Normal. (That's what makes the margin of error bigger.) As the degrees of freedom increase, the t models look more and more like the Normal. In fact, the t model with infinite degrees of freedom is exactly Normal. [3] This is great news if you happen to have an infinite number of data values. Fortunately, above a few hundred degrees of freedom it's very hard to tell the difference.

Finding t Values by Hand

The Student's t model is different for each value of degrees of freedom. We might print a table like the old Normal tables for each degrees of freedom value, but that's a lot of boring pages, and not likely to be a best-seller. One way to shorten the book is to admit that while it might be nice to be able to get a critical value for a 93.4% confidence interval, in practice we usually limit ourselves to 90%, 95, 99%, and 99.9% confidence levels. So statistics books usually have one table of t-model critical values for selected confidence levels. (And so does this one; see Appendix T). The tables run down the page for as many degrees of freedom as they can fit, and they are actually much easier to use than the Normal tables.

Then they get to the bottom of the page and run out of room. Of course, for *enough* degrees of freedom, the t model gets closer and closer to the

---

[3] Formally, in the limit as n goes to infinity.

Normal, so the tables give a final row with the critical values from the Normal model.

Or we could use technology. Any graphing calculator or statistics program can give critical values for a *t*-model for any number of degrees of freedom and for any confidence level you please. And they can go straight to P-values when we test a hypothesis.

Assumptions & Conditions

Gosset found the *t* model by simulation. Years later, when Sir R.A. Fisher showed mathematically that Gosset was right, he needed to make some assumptions to make the proof work. Disagreeing with Sir Ronald never did anyone's career any good, so we'll go along with his conditions and assumptions too.

Independence Assumption

The data values should be mutually independent of each other. There is really no way to check independence from the data. But we can check the

Randomization Condition: The data arise from a random sample or suitably randomized experiment. Randomly sampled data – and especially data from an SRS – are ideal.

When a sample is drawn without replacement, technically, we ought to check the

10% Condition: The sample is no more than 10% of the population. When making inferences about proportions, this condition was crucial. But for means, this is rarely a problem in practice. We can estimate means more reliably than proportions, so we almost never need to take that large a fraction of the population as our sample. We won't mention it again for means – but don't forget about it if you have a small population.

Normal Population Assumption

To use a Student's *t* model, we are formally required to assume that the data are from a population that follows a Normal model. Practically speaking, there is no way to be certain that this is true.

And it is almost certainly *not* true. Models are idealized; real data are…real. But the good news is that even for small samples, it is good enough to check the

Nearly Normal Condition: The data come from a distribution that is unimodal and symmetric. Check this by making a histogram or normal probability plot[4].

---

[4] There are tests of Normality, but they don't really help. When we have a small sample—just when we really care about checking Normality—these tests have very

DRAFT: Do not distribute or copy

The importance of Normality for Student's *t* depends upon the sample size. Just our luck; it matters most where it is hardest to check.

For very small samples (say n < 15 or so), the data should follow a Normal model pretty closely. Of course, with so little data, it's pretty hard to tell. But if you do find outliers or strong skewness, you should not use these methods.

For moderate sample sizes (say *n* between 15 and 40 or so), the *t* methods will work well if the data are unimodal and reasonably symmetric. Make a histogram.

When the sample size is larger than 40 or 50, the *t* methods are safe to use even if the data are skewed. But if you find outliers in the data, it is always a good idea to remove them and report them separately, even for large samples. They may well hold additional information about the data that deserves special attention.

A One-Sample *t*-Interval for the Mean, Step-by-Step

Let's build a 90% confidence interval for the mean speed of all vehicles traveling on Triphammer Rd. The interval that we'll make is called the **one sample *t*-interval.**

Think

Parameter: Identify the parameter you wish to estimate.

Choose and state a confidence level

Of course, we start by looking at the data.

✓ **Reality Check**

The histogram centers around 30 mph and the data lie between 20 and 40 mph. We'd expect a confidence interval to place the population mean within a few mph of 30.

We wish to find a 90% confidence interval for the mean speed, μ, of vehicles driving on Triphammer road.

Here's a histogram of the 23 speeds.

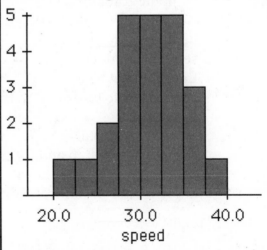

Plan: Check the conditions.

- **Random Sample Condition:** We know we have a convenience sample, but we have

little power. So it doesn't make much sense to use them to judge whether to perform a t-test.

Copyright © 2001, Dick De Veaux and Paul Velleman

reason to believe that it is representative.

- **Nearly Normal Condition:** The histogram of the speeds is unimodal and symmetric.

Under these conditions the sampling distribution of the mean can be modeled by a Student's *t* model with (*n* - 1) = 22 degrees of freedom.

We will use a **one sample *t*-interval for the mean.**

We know:

$n = 23$ cars

$\bar{y} = 31.04$ miles per hour

$s = 4.25$ mph

We estimate the standard error of $\bar{y}$:

$$SE(\bar{y}) = \frac{s}{\sqrt{n}} = \frac{4.25}{\sqrt{23}} = 0.886 \text{mph}$$

The 90% critical value for t_{22} is 1.717.

From these, we find that the margin of error is

$$ME = t_{22}^{*} \, SE(\bar{y}) = 1.717 \times 0.886 = 1.521 \text{mph}$$

So the 90% confidence interval for the mean speed is:

31.0 ± 1.5 mph or

[29.5 mph, 32.5 mph]

We are 90% confident that the confidence interval from 29.5 to 32.5 miles per hour captures the true mean speed of all

---

- State the sampling distribution model for the statistic.

- Choose your method.

Show

Mechanics: Construct the confidence interval.

Be sure to include the units along with the statistics

The critical value we need to make a 90% interval comes from a Student's *t* table, a computer program, or a calculator. We have 23 - 1 = 22 degrees of freedom. The selected confidence level says that we want 90% of the probability to be caught in the middle, so we exclude 5% in *each* tail for a total of 10%. The degrees of freedom and 5% tail probability are all we need to know to find the critical value.

✓ Reality Check The result looks plausible and in line with what we thought.

Tell

Interpretation: Tell what the confidence interval means.

When we construct confidence

intervals in this way, we expect 90% of them to cover the true mean, and 10% to miss the true value. This particular interval is one constructed in this way, so, in this sense, it has a 90% chance of covering the true mean.

vehicles on Triphammer Rd.

Caveat: This was not a random sample of vehicles. It was a convenience sample taken at one time on one day. And the participants were not blinded. (Thank goodness.) Drivers could see the police device and some may have slowed down.

Here's the part of the Student's *t* table that gives the critical value we needed. This table is part of the interactive software on the CD-ROM included with the book. You can find similar technology on a TI-83 calculator. Many books print static t-tables that look much the same.

To find a critical value, locate the row of the table corresponding to the degrees of freedom and the column corresponding to the probability you want. Our 90% confidence interval leaves 5% of the values on either side, so we look across to the ".05" column. The value in the table at that intersection is the critical value we need: 1.717.

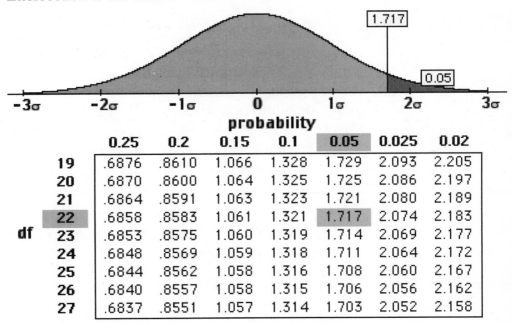

df	0.25	0.2	0.15	0.1	0.05	0.025	0.02
19	.6876	.8610	1.066	1.328	1.729	2.093	2.205
20	.6870	.8600	1.064	1.325	1.725	2.086	2.197
21	.6864	.8591	1.063	1.323	1.721	2.080	2.189
22	.6858	.8583	1.061	1.321	1.717	2.074	2.183
23	.6853	.8575	1.060	1.319	1.714	2.069	2.177
24	.6848	.8569	1.059	1.318	1.711	2.064	2.172
25	.6844	.8562	1.058	1.316	1.708	2.060	2.167
26	.6840	.8557	1.058	1.315	1.706	2.056	2.162
27	.6837	.8551	1.057	1.314	1.703	2.052	2.158

Another Caution About Interpreting Confidence Intervals

Don't Tell

Confidence intervals for means offer new tempting wrong interpretations. Here are some things you *shouldn't* say.

- **Don't** say "*90% of all the vehicles* on Triphammer Road drive at a speed between 29.52 and 32.56 miles per hour." The confidence interval is about the *mean* speed, not about the actual speeds of individual vehicles.

- **Don't** say "We are 90% confident that *a randomly selected vehicle* will have a speed between 29.52 and 32.56 miles per hour." This false interpretation is also about individual vehicles rather than about the *mean* of the speeds. We *are* 90% confident that the *mean* speed of all vehicles on Triphammer Road is between 29.52 and 32.56 mph.

- And **don't** say "The mean speed of the vehicles is 31.04 mph 90% *of the time*". That's about means, but still wrong. It implies that the mean varies, when in fact it is the confidence interval that would have been different had we gotten a different sample.

- Finally, **don't** say "90% *of all samples* will have mean speeds between 29.52 and 32.56 mph". That statement suggests that *this* interval somehow sets a standard for every other interval. In fact, this interval is no more (or less) likely to be correct than any other. You could say that 90% of all possible samples will produce intervals that actually do contain the true mean speed. (The problem is that because we'll never know where the true mean speed really is we can't know if our sample was one of those 90%.)

Make a picture, Make a picture, Make a picture

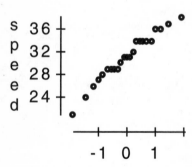

The only reasonable way to check the Nearly Normal Condition is with graphs of the data. Make and check a histogram of the data to see that the distribution is unimodal and symmetric and that it has no outliers. You may also want to make a normal probability plot and check that it is reasonably straight. You'll be able to see deviations from the Normal model more easily with a normal probability plot, but it's easier to understand the particular nature of the deviations from a histogram.

If you have a computer or graphing calculator doing the work, there's no excuse not to look at *both* displays as part of checking the Nearly Normal condition.

A One-Sample *t*-Test for the Mean, Step-by-Step

The residents along Triphammer road have a more specific concern. It appears that the mean speed along the road is higher than it ought to be. But to get the police to patrol more frequently, they'll need to show that the true mean speed is in fact greater than the 30 mile per hour speed limit. This calls for a hypothesis test called the **one-sample t-test for the mean.**

Think	**Hypotheses:** State what we want to know. Make clear what the population and parameter are.	We want to know whether the mean speed of vehicles on Triphammer road exceeds the posted speed limit of 30 mph.
	The null hypothesis is that the true mean speed is equal to the limit.	

     DRAFT: Do not distribute or copy

Because we're interested in whether the vehicles are speeding, the alternative is one-sided.

Reality check: The histogram of the observed speeds is clustered around 30, so we'd be surprised to find that the mean was much higher than that. (The fact that 30 is within the confidence interval that we've just found confirms this suspicion.)

Plan: State the **Null Model.**

Check the **conditions**

State the sampling distribution.

Choose your method.

Show

Mechanics: Be sure to include the units when you write down what you know from the data.

We use the null model to find the **P-value.**

Here is the place in the mechanics where we use the hypothesized

---

Ho: Mean speed, $\mu = 30$ mph

H$_A$: The mean speed, $\mu > 30$ mph

- **Random Sample Condition:** Although we have a convenience sample, we have reason to believe that it is a representative sample.

- **Nearly Normal Condition:** The histogram of the speeds (seen earlier, or we'd include it here) is unimodal and symmetric. This is close enough to Normal for our purposes.

Under these conditions the sampling distribution of the mean can be modeled by Student's t with $(n - 1) = 22$ degrees of freedom.

We will use a **one-sample t-test for the mean.**

We know:

$n = 23$ cars

$\bar{y} = 31.0$ miles per hour

$s = 4.25$ mph

Because the conditions are satisfied, we estimate the standard error of $\bar{y}$:

$$SE(\bar{y}) = \frac{s}{\sqrt{n}} = \frac{4.25}{\sqrt{23}} = 0.886 \text{mph}$$

value of the mean. We couldn't complete this calculation without it. The *t*-statistic calculation is just a standardized value. We subtract the hypothesized mean and divide by the estimated standard deviation (of the sampling distribution of the mean).

The P-value is the probability of observing a sample mean as large as 31.04 (or larger) *if* the true mean were 30.0, as the null hypothesis states. That is, $P = P(t_{22} > 1.13)$, the probability of observing a value more than 1.13 in a Student's *t* model on 22 degrees of freedom. We can learn from a table, calculator, or computer program that this probability is 0.136.

Reality check: We're not surprised that the difference isn't statistically significant.

Tell

Conclusion: State the conclusion.

Unfortunately for the residents, there is no course of action associated with failing to reject this particular null hypothesis.

The *t*-statistic is

$$t = \frac{\bar{y} - \mu_0}{SE(\bar{y})} = \frac{31.0 - 30.0}{0.886} = 1.13$$

So the observed mean is 1.13 standard errors above the hypothesized value.

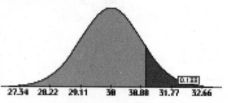

27.34 28.22 29.11 30 30.88 31.77 32.66

The corresponding P-value is 0.136.

The P-value of 0.136 says that if the true mean speed of vehicles on Triphammer road were 30 mph, samples of 21 vehicles can be expected to have an observed mean of at least 31.0 mph 13.6% of the time. That P-value is not small enough for us to reject the hypothesis that the true mean is 30mph. We conclude that there is not enough evidence to say that the average speed is too high.

Significance and Importance

Recall our warning that "statistically significant" does not mean "actually important" or "meaningful" even though it sort of sounds that way. In this example, it does seem that speeds may be a bit above 30 miles per hour. Possibly a larger sample would show statistical significance.

But is this really the right decision? The difference between 31 miles per hour and 30 miles per hour doesn't seem meaningful, and rejecting the null hypothesis wouldn't change that. Even with a statistically significant result, it would be hard to convince the police that vehicles on Triphammer road were driving at dangerously fast speeds. It would probably also be difficult to persuade the town that spending more money to lower the speed on Triphammer road was a good use of the town's resources. Looking at the confidence interval, we can say that with 90% confidence, the mean speed is somewhere between 29.5 and 32.5 mph. Even at the worst case, if the mean speed is 32.5 mph, would this be a bad enough situation to convince the town to spend more money? Probably not. It's always a good idea when we test a hypothesis to check the confidence interval to see the *range* of probable values for the mean.

Intervals and Tests

The 90% confidence interval for the mean speed was 31.0 mph ± 1.5 or [29.5 mph, 32.5 mph]. If someone hypothesized that the mean speed was really 30 mph how would you feel about it? How about 35 mph?

Because the confidence interval included the speed limit of 30 mph, it certainly looked like 30 mph might be a plausible value for the true mean speed of the vehicles on Triphammer road. In fact, 30 mph gave a P-value of 0.136, too large to reject the null hypothesis. We should have seen this coming. The hypothesized mean of 30 mph lies *within the confidence interval*. It's one of the reasonable values for the mean.

Confidence intervals and significance tests are built from the same calculations. In fact, they are really complementary ways of looking at the same question. Here's the connection. The confidence level contains all the null hypothesis values you can't reject.

More precisely, a level C confidence interval contains *all* of the possible null hypothesis values for which the two sided P-values would turn out to be *bigger* than 1 – C. Confidence intervals are naturally two sided, so they match exactly with two-sided hypothesis tests. When, as in our example, the hypothesis is one-sided, the corresponding P-values are bigger than (1 – C)/2.

Our 90% confidence interval was 29.5 to 32.5 mph. If we had selected any of these values as the null hypothesis for the mean, then the corresponding one sided P-value for our observed mean of 31 mph would be greater than $\frac{1-.90}{2} = .05$. So, we would fail to reject any hypothesized value between 29.5 and 32.5 mph.

Degrees of Freedom*

Some calculators offer an alternative button for standard deviation that divides by *n* instead of *n-1*. We recommend that you stick a piece of gum over that button so you won't be tempted to use it.

The number of degrees of freedom, *(n – 1)* might have reminded you of the value we divide by to find the standard deviation of the data (since, in fact, it's the same number). We promised back when we introduced that formula to say a bit more about why we divide by $n - 1$ rather than by n. The reason is closely tied to the reasoning of the *t*-distribution.

If only we knew the true population mean, μ, we would find the sample standard deviation as

$$\sqrt{\frac{\sum(y-\mu)^2}{n}}. \quad \text{(Equation 23.1)[5]}$$

But we use $\bar{y}$ instead of μ, and that causes a problem. For any sample, the data values will generally be closer to their own sample mean than to the true population mean, μ. Why is that? Imagine that we take a random sample of 10 high school seniors. The mean SAT verbal score is 500 in the U.S. But the sample mean, $\bar{y}$, for these 10 seniors won't be exactly 500. Are the 10 seniors scores closer to 500 or $\bar{y}$? They'll be closer to $\bar{y}$. So if we used $\sum(y-\bar{y})^2$ instead of $\sum(y-\mu)^2$ in equation 23.1 to calculate *s*, our standard deviation estimate would be too small. How can we fix it? The amazing mathematical fact is that we can compensate for this exactly by dividing by *n-1* instead of by *n*. So that's all the *n-1* is doing in the denominator of *s*. And we call *n-1* the degrees of freedom.

What Can Go Wrong?

Ways to not be Normal

Student's t methods only work when the Normality assumption is true. So naturally, many of the ways things can go wrong is for that assumption to fail. It's always a good idea to look for the most common kinds of failure. It turns out that you can even fix some of them.

- *Beware multimodality.* The Nearly Normal condition clearly fails if a histogram of the data has two or more modes. When you see this, look for the possibility that your data come from two groups. If so, your best bet is to try to separate the data into its separate groups. (Use the variables to help distinguish the modes if possible. For example, if the modes mostly seem to be men in one and women in the other, split the data according to sex.) Then analyze each group separately.

---

[5] Statistics textbooks usually have equation numbers so they can talk about equations by name. We haven't needed equation numbers yet, but, we admit it's useful here, so this is our first.

- *Beware skewed data.* Make a normal probability plot and a histogram of the data. If the data are very skewed, you might try re-expressing the variable. Re-expressing may yield a distribution that is unimodal and symmetric, more appropriate for the inference methods for means. Re-expression cannot help if the sample distribution is not unimodal. Some people may object to re-expressing the data, but unless your sample is very large, you just can't use the methods of this chapter on skewed data.

As tempting as it is to get rid of annoying values, you can't just throw away outliers. It isn't appropriate to lop off the highest or lowest values just to improve your inference results.

- *Set Outliers Aside.* The Nearly Normal condition also fails if the data have outliers. If you find outliers in the data, you may want to set them aside before using Student's *t* methods. Once they are singled out, you should look at them carefully. Sometimes, it's obvious that a data value is wrong and the justification for removing or correcting it is clear. But, when there's no clear justification for removing outliers, you might want to run the analysis both with and without the outliers and report any differences to your conclusions. Any time data values are set aside, you *must* report on them individually. Often they will turn out to be the most informative part of your report on the data.[6]

...And of course

- *Make sure data are independent.* Student's *t* methods also require that the sampled values be mutually independent. We check for random sampling and the 10% condition. But you should think hard about whether there are likely violations of independence in the data collection method. If there are, be very cautious about using these methods.

- *Make sure that data are from an appropriately randomized sample.* Ideally, all data that we analyze are drawn from a simple random sample. When they're not, be careful about making inferences from them. You may still compute a confidence interval correctly, or get the mechanics of the P-value right, but this might not save you from making a serious mistake in inference.

---

[6] This suggestion may be controversial in some disciplines. Setting aside outliers is seen by some as "cheating" because the result is likely to be a narrower confidence interval or a smaller P-value. But an analysis of data with outliers left in place is *always* wrong. The outliers violate the Nearly Normal condition and also the implicit assumption of a homogeneous population, so they invalidate inference procedures. An analysis of the non-outlying points along with a separate discussion of the outliers is often much more informative, and often can reveal important aspects of the data.

Inference for Means and the Computer

Statistics packages offer convenient ways to make histograms of the data. Even better for assessing near Normality is a normal probability plot. When you work on a computer there is simply no excuse for skipping the step of plotting the data to check that it is nearly Normal.

Any standard statistics package can complete such a hypothesis test. Here's what the package output might look like in general (although no package we know gives the results in exactly this form:)

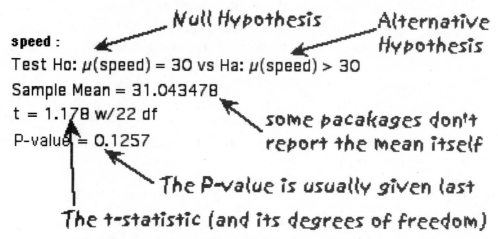

The package will compute the sample mean and sample standard deviation of the variable and find the P-value from the *t*-distribution based on the appropriate number of degrees of freedom. All modern statistics packages report P-values. The package output may also provide additional information such as the sample mean, sample standard deviation, *t*-statistic value, and number of degrees of freedom. These are useful for interpreting the resulting P-value and telling the difference between a meaningful result and one that is merely statistically significant.

Statistics packages that report the estimated standard deviation of the sampling distribution almost always label it "standard error" or "SE".

DRAFT: Do not distribute or copy

The commands to do inference for means on common statistics programs and calculators are not always obvious. (By contrast, the resulting output is usually clearly labeled and easy to read.) Here's a table to help you start navigating.

Package	Commands & Location	Comments
Data Desk	Select variables From the Calc menu, choose Estimate for confidence intervals or Test for hypothesis tests. Select the interval or test from the drop-down menu and make other choices in the dialog.	
Excel	Specify formulas. Find t* with the TINV(alpha, df) function	Not really automatic. There is no easy way to find P-values in Excel.
JMP	From the Analyze menu select Distribution. For a confidence interval, scroll down to the "Moments" section to find the interval limits. For a hypothesis test, click the red triangle next to the variable's name and choose Test Mean from the menu, then fill in the resulting dialog.	"Moment" is a fancy statistics term for means, standard deviations, and other related statistics. You don't need to know this term.
Minitab	From the Stat menu choose the Basic Statistics submenu. From that menu, choose 1-sample t... Then fill in the dialog.	The dialog offers a clear choice between confidence interval and test.
SPSS	From the Analyze menu choose the Compare Means submenu. From that, choose the One-Sample t-test command.	The commands suggest neither a single mean nor an interval. But the results provide both a test and an interval.
TI-83	Under STAT TESTS choose 8: Tinterval	

Connections

- The steps for finding a confidence interval or hypothesis test are identical to the corresponding steps for proportions. Even the form of the calculations is similar. The t-statistic, like the z-statistic for proportions, tells us how many standard errors our statistic is from the hypothesized mean. But for means we have to estimate the standard error separately from the mean. This added uncertainty changes the model for the sampling distribution from z to t.

- As with all of our inference methods, the randomization applied in drawing a random sample or in randomizing a comparative experiment is what generates the sampling distribution. So randomization is what makes inference in this way possible at all.

- The new concept of degrees of freedom connects back to the denominator of the sample standard deviation calculation, as shown earlier.

- There's just no escaping histograms and normal probability plots. The Nearly Normal condition required to use Student's t can only be checked by making appropriate displays of the data. Back when we first used histograms, we looked at their shape and in particular checked whether they were unimodal and symmetric and whether they showed any outliers. Those are just the features we check for here. The normal probability plot zeros in on the Normal model a little closer.

Key Concepts

Student's *t* distribution **Degrees of freedom**	A family of distributions indexed by their degrees of freedom. *t*-models are unimodal, symmetric, and bell-shaped, but generally have longer tails and a narrower center than the Normal model. As the degrees of freedom increase, *t*-distributions approach the Normal.
One sample *t*-interval	A confidence interval for the mean based on a statistic that follows a *t*-distribution.
One sample *t*-test	A significance test for a mean based on a statistic that follows a *t*-distribution.

Skills

At the end of this chapter you should:

Think

- Know the assumptions required for *t*-tests and *t*-based confidence intervals.

- Know how to examine your data for violations of conditions that would make inference about the population mean unwise or invalid.

- Understand that a confidence interval and a hypothesis test are essentially equivalent. You can do a two-tailed hypothesis test at level of significance α with a 100-α confidence interval, or a one-tailed test with a 100-2α confidence interval.

Show

- Be able to compute and interpret a *t*-test for the population mean using a statistics package or working from summary statistics for a sample.

- Be able to compute and interpret a *t*-based confidence interval for the population mean using a statistics package or working from summary statistics for a sample.

Tell

DRAFT: Do not distribute or copy

- Be able to summarize the meaning of a confidence interval for a population mean. Make clear that the randomness associated with the confidence level is a statement about the interval bounds and not about the population parameter value.

- Understand that a 95% confidence interval does not trap 95% of the sample values.

- Be able to interpret the result of a test of a hypothesis about a population mean.

- Know that we do not "accept" a null hypothesis if we cannot reject it. We only fail to reject it, or "retain" it.

- Understand that P-value of a test does not give the probability that the null hypothesis is correct.

Exercises

1. *t*-models (Part I) Using the *t*-tables, software, or a calculator, estimate:
   a) the critical value of *t* for a 90% confidence interval with df = 17.
   b) the critical value of *t* for a 98% confidence interval with df = 88.
   c) the P-value for $t \geq 2.09$ with 4 degrees of freedom.
   d) the P-value for $|t| > 1.78$ with 22 degrees of freedom.

2. *t*-models (Part II) Using the *t*-tables, software, or a calculator, estimate:
   a) the critical value of *t* for a 95% confidence interval with df = 7.
   b) the critical value of *t* for a 99% confidence interval with df = 102.
   c) the P-value for $t \leq 2.19$ with 41 degrees of freedom.
   d) the P-value for $|t| > 2.33$ with 12 degrees of freedom.

3. *t*-models (Part III) Describe how the shape, center, and spread of *t*-models change as the number of degrees of freedom increases.

4. *t*-models (Last One!) Describe how the critical value of *t* for a 95% confidence interval changes as the number of degrees of freedom increases.

5. **Cattle** Livestock are given a special feed supplement to see if it will promote weight gain. The researchers report that the 77 cows studied gained an average of 56 pounds, and that a 95% confidence interval for the mean weight gain this supplement produces has a margin of error of ±11 pounds. Some students wrote the following conclusions. Did anyone interpret the interval correctly? Explain any misinterpretations.
   e) 95% of the cows studied gained between 45 and 67 pounds.

f) We're 95% sure that a cow fed this supplement will gain between 45 and 67 pounds.

g) We're 95% sure that the average weight gain among the cows in this study was between 45 and 67 pounds.

h) The average weight gain of cows fed this supplement will be between 45 and 67 pounds 95% of the time.

i) If this supplement is tested on another sample of cows there is a 95% chance that their average weight gain will be between 45 and 67 pounds.

6. **Teachers** Software analysis of a random sample of 288 Nevada teachers produced the confidence interval shown below. Which conclusion is correct? What is wrong with the others?

t-Interval for μ: with 90.00% Confidence, 38944 < μ(TchPay) < 42893

a) If we took many random samples of Nevada teachers, about nine out of ten of them would produce this confidence interval.

b) If we took many random samples of Nevada teachers, about nine out of ten of them would produce a confidence interval that contained the mean salary of all Nevada teachers.

c) About 9 out of 10 Nevada teachers earn between $38,994 and $42,893.

d) About 9 out of 10 of the teachers surveyed earn between $38,994 and $42,893.

e) We are 90% confident that the average teacher salary in the US is between $38,994 and $42,893.

7. **Pulse Rates** A medical researcher measured the pulse rates (beats per minute) of a sample of randomly selected adults.

t-Interval for Individual μ's
With 95.00% Confidence, 70.887604 < μ(Pulse) < 74.497011

a) Explain carefully what the software output means.

b) What is the margin of error for this interval?

c) If the researcher had calculated a 99% confidence interval, would the margin of error be larger or smaller?

8. **Crawling** Data collected by child development scientists produced this confidence interval for the average age (in weeks) at which babies begin to crawl.

t-Interval for μ (95.00% Confidence): 29.202 < μ(age) < 31.844

a) Explain carefully what the software output means.

b) What is the margin of error for this interval?

c) If the researcher had calculated a 90% confidence interval, would the margin of error be larger or smaller?

9. **Normal Temperature** The researcher described in Exercise 7 also measured the body temperatures of that randomly selected group of adults. The data he collected are summarized below. We wish to estimate the average (or "normal") temperature among the adult population.

DRAFT: Do not distribute or copy

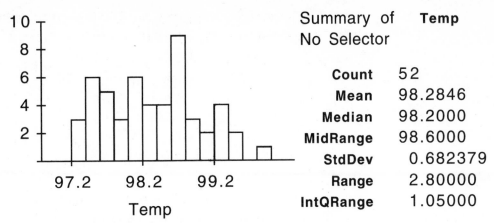

Summary of **Temp**
No Selector

Count	52
Mean	98.2846
Median	98.2000
MidRange	98.6000
StdDev	0.682379
Range	2.80000
IntQRange	1.05000

a. Are the necessary conditions satisfied? Explain.
b. Find a 98% confidence interval for mean body temperature.
c. Explain the meaning of that interval.
d. Explain what "98% confidence" means in this context.
e. 98.6 degrees is commonly assumed to be "normal". Do these data suggest otherwise? Explain.

10. **Parking** A city builds a new public parking garage in the central business district, hoping to lure more shoppers downtown. They plan to pay for the structure through parking fees. During a two-month period (44 weekdays), daily fees collected averaged $126 with a standard deviation of $15.
   a. What assumptions must you make in order to use these statistics for inference?
   b. Write a 90% confidence interval for the mean daily income this parking garage will generate.
   c. Explain in context what this confidence interval means.
   d. Explain what "90% confidence" means in this context.
   e. The consultant who advised the city on this project predicted that parking revenues would average $130 per day. Based on your confidence interval, do you think the consultant could have been correct? Why?

11. **Normal Temperatures, Part II** Consider again the statistics about human body temperature in Exercise 9.
   a. Would a 90% confidence interval be wider or narrower than the 98% confidence interval you calculated before? Explain. (You should not need to compute the new interval.)
   b. What are the advantages and disadvantages of the 98% confidence interval?
   c. If we conduct further research, this time using a sample of 500 adults, how would you expect the 98% confidence interval to change? Explain.

Copyright © 2001, Dick De Veaux and Paul Velleman

    d. How large a sample would you need to estimate the mean body temperature to within 0.1 degrees with 98% confidence?

12. **Parking II** Suppose that for budget planning purposes the city in Exercise 10 needs a better estimate of the mean daily income from parking fees.

    a. Someone suggests they use their data to create a 95% confidence interval instead of the 90% interval they first created. How would this interval be better for them? (You need not actually create the new interval.)

    b. How would the 95% interval be worse for the planners?

    c. How could they achieve an interval estimate that would better serve their planning needs?

    d. How many days worth of data must they collect to have 95% confidence of estimating the true mean to within $3?

13. **Hot Dogs** A nutrition laboratory tests 40 "reduced sodium" hot dogs, finding that the mean sodium content is 310 mg with a standard deviation of 36 mg.

    a. Find a 95% confidence interval for the mean sodium content of this brand of hot dog.

    b. What assumptions have you made in this inference? Are the appropriate conditions satisfied?

    c. Explain clearly what your interval means.

14. **Speed of Light** In 1882 Michelson measured the speed of light (usually denoted "C" as in the famous statement $e = mC^2$). His values are in km/sec and have 299,000 subtracted from them. He reported the results of 23 trials with a mean of 756.22 and a standard deviation of 107.12.

    a. Find a 95% confidence interval for the true speed of light from these statistics.

    b. State in words what this interval means. Keep in mind that the speed of light is a physical constant that, as far as we know, has a true value that is true throughout the universe.

    c. What assumptions must you make in order to use your method?

15. **Second Dog** The nutrition lab in Exercise 13 tests the hot dogs again, this time using a sample of 60 "reduced sodium" frankfurters. The new sample produces a mean of 318 mg of sodium, and the standard deviation is 32 mg.

    a. What is the standard error of the mean sodium content?

    b. Find and interpret a 95% confidence interval.

    c. Food labeling regulations require that any food identified as "reduced sodium" must have at least 30% less sodium than its regular counterpart. If regular franks average 465 mg of sodium, should this brand be labeled "reduced"? Explain, using your confidence interval.

16. **Better Light** After his first attempt to determine the speed of light (described in Exercise 14) Michelson conducted an "improved" experiment. In 1897 he reported results of 100 trials with a mean of 852.4 and a standard deviation of 79.0.
    a. What is the standard error of the mean for these data?
    b. Without computing it, how would you expect a 95% confidence interval for the second experiment to differ from the confidence interval for the first? Note at least three specific reasons why they might differ, and indicate the ways in which these differences would change the interval.
    c. According to Stigler (who reports these values), the true speed of light is 299,710.5, corresponding to a value of 710.5 for Michelson's 1897 measurements. What does this indicate about Michelson's experiments? Explain, using your confidence interval.

17. **TV Safety** The manufacturer of a metal stand for home sets must be sure that their product will not fail under the weight of the TV. Since some larger sets weigh nearly 300 pounds, the company's safety inspectors have set a standard of insuring that the stands can support an average of over 500 pounds. Their inspectors regularly subject a random sample of the stands to increasing weight until they fail. They test the hypothesis $H_0: \mu = 500$ against $H_0: \mu > 500$, using the level of significance $\alpha = 0.01$. If the sample of stands fail to pass this safety test the inspectors will not certify the product for sale to the general public.
    a. Is this an upper-tail or lower-tail test? In the context of the problem, why do you think this is important?
    b. Explain what will happen if the inspectors commit a Type I error.
    c. Explain what will happen if the inspectors commit a Type II error.

18. **Catheters** During an angiogram, heart problems can be examined via a small tube (a catheter) threaded into the heart from a vein in the patient's leg. It is important that the company who manufactures the catheter maintain a diameter of 2.00 mm. (The standard deviation is quite small.) Each day quality control personnel make several measurements to test $H_0: \mu = 2.00$ against $H_0: \mu \neq 2.00$ at a significance level of $\alpha = 0.05$. If they discover a problem they will stop the manufacturing process until it is corrected.
    a. Is this a one-sided or 2-sided test? In the context of the problem, why do you think this is important?
    b. Explain in this context what happens if the quality control people commit a Type I error.
    c. Explain in this context what happens if the quality control people commit a Type II error.

19. **TV Safety Revisited** The manufacturer of the metal TV stands in Exercise 17 is thinking of revising its safety test.

Copyright © 2001, Dick De Veaux and Paul Velleman

    a. If the company's lawyers are worried about being sued for selling an unsafe product, should they increase or decrease the value of α? Explain.

    b. In this context, what is meant by the power of the test?

    c. If the company wants to increase the power of the test, what options do they have? Explain the advantages and disadvantages of each option.

20. **Catheters Again** The catheter company in Exercise 18 is reviewing its testing procedure.

    a. Suppose they change the significance level to $\alpha = 0.01$. Will the probability of Type II error increase, decrease, or remain the same?

    b. What is meant by the power of the test they conduct?

    c. Suppose the manufacturing process is slipping out of proper adjustment. As the actual mean diameter of the catheters produced gets farther and farther above the desired 2.00 mm, will the power of the quality control test increase, decrease, or remain the same?

    d. What could they do to improve the power of their test?

21. **Marriage** In 1960, census results indicated that the age at which American men first married had a mean of 23.3 years. It is widely suspected that young people today are waiting longer to get married. We want to find out if the mean age of first marriage has increased during the past 40 years.

    a. Write appropriate hypotheses.

    b. We plan to test our hypothesis by selecting a random sample of 40 men who married for the first time last year. Do you think the necessary assumptions for inference are satisfied? Explain.

    c. Describe the approximate sampling distribution model for the mean age in such samples.

    d. The men in our sample married at an average age of 24.2 years with a standard deviation of 5.3 years. What is the P-value for this result?

    e. Explain (in context) what this P-value means.

    f. What is your conclusion?

22. **Fuel Economy** A company with a large fleet of cars hopes to keep gasoline costs down, and sets a goal of attaining a fleet average of at least 26 miles per gallon. To see if the goal is being met they check the gasoline usage for 50 company trips chosen at random, finding a mean of 25.02 mpg and a standard deviation of 4.83 mpg. Is this strong evidence that they have failed to attain their fuel economy goal?

    a. Write appropriate hypotheses.

    b. Are the necessary assumptions to perform inference satisfied?

    c. Describe the sampling distribution model of mean fuel economy for samples like this.

    d. Find the P-value.

    e. Explain what the P-value means in this context.

    f. State an appropriate conclusion.

23. **Ruffles** Students investigating the packaging of potato chips purchased 6 bags of Lay's Ruffles marked with a net weight of 28.3 grams. They carefully weighed the contents of each bag, recording the following weights (in grams): 29.3, 28.4, 29.1, 28.7, 29.0, 28.5
    a. Do these data satisfy the assumptions for inference? Explain.
    b. Find the mean and standard deviation of the observed weights.
    c. Create a 95% confidence interval for the mean weight of such bags of chips.
    d. Explain in context what your interval means.
    e. Comment on the company's stated net weight of 28.3 grams.

24. **Doritos** The students also checked 6 bags of Doritos marked with a net weight of 28.3 grams. They carefully weighed the contents of each bag, recording the following weights (in grams): 29.2, 28.5, 28.7, 28.6, 29.1, 29.5
    a. Do these data satisfy the assumptions for inference? Explain.
    b. Find the mean and standard deviation of the observed weights.
    c. Create a 95% confidence interval for the mean weight of such bags of chips.
    d. Explain in context what your interval means.
    e. Comment on the company's stated net weight of 28.3 grams.

25. **Cars** One of the important factors in auto safety is the weight of the vehicle. Insurance companies are interested in knowing the average weight of cars currently licensed in the US; they believe it is 3000 pounds. To see if that estimate is correct, they checked a random sample of 91 cars. For that group the mean weight was 2919 pounds, with a standard deviation of 531.5 pounds. Is this strong evidence that the mean weight of all cars is not 3000 pounds?

26. **Portable Phones** A manufacturer claims that a new design for their portable phone has increased the range to 150 feet, allowing many customers to use the phone throughout their homes and yards. An independent testing laboratory found that a random sample of 44 of these phones worked over an average distance of 142 feet, with a standard deviation of 12 feet. Is there evidence that the manufacturer's claim is false?

27. **Chips Ahoy** In 1998, as an advertising campaign, the Nabisco Company announced a "1000 Chips Challenge", claiming that every 18-ounce bag of their Chips Ahoy cookies contained at least 1000 chocolate chips. Dedicated statistics students at the Air Force Academy (no kidding) purchased some randomly selected bags of cookies, and counted the chocolate chips. Some of their data are given below. [Chance, Volume 12, No. 1, 1999]

1219	1214	1087	1200	1419	1121	1325	1345
1244	1258	1356	1132	1191	1270	1295	1135

a. Check the assumptions and conditions for inference.
b. Create a 95% confidence interval for the average number of chips in bags of Chips Ahoy cookies.
c. What does this evidence say about Nabisco's claim? Use your confidence interval to test an appropriate hypothesis and state your conclusion.

28. **Yogurt** *Consumer Reports* tested 14 brands of vanilla yogurt and found the following numbers of calories per serving:

160	200	220	230	120	180	140
130	170	190	80	120	100	170

a. Check the assumptions and conditions for inference.
b. Create a 95% confidence interval for the average calorie content of vanilla yogurt.
c. A diet guide claims that you will get 120 calories from a serving of vanilla yogurt. What does this evidence indicate? Use your confidence interval to test an appropriate hypothesis and state your conclusion.

29. **Maze** Psychology experiments sometimes involve testing the ability of rats to navigate mazes. The mazes are classified according to difficulty, as measured by the mean length of time it takes rats to find the food at the end. One researcher needs a maze that will take rats an average of about one minute to solve. He tests one maze on several rats, collecting the data at the right.

a. Plot the data. Do you think the conditions for inference are satisfied? Explain.
b. Test the hypothesis that the mean completion time for this maze is 60 seconds. What is your conclusion?
c. Eliminate the outlier, and test the hypothesis again. What is your conclusion?
d. Do you think this maze meets the "one-minute average" requirement? Explain.

Time (sec)
38.4
46.2
72.5
38.0
82.8
33.9
50.4
35.0
32.8
60.1
75.1
57.6
55.5
49.5
40.9
44.3
93.8
47.9
75.2
46.2
56.3

30. **Braking** A tire manufacturer is considering a newly designed tread pattern for its all-weather tires. Tests have indicated that these tires will provide better gas mileage and longer tread life. The last remaining test is for braking effectiveness. The company hopes the tire will allow a car traveling at 60 mph to come to a complete stop within an average of 125 feet after the brakes are applied. They will adopt the new tread pattern unless there is strong evidence that the tires do not meet this objective. The distances (in feet) for 10 stops on a test track were 129, 120, 130, 132, 135, 123, 128, 102, 128, and 130. Should the company adopt the new tread pattern? Test an appropriate hypothesis and state your conclusion. Explain how you dealt with the outlier, and why you made the recommendation you did.

24 Comparing Means

S HOULD YOU BUY GENERIC RATHER THAN BRAND-NAME BATTERIES? A statistics student tested battery life by keeping a battery-powered CD player with the same CD running continuously, fixing the volume control at 5. For the experiment, he used six pairs of AA alkaline batteries from two major battery manufacturers: a well-known brand name and a generic brand. He measured the time until no more music was heard through the headphones. (He ran an initial trial to find out approximately how long that would take, so that he didn't have to spend the first 3 hours of each run listening to the same CD). Here are his data:

Brand Name	Generic
194.0	190.7
205.5	203.5
199.2	203.5
172.4	206.5
184.0	222.5
169.5	209.4

Who: AA alkaline batteries

What: Battery life playing a CD continuously

Unit: Minutes

Why: Class project

When: ??

Experiments that compare two groups are common throughout both science and industry. We might want to compare the effects of a new drug with the traditional therapy, the fuel efficiency of two car engine designs, or the amount of sales of new product in two different test cities. In fact, battery manufacturers perform such experiments themselves.

Plot the Data

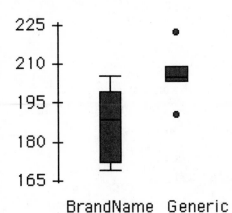

The natural display for comparing two groups is boxplots of the data for the two groups, side-by-side. Although we can t make a confidence interval or test a hypothesis from the boxplots themselves, you should always start with boxplots when comparing groups. Here are boxplots of the battery test data:

It sure looks like the generic batteries lasted longer. And we can see that they were also more consistent. But is the difference large enough to change our battery buying behavior? Can we be confident that the difference is more than just random fluctuation? That s why we need statistical inference.

The boxplot for the generic data identifies two possible outliers. That s interesting, but with only six measurements in each group, the outlier nomination rule is not very reliable, and neither of the extreme values is unreasonable.

Comparing Two Means

Comparing two means is not very different from comparing two proportions. In fact, it s not different in concept from any of the methods we ve seen. But here, the population model parameter of interest is the difference between the mean battery lifetimes of the two brands, $\mu_1 - \mu_2$.

The rest is the same as before. The statistic of interest is the difference in the two observed means, $\bar{y}_1 - \bar{y}_2$. We ll need to know its standard deviation and its sampling model. Then we can build confidence intervals and find P-values for hypothesis tests.

We know that for independent random quantities, variances add. It worked for proportions; it works for means. To find the standard deviation of the difference between the two sample means we add their variances and then take a square root:

$$SD(\bar{y}_1 - \bar{y}_2) = \sqrt{Var(\bar{y}_1) + Var(\bar{y}_2)}$$

$$= \sqrt{\left(\frac{\sigma_1}{\sqrt{n_1}}\right)^2 + \left(\frac{\sigma_2}{\sqrt{n_2}}\right)^2}$$

$$= \sqrt{\frac{\sigma_1^2}{n_1} + \frac{\sigma_2^2}{n_2}}$$

Of course, we still don t know the true standard deviations σ_1 and σ_2, so as usual, we ll use the estimates, s_1 and s_2. Using the estimates give us the *standard error,*

$$SE(\bar{y}_1 - \bar{y}_2) = \sqrt{\frac{s_1^2}{n_1} + \frac{s_2^2}{n_2}}.$$

We ll use this to see how big the difference really is. Because we are working with means and estimating the standard error of their difference using the data, we shouldn t be surprised that the sampling model is a Student s t.

The confidence interval we build is called a **two-sample t-interval** (for the mean). The hypothesis test is called a **two-sample t-test**.

The confidence interval looks just like all the others we ve seen; the statistic plus or minus an estimated margin of error:

$$\bar{y}_1 - \bar{y}_2 \pm ME$$

$$where \quad ME = t^* SE(\bar{y}_1 - \bar{y}_2)$$

Compare this formula to the one for the confidence interval for the difference of two proportions we saw in chapter 22. It is almost the same except that now we use a Student s *t* model instead of a *z** from the Normal model because here the estimated standard deviations are not linked to the estimated means as they were for proportions.

What are we missing? Only the degrees of freedom for the Student s *t* model, so we can find the critical t* value corresponding to our chosen confidence level. Unfortunately, *that* formula is strange.

The deep, dark secret is that the sampling model isn t *really* Student s *t,* but only something close to that. But by using a special degrees of freedom calculation, we can make it so close to the appropriate Student s *t* model that nobody could tell the difference The approximation formula is straightforward, but doesn t help us understand anything, so we leave it to the computer or calculator. (If you are curious and really want to see the formula, look in this footnote.)[1]

An Easier Rule?

Because the formula for the degrees of freedom of the sampling distribution of the difference between two means is so complicated, some books teach an easier rule: The number of degrees of freedom is always at *least* the smaller of the two *n*'s, minus1. The problem with using this method is that it can be off by more than 50%. If you *need* to put a number down and don't have the formula at hand use this worst case approximation, but realize that the approximation formula is much better.

Assumptions and Conditions

Now we ve got everything we need. But before we can do a **two-sample *t*-interval** or a **two-sample *t*-test**, we ll need to check the assumptions and conditions.

Independence Assumption

The data in each group must be drawn independently and at random from a homogeneous population, or generated by a randomized comparative experiment. We can t expect that the data, taken as one big group, come from a homogeneous population, because that s what we re trying to check. But

---

[1]

$$[1] \quad df = \frac{\left(\dfrac{s_1^2}{n_1} + \dfrac{s_2^2}{n_2}\right)^2}{\dfrac{1}{n_1-1}\left(\dfrac{s_1^2}{n_1}\right)^2 + \dfrac{1}{n_2-1}\left(\dfrac{s_2^2}{n_2}\right)^2}$$

Bet you wish you didn't look. Notice that this formula usually doesn t give a whole number. We usually round down. But in fact, the approximation formulas that computers use for the Student s *t* distribution can deal with fractional degrees of freedom, and it s OK to pass the fractional form through to those formulas.

without randomization of some sort, there are no sampling distribution models and no inference. We check the

Randomization Condition: were the data collected with suitable randomization? For surveys, are they a representative random sample? For experiments, was the experiment randomized?

10% Condition to check that we have not violated the independence assumption by sampling too large a fraction of the population.

Normal Population Assumption

And, as we did before with Student s *t* models, we should check the assumption that the underlying populations are *each* Normally distributed. We check the

Nearly Normal Condition. We must check this for *both* samples; a violation by either one violates the condition. As we saw for single sample means, the Normality assumption matters most when sample sizes are small. For samples of $n < 15$ in either group, you should not use these methods if the histogram or normal probability plot shows severe skewness. For samples of n less than 40, a mildly skewed histogram is OK, but you should remark on any outliers you find and not work with severely skewed data. When both samples are bigger than 40, the Nearly Normal Condition assumption matters less, but you should still treat outliers carefully because they may provide useful information.

Independent Samples Assumption

As for the two proportion z interval, the two groups we are comparing here must be independent of each other. There is no statistical test for this. You have to think about how the data were collected. This assumption would be violated, for example, if we compared husbands with their wives. Or if we compared subjects performances before some treatment with their performances after the treatment. In cases such as these, where the observational units in the two groups are related, the two-sample methods of this chapter can t be applied. When this happens we need a different procedure, as we ll see in the next chapter.

A Two Sample *t* Interval, Step-by-Step

Judging from the boxplot, the generic batteries seem to have lasted about 20 minutes longer than the brand-name batteries. But should we change our buying habits? What should we expect to happen with the next batteries we buy? How much longer might the generics last? Let s make a confidence interval for the differences of the means.

Think **Parameter:** Identify the *parameter* you wish to estimate. Here the parameter is the difference in the means of the populations to which the two groups belong.

We wish to find an interval that is likely with 95% confidence to contain the true difference $\mu_G - \mu_B$ between the mean lifetime of the generic brand AA

DRAFT: Do not distribute or copy

batteries and the mean lifetime of the brand-name batteries.

Choose and state a confidence level

Reality Check

From the box plot, our confidence interval should be centered near 20 minutes. We don t have a lot of intuition about how far the interval should extend either side of 20.

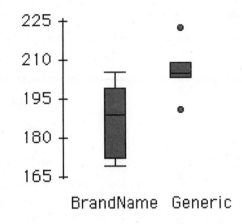

BrandName   Generic

Plan

Check the conditions.

✓ **Independent Samples Assumption:** Batteries manufactured by two different companies from separate packages should be independent.

✓ **Random Sample Condition:** The batteries were selected at random from those available for sale. Not exactly an SRS, but a reasonably representative random sample. But the batteries do come in packs, so they may not be independent. For example, a storage problem might affect all the batteries in the same pack. To make our case stronger, we might want to repeat the experiment for several different packs of batteries.

✓ **10% Condition:** Although sampling was necessarily without replacement, there are many more batteries than were sampled.

✓ **Nearly Normal Condition:** The samples are small, but histograms look unimodal and symmetric:

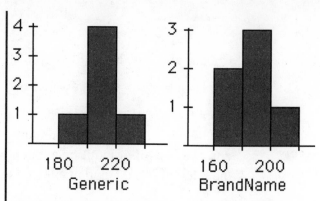

Generic   BrandName

Under these conditions the sampling model of the difference in the sample means can be modeled by a Student's t model on about 9 degrees of freedom.

We will use a **two-sample t-interval**.

State the sampling distribution model model for the statistic. Here the degrees of freedom come from the approximation formula.

Choose your method.

Show **Mechanics:** Construct the confidence interval.

We know:

$$n_1 = 6 \qquad n_2 = 6$$
$$\bar{y}_1 = 206.0 \quad \bar{y}_2 = 187.4$$
$$s_1 = 10.3 \qquad s_2 = 14.6$$

Because we think the independence condition is OK, we can say that:

$$SE(\bar{y}_1 - \bar{y}_2) = \sqrt{SE^2(\bar{y}_1) + SE^2(\bar{y}_2)}$$

$$= \sqrt{\frac{s_1^2}{n_1} + \frac{s_2^2}{n_2}}$$

$$= \sqrt{\frac{10.3^2}{6} + \frac{14.6^2}{6}}$$

$$= \sqrt{\frac{106.13}{6} + \frac{213.48}{6}}$$

$$= \sqrt{53.268}$$

$$= 7.3$$

The sampling model has 8.98 degrees of freedom (from the approximation formula).

---

[3] This claim is a good example of what is called a research hypothesis in many social sciences. The only way to check it is to deny that it is true and see where the resulting null hypothesis leads us.

DRAFT: Do not distribute or copy

We have three choices for degrees of freedom. The best alternative is to let the computer or calculator use the approximation formula. This gives a fractional degree of freedom (here df = 8.98), but the technology can find a corresponding critical value. In this case it is t* = 2.263.

Or we could round the approximation formula s df value down to an integer so we can use a t-table. That gives 8 df and a critical value, t* = 2.306.

The easy(?) rule says to use only 6 — 1 = 5 df. That gives a critical value t* = 2.571. The corresponding confidence interval is about 14% wider a high price to pay for a small savings in effort.

The corresponding critical value for a 95% confidence level from a Student's t model on 8.98 df is $t^* = 2.263$

From these, we find the margin of error:
$$ME = t^* \times SE(\bar{y}_1 - \bar{y}_2)$$
$$= 2.263 \times 7.3$$
$$= 16.52$$

So the 95% confidence interval is:

(206.0 – 187.4) ± 16.5 minutes

or 18.6 ± 16.5 minutes

= [2.1, 35.1] minutes

Tell

Interpretation: Tell what the confidence interval means.

We are 95% confident that the mean useful life of the generic batteries is between 2.1 minutes and 35.1 minutes longer than the mean useful life of the brand-name batteries for this task. If generic batteries are cheaper, there seems little reason not to use them. If it is more trouble or costs more to buy them, then you should consider whether the additional performance is worth it.

Another One Just Like the Other Ones?

Yes. That s been our point all along. Once again we see a statistic – margin of error. And the ME is just a critical value times the standard error. Just look out for that crazy degrees of freedom formula.

Testing the Difference Between Two Means

If you bought a used camera in good condition from a friend, would you pay the same as you would if you bought the same item from a stranger? A researcher at Cornell University wanted to know how friendship might affect simple sales such as this. (Halpern, J.J. (1997). The transaction index: A method for standardizing comparisons of transaction characteristics across different contexts, *Group Decision and Negotiation*, 6(6), 557-572.) She randomly divided subjects into two groups and gave each group descriptions of items that they might want to buy. One group was told to imagine buying from a friend whom they expected to see again. The other group was told to imagine buying from a stranger.

Here are the prices they offered for a used camera in good condition:

Buying from a Friend	Buying from a Stranger
$275	$260
300	250
260	175
300	130
255	200
275	225
290	240
300	

Who: University Students
What: Prices offered for a used camera.
Unit: Dollars
Why: Study of the effects of friendship on transactions.
When: 1990's
Where: Cornell University

It looks like there s a difference. Here are the boxplots:

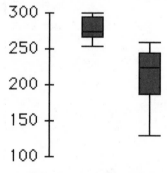

Buy from Friend
Buy from Stranger

But is the difference statistically significant? Should we really be careful when buying items from a friend? Let s perform a hypothesis test.

A Two-Sample *t*-test for the Mean, Step-By-Step

The usual null hypothesis is that there s no difference. That s just what we hope to find out here.

DRAFT: Do not distribute or copy

Think

Hypotheses: State what we want to know.

We want to know whether people are likely to offer a different amount for a used camera when buying from a friend than when buying from a stranger.

Claim: Friendship changes what people are willing to pay[3].

We didn t start with any knowledge of whether friendship might increase or decrease the price, so we choose a two-sided alternative

H_0: The difference in mean price offered to friends and the mean price offered to strangers is zero; $\mu_F - \mu_S = 0$

H_A: The difference in mean prices is not zero: $\mu_F - \mu_S \neq 0$.

Reality Check:

Looks like the prices are higher if you buy from a friend, but it s hard to be sure. The two ranges barely overlap so we d be pretty surprised if we don t reject the null hypothesis.

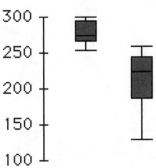

Buy from Friend

Buy from Stranger

Plan: State the **Null Model.**

Check the **conditions**

✓ **Independent Groups Assumption:** Randomization gives us independent groups

✓ **Random Sampling Condition:** The experiment was randomized. Subjects were assigned to treatment groups at random.

✓ **10% Condition:** The experiment observes some of what could be a very large number of subjects.

✓ **Nearly Normal Condition:** Histograms of the two sets of prices are unimodal and symmetric:

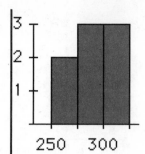 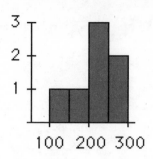

Buy from Friend   Buy from Stranger

State the sampling distribution model of the statistic.

Because the conditions are satisfied, it is appropriate to model the sampling distribution of the difference in the means with a Student's *t* model.

Choose your method.

We will perform a **two-sample *t*-test.**

Show Mechanics:

We know:

$$n_1 = 8 \qquad n_2 = 7$$
$$\bar{y}_1 = \$281.88 \quad \bar{y}_2 = \$211.43$$
$$s_1 = \$18.31 \qquad s_2 = \$46.43$$

We use the null model to find the **P-value**.

Because the independence condition appears to be satisfied, we can say that:

$$SE(\bar{y}_1 - \bar{y}_2) = \sqrt{SE^2(\bar{y}_1) + SE^2(\bar{y}_2)}$$

$$= \sqrt{\frac{s_1^2}{n_1} + \frac{s_2^2}{n_2}}$$

$$= \sqrt{\frac{18.31^2}{8} + \frac{46.43^2}{7}}$$

$$= \sqrt{349.87}$$

$$= 18.70$$

A statistics program or graphing calculator can find the P- value using the fractional degrees of freedom from the approximation formula.

The sampling distribution model has 7.73 degrees of freedom (from the approximation formula).

The test statistic is

$$t = \frac{(\bar{y}_1 - \bar{y}_2) - (0)}{SE(\bar{y}_1 - \bar{y}_2)} = \frac{70.44}{18.70} = 3.77$$

If you are doing a test like this without software, you could use the smaller sample size to determine degrees of

The P-value corresponding to this statistic (found from a Student's *t* model on 7.73 df) is 0.006.

freedom. In this case $n_2 - 1 = 6$.

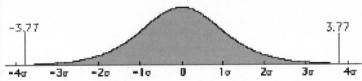

Tell

Conclusion: State the conclusion.

The P-value tells us that, if the null hypothesis were true and there were no difference in the mean prices, the difference we have observed would occur only 6 times in 1000. That's too rare for most folks to believe, so we reject the null hypothesis and conclude that people are likely to pay more to a friend for a used camera (and possibly for other similar items.)

If possible, propose a course of action.

We may want to take special care not to pay too much when buying an item such as this from a friend.

Back Into the Pool

When we tested whether two proportions were equal, we could assume that their variances were equal. This led us to pool our data. For means, if we are willing to make the equivalent assumption, we can use a **pooled t test.** For the pooled t, the degrees of freedom formula is simpler. But be careful. Means don t have any link between their value and their variance. Just because two means are equal doesn t say anything about their variances. But we can pool our data if we are willing to make that additional assumption.

Equal Variance Assumption:

The variances of the two populations from which the samples have been drawn are equal. That is, $\sigma_1^2 = \sigma_2^2$. (Of course, we can think about the standard deviations being equal instead.)

If we can assume equal variances, then we can find a standard error based on pooling the data. We can find it from the numbers we already have:

$$s_{pooled}^2 = \frac{(n_1 - 1)s_1^2 + (n_2 - 1)s_2^2}{(n_1 - 1) + (n_2 - 1)}$$

(Notice that if the two sample sizes are equal, this is just the average of the two variances.)

Now we just substitute this pooled variance for each of the variances in the standard error formula:

$$SE(\bar{y}_1 - \bar{y}_2) = \sqrt{\frac{s_1^2}{n_1} + \frac{s_2^2}{n_2}},$$

After substituting, the standard error formula now looks like this:

$$SE_{pooled}(\bar{y}_1 - \bar{y}_2) = \sqrt{\frac{s_{pooled}^2}{n_1} + \frac{s_{pooled}^2}{n_2}} = s_{pooled}\sqrt{\frac{1}{n_1} + \frac{1}{n_2}}$$

The formula for degrees of freedom for the Student s t model is simpler too. It was so complicated for the two-sample t that we stuck it in a footnote. Now it s just $n_1 + n_2 - 2$, which is usually a bit bigger than you d get by using a two-sample t.

Substitute the pooled-t estimate of the standard error and its degrees of freedom into the steps of the confidence interval or hypothesis test and you ll be using the pooled-t methods. Of course, if you decide to use a pooled-t method, you must defend your assumption that the variances of the two groups are equal.

But how can we defend an assumption like that? We re testing whether the means are equal, so we admit that we don t *know* whether they are equal. Isn t it a bit much to just *assume* that the variances are equal?

Is the Pool all Wet?

So when *should* you use pooled t methods rather than two-sample t methods?

Never.

What, never?

Well, hardly ever.

You see, when the variances of the two groups are in fact equal, the two methods give pretty much the same result. Pooled methods have a small advantage (slightly narrower confidence intervals, slightly more powerful tests) mostly due to the increased degrees of freedom, but the advantage is slight.

And when the variances are *not* equal the pooled methods are just not valid, and can give poor results. You have to use the two-sample methods instead.

Because the advantages of pooling are small, and you are allowed to pool only rarely (when the equal variances assumption is met), don't.

It's never wrong *not* to pool.

As the sample sizes get bigger, the advantages that come from a few more degrees of freedom make less and less difference. So the advantage (such as it is) of the pooled method is greatest when the samples are small just when it is hardest to check the conditions. So, our advice is to use the two-sample t methods to compare means.

So, why did we devote a whole section to a method that we don t recommend using? Good question. The answer is that pooled methods are actually very important in Statistics. We ll see important pooled methods in coming chapters. It s just that the simplest of the pooled methods the methods for comparing two means have good alternatives in the two-sample methods that don t

DRAFT: Do not distribute or copy

require the extra assumption. Without the burden of the equal variances assumption, the two-sample methods apply to more situations and are safer to use.

Why not Test the Condition that the Variances are Equal?

There is a hypothesis test that would do this. But it is very sensitive to failures of the assumptions and works poorly for small sample sizes just the situation where we might care about a difference in the methods. When the choice between two sample and pooled *t* methods makes a difference (that is, when the sample sizes are small), the test for whether the variances are equal hardly works at all.

Is There Ever a Time when Assuming Equal Variances Makes Sense?

Yes. In a randomized comparative experiment, we start out by assigning our experiment units to treatments at random. We know that at the start of the experiment each treatment group is a random sample from the same population, so each treatment group starts with the same population variance. In this case, assuming equal variances is equivalent to assuming that the treatment doesn t change the variance. When we test the difference between the means, the null hypothesis is almost always that the true means are equal. If we are willing to stretch that idea to saying that the treatments made no difference *at all* (for example, that the treatment is no different from the placebo offered as a control), then it is reasonable to assume that the variances have remained equal. It s still an assumption and there are conditions that need to be checked, but at least it s a plausible assumption.

This line of reasoning is important. The methods used to analyze comparative experiments *do* pool variances in exactly this way and defend the pooling with a version of this argument.

Tukey s Quick Test*

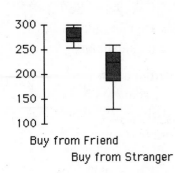

Buy from Friend
Buy from Stranger

The famous statistician John Tukey[4] was once challenged to come up with a simpler alternative to the two-sample t-test that, like the 68-95-99.7 rule, could be easily remembered. The test he came up with asks you only to count and remember three numbers: 7, 10, and 13.

When you first looked at the boxplots of the price data, you might have noticed that they didn t overlap very much. That s the basis for Tukey s test.

---

[4] You know some of his other work. Tukey originated the stem-and-leaf display and the boxplot in the form we use here and published theoretical work on data re-expression that justifies the recommendations of Chapter 10.

Buying from a Friend	Buying from a Stranger
$275	$260
300	250
260	175
300	130
255	200
275	225
290	240
300	

To use this test, one group must have the highest value and the other, the lowest. We just count how many values in the high group are higher than *all* the values of the lower group. Add to this the number of values in the low group that are lower than *all* the value of the higher group. (You can count ties as $\frac{1}{2}$.) Now if this total is 7 or more, we can reject the null hypothesis of equal means at $\alpha = .05$. The critical values of 10 and 13 give us α s of .01 and .001.

Let s try it. The Friend group has the highest value ($300) and the Stranger group has the lowest ($130). Six of the values in the Friend group are higher than the highest value of the Stranger group ($260) and one is a tie. Six of the Stranger values are lower than the lowest value for Friends. That s a total of $12\frac{1}{2}$ values.

That s more than 10, but less than 13. So the P-value is between .01 and .001 — just what we found with the two-sample t.

This is a remarkably good test, and the only assumption it requires is that the two samples are independent. And it is so simple to do that there is no reason not to do one to check your two-sample t results. If they disagree, check the assumptions. But Tukey s quick test is not as widely known or accepted as the two-sample t test, so you still need to know and use the two-sample t.

What Can Go Wrong

- *Watch out for Paired Data*. The **Independent Samples Assumption** deserves special attention. A failure of this condition disqualifies these methods. This is probably the main thing that can go wrong when using these two—sample methods. Suppose you wanted to test a diet program. You select 10 people at random to take part in your diet. You measure their weights at the beginning of the diet and after 10 weeks of the diet. So, you have two columns of weights, one for *before* and one for *after.* Can you use these methods to test whether the mean has gone down? No! The data are paired. Certainly someone s weight before and after the 10 weeks will be related (whether the diet works or not). The methods of this chapter can be used *only* if the observations in the two groups are *independent*. Paired data arise often and are important. We ll devote another chapter to them.

  Look at the Plots The usual (by now) warnings about checking for outliers and non-normal distributions apply, of course.

Do what we say, not what we do…

Precision machines used in industry often have a bewildering number of parameters that have to be set, so experiments are preformed in an attempt to try to find the best settings. Such was the case for a hole-punching machine used to make printed circuit boards by a well-known computer manufacturer. The data were analyzed by one of the authors, but because he was in a rush, he didn't look at the box plots first and just performed t-tests on the experimental factors. When he found very very small P-values even for factors that made no sense, he plotted the data. Sure enough, there was one observation 1,000,000 times bigger than the others. It turns out that it had been recorded in microns (millionths of an inch) while all the rest were in inches.

DRAFT: Do not distribute or copy

The simple defense is to make and examine boxplots. You may be surprised how often this simple step saves you from the wrong or even absurd conclusions that can be generated by a single undetected outlier. Concluding that two methods have very different means just because one observation is atypical is not something that you want to do.

•

Two-Sample Methods and the Computer

Here s some typical computer package output with comments:

May just say "difference of means"

2-Sample t-Test of µ1-µ2 ←

Difference Between Means = 0.99145299 t-Statistic = 1.540
w/196 df   *Test Statistic*
Fail to reject Ho at Alpha = 0.05
P = 0.9374

Many programs give far too many digits. Ignore the excess ones.

df found from approximation formula

Some programs will draw a conclusion about the test. Others just give the P-value and let you decide for yourself.

Most statistics packages compute the test statistic for you and report a P-value corresponding to that statistic. And, of course, statistics packages make it easy to examine the boxplots of the two groups, so you have no excuse for skipping this important check.

Some statistics software automatically tries to test whether the variances of the two groups are equal. Some automatically offer both the two-sample t and pooled-t results. Ignore the test for the variances; it is not valid for any situation in which its results could matter. If the pooled and two-sample methods are different in any important way, you should stick with the two-sample method. Most likely, the equal variance assumption needed for the pooled method has failed.

The degrees of freedom approximation usually gives a fractional value. Most packages seem to round the approximate value down to the next smallest integer (although they may actually compute with the fractional value, gaining a tiny amount of power).

There are two ways to organize data when we want to compare two independent groups. The data can be in two lists, as in the table at the start of this chapter.

Each list can be thought of as a variable. In this case, the variables would be *brand name* and *generic*. Graphing calculators usually prefer this form, and some computer programs can use it as well.

But there is another way to think about the data. What is the response variable here? It s the time until the music stopped. But this is in both columns. And actually there s a predictor variable here too; namely, the brand of the battery. So, we could think of the data as being in two different columns, one with the *times* in it and one with the *brand*. Then the data would look like this:

Time	Brand
169.5	Brand Name
205.5	Brand Name
184.0	Brand Name
172.4	Brand Name
194.0	Brand Name
199.2	Brand Name
190.7	Generic
203.5	Generic
203.5	Generic
206.5	Generic
222.5	Generic
209.4	Generic

This way of organizing the data makes sense as well. Now the predictor and the response variables are clearly visible. You ll have to check to see which method your program requires. Some packages even allow you to enter the data either way depending on which part of the package you re using to analyze the difference between two means.

The commands to do inference for two independent groups on common statistics technology are not always found in obvious places.

DRAFT: Do not distribute or copy

Package	Commands & Location	Comments
Data Desk	Select variables From the Calc menu, choose Estimate for confidence intervals or Test for hypothesis tests. Select the interval or test from the drop-down menu and make other choices in the dialog.	Data Desk expects the two groups to be in separate variables.
Excel	From the Tools menu, choose Data Analysis. From the Data Analysis menu, choose t-test: two-sample assuming unequal variances Fill in the cell ranges for the two groups, the hypothesized difference, and the alpha level.	Excel expects the two groups to be in separate cell ranges. Notice that, contrary to Excel's wording, we need not assume that the variances are *not* equal; we simply choose not to assume that they *are* equal.
JMP	From the Analyze menu select Fit y by x. Select variables: a y-Response variable that holds the data and an x-Factor variable that holds the group names. JMP will make a dotplot. Click the red triangle in the dotplot title, and choose Unequal variances. The t-test is at the bottom of the resulting table. Find the P-value from the Prob>F section of the table (they are the same.)	JMP expects data in one variable and category names in the other. The P-value hides in an unusual place.
Minitab	From the Stat menu choose the Basic Statistics submenu. From that menu, choose 2-sample t... Then fill in the dialog.	The dialog offers a choice of data in two variables or data in one variable and category names in the other.
SPSS	From the Analyze menu choose the Compare Means submenu. From that, choose the Independent-Samples t-test command. Specify the data variable and "group variable". Then type in the labels used in the group variable. SPSS offers both the two-sample and pooled t results in the same table.	SPSS expects the data in one variable and group names in the other. If there are more that two group names in the group variable, only the two that are named will be compared.
TI-83	Under STAT TESTS choose 2-Samp Tint or 2-Samp Ttest	The TI-83 expects the data in two separate lists, one for each group.

Connections

- The two sample t-test for means is essentially the same as the two-proportion z-test. Much of the reasoning is the same. But because means don t have the link between their value and their variance, we use the Student s t model for the sampling distribution.

- We first learned about side-by-side boxplots in chapter 5. There we made general statements about the shape, center, and spread of each group. When we compared groups we asked whether their centers looked different compared to how spread out the distributions were. Now we ve made that kind of thinking precise. We ve added confidence intervals for the difference and tests of whether the means are the same.

- We use Student s t as we did for single sample means, and for the same reasons. We are using standard deviations from the data to estimate the standard deviation of the sampling model. As before, we need to check the Nearly Normal condition. Histograms and normal probability plots are the best method for such checks.

- As always, we ve decided whether a statistic is large by comparing it to its standard error. Here our statistic is the difference in means.

Key Concepts

Two-sample t Methods	Two-sample t methods enable inference about the difference between the means of two independent groups. The two-sample methods make relatively few assumptions about the underlying populations, so they are usually the method of choice for comparing two sample means. However, the Student s t models are only an approximate model for their true sampling distribution. To make that model work well, the two-sample t methods have a special rule for estimating degrees of freedom.
Pooling	Data from two or more populations may sometimes be combined or *pooled* to estimate a statistic (typically a pooled variance) when one can reasonably assume that the estimated value is the same in both populations. The resulting larger sample size may lead to an estimate with lower sample variance. However, pooled estimates are only appropriate when the required assumptions are true.
Pooled t Methods	Pooled t-methods provide inference about the difference between the means of two independent populations under the assumption that both populations have the same standard deviation. When the assumption is justified, pooled t-methods generally produce slightly narrower confidence intervals and more powerful significance tests than two-sample t-methods. When the assumption is not justified, they generally produce worse results -- sometimes substantially worse.

DRAFT: Do not distribute or copy

Skills:

Upon completing this Lesson you should:

> ### *Think*
>
> - Recognize situations where we want to do inference on the true difference between the means of two independent groups.
>
> - Know how to examine your data for violations of conditions that would make inference about the difference between two population means unwise or invalid.
>
> - Recognize when a poole-t procedure might be appropriate and be able to explain why you decided to use a two-sample method anyway.
>
> ### *Show*
>
> - Be able to perform a two-sample *t*-test using a statistics package or calculator (at least for finding the degrees of freedom).
>
> - Be able to perform a pooled *t*-test. using a statistics package or calculator.
>
> ### *Tell*
>
> - Be able to interpret a test of the null hypothesis that the true means of two independent groups are equal. If the test is a pooled *t*-test, your interpretation should include a defense of your assumption of equal variances.

Exercises

1. **Learning Math** The Core Plus Mathematics Project (CPMP) is an innovative approach to teaching mathematics that engages students in group investigations and mathematical modeling. After field tests in 36 high schools over a three-year period, researchers compared the performances of CPMP students to those taught using a traditional curriculum. In one test students had to solve applied algebra problems using calculators. Scores for 320 CPMP students were compared to a control group of 273 students in a traditional math program. Computer software was used to create a confidence interval for the difference in mean scores. (Journal for Research in Mathematics Education, 2000, Vol. 31 No 3)

   Conf level: 95%   Variable: Mu(CPMP) - Mu(Ctrl)   Interval: (5.573, 11.427)

   a) What is the margin of error for this confidence interval?
   b) If we had created a 98% CI would the MOE be larger or smaller?
   c) Explain what the calculated interval means in this context.
   d) Does this result suggest that students who learn mathematics with CPMP will have significantly higher mean scores in algebra than those in traditional programs? Explain.

2. **Stereograms** Stereograms appear to be composed entirely of random dots. However, they contain separate images that a viewer can fuse into a three-dimensional image by staring at the dots while defocusing the eyes. An experiment was performed to determine whether knowledge of the form of the embedded image affected the time required for subjects to fuse the images. One group of subjects (group NV) received no information or just verbal information about the shape of the embedded object. A second group (group VV) received both verbal information and visual information (specifically, a drawing of the object). The experimenters measured how many seconds it took for the subject to report that he or she saw the 3D image.

   2-Sample t-Interval for 1- 2   df = 70   Conf level = 90%
   Mu(VV) —Mu(NV) interval: (0.55, 5.47)

   a) Interpret your interval in context.
   b) Does it appear that viewing a picture of the image helps people see the 3D image in a stereogram?
   c) What is the margin of error for this interval?
   d) Explain carefully what the 90% confidence level means.
   e) Would you expect a 99% confidence level to be wider or narrower? Explain.
   f) Might that change your conclusion in part b)? Explain.

3. **CPMP, Again.** During the study described in Exercise 1, students in both CPMP and traditional classes took an other algebra test that did not allow them to use calculators. The table below shows the results. Are the mean scores of the two groups significantly different? Test an appropriate hypothesis and state your conclusion.

Math program	n	Mean	SD
CPMP	312	29.0	18.8
Traditional	265	38.4	16.2

Performance on Algebraic Symbolic Manipulation
Without Use of Calculators

a) Write an appropriate hypothesis.
b) Do you think the assumptions for inference are satisfied? Explain.
c) Here is computer output for this hypothesis test. Explain what the P-value means in this context.

   2-Sample t-Test of $\mu 1 - \mu 2 \neq 0$
   t-Statistic = -6.496 w/583 df
   P < 0.0001

d) State a conclusion about the CPMP program.

4. **CPMP and Word Problems** The study of the new CPMP mathematics methodology described in Exercise 1 also tested students abilities to solve word problems. This table shows how the CPMP and traditional groups performed. What do you conclude?

Math program	n	Mean	SD
CPMP	320	57.4	32.1
Traditional	273	53.9	28.5

5. **Commuting** A man who moves to a new city sees that there are two routes he could take to work. A neighbor who has lived there a long time tells him Route *A* will average 5 minutes faster than Route *B*. The man decides to experiment. Each day he flips a coin to determine which way to go, driving each route 20 days. He finds that Route *A* took an average of 40 minutes with standard deviation 3 minutes, and Route *B* took an average of 43 minutes with standard deviation 2 minutes. Histograms of travel times for the routes are roughly symmetric and show no outliers.

a) Find a 95% confidence interval for the difference in average commuting time for the two routes.
b) Should the man believe the old-timer s claim that he can save an average of 5 minutes a day by always driving Route *A*? Explain.

6. **Pulse Rates** A researcher wanted to see of there is a significant difference in resting pulse rates for men and women. The data she collected are displayed in the boxplots and summarized below.

PULSE RATES	Gender	
	Male	Female
Count	28	24
Mean	72.75	72.625
Median	73	73
StdDev	5.37225	7.69987
Range	20	29
IQR	9	12.5

a) What do the boxplots suggest about any gender differences in pulse rates?
b) Is it appropriate to analyze these data using the methods of inference discussed in this chapter? Explain.
c) Create a 90% confidence interval for the difference in mean pulse rates.
d) Does the confidence interval confirm your answer to part (a)? Explain.

7. **Cereal** The data below show the sugar content (as a percentage of weight) of several national brands of children s and adult s cereals. Create and interpret a 95% confidence interval for the difference in mean sugar content. Be sure to check the necessary assumptions and conditions.

Children's Cereals: 40.3, 55, 45.7, 43.3, 50.3, 45.9, 53.5, 43, 44.2, 44, 47.4, 44, 33.6, 55.1, 48.8, 50.4, 37.8, 60.3, 46.6, 10, 15.6

Adult's Cereals: 20, 30.2, 2.2, 7.5, 4.4, 22.2, 16.6, 14.5, 21.4, 3.3, 6.6, 7.8, 10.6, 16.2, 14.5, 4.1, 15.8, 4.1, 2.4, 3.5, 8.5, 10, 1, 4.4, 1.3, 8.1, 4.7, 18.4

8. **Egyptians** Some archaeologists theorize that ancient Egyptians interbred with several different immigrant populations over thousands of years. To see if there is any indication of changes in body structure that might result, they measured 30 skulls of male Egyptian dated from 4000 B.C.E. and 30 others dated from 200 B.C.E. [Thomson, A. and Randall-Maciver, R. (1905) *Ancient Races of the Thebaid*, Oxford: Oxford University Press.]

a) Are these data appropriate for inference? Explain.
b) Create a 95% confidence interval for the difference in mean skull breadth between these two eras.
c) Do these data provide evidence that the mean breadth of males skulls changed over this time period? Explain.

Egyptian Maximum Skull Breadth	
4000 BCE	200 BCE
131	141
125	141
131	135
119	133
136	131
138	140
139	139
125	140
131	138
134	132
129	134
134	135
126	133
132	136
141	134
131	131
135	129
132	136
139	131
132	139
126	144
135	141
134	130
128	133
130	138
138	131
128	136
127	132
131	135
124	141

9. **Reading** An educator believes that new reading activities for elementary school children will improve reading comprehension scores. She randomly assigns third graders to an 8-week program in which some will use these activities and others will experience traditional teaching methods. At the end of the experiment, both groups take a reading comprehension exam. Their scores are shown in the back-to-back stem-and-leaf display. Do these results suggest that the new activities are better? Test an appropriate hypothesis and state your conclusion.

New Activities		Control
	1	07
4	2	068
3	3	377
96333	4	122238
9876432	5	355
721	6	02
1	7	
	8	5

10. **Hurricanes** The data below show the number of hurricanes recorded annually before and after 1970. Create an appropriate visual display and test whether there has been a change in the frequency of hurricanes.

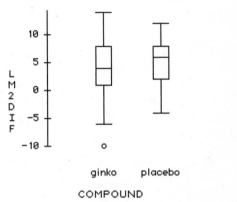

1944 - 1969	1970 - 2000
3, 2, 1, 2, 4, 3, 7, 2, 3, 3, 2, 5, 2, 2, 4, 2, 2, 6, 0, 2, 5, 1, 3, 1, 0, 3	2, 1, 0, 1, 2, 3, 2, 1, 2, 2, 2, 3, 1, 1, 1, 3, 0, 1, 3, 2, 1, 2, 1, 1, 0, 5, 6, 1, 3, 5, 3

11. **Memory** Does Ginko Biloba enhance memory? In an experiment to find out, subjects were assigned randomly to take Ginko Biloba supplements or a placebo. Their memory was tested to see whether it improved. Here is a boxplot comparing the two groups and some computer output from a two-sample *t*-test computed for the data.

    2-Sample t-Test of μ1-μ2 > 0
    Difference Between Means = 0.9914
    t-Statistic = 1.540 w/196 df
    P = 0.9374

   a) Explain in this context what the P-value means.
   b) State your conclusion about the effectiveness of Gingko Biloba.
   c) Proponents of Ginkgo Biloba continue to insist that it works. What type of error do they claim your conclusion makes?

12. **Streams** Researchers collected samples of water from streams in the Adirondack mountains to investigate the effects of acid rain. They measured the pH (acidity) of the water and classified the streams with respect to the kind of substrate (type of rock over which they flow). Here is a plot of the pH of the streams by substrate (limestone, mixed, or shale):

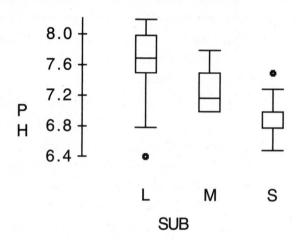

Here are selected parts of a software analysis comparing the pH of streams with Limestone and Shale substrates:

2-Sample t-Test of 1- 2
Difference Between Means = 0.735   t-Statistic = 16.30 w/133 df
p † 0.0001

a) State the null and alternative hypotheses for this test.
b) From the information you have, do the assumptions and conditions appear to be met?
c) What conclusion would you draw?

13. **Baseball** American League baseball teams play their games with the designated hitter rule, meaning that pitchers do not bat. The League believes that replacing the pitcher, traditionally a weak hitter, with a another player in the bating order produces more runs and generates more interest among fans. Below are the average numbers of runs scored in American League and National League stadiums for the first half of the 2001 season.

American				National			
11.1	10.8	10.8	10.3	14.0	11.6	10.4	10.3
10.3	10.1	10.0	9.5	10.2	9.5	9.5	9.5
9.4	9.3	9.2	9.2	9.5	9.1	8.8	8.4
	9.0	8.3		8.3	8.2	8.1	7.9

a) Create an appropriate display of these data. What do you see?
b) Estimate the mean number of runs scored in American League games with a 95% confidence interval.

DRAFT: Do not distribute or copy

c) What concerns do you have about making a similar confidence interval for National League games? What could you do?

d) Coors Field, in Denver, stands a mile above sea level, an altitude far greater than any other major league ballpark. Some believe that the thinner air makes it harder for pitchers to throw curve balls and easier for batters to hit the ball a long way. Do you think the 14 runs scored per game at Coors is unusual? Explain.

e) Explain why you should not use two separate confidence intervals to decide whether the two leagues differ in average number of runs scored.

14. **Handy** A factory hiring people to work on an assembly line gives job applicants a test of manual agility. This test counts how many strangely shaped pegs the applicant can fit into matching holes in a one-minute period. The table below summarizes the data by gender of the job applicant. Assume all conditions necessary for inference are met.

	Male	Female
Number of Subjects	50	50
Pegs Placed:		
Mean	19.09	18.21
Standard Deviation	2.52	3.39

a) Find 95% confidence intervals for the average number of pegs that males and females can each place.

b) Those intervals overlap. What does this suggest about any gender-based difference in manual agility?

c) Find a 95% confidence interval for the difference in the mean number of pegs that could be placed by men and women.

d) What does this interval suggest about any gender-based difference in manual agility?

e) The two results seem contradictory. Which method is correct: doing two-sample inference, or doing one-sample inference twice?

f) Why don t the results agree?

15. **Double Header** Do the data in Exercise 13 suggest that the American League s designated hitter rule may lead to more runs?

a) Estimate the difference between the mean number of runs scored in American and National league games with a 95% confidence interval.

b) Interpret your interval.

c) Does that interval suggest that the two leagues may differ in average number of runs scored per game?

d) Does omitting the 14 runs scored per game at Coors field affect your decision?

16. **Hard Water** In an investigation of environmental causes of disease, data were collected on the annual mortality rate (deaths per 100,000) for males in 61 large towns in England

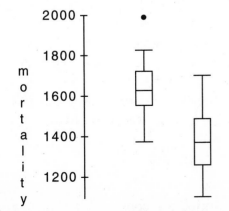

and Wales. In addition, the water hardness was recorded as the calcium concentration (parts per million, ppm) in the drinking water. The dataset also notes for each town whether it was south or north of Derby. Is there a significant difference in mortality rates in the two regions? Here are the summary statistics.

Summary of   **mortality**
For categories in   **Derby**
No Selector

Group	Count	Mean	Median	StdDev
North	34	1631.59	1631	138.470
South	27	1388.85	1369	151.114

a) Test appropriate hypotheses and state your conclusion.

b) The boxplot of the two distributions shows an outlier among the data North of Derby. What effect might that have had on your test?

17. **Job Satisfaction** A company institutes an exercise break for its workers to see if this will improve job satisfaction, as measured by a questionnaire that assesses workers satisfaction. Scores for ten randomly selected workers before and after the implementation of the exercise program are shown. The company wants assess the effectiveness of the exercise program Explain why you cannot use the methods discussed in this chapter to do that. (Don t worry, we ll give you another chance to do this the right way.)

Worker number	Job Satisfaction Index	
	Before	After
1	34	33
2	28	36
3	29	50
4	45	41
5	26	37
6	27	41
7	24	39
8	15	21
9	15	20
10	27	37

18. **Summer School** Having done poorly on their math final exams in June, six students repeat the course in summer school, then take another exam in August. If we consider these students to be representative of all students who might attend this summer school in other years, do these results provide evidence that the program is worthwhile?

June	54	49	68	66	62	62
Aug	50	65	74	64	68	72

19. **Sex and Violence** In June 2002 the *Journal of Applied Psychology* reported on a study that examined whether the content of TV shows influenced the ability of viewers to recall brand names of items featured in the commercials. The researchers randomly assigned volunteers to watch one of three programs, each containing the same 9 commercials. One of the programs had violent content, another sexual content, and the third neutral content. After the shows ended the subjects were asked to recall the brands of products that were advertised. Results are summarized below.

	Program Type

DRAFT: Do not distribute or copy

	Violent	Sexual	Neutral
No of Subjects	108	108	108
Brands Recalled			
Mean	2.08	1.71	3.17
St Dev	1.87	1.76	1.77

a) Do these results indicate that viewer memory for ads may differ depending on program content? A test of the hypothesis that there is no difference in ad memory between programs with sexual content and those with violent content has a P-value of 0.136. State your conclusion.

b) Is there evidence that viewer memory for ads may differ between programs with sexual content and those with neutral content? Test an appropriate hypothesis and state your conclusion.

20. **Ad Campaign** You are a consultant to the marketing department of a business preparing to launch an ad campaign for a new product. The company can afford to run ads during one TV show, and has decided not to sponsor a show with sexual content. You read the study described in Exercise 19, then use a computer to create a confidence interval for the difference in mean number of brand names remembered between the groups watching violent shows and those watching neutral shows.

> TWO SAMPLE T
> 95% CI FOR MU viol – MU neut: (-1.578, -0.602)

a) At the meeting of the marketing staff you have to explain what this output means. What will you say?

b) What advice would you give the company about their upcoming ad campaign?

21. **Sex and Violence II** In the study described in Exercise 19 the researchers also contacted the subjects again, 24 hours later, and asked them to recall the brands advertised. Results are summarized below.

	Program Type		
	Violent	Sexual	Neutral
No of Subjects	101	106	103
Brands Recalled			
Mean	3.02	2.72	4.65
St Dev	1.61	1.85	1.62

a) Is there a significant difference in viewers abilities to remember brands advertised in shows with violent vs neutral content?

b) Find a 95% confidence interval for the difference in mean number of brand names remembered between the groups watching shows with sexual content and those watching neutral shows. Interpret your interval in this context.

22. **Ad Recall** In Exercises 19 and 21 we see the number of advertised brand names people recalled immediately after watching TV shows and 24 hours later. Strangely enough, it appears that they remembered more about the ads the next

day. Should we conclude this is true in general about people s memory of TV ads?

a) Suppose one analyst conducts a 2-sample hypothesis test to see if memory of brands advertised during violent TV shows is higher 24 hours later. The P-value of his test is 0.00013. What might he conclude?

b) Explain why his procedure was inappropriate. Which of the assumptions for inference was violated?

c) How might the design of this experiment have tainted these results?

d) Suggest a design that could compare brand name recall immediately to one day later.

23. **Lower Scores?** Newspaper headlines recently announced a decline in science scores among high school seniors. In 2000, 15109 seniors tested by The National Assessment in Education Program tested scored a mean of 147 with standard deviation. Four years earlier 7537 seniors had averaged 150 points. The standard error of the difference in the mean scores for the two groups was 1.22.

a) Have the science scores declined significantly? Cite appropriate statistical evidence to support your conclusion.

b) The sample size in 2000 was almost double that in 1996. Does this make the results more convincing, or less? Explain.

24. **The Internet** The NAEP report described in Exercise 23 compared science scores for students with home internet access to those without, as shown in the graph. They report that the differences are statistically significant.

a) Explain what statistically significant means in this context.

b) If their conclusion is incorrect, which type of error did the researchers commit?

c) Does this prove that using the internet at home can improve a student s performance in science?

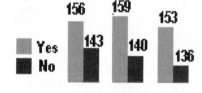

NAEP scores by grade and internet access.

25. **Statistics Journals** When a professional statistician has information to share with colleagues he or she will submit an article to one of several statistics journals for publication. This can be a lengthy process; typically the article must be circulated for peer review and perhaps edited before being accepted for publication. Then the article must wait in line with other articles before actually appearing in print. In the Winter 1998 issue of *Chance* magazine, Eric Bradlow and Howard Wainer reported about this delay for several journals between 1990 and 1994. For 29 articles published in *The American Statistician* the mean length of time between initial submission and publication was 21 months, with a standard deviation of 7 months. For *Applied Statistics* articles, the mean time to publication was 31 months with a standard deviation of 12 months. Create and interpret a 90% confidence interval for the

DRAFT: Do not distribute or copy

difference in mean delay, and comment on the assumptions that underlie your analysis.

26. **Music and Memory** Is it a good idea to listen to music when studying for a big test? In a study conducted by some statistics students, 62 people were randomly assigned to listen to rap music, Mozart, or no music while attempting to memorize objects pictured on a page. They were then asked to list all the objects they could remember. Here are summary statistics for each group:

	Rap	Mozart	No Music
Count	29	20	13
Mean	10.72	10.0	12.77
StDev	3.99	3.19	4.73

a) Does it appear that it is better to study while listening to Mozart than to rap music? Test an appropriate hypothesis and state your conclusion.

b) Create a 90% confidence interval for the mean difference in memory score between students who study to Mozart and those who listen to no music at all. Interpret your interval.

27. **Mozart** Using the results of the experiment described in Exercise 26, does it matter whether one listens to Rap music while studying, or is it better to study without music at all?

a) Test an appropriate hypothesis and state your conclusion.

b) If you concluded there is a difference, estimate the size of that difference with a confidence interval and explain what your interval means.

28. **Cuckoos** Cuckoos lay their eggs in other birds nests, tricking those birds into hatching and raising the baby cuckoos. It would seem that the ruse might not work because the eggs would look different, but a 1940 investigation called *The Truth About the Cuckoo* observed that cuckoos may lay eggs of different sizes in nests of different species! The authors suggest that natural selection would lead to the survival of cuckoos whose eggs get adopted by a particular foster-parent species. The table shows some of the data collected. Lengths of cuckoo eggs found in the nests of three other species are given in millimeters. Is there evidence that the mean length of the cuckoo eggs may be different for some foster species? Investigate, and state your conclusion.

Cuckoo Egg Length (mm)

Foster parent Species

Sparrow	Robin	Wagtail
20.85	21.05	21.05
21.65	21.85	21.85
22.05	22.05	21.85
22.85	22.05	21.85
23.05	22.05	22.05
23.05	22.25	22.45
23.05	22.45	22.65
23.05	22.45	23.05
23.45	22.65	23.05
23.85	23.05	23.25
23.85	23.05	23.45
23.85	23.05	24.05
24.05	23.05	24.05
25.05	23.05	24.05
	23.25	24.85
	23.85	

25 Paired Samples and Blocks

DO FLEXIBLE SCHEDULES REDUCE THE DEMAND FOR RESOURCES? The Lake County (IL) Health Department experimented with a flexible four-day workweek. They recorded the mileage driven by 11 field workers for a year on an ordinary five-day workweek. Then they changed to a flexible four-day workweek and recorded mileage for another year.[1]

Here are the data:

Who: 11 Healthcare workers

What: annual mileage driven

When: 1993-1994

Where: Illinois

Why: experiment to see whether change in workweek increased efficiency.

name	5 mileage	4 mileage
Jeff	2798	2914
Betty	7724	6112
Roger	7505	6177
Tom	838	1102
Aimee	4592	3281
Greg	8107	4997
Larry G	1228	1695
Tad	8718	6606
Larry M	1097	1063
Leslie	8089	6392
Lee	3807	3362

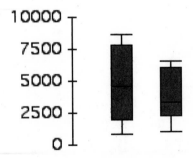

Boxplots of the mileages don t show much. Neither would a two-sample *t*-test. (It would find a P-value of 0.4, clearly not evidence of a difference.) But, wait a minute. The two-sample t is not valid here. We have 11 individuals and we know their mileage *before and after* the change in schedule. These data are not independent; they are paired.

[1] Catlin, Charles S, Four-day Work Week Improves Environment, *Joural of Environmental Health*, Denver, March 1997 **59**:7.

Paired Data

But this isn t a problem, it s an opportunity. The independence assumption is violated, but we can actually do much better than the two-sample t-test. After all, we should be focusing on the *changes* in driving mileage.

Data such as these are called **paired.** We have each worker s mileage both before and after the work schedule change. Paired data arise in a number of ways. Perhaps the most common is to compare subjects with themselves before and after a treatment. When pairs arise from an experiment, the pairing is a type of *blocking.* When they arise from an observational study it is a form of *matching*

If you know the data are paired, you can take advantage of that fact in fact, you *must* take advantage of it. You *may not* use the two-sample and pooled methods of the previous chapter when the data are paired. But there is no test for whether the data are paired. You must decide whether the data are paired from understanding how the data were collected.

Once we recognize that the mileage data are matched pairs, it makes sense to consider the change in annual miles driven for each worker as the work schedule changed. So we look at the collection of *pairwise* differences:

name	5 mileage	4 mileage	difference
Jeff	2798	2914	-116
Betty	7724	6112	1612
Roger	7505	6177	1328
Tom	838	1102	-264
Aimee	4592	3281	1311
Greg	8107	4997	3110
Larry G	1228	1695	-467
Tad	8718	6606	2112
Larry M	1097	1063	34
Leslie	8089	6392	1697
Lee	3807	3362	445

Jeff actually drove a bit farther under the 4-day plan. But Greg (who started out driving a far greater distance) reduced his mileage substantially. Now we ll treat these differences as if they were the original data. Since we have only one column of values to consider, we can use a simple one-sample *t*-test. Mechanically, a **matched pairs *t*-test** is just a one-sample *t*-test on the pairwise differences.

DRAFT: Do not distribute or copy

Assumptions and Conditions

Paired Data Assumption

The data must be paired. You can t just decide to pair data when in fact the samples are independent. Be prepared to justify your claim that the data are paired.

Independence Assumption

The data are paired, so the groups are *not* independent. But the *differences* must be independent of each other. In our example, the fact that Jeff drove further doesn t affect how far Betty drove. (If Jeff and Betty carpooled for part of the year, this wouldn t be true and the assumption would be violated.)

Randomization Condition. Randomness may arise one of two ways. The individuals may be a random sample, or randomly assigned to treatments in an experiment, or the randomness may arise in the individual measurements themselves. What we want to know usually focuses our attention on where the randomness can be found. In our example, we could have both. But our main concern is testing whether a 4-day work week changes driving patterns. The randomness comes from all the many random driving events that make up the annual totals. If we were to repeat the experiment in two other years, we would find different mileage totals, but (we hope) the same overall pattern of change.

If we also wanted to claim that this change would be typical of all State employees, then we might be concerned with how the workers were selected. Are they a random sample of Illinois workers, or was this Department selected randomly? If not, our inference may be restricted only to these 11 individuals.

10% Condition. When the inference is about a population from which the paired individuals are drawn, we must be sure that we have sampled no more than 10% of that population. If we hoped to generalize our conclusions to all State healthcare workers, we d want to verify that these 11 were not more than 10% of that group.

Normal Population Assumption

We need to assume that the population of differences has a Normal model. We don t need to check the individual columns. In practice, the

Nearly Normal Condition can be checked with a histogram or normal probability plot of the differences. As with the one-sample *t* methods, this assumption matters less as we have more pairs to consider. You may be pleasantly surprised when you check this condition. Measurements that are skewed or bimodal may, after we take pairwise difference, yield nearly Normal differences. After all, the individual who was way out in the tail on one measurement is likely to still be out there on the second one, giving a perfectly ordinary pairwise difference.

Performing a Paired *t*-test, Step-by-Step

The steps of testing a hypothesis for paired differences are very much like the steps for a one-sample *t*-test for a mean. Only now we first take the pairwise differences, and work with them as our data values.

Think

Hypothesis: The parameter is the mean of the pairwise differences in the mileage driven.

Although we hope for a reduction in miles driven, we have no reason to suppose that the difference must be in that direction, so we d better test a two-sided alternative.

Reality Check:
The individual differences are all in the hundreds to low thousands of miles. We should expect the mean difference to be comparable in magnitude.

Plan: Check the conditions.

State why you think the data are paired. Simply having the same number of individuals in each group displaying them in side-by-side columns doesn t make them paired.

Think about what we hope to learn and where the randomization comes from. Here, the randomization comes from the random events that happen to each driver during the study.

We would need to check the 10% condition if we hoped to extend our inference to, for example, all

Ho: The mileage driven by each Health Department worker under a four-day workweek is the same as his or her mileage under the original five-day workweek; the mean difference is zero. $\mu_d = 0$

H_A: The mean difference is different from zero: $\mu_d \neq 0$.

- **Paired Data Assumption:** The data are paired because they are measurements on the same individuals before and after a change in work schedule.

- **Independence Assumption:** The behavior of any individual is independent from the behavior of the others, so the differences are mutually independent.

- **Randomization Condition:** The measured values are the sums of individual trips, each of which experienced random events that arose while driving. Repeating the experiment in two new years would give randomly different values.

- **10% Condition:** Our inference is about driving amounts not about the workers so

DRAFT: Do not distribute or copy

State health workers.

For paired data we work with the differences. So it is the normality of the differences that we care about. The distributions of the individual measurements don t matter for this method only the distribution of the differences.

driving amounts, not about the workers, so we don't need to check this condition here

- **Nearly Normal condition:** The histogram of the differences is unimodal and symmetric.

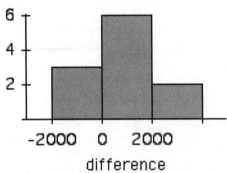

Under these conditions the sampling distribution of the differences can be modeled by a Student's *t* model with (n - 1) = 10 degrees of freedom.

- Specify the sampling distribution.

We will use a **paired-*t* test.**

- Choose the method.

We find from the data:

$n = 11$

$\bar{d} = 982$ miles

$s_d = 1139.6$ miles

Show

Mechanics:

$\bar{d}$ is the sample mean of the pairwise differences.

s_d is the standard deviation of the pairwise differences.

n is the number of *pairs;* in this case, the number of workers.

There is nothing new in the mechanics of the paired-*t* methods. These are the mechanics of the *t*-test for a mean applied to the pairwise differences.

We estimate the standard error of $\bar{d}$:

$$SE(\bar{d}) = \frac{s}{\sqrt{n}} = \frac{1139.6}{\sqrt{11}} = 343.6$$

The test statistic is

$$t_{(11-1)} = \frac{\bar{d} - 0}{SE(\bar{d})} = \frac{982.0}{343.6} = 2.86$$

We refer to a Student's *t* model on 10 df.

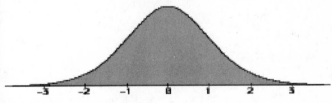

The *t*-ratio gives the distance from the hypothesized value in standard deviation units.

The P-value is 0.017.

Reality Check: The mean difference is 982 miles. That s more than twice the SE of 344, so it looks like the change is real. The t value of 2.86 and P-value of .017 are consistent with that.

Tell

Interpretation: State your conclusions.

With a P-value this small, we can reject the null hypothesis. We conclude that the change in workweek does lead to a change in driving mileage.

If possible, propose a course of action.

Without a confidence interval, it is hard to know whether the difference in mileage is important in the sense of reducing air pollution or cost, or merely statistically significant. So we'd recommend finding a confidence interval. If the difference in mileage proves to be large in a practical sense, then we might recommend a change in schedule for the rest of the Department.

Confidence intervals for matched pairs

In developed countries, the average age of women is generally higher than the average age of men. After all, women tend to live longer. But, if we look at *married couples*, husbands tend to be slightly older than wives. How much older on average is the husband? We have data from a random sample of 170 British couples, the first 16 of which are shown below. Let s form a confidence interval for the mean difference of husband s and wife s age.

Who: 170 randomly sampled couples.

What: ages

When: recently

Where: Britain

Wife's age	Husband's Age
43	49
28	25
30	40
57	52
52	58
27	32
52	43
43	47
23	31
25	26
39	40
32	35
35	35

25-6 **DRAFT: Do not distribute or copy**

33	35
43	47
35	38

These data are obviously paired. It would not be interesting to know whether the collection of husbands was, on average, older than the collection of wives. Instead, we care about the mean age *difference* within couples. How would we construct a confidence interval for the true mean difference in ages?

A Matched-Pairs *t*-Interval, Step-by-Step

Making confidence intervals for matched pairs follows exactly the steps for a one-sample *t*-interval.

Think

Parameter: Identify the *parameter* you wish to estimate.

We wish to find an interval that is likely with 95% confidence to contain μ_d, the true mean difference in ages of husbands and wives.

For a paired analysis, the parameter of interest is the mean of the differences. The population of interest is the population of differences.

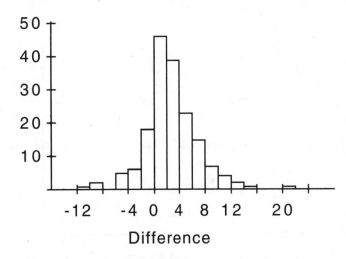

Reality Check:

The histogram shows husbands are often older than wives (because most of the differences are greater than 0). The mean difference seen here of about 2 years is reasonable.

Plan:

Check the conditions.

• **Paired Data Assumption:** The data are paired because they are on members of married couples.

• **Randomization condition:** Couples were randomly sampled from a much larger population.

• **10% Condition** The sample is less than 10% of the population of married couples in Britain.

• **Nearly Normal Condition:** The histogram of the husband - wife differences is unimodal and symmetric.

State the sampling distribution model for the statistic.

Choose your method.

Under these conditions the sampling distribution of the differences can be modeled by a Student's *t* model with *(n - 1) = 169* degrees of freedom.

We will find a **paired *t*-interval.**

Show

Mechanics: $\bar{d}$ is the sample mean of the pairwise differences.

s_d is the standard deviation of the pairwise differences.

n is the number of *pairs,* here, the number of couples.

Be sure to include the units along with the statistics

This is a *t*-interval for a mean applied to the differences.

The critical value we need to make a 95% interval comes from a Student s *t* table, a computer program, or a calculator.

$$n = 170$$

$$\bar{d} = 2.2 \ \text{years}$$

$$s_d = 4.1 \ \text{years}$$

We estimate the standard error of $\bar{d}$ as:

$$SE(\bar{d}) = \frac{s_d}{\sqrt{n}} = \frac{4.1}{\sqrt{170}} = 0.31 \ \text{years}$$

The *df* for the *t*-model is *n-1* = 169.

The 95% critical value for t_{169} (from the table) is 1.97

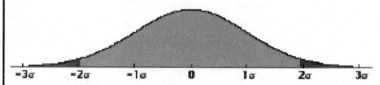

From these, we find the margin of error to be

$$ME = t^*_{169} SE(\bar{d}) = 1.97 \times 0.31 = 0.61$$

Reality Check:

This result makes sense. Our everyday experience confirms that an age difference of about 2 years is reasonable.

So the 95% confidence interval is:

2.2± 0.6 years

or an interval of [1.6, 2.8] years.

Tell

Interpretation: Tell what the confidence interval means.

We are 95% confident that in married couples in Britain, the husband is, on average, between 1.6 to 2.8 years older.

Blocking

Because the sample includes both older and younger couples, there s a lot of variation in the ages of the men and in the ages of the women. In fact, that variation is so great that a boxplot of the two groups would show no difference. But that would be the wrong plot. It s the difference we care about. Pairing removes the extra variation and allows us to focus on the individual differences. In experiments, we *block* to separate the variability between the experimental units from the variability in the response. Matching in observed data has much the same purpose.

When we pair, we have only half the degrees of freedom of a two-sample test. You may see discussions that suggest that in choosing a paired analysis we gave up these degrees of freedom. But this isn t really true. If the data are paired, then there never were additional degrees of freedom, and we had no choice . The fact of the pairing determined how many df were available.

Matching pairs generally removes so much extra variation that it more than compensates for having only half the degrees of freedom. Of course, inappropriate matching when the groups are in fact independent (say, by matching on first letter of the last name of subjects) would cost degrees of freedom without the benefit of reducing the variance. When you design a study or experiment, you should use paired matching if possible.

What Can Go Wrong

Don't use a two-sample t-test for paired data. See the What Can Go Wrong discussion in the previous chapter.

Don't use a paired t method when the samples aren't matched. When two groups don t have the same number of values, it s pretty easy to see that they can t be paired. But just because two groups have the same number of observations, doesn t mean they can be paired even if they are shown side-by-side in a table. We might have 25 men and 25 women in our study, but they might be completely independent of one-another. But if they were siblings or spouses, we could consider them to be paired. But you cannot *choose* which method to use based on your preferences. If the data are from two independent samples, use a two-sample *t*-test. If the data are from an experiment where observations were paired, you must use a paired method. If the data are from an observational study, you must be able to defend your choice to used matched pairs.

Don't forget outliers. The outliers we care about now are in the differences. A subject who is extraordinary both before and after a treatment may still have a perfectly typical difference. But one outlying difference can completely distort our conclusions. Be sure to plot the differences (even if you also plot the data.)

Don't look for the difference in side-by-side boxplots. The point of the paired analysis is to remove extra variation. The boxplots of each group still contain that variation. Comparing them is likely to be misleading.

Paired *t* and the Computer

Most statistics programs offer to compute paired *t* analyses. Some may want you to find the pairwise differences yourself and use the one-sample *t*-methods.

Those that perform the entire procedure will need to know the two variables to compare. The computer, of course, cannot check that the variables are naturally paired. Most programs will at least check that the two variables have the same number of observations.[2]

Computers make it easy to examine the boxplots of the two groups[3] and the histogram of the differences — both important steps.

Needs ACO

Connections

o The most important connection is to the concept of blocking that we first discussed when we considered designed experiments. Pairing is a basic and very effective form of blocking.

o Of course, the details of the mechanics for both tests and intervals are identical to those for the one-sample *t*-methods. Everything we know about those methods applies here.

o The connection to the two-sample and pooled methods of the previous chapter is that when the data are naturally paired, those methods are not appropriate because paired data fails the required condition of independence.

Key Concepts

Paired Data	Data are paired when pairs of values can be grouped together so that the differences among the groups can be meaningfully separated from the variability within each group.
	The simplest form of pairing is to measure each subject twice — often before and after a treatment is applied. More sophisticated forms of pairing in experiments are a form of blocking and arise in other contexts.
	Observational data can often be stratified. When the same measurement is taken twice within each stratum, the data may be regarded as paired.
Matched Pairs Confidence	Regardless of the nature of the pairing, when two

[2] Beware of programs that do not deal with missing values well. Some statistics programs just skip missing values as if they were not there at all. If one variable has a missing value in one case and the other has a missing value at a different case, the two variables still have the same count of non-missing values. But a na ve program might mis-match them for pairing. At the time of writing, the statistics add-on provided by Microsoft for the Excel spreadsheet program makes this error.

[3] Even though our concern is with the differences of the pairs, you should examine the boxplots of the two groups separately to look for any outliers or other unusual pairs.

DRAFT: Do not distribute or copy

Interval	groups to be compared are naturally paired, the best way to do inference is with a matched pairs *t*-procedure. Creating a confidence interval for the mean difference or testing whether their means are equal is mechanically equivalent to performing a one-sample *t*-procedure on the pairwise differences.
Matched Pairs *t*-test	

Skills

Upon completing this Lesson you should:

> *Think*
>
> - Be able to recognize whether a design that compares two groups is paired or not.
>
> *Show*
>
> - Be able to find a paired confidence interval, recognizing that it is mechanically equivalent to doing a one-sample *t*-interval applied now to the pairwise differences.
>
> - Be able to perform a paired t-test, recognizing that it is mechanically equivalent to a one-sample *t*-test applied now to the pairwise differences.
>
> *Tell*
>
> - Be able to interpret a paired t-test, recognizing that the hypothesis tested is about the mean of the differences between paired values rather than about the differences between the means of two independent groups.

Exercises

1. **More Eggs?** Can a food additive increase egg production? Agricultural researchers want to design an experiment to find out. They have 100 hens available. They have two kinds of feed — the regular feed and the new feed with the additive. They plan to run their experiment for a month, recording the number of eggs each hen produces.
   a) Design an experiment that will require a 2-sample t-procedure to analyze the results.
   b) Design an experiment that will require a matched pairs t-procedure to analyze the results.
   c) Which experiment would you consider to be the stronger design? Why?

2. **MTV** Some students do homework with the TV on. (Anyone come to mind?) Some researchers want to see if people can work as effectively with as without distraction. They will time some volunteers to see how long it takes them to complete some relatively easy crossword puzzles. During some of the trials the room will be quiet, during other trials in the same room a TV will be on, tuned to MTV.
   d) Design an experiment that will require a 2-sample *t*-procedure to analyze the results.
   e) Design an experiment that will require a matched pairs *t*-procedure to analyze the results.
   f) Which experiment would you consider to be the stronger design? Why?

3. **Women** Values for the Labor force participation rate of women (LFPR) are published by the U.S. Bureau of Labor Statistics. We are interested in whether there was a difference between female participation in 1968 and 1972, a time of rapid change for women. We check LFPR values for 19 randomly selected cities for 1968 and 1972. Shown below is software output for two possible tests.

   Paired t-Test of $\mu(1 - 2)$
   Test Ho: $\mu(1972-1968) = 0$ vs Ha: $\mu(1972-1968) \neq 0$
   Mean of Paired Differences = 0.0337 t-Statistic = 2.458 w/18 df
   p = 0.0244

   2-Sample t-Test of $\mu1-\mu2$
   Ho: $\mu1-\mu2 = 0$ Ha: $\mu1-\mu2 \neq 0$
   Test Ho: $\mu(1972)-\mu(1968) = 0$ vs Ha: $\mu(1972)-\mu(1968) \neq 0$
   Difference Between Means = 0.0337 t-Statistic = 1.496 w/35 df
   p = 0.1434

   a) Which of these tests is appropriate for these data? Explain.
   b) Using the test you select, state your conclusion.

4. **BST** Many dairy cows now receive injections of BST, a hormone intended to spur greater milk production. After the first injection a test group of 60 Ayrshire cows increased their mean daily production from 47 pounds to 61 pounds of milk. The standard deviation of the increases was 5.2 pounds. We want to estimate the mean increase a farmer could expect in his own cows.

a) Check the assumptions and conditions for inference.

b) Write a 95% confidence interval.

c) Explain what your interval means in this context.

d) Given the cost of BST, a farmer believes he cannot afford to use it unless he is sure of attaining at least a 25% in milk production. Based on your confidence interval, what advice would you give him?

5. **Rain** Simpson, Alsen, and Eden (*Technometrics* 1975) report the results of trials in which clouds were seeded and the amount of rainfall recorded. 26 seeded and 26 unseeded clouds are reported. They are reported by the authors in order of the amount of rainfall, largest amount first. Here are two possible tests to study the question of whether cloud seeding works. Which test is appropriate for these data? Explain your choice. Using the test you select, state your conclusion.

> Paired t-Test of $\mu(1 - 2)$
> Mean of Paired Differences = -277.39615 t-Statistic = -3.641 w/25 df
> p = 0.0012
>
> 2-Sample t-Test of $\mu1-\mu2$
> Difference Between Means = -277.4 t-Statistic = -1.998 w/33 df
> p = 0.0538

a) Which of these tests is appropriate for these data? Explain.

b) Using the test you select, state your conclusion.

6. **BST II** In the experiment about hormone injections in cows described in Exercise 4, a group of 52 the Jersey cows increased average milk production from 43 pounds to 52 pounds per day, with a standard deviation of 4.8 pounds. Is there evidence that the hormone may be more effective in one breed than the other? Test an appropriate hypothesis and state your conclusion. Be sure to discuss any assumptions you make.

7. **Temperatures** The table below gives the average high temperatures in January and July for several European cities. Write a 90% confidence interval for the mean temperature difference between summer and winter in Europe. Be sure to check conditions for inference, and clearly explain what your interval means.

City	Jan	July
Vienna	34	75
Copenhagen	36	72
Paris	42	76
Berlin	35	74
Athens	54	90
Rome	54	88
Amsterdam	40	69
Madrid	47	87
London	44	73
Edinburgh	43	65
Moscow	21	76
Belgrade	37	84

8. **Marathons** Shown are the winning times (in minutes) for men and

Year	Men	Women
1978	132.2	152.5
1979	131.7	147.6
1980	129.7	145.7
1981	128.2	145.5
1982	129.5	147.2
1983	129.0	147.0
1984	134.9	149.5
1985	131.6	148.6
1986	131.1	148.1
1987	131.0	150.3
1988	128.3	148.1
1989	128.0	145.5
1990	132.7	150.8
1991	129.5	147.5
1992	129.5	144.7
1993	130.1	146.4
1994	131.4	147.6
1995	131.0	148.1
1996	129.9	148.3
1997	128.2	148.7
1998	128.8	145.3

women in the New York City marathon between 1978 and 1998. Assuming that performances in the Big Apple resemble performances elsewhere, we can think of these data as a sample of performance in marathon competitions. Create a 90% confidence interval for the mean difference in winning times for male and female marathon competitors. [Chance, Vol 12, No 4, 1999]

9. **Push-Ups** Every year the students at Gossett High School take a physical fitness test during their gym classes. One of the components of the test asks them to do as many pushups as they can. Results for one class are shown below, according to gender. Assuming that students at Gossett are assigned to gym classes at random, create a 90% confidence interval for how many more pushups boys there can do than girls, on average.

Boys	17	27	31	17	25	32	28	23	25	16	11	34
Girls	24	7	14	16	2	15	19	25	10	27	31	8

10. **Exercise** In an August 2001 article the journal *Medecine and Science in Sports and Exercise* compared how long it would take men and women to burn 200 calories during light or heavy workouts on various kinds of exercise equipment. The results summarized in the table are the average times for a group of physically active young men and women whose performances were measured on each type of equipment.

Machine Type	Average Minutes to Burn 200 Calories			
	Hard Exertion		Light Exertion	
	Men	Women	Men	Women
Treadmill	12	17	14	22
X-C Skier	12	16	16	23
Stair Climber	13	18	20	37
Rowing Machine	14	16	21	25
Exercise Rider	22	24	27	36
Exercise Bike	16	20	29	44

11. **Job Satisfaction** (When you first read about this exercise break plan in the last chapter you did not have an inference method that would work. Try again now.) A company institutes an exercise break for its workers to see if this will improve job satisfaction, as measured by a questionnaire that assesses workers satisfaction. Scores for ten randomly selected workers before and after the implementation of the exercise program are shown.

Worker number	Job Satisfaction Index	
	Before	After
1	34	33
2	28	36
3	29	50
4	45	41
5	26	37
6	27	41
7	24	39
8	15	21
9	15	20
10	27	37

a) Identify the procedure you would use to assess the effectiveness of the exercise program, and check to see if the conditions allow use of that procedure.

b) Test an appropriate hypothesis and state your conclusion.

DRAFT: Do not distribute or copy

12. **Summer School** (When you first read about the summer school issue in the last chapter you did not have an inference method that would work. Try again now.) Having done poorly on their math final exams in June, six students repeat the course in summer school and take another exam in August. If we consider these students to be representative of all students who might attend this summer school in other years, do these results provide evidence that the program is worthwhile?

June	54	49	68	66	62	62
Aug	50	65	74	64	68	72

13. **Sleep** W.S. Gosset (Student) refers to data recording the number of hours of additional sleep gained by 10 patients from the use of *laevohysocyamine hydrobromide*. We want to see if there is strong evidence that the herb can help people get more sleep.
    a) State the null and alternative hypotheses clearly.
    b) A t-test of the null hypothesis of no gain has a t-statistic of 3.680 with 9 degrees of freedom. Find the P-value.
    c) Interpret this result by explaining the meaning of the P-value.
    d) State your conclusion regarding the hypotheses.
    e) This conclusion, of course, may be incorrect. If so, which type of error was made?

14. **Gasoline** Many drivers of cars that can run on regular gas actually buy premium believing that they will get better gas mileage. To test that belief we use 10 cars in a company fleet. Each car is filled first with either regular or premium gasoline, decided by a coin toss, and the mileage for that tankful recorded. Then the mileage is recorded again for the same cars for a tankful of the other kind of gasoline. We don t let the drivers know about this experiment. Here are the results (miles per gallon):

Car #	1	2	3	4	5	6	7	8	9	10
Regular	16	20	21	22	23	22	27	25	27	28
Premium	19	22	24	24	25	25	26	26	28	32

   a) Is there evidence that cars get significantly better fuel economy with premium gasoline?
   b) How big might that difference be? Check a 90% confidence interval.
   c) Even if the difference is significant, why might the company choose to stick with regular gasoline?
   d) Suppose you had done a Bad Thing. (We re sure you didn t.) Suppose you had mistakenly treated these data as two independent samples instead of matched pairs. What would the significance test have found? Carefully explain why the results are so different.

15. **Yogurt** Do these data suggest that there is a significant difference in calories between servings of strawberry and vanilla yogurt? Test an appropriate

hypothesis and state your conclusion. Don t forget to check assumptions and conditions!

Brand	Calories per serving	
	Strawberry	Vanilla
America's Choice	210	200
Breyer's Lowfat	220	220
Columbo	220	180
Dannon Light 'n Fit	120	120
Dannon Lowfat	210	230
Dannon laCreme	140	140
Great Value	180	80
La Yogurt	170	160
Mountain High	200	170
Stonyfield Farm	100	120
Yoplait Custard	190	190
Yoplait Light	100	100

16. **Caffeine** A student experiment investigating the potential impact of caffeine on studying for a test involved 30 subjects, randomly divided into two groups. Each group took a memory test. The subjects then each drank two cups of regular (caffeinated) cola or caffeine-free cola. Thirty minutes later they each took another version of the memory test, and the changes in their scores were noted. Among the 15 subjects who drank caffeine scores fell an average of —0.933 points, with a standard deviation of 2.988 pointsAmong the no-caffeine group scores went up an average of 1.429 points with a standard deviation of 2.441 points. Assumptions of normality were deemed reasonable based on histograms of differences in scores.
    a) Did scores change significantly for the group who drank caffeine? Test an appropriate hypothesis and state your conclusion.
    b) Did scores change significantly for the no-caffeine group? Test an appropriate hypothesis and state your conclusion.
    c) Does this indicate that some mystery substance in non-caffeinated soda may aid memory? What other explanation is plausible?

17. **Braking** In a test of braking performance a tire manufacturer measured the stopping distance for one of their tire models. On a test track, a car made repeated stops from 60 miles per hour. The test was run on both dry and wet pavement, with results as shown in the table. (Note that actual *stopping distance*, which takes into account the driver s reaction time, is much longer, typically nearly 300 feet at 60 mph!)

Stopping Distance (feet)	
Dry Pavement	Wet Pavement
145	211
152	191
141	220
143	207
131	198
148	208
126	206
140	177
135	183
133	223

    a) Write a 95% confidence interval for the mean dry pavement stopping distance. Be sure to check the appropriate assumptions and conditions, and explain what your interval means.

DRAFT: Do not distribute or copy

b) Write a 95% confidence interval for the mean increase in stopping distance on wet pavement. Be sure to check the appropriate assumptions and conditions, and explain what your interval means.

18. **Brain Waves** An experiment was performed to see whether sensory deprivation over an extended period of time has any effect on the alpha-wave patterns produced by the brain. To determine this, 20 subjects, inmates in a Canadian prison, were randomly split into two groups. Members of one group were placed in solitary confinement. Those in the other group were allowed to remain in their own cells. Seven days later alpha-wave frequencies were measured for all subjects as shown in the following table:

a) What are the null and alternative hypotheses? Be sure to define all the terms and symbols you use.

b) Are the assumptions necessary for inference met?

c) Perform the appropriate test, indicating the formula you used, the calculated value of the test statistic, and the P-value.

d) State your conclusion.

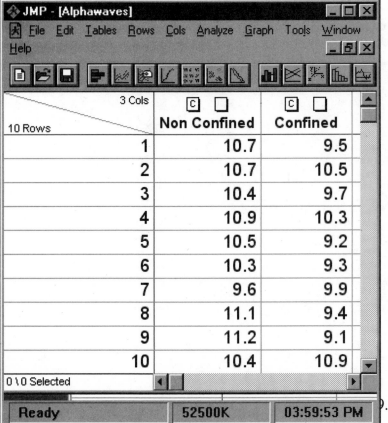

3 Cols / 10 Rows	Non Confined	Confined
1	10.7	9.5
2	10.7	10.5
3	10.4	9.7
4	10.9	10.3
5	10.5	9.2
6	10.3	9.3
7	9.6	9.9
8	11.1	9.4
9	11.2	9.1
10	10.4	10.9

19. **Braking, Test 2** For another test of the tires in Exercise 17, the company tried them on ten different cars, recording the stopping distance for each car on both wet and dry pavement. Results are shown in the table.

a) Write a 95% confidence interval for the mean dry pavement stopping distance. Be sure to check the appropriate assumptions and conditions, and explain what your interval means.

Car #	Stopping Distance (feet)	
	Dry Pavement	Wet Pavement
1	150	201
2	147	220
3	136	192
4	134	146
5	130	182
6	134	173
7	134	202
8	128	180
9	136	192
10	158	206

b) Write a 95% confidence interval for the mean increase in stopping distance on wet pavement. Be sure to check the appropriate assumptions and conditions, and explain what your interval means.

20. **Tuition** How much more do public colleges and universities charge out-of-state students for tuition? A random sample of 19 public colleges and universities listed in the *Information Please Almanac* found the data shown below. Tuition figures are rounded to the nearest hundred dollars.

a) Create a 90% confidence interval for the mean difference in cost. Be sure to justify the procedure you use.
b) Interpret your interval in context.
c) A national magazine claims that public institutions charge state residents an average of $4000 less for tuition each semester. What does your confidence interval indicate about the validity of this assertion?

Institution	Resident	Non-Res
Univ of Akron (OH)	3200	7900
Athens State (GA)	3800	7500
Ball State (IN)	3000	7800
Bloomsburg U (PA)	3700	8500
UC Irvine (CA)	4300	12000
Central Ohio St	2900	6400
Clarion U (PA)	3900	8600
Dakota State	2500	4600
Fairmont State (WV)	1800	4500
Johnson State (VT)	4000	8600
Lock Haven U (PA)	7400	12100
New College of S. Fla.	2000	7900
Oakland U (MI)	3100	8700
U Pittsburgh	5400	11200
Savannah State (GA)	2000	5200
SW Louisiana	1900	4900
W Liberty State (WV)	1900	4500
W Texas State	1600	6000
Worcester State (MA)	2700	6200

State	'99 – '00	'00-'01
AL	13.3	13.2
AK	18.6	17.3
AZ	18.6	17.3
AR	14.4	15.2
CA	19.0	19.0
CO	14.9	14.9
CT	9.4	10.0
DE	9.6	9.2
DC	14.1	13.4
FL	17.6	17.9
GA	14.7	15.5
HI	9.8	9.5
ID	16.8	15.7
IL	13.6	13.7
IN	10.3	11.5
IA	8.2	8.2
KS	11.4	11.1
KY	13.4	13.0
LA	19.9	18.7
ME	10.8	10.6
MD	10.8	11.3
MA	9.0	8.5
MI	9.7	9.8
MN	7.8	8.1
MS	14.6	15.0
MO	8.1	9.9
MT	17.3	15.2
NE	17.7	16.5
NV	17.7	16.5
NH	8.7	8.9
NJ	12.1	12.6
NM	24.4	22.4
NY	15.9	15.9
NC	14.0	14.0
ND	11.5	10.5
OH	10.7	11.2
OK	17.7	18.6
OR	13.3	12.7
PA	8.5	9.0
RI	6.9	7.6
SC	13.8	12.2
SD	10.9	10.2
TN	10.6	11.1
TX	22.7	23.2
UT	13.0	13.7
VT	9.8	9.1
VA	12.4	11.3
WA	13.7	13.3
WV	14.7	13.6
WI	8.9	7.6
WY	15.4	15.8

21. **Strikes** Advertisements for an instructional video claim that the techniques will improve the ability of Little League pitchers to throw strikes, and that after undergoing the training players will be able to throw strikes on at least 60% of their pitches. To test this claim we have 20 Little Leaguers throw 50 pitches each, and we record the number of strikes. After the players participate in the training program we repeat the test. The table shows the number of strikes each player threw before and after the training.

a) Is there evidence that after training players can throw strikes more than 60% of the time?

b) Is there evidence that the training is effective in improving a player s ability to throw strikes?

Number of strikes (out of 50)	
Before	After
28	35
29	36
30	32
32	28
32	30
32	31
32	32
32	34
32	35
33	36
33	33
33	35
34	32
34	30
34	33
35	34
36	37
36	33
37	35
37	32

22. **Uninsured** During the economic recession of 2000-01 unemployment increased and job benefits were scaled back. The table shows the percentage of people in each state who lacked health insurance during the 99- 00 and 00- 01, as reported by the US Census Bureau. Is there any evidence that more people were without health insurance?

a) On average, how many minutes longer than a man must a woman exercise at a light exertion rate in order to burn 200 calories? Give a 95% confidence interval.

b) Estimate the average number of minutes longer a woman must work out at light exertion than at heavy exertion to get the same benefit. Give a 95% confidence interval.

26 Comparing Counts

DOES YOUR ZODIAC SIGN DETERMINE HOW SUCCESSFUL you will be in later life? Fortune magazine collected the zodiac signs of 256 heads of the largest 400 companies. Here are the number of births for each sign:

Births	Sign
23	Aries
20	Taurus
18	Gemini
23	Cancer
20	Leo
19	Virgo
18	Libra
21	Scorpio
19	Saggitarius
22	Capricorn
24	Aquarius
29	Pices

Birth totals by sign for
256 Forbes 400 executives

We can see some variation in the number of births per sign and there *are* more Pices, but is it enough to claim that successful people are more likely to be born under some star signs than others?

Goodness-of-fit

If births were uniformly distributed across the year, we would expect about 1/12 of them to occur under each sign of the zodiac. That suggests 256/12, or about 21.3 births per month. How close is the observed distribution of births to this simple null pattern?

A hypothesis test to address this question is called a test of goodness-of-fit. The name suggests a certain badness-of-grammar, but it is quite standard. And, after all, we are asking whether the model that births are uniformly distributed over the signs fits the data good, er, well. Goodness-of-fit involves testing a hypothesis. We have specified a model for the distribution and want to know whether it fits. There is no parameter to estimate, so a confidence interval wouldn t make much sense.

If the question were about only one astrological sign (for example are Pisces more likely to be executives? [1]), we could use a one-proportion z-test and ask if the true proportion of executives with that sign is equal to 1/12. But here we have 12 hypothesized proportions, one for each sign. We need a test that considers all of them together and gives an overall idea of whether the observed distribution differs from the hypothesized one.

Assumptions and Conditions

These data are organized differently from the data we ve looked at for other inference methods, and the assumptions and conditions reflect that.

Counted Data Condition:

The first condition is just to check that the data are *counts* for the categories of a categorical variable. This might seem a simplistic, even silly condition. But many kinds of values can be assigned to categories, and it is unfortunately common to find the methods of this chapter applied incorrectly to proportions or amounts. So check to be sure you have counts.

Independence Assumption

The individuals who are counted in the cells must be sampled independently of each other. We can t test for this, but we can check the

Randomization Condition: The individuals who have been counted and whose counts are available for analysis should be a random sample from some population.

Sample Size Condition:

We must have enough data for the methods to work. That turns out not to be a simple question. We usually check the

Expected Cell Frequency Condition: We should expect to see at least 5 individuals in each cell. Because we start all of the chi square analyses by proposing expected counts for each cell, this condition is easy to check.

The Expected Cell Frequency Condition sounds like and is, in fact quite similar to the condition that np and nq be greater than 10 when we tested proportions.

---

[1] A question actually asked us by someone who was-undoubtedly-a Pisces.

DRAFT: Do not distribute or copy

Calculations

We have observed a count in each category from the data, and have an expected count for each category from the hypothesized proportions. The test statistic, naturally enough, considers the *differences* between these observed and expected counts. Because the difference between these numbers gets larger the more data we have, we need to divide by something to get an idea of the *relative* sizes of the differences.

For each category, we start by computing its **standardized residual**:

$$c = \frac{(Obs - Exp)}{\sqrt{Exp}}.$$

The test statistic, called **chi-square (or chi-squared)** statistic, is found by adding up the sum of the squares of these standardized residuals:

$$\chi^2 = \sum_{all\ cells} c^2 = \sum_{all\ cells} \frac{(Obs - Exp)^2}{Exp}$$

The chi square statistic is denoted χ^2 where χ is the Greek letter chi (pronounced ki as in sky , not chai as in tea). It refers to a family of sampling distribution models we have not seen before called (remarkably enough) the chi-square models.

Its sampling distribution is a family of models, like the Student s *t* models, that differ only in the number of degrees of freedom. As with Student s *t,* the number of degrees of freedom for a goodness-of-fit test is *n — 1*. But here *n* is *not* the sample size, but, instead, is the number of categories.

> **Notation Alert**
>
> There goes another perfectly good letter. But this time it's only the Greek letter χ . Its only use in Statistics is to represent this statistic and the associated sampling distribution.
>
> This is another violation of our rule that Greek letters represent population parameters. Here we are using a Greek letter simply to name a family of distribution models and a statistic.

> **Notation Alert**
>
> We compare the counts observed in each cell with the counts we expect to observe. The usual notation uses O's and E's or abbreviations such as those we've used here. The way the expected counts are found depends on the model.

One-sided or two-sided?

The chi-square statistic is used only for testing, not for constructing confidence intervals. If the observed counts don t match the expected, the statistic will be large. And it can t be too small . That would just mean that our data *really* fit the hypothesis well. So, the chi-square test is always one-sided. If it s large enough, we ll reject the null hypothesis. What could be simpler?

But even though it behaves like a one-sided test, when we reject the null hypothesis, we really don t know *how* our data differ from the null model. There s no direction to the rejection. We just know that it doesn t fit.

A Chi-Square Test for Goodness-of-fit, Step-by-Step

We have counts of 256 executives in 12 Zodiac sign categories. The natural null hypothesis is that executive births should be equally divided among all the Zodiac signs. The test statistic looks at how closely the observed data match this idealized situation.

Think

Hypotheses:

State what we want to know.

We want to know whether births of successful people are *uniformly* distributed across the signs of the zodiac.

H_0: Births are uniformly distributed over Zodiac signs.[2]

H_A: Births are not uniformly distributed over Zodiac signs.

Plan

State the **Null** Model

Check the **conditions**

- **Counted Data Condition:** We have counts of the number of executives in categories.

- **Randomization Condition:** We have a convenience sample of executives, but no reason to suspect bias.

- **Expected Cell Frequency Condition:** The null hypothesis expects 1/12 of the 256 births, or 21.3, should occur in each sign. These values are all greater than 5, so the condition is satisfied.

State the statistic and sampling distribution.

Name the test you will use.

Under these conditions the sampling distribution of the test statistic is χ^2 on 12-1 = 11 degrees of freedom.

We will perform a **chi square goodness-of-fit test**.

Show

Mechanics

We find the standardized

Aries: $c = \dfrac{(23 - 21.33)}{\sqrt{21.33}} = 0.362$,

---

[2] It may seem that we have broken our rule of thumb that null hypotheses should specify parameter values. If you want to get formal about it, the null hypothesis is that:

$$p_{Jan} = p_{Feb} = \ = \ p_{Dec}$$

That is, we hypothesize that the true proportions of births in each month are equal. But the role of the null hypothesis is to specify the values we need so that we can compute the test statistic. That s what this one does.

DRAFT: Do not distribute or copy

residuals for each Zodiac sign, and sum their squares. If you prefer not to write out the whole equation, it can be helpful to do the calculation as a table. We show one after the Step-by-Step.

The χ^2 models are skewed to the high end, and change shape depending on the degrees of freedom. The P-value considers only the right tail. Big χ^2 statistic values correspond to small P-values, which lead us to reject the null hypothesis.

Taurus: $c = \dfrac{(28 - 21.33)}{\sqrt{21.33}} = 1.44$,

Gemini: $c = \dfrac{(18 - 21.33)}{\sqrt{21.33}} = -0.721$, etc.

$$\chi^2 = 0.362^2 + 1.44^2 + (-0.721)^2 + ... = 5.094$$

The chi-square statistic comes out to 5.094,

The P-value is the area in the upper tail of the χ^2 model for 12-1 = 11 degrees of freedom above the computed χ^2 value.

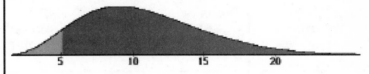

The P-value is 0.927.

Tell

Conclusion

Remember to state the conclusion in terms of what the data mean rather than just making statement about the distribution of counts.

The P-value of 0.927 says that if the Zodiac signs of executives were in fact distributed uniformly, an observed chi square value of 5.09 or higher would occur about 93% of the time. We conclude that these data show virtually no evidence of non-uniform distribution of Zodiac signs among executives.

The Chi-Square Calculation

Let s make the chi square procedure very clear. Here are the steps:

1. **Find the expected values.** These come from the null hypothesis model. Every model gives a hypothesized proportion for each cell. The expected value is the product of the total number of observations times this proportion.

   For our example, the null model hypothesizes *equal* proportions. So, with twelve signs, there should be 1/12 of the 256 executives in each sign. The expected number for each sign is 21.33.

2. **Compute the standardized residuals.** Once you have the expected values, compute the standardized residual for each cell.

3. **Square the standardized residuals and add them up.** Now you have the chi square statistic.

4. **Find the degrees of freedom.** It s equal to the number of cells minus one. For the zodiac signs that s 12-1=11 degrees of freedom.

5. **Test the hypothesis.** Large statistic values mean lots of deviation from the hypothesized distribution so they give small P-values. Look up the critical value from a table of Chi-square values, or use technology to find the P-value directly.

The steps of the Chi square calculations are often laid out in tables. Use one row for each category, and columns for observed counts, expected counts, and squares of the standardized residuals, like this:

Sign	Observed	Expected	Observed-Expected	Standardized residual	Std Resid Squared
Pisces	29	21.333	7.667	1.660733	2.758036
Aquarius	24	21.333	2.667	0.578117	0.334219
Aries	23	21.333	1.667	0.361594	0.13075
Cancer	23	21.333	1.667	0.361594	0.13075
Capricorn	22	21.333	0.667	0.145071	0.021045
Scorpio	21	21.333	-0.333	-0.07145	0.005105
Taurus	20	21.333	-1.333	-0.28798	0.08293
Leo	20	21.333	-1.333	-0.28798	0.08293
Saggitarius	19	21.333	-2.333	-0.5045	0.254519
Virgo	19	21.333	-2.333	-0.5045	0.254519
Libra	18	21.333	-3.333	-0.72102	0.519873
Gemini	18	21.333	-3.333	-0.72102	0.519873

But I Believe the Model

Goodness-of-fit tests are likely to be performed by people who have a theory of what the proportions *should* be in each category, and who believe their theory to be true. Unfortunately, the only *null* hypothesis available for a Goodness-of-Fit test is that the theory is true. And as we know, the hypothesis testing procedure only allows us to *reject* the null or *fail to reject* it. We can never confirm that a theory is in fact true.

At best, we can only point out that the data are consistent with the theory being proposed. But this doesn t prove it and isn t what most people want to say about their theory.

Unfortunately, they re stuck. The alternative hypothesis is that the model is not true — and the model can be not true in many, many ways. So there s no way to frame a null hypothesis the other way around. There s just no way to prove that their favored model is true.

Why we can't prove the null

A biologist wants to show that her inheritance theory about fruit flies is valid. It says that _ of the flies should be type 1, _ type 2 and _ type 3. After her students collected data on 100 flies, she did a goodness-of-fit test and found a P-value of .07. She started celebrating since her null hypothesis was retained – that is, until her students collected data on 100 more flies. With 200 flies, the P-value dropped to .02. Although she knew the answer was probably no, she asked the statistician hopefully if she could just ignore half the data and stick with the original 100.

By this reasoning you could always "prove the null" just by not collecting much data. With only a little data, the chances are good that they'll be consistent with almost anything. But they also have little chance of disproving anything as well. In this case we say the test had no "power". Don't let yourself be lulled into this scientist's reasoning. More data is always better. You just can't ever prove the

---

"Statisticians, like artists, have the bad habit of falling in love with their models" -- George Box

Comparing Observed Distributions

Sometimes we don t have a theoretical model for the distribution of counts. We just have several sets of counts for the same variable under two or more circumstances. Now our question is about whether the populations are the same or whether they differ.

It turns out that we can use a very similar statistic in this case. In fact, the formula for it is *identical* to the Chi-square statistic for goodness-of-fit that we just saw. (How similar can you get?). But now we have no model. So we find the expected counts for each category directly from the data. And as a result, we count up the degrees of freedom slightly differently as well.

Many high schools survey graduating classes to determine the plans of the graduates. We might wonder whether the plans of students have stayed roughly the same over past decades or whether they have changed. Here is a summary table from one high school. Each **cell** of the table shows how many students from a particular graduating class (the column) made a certain choice (the row).

	1980	1990	2000	Total
College/Post HS Education	320	245	288	853
Employment	98	24	17	139
Military	18	19	5	42
Travel	17	2	5	24
Total	453	290	315	1058

Who: High School Graduates

What: Post Graduation Activities

When: 1980, 1990, 2000

Why: Regular survey for general information

Activities of graduates of a high school reported a year after graduation, by graduation year. (Source: IHS)

We might wonder about changes in the choice of Military service as a post-high school activity. The numbers for 1980 and 1990 look similar, until you notice the class sizes are quite different. The 18 seniors in 1980 who chose military service were only about 4% of the graduating class. In 1990, the 19 seniors making the same choice represented 6.6% of the class. Because the class sizes change so much, we re probably better off examining the proportions rather than the counts:

	1980	1990	2000	total
College	70.6	84.5	91.4	**80.6**
Employment	21.6	8.28	5.40	**13.1**
Military	3.97	6.55	1.59	**3.97**
Travel	3.75	0.690	1.59	**2.27**
total	100	100	100	100

Activities of graduates of a high school reported a year after graduation, as percentage of the class.

We already know how to test whether *two* proportions are the same. For example, we could consider whether the proportion of students choosing military service was the same between 1980 and 1990 with a two-proportion z-test. But here we are interested in differences among *all* of the proportions. We can address the general question with a version of the chi-square test called a **test of homogeneity**.

The name homogeneity means that things are the same. Here, we ask whether the post-high school choices made by students are the same for these three graduating classes.

Assumptions and Conditions

The assumptions and conditions here are the same as for the chi square test for goodness-of-fit. In particular, these data must be counts. You can t do a test of homogeneity on measurements. For example, if we had recorded mean GPA s for these same groups over the same time span, we wouldn t be able to test whether GPA s had changed using this test.

Calculations

We base the expected counts on the null hypothesis, which says that the proportions of graduates choosing each alternative should be the same for all three classes. First we find the overall proportion of students making a certain choice. Those fractions of each graduating class are our expected counts.

For example, of the 1058 students covered by these three surveys, 139, or about 13.14% were employed. If the distributions are homogeneous (as the null hypothesis asserts), then 13.13% of the 453 students in the class of 1980 (or about 59.51) should be employed. Similarly, 13.13% of the 290 students in the class of 1990 (or about 38.1) should be employed.

Working in this way, we (or more likely, the computer) can fill in expected values for each cell. Because these are theoretical values, there is no requirement that they be integers. The expected values look like this:

	1980	1990	2000	total
College	365.226	233.809	253.965	853
Employment	59.5151	38.1002	41.3847	139
Military	17.9830	11.5123	12.5047	42
Travel	10.2760	6.57845	7.14556	24
total	453	290	315	1058

Following the pattern of the goodness-of-fit test, we compute for each cell of the table the **standardized residual**. For the first cell, 1980 college-bound students, that s

$$c = \frac{(Obs - Exp)}{\sqrt{Exp}} = \frac{(320 - 365.226)}{\sqrt{365.226}} = -2.367$$

The chi square statistic adds up the sum of squared standardized residuals:

$$\chi^2 = \sum_{all\ cells} c^2 = \sum_{all\ cells} \frac{(Obs - Exp)^2}{Exp}$$

Because the column totals are fixed, as in the goodness-of-fit test, the number of **degrees of freedom** involves one less than the number of rows. (If we know the totals for a given class year for all choices but one, we can find the missing count by subtraction.) And the row totals are also fixed. Why? The null hypothesis says that the proportion of students making each choice has stayed the same, so the proportions in each row are fixed[3]. And because the total number of students in the table is known, the row totals are also fixed. That means that if we know two of the three numbers in any row, we can find the remaining one.

So we have 3 independent choices in each column by 2 independent choices in each row, for a total of 2 x 3 = 6 degrees of freedom. In general, a table with R rows and C columns has $(R — 1)(C — 1)$ degrees of freedom.

A Chi-Square Test for Homogeneity, Step-by-Step

We have counts of 1058 students observed in three different years a decade apart and categorized according to their post-graduation activities.

Think

Hypotheses: State what we want to know.

State the hypotheses.

The homogeneity test comes with a built-in null hypothesis. We hypothesize that the distribution does not change from group to group. The test looks for differences large enough to step beyond what we might expect from random sample-to-sample variation. It will notice a large deviation in a single category or small but persistent differences over all the categories or anything in between.

We want to know whether the choices made by high school graduates in what they do after high school have changed between 1980 and 2000.

H_0: The post-high school choices made in 1980, 1990, and 2000 have the same distribution (are homogeneous).

H_A: The post-high school choices made in 1980, 1990, and 2000 do not have the same distribution.

Plan

State the **Null Model.**

Check the **conditions**

Counted Data Condition: We have counts of the number of students in categories.
Random Sample Condition: We have the full graduating classes from one high school in three different years. They could be viewed as a representative sample of high school graduates from similar communities in those years.
Expected Cell Frequency Condition: The

---

[3] We find the row proportions as *pooled proportions,* combining the counts across each row.

DRAFT: Do not distribute or copy

State the statistic and sampling distribution.

Name the test you will use.

Show

Mechanics

The shape of a χ^2 model depends on the degrees of freedom. A χ^2 model on 6 df is skewed to the high end. The P-value considers only the right tail.

In this case the statistic value is off the scale, so the P-value is quite small.

expected values (found earlier) are all sufficiently large.

Under these conditions the sampling distribution of the test statistic is χ^2 on (3-1) x (4-1) = 6 degrees of freedom. We will perform a chi square test of homogeneity.

We find the expected frequencies for all cells using the null hypothesis. The sum of the squared standardized residuals comes out to $\chi^2 = 72.77$.

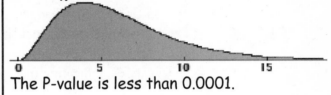

The P-value is less than 0.0001.

Tell

Conclusion

State your conclusion in terms of the data. It should specifically talk about whether the distributions for the groups appear to be different.

The P-value is very small, indicating that the pattern we see would be very unlikely to occur by chance were post-high school choices homogeneous. We reject the null hypothesis, and conclude that the choices made by high school graduates have indeed changed over the two decades examined.

If you find that simply rejecting the hypothesis of homogeneity a bit unsatisfying, you are in good company. It is hardly a shock that high school students made different choices in 2000 than in 1980. What we d really like to know is how big the differences were, where they were greatest and where they were smallest. The test for homogeneity doesn t answer these very interesting questions, but there is some evidence that can help us.

Examining the Residuals

It is always a good idea to examine the standardized residuals when we reject the null hypothesis for a chi square test. (We don t need to do this when we fail to reject because if the χ^2 value is small, all of its components must have been small.) The residuals give us a chance to think about the underlying patterns and to consider the ways in which the distribution may have changed from class to class.

Here are the residuals for the high school data:

Remember: the standardized residuals are

$$c = \frac{(Obs - Exp)}{\sqrt{Exp}}$$

	1980	1990	2000
College	-2.366	0.7319	2.136
Employment	4.988	-2.284	-3.790
Military	0.0040	2.207	-2.122
Travel	2.098	-1.785	-0.8026

The row for Employment immediately attracts our attention. It holds the largest (in magnitude) two residuals and three of the four largest residuals. It looks like employment was a more common choice for the class of 1980 and a less common choice for the classes of 1990 and 2000. This trend may have been influenced by changes in the economy or by a growing sense of the importance of post-secondary education. We can see an opposite trend in the College row, from moderate negative residual to moderate positive residual across the three classes, indicating that going to college has become more common.

Independence

A study from the University of Texas Southwestern Medical Center examined whether the risk of hepatitis C was affected by whether people had tattoos and by where they got their tattoos. Hepatitis C causes about 10,000 deaths each year in the United States, but often lies undetected for years after infection.

The data from this study can be summarized in a two-way table as follows

Who: Patients being treated for non-blood related disorders.

What: Tattoo status and Hepatitis C status

When 1991, 1992

Where Texas

	Hep C	no Hep C	Total
Tattoo, Parlor	17	35	**52**
Tattoo, Elsewhere	8	53	**61**
None	22	491	**513**
Totals	**47**	**579**	**626**

Number of patients testing positive or negative for hepatitis C according to whether they had a tattoo from a tattoo parlor, from another source, or no tattoo.

These data differ from the kinds of data we've considered before in this chapter because they categorize subjects on *two* categorical variables rather than on only one. The categorical variables here are hepatitis C status (Hep C or no Hep C) and Tattoo status (Parlor , Elsewhere , None). Although we've summarized the data in a two-way table for all three versions of the chi-square test, it is this version that deserves the special name **contingency table**. Contingency tables categorize counts on two (or more) variables so that we can see whether the distribution of counts on one variable is contingent on the other.

DRAFT: Do not distribute or copy

The natural question to ask of these data is whether the chance of having hepatitis C is *independent* of tattoo status. Recall that for events A and B to be independent, P(A) must equal P(A|B). Here, that means that the probability that a randomly selected patient has hepatitis C should not change conditional on learning that patient s tattoo status. We examined the question of independence in just this way back in Chapter 17, but we lacked a way to test it. The rules for independence are much too precise and absolute to work well with real data.

Now we can construct the test that we wanted back then. Where we computed relative frequencies and thought about them as probabilities, we now find the same relative frequencies and think of them as proportions. In that form, the condition of independence just means that the proportion (think relative frequency) of patients with hepatitis C should be the same for all tattoo status categories. This is the same pattern as the one we hypothesized in the test for homogeneity. In fact, the mechanics of the test for independence are the same as for the test for homogeneity.

This is an unusual case. Here is a new test that is in every way computationally identical to one we already know, and yet is conceptually different. These differences are important. First, the data are structured differently. For the independence test we have two categorical variables measured on a single population. For the homogeneity test we have a single categorical variable measured independently on two or more populations. And then we ask different questions: Are the variables independent? *vs* Are the groups homogeneous?

> The only difference between the test for homogeneity and the test for independence is in what you...
>
> **Think**

A Chi-Square Test for Independence, Step-by-Step

We have counts of 626 individuals categorized according to their tattoo status and their hepatitis status .

Think

Hypotheses: State what we want to know.	We want to know whether the categorical variables "tattoo status" and "hepatitis status" are statistically independent.
We perform a test of independence when we do not really believe the variables are independent. We are on the familiar ground of making a claim (that knowing tattoo status	H_0: Tattoo status and hepatitis status are independent[4]. H_A: Tattoo status and hepatitis status are not independent.

---

[4] Once again, parameters are hard to find. The hypothesis of independence itself tells us how to find expected values for each cell of the contingency table. That s all we need

will change probabilities for hepatitis C status), but testing the null hypothesis that it is *not* true. The interesting result in a test of independence is almost always that the variables are not independent

Plan

Check the **conditions**

Counted Data Condition: We have counts of individuals in categories of two categorical variables.

Random Sample Condition: These data are from a retrospective study of patients being treated for something unrelated to hepatitis. Although they are not an SRS, they were selected to avoid biases and should be representative of the general population.

Expected Cell Frequency Condition: The expected values do not meet the condition that all are bigger than 5. We will return to this later.

	Hepatitis C	No Heptatitis	Total
Tattoo, Parlor	3.904	48.096	**52**
Tattoo, no parlor	4.580	56.420	**61**
None	38.516	474.48	**513**
Total	47	579	**626**

State the **Null Model.**

Name the test you will use.

Under these conditions the sampling distribution of the test statistic is c^2 on $(3-1) \times (2-1) = 2$ degrees of freedom.

We will perform a chi square test of independence.

Show

Mechanics

The shape of a chi square model depends on its degrees of freedom. With 2 df, the model looks quite different, as you can see here. We still care only

The sum of the squared standardized residuals is $c^2 = 57.91$.

about the right tail.

The P-value for this statistic is small—less than 0.0001.

Tell

Conclusion

State your conclusion about the independence of the two variables.

The P-value is very small, indicating that if these variables were independent the pattern we have seen would be very unlikely to occur by chance. We conclude that the hepatitis status is not independent of tattoo status. But we'll want to check that the two cells with small expected counts did not influence our result too greatly.

Examine the Residuals

Each cell of the contingency table contributes a term to the chi square sum. As we did earlier, we should examine the residuals because we have rejected the null hypothesis. Here, we have an additional concern that the cells with small expected frequencies not be the ones that make the chi square statistic large.

Our concern with the data arises from the potential for improving public health. If patients with tattoos are more likely to test positive for hepatitis C, perhaps physicians should be advised to suggest blood tests for such patients.

The residuals look like this:

	Hepatitis C	No Heptatitis
Parlor	6.628	-1.888
Tattoo, no parlor	1.598	-0.455
None	-2.661	0.758

The chi square value of 57.91 is the sum of the squares of these six values. The cell for patients with tattoos obtained in a tattoo parlor who have hepatitis C is large and positive, indicating that there are more patients in that cell than the null hypothesis of independence would predict. This result suggests that a principle source of infection may be tattoo parlors.

The second largest component is a negative value for those with no tattoos who test positive for hepatitis C. A negative value says that there are fewer patients in this cell than independence would expect. That is, those who have no tattoos are less likely to be infected with hepatitis C than we might expect from a simple hypothesis of independence.

What about the cells with small expected counts? The formula for the chi square standardized residuals divides by the square root of the expected frequency. Too small an expected frequency will arbitrarily inflate the residual, and lead to an inflated chi square statistic. So, any expected count close to the arbitrary minimum of 5 calls for checking that cell s standardized residual to be sure that it is not particularly large. In this case, the standardized residual for Hep C and no Parlor is not particularly large, but the standardized residual for Hep C and tattoo parlor is large.

Tell all

We might choose not to report the results because of concern with the small expected frequency. Alternatively, we could include a warning along with our report of the results. Yet another approach is to combine appropriate categories to get a larger sample size and correspondingly larger expected frequencies. Here, we might naturally combine the two rows for tattoos, obtaining a 2 x 2 table:

	Hepatitis C	No Heptatitis	total
None	22	491	**513**
Tattoo	25	88	**113**
total	**47**	**579**	**626**

This table has expected values greater than 5 in every cell and a chi-square value of 42.42 on 1 degree of freedom. The corresponding P-value is found to be † 0.0001 by the computer.

So we conclude that tattoo status and hepatitis C status are not independent. The data suggest that tattoo parlors may be a particular problem, but we haven t enough data to be certain of that.

Chi Square and Causation

Don't Tell

Chi square tests are common. Tests for independence are especially widespread. Unfortunately, a rejection of the independence hypothesis is often interpreted as proof of causation. Just as correlation between quantitative variables does not demonstrate causation, a failure of independence between two categorical variables does not show a cause-and-effect relationship between them. And for the same reasons.

The chi square test for independence treats the two variables symmetrically. There is no way to differentiate the direction of any possible causation from one variable to the other. In our example, it is unlikely that having hepatitis causes one to crave a tattoo, but other examples are not so clear.

Nor is there any way to eliminate the possibility that a third (lurking) variable is responsible for the observed lack of independence. For example, it might be that people who have body piercings or those who inject drugs are both more likely to get tattooed and more likely to contract hepatitis C. Even a small subpopulation of drug users among those with tattoos might be enough to create the observed result.

In some sense, a failure of independence between two categorical variables is less impressive than a strong, consistent, linear association between quantitative

DRAFT: Do not distribute or copy

variables. There are many ways two categorical variables can fail the test of independence, and many of these show no consistent pattern of failure. Examination of the chi square residuals can help you to think about the underlying patterns.

What Can Go Wrong

Don't use Chi-square methods if you don't have counts. All three of the chi square tests considered here apply only to counts. Other kinds of data can be arrayed in two-way tables. Just because numbers are in a two-way table, doesn t make them suitable for chi square analysis. Data reported as proportions or percentages can be suitable for chi square procedures, *but only after they are converted to counts.* If you try to do the calculations without first finding the counts, your results will be wrong.

Beware large samples. The chi square distributions are unusual because the degrees of freedom depend on the dimensions of the table and not on the sample size. Larger sample sizes do tend to generate larger chi square statistic values because they make it possible to discern smaller deviations from the (null) hypothesized value. But deviations that are smaller are usually of less practical importance. You should be wary of chi square tests performed on very large samples. No two variables are completely independent, no two groups are exactly homogeneous, and no hypothesized distribution fits perfectly. With a sufficiently large sample size, a chi square test can always reject the null hypothesis. If that rejection depends on a large sample size, you should not be impressed with the test result unless the magnitude of the effect is itself large.

Chi Square and the Computer

You may be able to fool a package into computing a goodness-of-fit chi square by entering values that exactly fit your model and testing for independence. That can give the right chi-square value, but the degrees of freedom (and thus the P-value) will be wrong.

Most statistics packages associate chi square tests with contingency tables. Often chi square is only available as an option when you make a contingency table. This organization can make it hard to locate the chi square test and may confuse the three different roles that the chi square test can take. In particular, chi square tests for goodness-of-fit may be hard to find or missing entirely. Chi square tests for homogeneity are computationally the same as chi square tests for independence, but you may have to find them as tests of independence.

Most statistics packages work with data on the individuals rather than with the summary counts. If the only information you have is the table of counts, you may find it more difficult to get a statistics package to compute chi square. Some packages offer a way to reconstruct the data from the summary counts so that they can then be passed back through the chi square calculation, finding the cell counts again. (Hey, whatever works.) Many package offer chi square standardized residuals (although they may be called something else).

Package	Commands & Location	Comments
Data Desk	Select variables From the Calc menu, choose Contingency Table. From the table's HyperView menu choose Table Options. (Or Choose Calc > Calculation Options > Table Options) In the dialog check for Chi Square and for Standardized Residuals. Data Desk will display the Chi Square and its P-value below the table, and the standardized residuals within the table.	Data Desk automatically treats variables selected for this command as categorical variables even if their elements are numerals. The Compute Counts command in the table's HyperView menu will make variables that hold the table contents (as selected in the Table Options dialog) including the standardized residuals.
Excel	Excel offers the function CHITEST(actual_range,expected_range), which computes a chi square test for homogeneity. Both ranges are of the form UpperleftCell:LowerRuightCell, specifying two rectangular tables that must hold counts (although Excel will not check for integer values). The two tables must be of the same size and shape.	Excel's documentation claims this is a test for independence and labels the input ranges accordingly, but Excel offers no way to find expected counts, so the function is not particularly useful for testing independence. You can only use this function if you already know both tables of counts or are willing to program additional calculations.
JMP	From the Analyze menu select Fit y by x. Select variables: a y-Response variable that holds responses for one variable, and an x-Factor variable that holds responses for the other. Both selected variables must be Nominal or Ordinal. JMP will make a plot and a contingency table. Below the contingency table, JMP offers a Tests panel. In that panel the Chi Square for independence is called a Pearson ChiSquare. The table also offers the P-value. Click on the Contingency Table title bar to drop down a menu that offers to include a Deviation and Cell Chi square in each cell of the table.	JMP will choose this result for y by x if both variables are nominal or ordinal (marked with an N or O), but not otherwise. Be sure the variables have the right type. Deviations are the observed − expected differences in counts. Cell chi squares are the squares of the standardized residuals. Refer tot he deviations for the sign of the difference.
Minitab	From the Stat menu choose the Tables submenu. From that menu, choose Cross Tabulation. In the Cross Tabulation dialog assign variables from the list to the Classification Variables box. The first selected specifies the rows; the second specifies columns. Click the Chi-Square analysis check box and choose the standardized residual option below it. Minitab will display the table and print the chi square value and its P-value below it.	
SPSS	From the Analyze menu choose the Descriptive Statistics submenu. From that submenu, choose Crosstabs... In the Crosstabs dialog, assign the row and column variables from the variable list. Both variables must be categorical. Click the Cells button to specify that standardized residuals should be displayed. Click the Statistics button to specify a Chi Square test.	SPSS only presents variables that it knows to be categorical in the variable list for the Crosstabs dialog. If the variables you want are missing, check that they have the right type.
TI-83		The TI-83 can calculate a Chi square, but it is a bit messy.

DRAFT: Do not distribute or copy

Connections

Chi-square methods relate naturally to inference methods for proportions. Indeed, we can think of a test of homogeneity as stepping from a comparison of two proportions to a question of whether three or more proportions are equal.

Independence is, of course, a fundamental statistics concept. But chi square tests do not offer a general way to check on independence for all those times when we have had to assume it.

There are few natural displays to accompany chi square tests. A histogram or boxplot of the standardized residuals can help locate extraordinary values, but few statistics packages offer this capability.

Key Concepts

Two-way Table	Each *cell* of a two-way table shows counts of individuals. One way classifies a sample according to a categorical variable. The other way can classify different groups of individuals according to the same variable, or classify the same sample according to a different categorical variable.
Contingency Table	A two-way table that classifies individuals according to two categorical variables is called a *contingency table*.
Standardized Residual	In two-way tables, a standardized residual is the difference between the observed count and the expected count divided by the square root of the expected count.
Chi-Square models	Chi-square models are skewed to the right. They are parameterized by their degrees of freedom, and become less skewed with increasing degrees of freedom.
Chi-Square statistic	The chi-square statistic is found by summing the squares of the standardized residuals. Chi square tests can be used to test goodness-of-fit, homogeneity, or independence.
Goodness-of-fit	A test of whether the distribution of counts in one categorical variable matches the distribution predicted by a model is called a test of Goodness-of-fit. A chi-square test of goodness-of-fit uses a chi-square model with $k - 1$ degrees of freedom, where k is the number of categories in the categorical

	variable.
Homogeneity	A test comparing the distribution of counts for two or more groups on the same categorical variable is called a test of *homogeneity*. A chi-square test of homogeneity uses a chi-square distribution with (*#Rows - 1*) * (*#Cols - 1*) degrees of freedom, where *#Rows* gives the number of categories and *#Cols* gives the number of independent groups.
Independence	A test of whether two categorical variables are independent examines the distribution of counts for one group of individuals classified according to both variables. A chi-square test of *independence* uses a chi-square distribution with (*#Rows - 1*) * (*#Cols - 1*) degrees of freedom, where *#Rows* gives the number of categories in one variable and *#Cols* gives the number of categories in the other.

Skills

Upon completing this Lesson you should:

Think

- Be able to recognize when a test of Goodness-of-fit, a test of Homogeneity, or a test of Independence would be appropriate for a table of counts.

- Understand that the degrees of freedom for a chi-square test depend on the dimensions of the table and not on the sample size. Understand that this means that increasing the sample size increases the ability of chi-square procedures to reject the null hypothesis.

Show

- Be able to display and interpret counts in a two-way table.

- Know how to use the chi-square tables to perform chi-square tests.

- Know how to compute a chi-square test using your statistics software or calculator.

- Be able to examine the standardized residuals to explain the nature of the deviations from the null hypothesis.

Tell

- Know how to interpret chi-square as a test of Goodness-of-fit in a few sentences.

- Know how to interpret chi-square as a test of Homogeneity in a few sentences.

> • Know how to interpret chi-square as a test of Independence in a few sentences.

Exercises

1. **Dice** After getting trounced by your little brother in a children s game, you suspect the die he gave you to roll may be unfair. To check, you roll it 60 times, recording the number of times each face appears. Do these results cast doubt on the die s fairness?

Face	Count
1	11
2	7
3	9
4	15
5	12
6	6

   a) If the die is fair, how many times would you expect each face to show?
   b) To see if these results are unusual, will you test goodness-of-fit, homogeneity, or independence?
   c) State your hypotheses.
   d) Check the conditions.
   e) How many degrees of freedom are there?
   f) Find χ^2 and the P-value.
   g) State your conclusion.

2. **M&Ms** As noted in Chapter 17, the Mars company says that yellow candies make up 20% of their plain M&M s, red another 20%, and orange, blue, and green are each 10%. The rest are brown. [www.m-ms.com/factory/history] On his way home from work the day he was writing these exercises, one of the authors bought a bag of plain M&M s. He got 29 yellow ones, 23 red ones, 12 orange, 14 blue, 8 green, and 20 brown ones. Is this sample consistent with the Mars company s stated proportions? Test an appropriate hypothesis and state your conclusion.

3. **Nuts** A company says their premium mixture of nuts contains 10% Brazil nuts, 20% cashews, 20% almonds, 10% hazelnuts, and the rest are peanuts. You buy a large can and separate the various kinds of nuts. Upon weighing them you find there were 112 grams of Brazil nuts, 183 grams of cashews, 207 grams of almonds, 71 grams of hazelnuts, and 446 grams of peanuts. You wonder whether your mix is significantly different from what the company advertises. Explain why the chi-square goodness-of-fit test is not an appropriate way to find out.

4. **NYPD and Race** Census data for New York City indicates that 29.2% of the under-18 population is White, 28.2% Black, 31.5%Latino, 9.1% Asian, and 2% other ethnicities. [http://mumford1.dyndns.org/cen2000] The New York Civil Liberties Union points out that of 26181 police officers, 64.8% are White, 14.5% Black, 19.1% Hispanic, and 1.4% Asian. [http://www.nyclu.org/blame6.html] Do the police officers reflect the ethnic

composition of the city's youth? Test an appropriate hypothesis and state your conclusion.

5. **NYPD and Gender** The table below shows the rank attained by male and female officers in the New York City Police Department. [http://www.nyclu.org/blame6.html] Do these data indicate that men and women are equitably represented at all levels of the department?

Rank	Male	Female
Officer	21900	4281
Detective	4058	806
Sergeant	3898	415
Lieutenant	1333	89
Captain	359	12
Higher ranks	218	10

a) What is the probability that a police officer selected at random from the NYPD is a female?
b) What is the probability that a police officer selected at random is a detective?
c) Assuming no bias in promotions, how many female detectives would you expect the NYPD to have?
d) To see if there is evidence of differences in ranks attained by males and females, will you test goodness-of-fit, homogeneity, or independence?
e) State the hypotheses.
f) Test the conditions.
g) How many degrees of freedom are there?
h) Find χ^2 and the P-value.
i) State your conclusion.
j) If you concluded that the distributions are not the same, analyze the differences.

6. **Grades** Two different professors teach an introductory statistics course. The table shows the distribution of final grades they reported. We wonder whether one of theses professors is an "easier" grader".

Grade	Dr. Alpha	Dr. Beta
A	3	9
B	11	12
C	14	8
D	9	2
F	3	1

a) Will you test goodness-of-fit, homogeneity, or independence?
b) Write appropriate null hypotheses.
c) Find the expected counts for each cell, and explain why the chi-square procedures are not appropriate for this table.

7. **Grades Again** In some situations where the expected cell counts are too small, as in the case of the grades given by Professors Alpha and Beta, we can complete an analysis anyway. We can often proceed after combining cells in some way that both makes sense and produces a table in which the conditions are satisfied. Here we create a new table displaying the same data, but calling D's and F's "Below C", as shown.

a) Find the expected counts for each cell in this new table, and explain why a chi-square procedure is now appropriate.

Grade	Dr. Alpha	Dr. Beta
A	3	9
B	11	12
C	14	8
Below C	12	3

b) With this change in the table, what has happened to the number of degrees of freedom?

c) Test your hypothesis about the two professors, and state an appropriate conclusion.

8. **Full Moon** Some people believe that a full moon elicits unusual behavior. The table shows the number of arrests made in a small town during weeks of 6 full moons and six other randomly selected weeks during the same year. Is there evidence of a difference in the types of illegal activity that takes place?

Offense	Full Moon	Not Full
Violent (murder, assault, rape, etc)	2	3
Property (burglary, vandalism, etc)	17	21
Drugs/Alcohol	27	19
Domestic Abuse	11	14
Other offenses	9	6

9. **Titanic** Here is a table showing who survived the sinking of the *Titanic* based on whether they were crew members, or passengers booked in first, second, or third class staterooms:

	Crew	First	Second	Third	Total
Alive	212	202	118	178	710
Dead	673	123	167	528	1491
Total	885	325	285	706	2201

a) If we draw an individual at random from this table, what is the probability that we will draw a member of the crew?

b) What is the probability of randomly selecting a third class passenger who survived?

c) What is the probability of a randomly selected passenger surviving, given that the passenger was a first class passenger?

If someone s chances of surviving were the same regardless of their status on the ship, how many members of the crew would you expect to have lived?

d) State the null and alternative hypotheses we would test here.

e) Give the degrees of freedom for the test.

f) The chi-square value for the table is 2109.4, and the corresponding P-value is barely greater than 0. State your conclusions about the hypotheses.

10. **Titanic, Redux** Newspaper headlines at the time, and traditional wisdom in the succeeding decades, have held that women and children escaped the *Titanic* in greater proportion than men. Here is a table

	Female	Male	Total
Alive	343	367	710
Dead	127	1364	1491
Total	470	1731	2201

with data by gender. Do you think that survival was independent of gender? Defend your conclusion.

11. **Survival and Gender, One More Time** In Exercise 9 you could have checked for a difference in the chances of survival for men and women using two-proportion z-procedures.
    a) Find the z—value for this approach
    b) Show that the square of your calculated value of z is the value of χ^2 you calculated in Exercise 19.
    c) Show that the resulting P-values are the same.

12. **Racial Steering** A subtle form of racial discrimination in housing is racial steering . Racial steering occurs when real estate agents only show prospective buyers homes in neighborhoods already dominated by that family s race. This violates the Fair Housing Act of 1968. According to an article in *Chance* magazine [Vol 14, No2 2001], tenants at a large apartment complex recently filed a lawsuit alleging racial steering. The complex is divided into two parts, Section A and Section B. The plaintiffs claimed that white potential renters were steered to Section A while African-Americans were steered to Section B. The table displays the data that were presented in court to show the locations of recently rented apartments. Do you think there is evidence of racial steering?
    a) Is this a test of goodness-of-fit, homogeneity, or independence?
    b) State the hypotheses.
    c) Test the conditions.
    d) How many degrees of freedom are there?
    e) Find χ^2 and the P-value.
    f) State your conclusion.

New Renters			
	White	Black	Total
Section A	87	8	95
Section B	83	34	117
Total	170	42	212

13. **Steering Revisited** You could have checked the data in Exercise 11 for evidence of racial steering using two-proportion z-procedures.
    a) Find the z—value for this approach, and show that when you square z you get the value of χ^2 you calculated in Exercise 11.
    b) Show that the resulting P-values are the same.

14. **Pregnancy** In 1998 a San Diego reproductive clinic reported 42 live births to 157 women under the age of 38, but only 7 successes for 89 clients aged

38 and older. Is this strong evidence of a difference in the effectiveness of the clinic s methods for older women?

a) Test the appropriate hypotheses using the 2-proportion z-procedure.

b) Repeat the analysis using an appropriate chi-square procedure.

c) Explain how the two results are equivalent.

15. **Race and Education** Data from the US Census Bureau show levels of education a sample of US residents attained by age 30.

	Not HS Grad	HS Diploma	College Grad	Adv. Degree
White	810	6429	4725	1127
Black	263	1598	549	117
Hispanic	1031	1269	412	99
Other	66	341	305	197

a) Do these data highlight significant differences in education levels attained by these groups?

b) What might explain the unusually high number of Hispanic Americans who have not finished high school?

16. **Race and Education, Part 2** Consider only the people who have graduated from high school. Do these data suggest there are significant differences in opportunities for Black and Hispanic Americans who have completed high school to pursue college or advanced degrees?

	HS Diploma	College Grad	Adv. Degree
Black	1598	549	117
Hispanic	1269	412	99

17. **Cranberry Juice** It is common folk wisdom that drinking cranberry juice can help prevent urinary tract infections in women. In 2001 the British Medical Journal reported the results of a Finnish study in which three groups of 50 women were monitored for these infections over 6-months. One group drank cranberry juice daily, another group drank a lactobacillus drink, and the third drank neither of those beverages, serving as a control group. 18 of the women in the control group developed at least one infection compared to 20 who consumed the lactobacillus drink and only 8 who drank cranberry juice. Does this study provide supporting evidence for the value of cranberry juice in warding off urinary tract infections?

a) Is this a survey, a retroactive study, a prospective study, or an experiment? Explain.

b) Will you test of goodness-of-fit, homogeneity, or independence?

c) State the hypotheses.

d) Test the conditions.

e) How many degrees of freedom are there?

f) Find χ^2 and the P-value.

g) State your conclusion.

18. **AP Statistics Scores** In 2001 over 41000 students nationwide took the Advanced Placement Examination. The national distribution of scores and the results at Ithaca High School are shown in the table.

Score	National Distribution	Ithaca High School Number of Boys	Number of Girls
5	11.5%	13	13
4	23.4%	21	15
3	24.9%	6	13
2	19.1%	7	3
1	21.1%	4	2

a) Did students at this high school perform significantly better than their peers nationwide?

b) Was there a significant difference between the performances of boys and girls at this school?

19. **Working parents** In July 1991 and again in April 2001 the Gallup poll asked random samples of 1015 adults about their opinions on working parents. The table summarizes responses to the question "Considering the needs of both parents and children, which of the following do you see as the ideal family in today's society?" Based upon these results, do you think there was a change in people's attitudes during the ten years between these polls?

Response	1991	2001
Both work fulltime	142	131
One works fulltime, other parttime	274	244
One works, other works at home	152	173
One works, other stays home for kids	396	416
No opinion	51	51

a) Is this a survey, a retroactive study, a prospective study, or an experiment? Explain.

b) Will you test goodness-of-fit, homogeneity, or independence?

c) State the hypotheses.

d) Test the conditions.

e) How many degrees of freedom are there?

f) Find χ^2 and the P-value.

g) State your conclusion.

20. **Fish diet** Medical researchers followed 6272 Swedish men for 30 years to see if there was any association between the amount of fish in their diet and prostate cancer. [*Fatty fish consumption and risk of prostate cancer*, Lancet, June 2001]

Fish consumption	Total subjects	Prostate cancers
Never/seldom	124	14
Small part of diet	2621	201
Moderate part	2978	209
Large part	549	42

DRAFT: Do not distribute or copy

a) Is this a survey, a retroactive study, a prospective study, or an experiment? Explain.
b) Do you see evidence of an association between the amount of fish in a man's diet and his risk of developing prostate cancer?
c) Does this study prove that eating fish can prevent prostate cancer? Explain.

21. **Pregnancies** Not all pregnancies result in live births; some are aborted, and others end in miscarriages or stillbirths. A June 2001 National Vital Statistics Report examined those outcomes in the U.S. during 1997, broken down by the age of the mother. The table shows counts consistent with that report. Is there evidence that the distribution of outcomes is not the same for these age groups?

Age of mother	Live births	Abortions	Fetal losses
Under 20	49	26	13
20 - 29	201	75	41
30 - 34	88	18	21
35 or over	49	14	21

27 Inferences for Regression

THREE PERCENT OF A MAN'S BODY is essential fat. (For a woman, the percentage is more like 12.5%). As the name implies, essential fat is necessary for a normal, healthy body. Fat is stored in small amounts throughout your body[1]. But too much body fat can be dangerous to your health. For men between 18 and 39 years old, a healthy percent body fat ranges from 8% to 19%. (For women of the same age, it's 21% to 32%.)

But measuring body fat can be tedious and expensive. The "standard reference" measurement is the Dual Energy X-Ray Absorptiometry (DEXA), which involves two low does X-ray generators and takes from 10 to 20 minutes.

How close can we get to a useable prediction of body fat from easily measurable variables such as height, weight or waist size? Here's a scatterplot of the percent body fat plotted against waist size for a sample of 250 males of various ages.

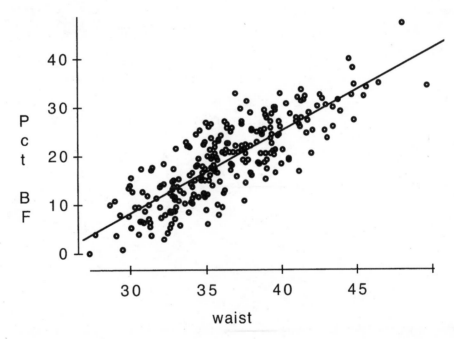

The least squares line for these data is shown in the plot and has the following equation:

$$\%Bod\hat{y}Fat = -42.7 + 1.7Waist$$

The slope says that, on average, % body fat grows at a rate of 1.7 percent for each added inch around the waist.

---

[1] http://www.shapeup.org/bodylab/

How useful is this model? We learned in Chapter 10 how to calculate these coefficients. Now we'd like to know what the regression model can tell us beyond the data at hand, here the 250 men in this study. To do that we'll need to make confidence intervals and test hypotheses about the slope and intercept of the regression line.

The Population and the Sample

What does inference for regression mean? We know better than to think that even if we knew every population value, the data would line up perfectly on a straight line. After all, even in our sample, not all men who have 38-inch waists have the same percent body fat. In fact, there's a whole distribution of %body fat for these men:

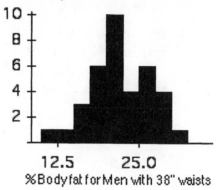

%Body fat for Men with 38" waists

And, of course, the same is true at each waist size. We could depict the distribution of %body fat at different waist sizes like this:

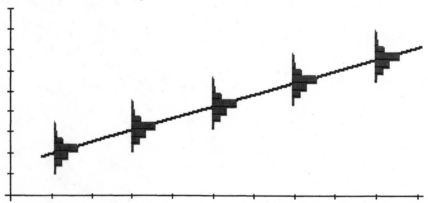

But we want to model the relationship between % body fat and waist size for *all* men. We imagine an **idealized regression line**. This model assumes that the means of the distributions of %body fat for each waist size fall along the line. We know that this model is not a perfect description of how the variables are associated, but it may be useful for predicting body fat and understanding how it is related to waist size.

If we had *all* the values in the population, we could find the slope and intercept of this *ideal regression line* explicitly by using least squares. Following our usual conventions, we write the ideal line with Greek

DRAFT: Do not distribute or copy

letters and consider the coefficients to be *parameters:* β_0 is the intercept and β_1 is the slope.

$$\mu_y = \beta_0 + \beta_1 x$$

Why μ_y? As we saw, there is a distribution of %body fat for each waist size, and we can model it. The idealized regression equation places the *means* of all of those models on the same straight line.

Of course, not all the individual y's are at these means. Some lie above and some below the line. So, like all models, this one makes **errors,** one at each point. These errors can be positive or negative, depending on which side of the line the data fall, (or even zero if the line passes right through a point). We denote the errors by ε.

We can put the errors into an equation for individual y's instead of means like this:

$$y = \beta_0 + \beta_1 x + \varepsilon.$$

This equation is now true for each data point (since the ε's soak up the deviations), and gives a value of y for any value of x.

For the body fat data, an idealized model such as this provides a summary of the relationship between %body fat and waist size. And like all models, it simplifies the real situation. We know there is more to body fat than waist size. But the advantage of models is that the simplification might help us to think about the situation or even to make educated guesses about %body fat from simpler measurements.

The statistical challenge is to come up with reasonable *estimates* of the parameters of this model from a random sample of data and to account for our uncertainty in how close they come. To do this, we need to make some assumptions about the model and the errors.

Assumptions and Conditions

We must make four assumptions to do inference in regression. Fortunately, we can check conditions to help us judge whether these assumptions are reasonable for our data.

Linearity Assumption:

Ideally, the relationship between the variables should be linear. Remember, our idealized regression model places all the means on the same straight line. If the true relationship is very far from linear and you use a straight line to fit the data, your entire analysis may be useless. Certainly your predictions will be far off. A scatterplot will let you check that the assumption is reasonable. If the shape of the scatterplot is linear, the

Check the scatterplot. The shape must be linear or we can't use regression at all.	**Straight Enough Condition** is satisfied. It's also a good idea to check linearity again *after* computing the regression when we can examine the residuals. For the %body fat data, the scatterplot is beautifully linear.
	If the scatterplot is straight enough, we can go on to some assumptions about the errors. (If not, stop here, or consider re-expressing the data to make the scatterplot more linear.)

Independence Assumption

The errors in the true underlying regression model must be mutually independent. As usual, there is no way to be sure that this assumption is true. It is reassuring if the

Random Sample condition is met for the y-variable. Ideally, we can assume we know the x-variable without any random variability. But this is often not strictly true.

Check the residuals plot.(Part 1) The residuals should appear to be randomly scattered.

We can also check displays of the regression residuals for evidence of patterns, trends, or clumping, any of which would suggest a failure of independence.

In the special case when the x-variable is related to time, make sure that the residuals do not have a pattern when plotted against the x variable. The %body fat data were collected on a sample of men. They were not related in any way, so we can be pretty sure that their measurements are independent.

Equal Variance Assumption

The variability of y should be about the same for all values of x. We need this assumption because we are going to estimate this variability with a standard deviation. In effect, this is a "pooled" estimate, and pooled estimates are only appropriate when the variance is constant. Practically, what we can check is the:

Check the residuals plot. (Part 2) The spread of the residuals should be uniform.

Does the Plot Thicken? Condition: A scatterplot of y against x offers a visual check. Make sure the spread around the line is nearly constant. Be alert for a "fan" shape or other tendency for the variability to grow or shrink in one part of the scatterplot. Often it is better to plot the residuals against x or against the predicted values, $\hat{y}$. With the slope of the line removed, the plot of the residuals can spread out to fill the display area and often reveals more about the data.

Normality Assumption

Check a histogram of the residuals. The distribution of the residuals should be unimodal and symmetric.

We assume the errors around the idealized regression line at each value of x follow a Normal model. We need this assumption so that we can use a Student's t model for inference. As with other times when we've used Student's t, we'll settle for the residuals satisfying the **Nearly Normal Condition:** Look at a histogram or Normal probability plot of the

DRAFT: Do not distribute or copy

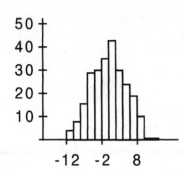

residuals. The histogram of residuals in the %body fat regression certainly looks nearly normal. And, as we have noted before, the Normality Assumption becomes less important as the sample size grows.

If these three assumptions are true, the model looks like this:

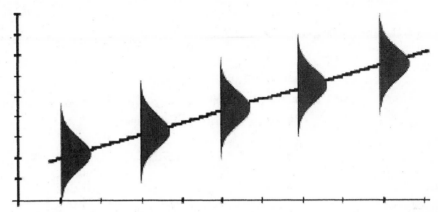

At each value of x there is a distribution of y-values that follow a Normal model, and each of these Normal models is centered on the line and has the same standard deviation.

Catch - 22

Note that many conditions require that we check the residuals, so we can only perform the checks *after* we compute the regression model. We must still check the conditions *before* doing inference on the model.

Intuition about Regression Inference

We know how to estimate the slope and intercept with least squares regression. To make confidence intervals and test hypotheses, we need to know how much these estimates vary from sample to sample. In other words, we'll need a sampling distribution model and we'll need to estimate its standard deviation with a standard error. Before we show you the formula for the standard error, let's see if our intuition can tell us what to expect. What aspects of a regression affect the variability of the slope and intercept from sample to sample?

- **Spread around the line:** Here are two situations in which we might do regression. Which situation would yield a more consistent slope? That is, if we were to sample over and over from these two underlying populations and compute all the slopes, which group of slopes would vary less?

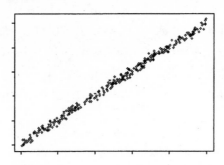
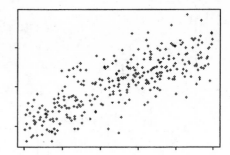

Clearly the one on the left.

- **Spread of the x's:** here are two more situations. Which of *these* would yield more consistent slopes?

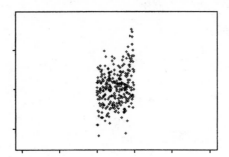
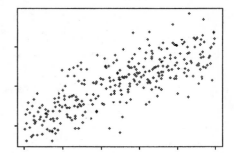

A plot like the one on the right has a broader range of *x*-values so it gives a more stable base for the slope. We'd expect the slopes of repeated samples to vary less.

- **Sample Size:** Here we go again. What about these two?

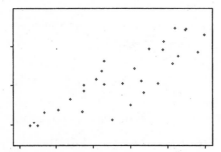
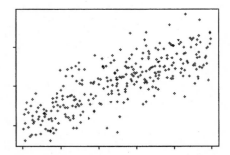

It shouldn't be a surprise that having more data gives a more consistent estimate.

So, three aspects of the scatterplot affect the standard error of the regression slope:

- Spread around the line;
- Range of *x* values;
- Sample Size.

DRAFT: Do not distribute or copy

It turns out that these are the only factors affecting the standard error of the slope. In fact, although you'll probably never have to calculate it by hand, the formula for the standard error is:

$$SE(b_1) = \frac{s(e)}{\sqrt{\sum(x-\bar{x})^2}} = \frac{s(e)}{\sqrt{n-1}\ s(x)}$$

We have written $s(e)$ for the standard deviation of the residuals and $s(x)$ for the standard deviation of the x's. The standard deviation of the residuals is in the numerator since spread around the line *increases* the slope's standard error and the denominator has both a sample size term (with a $\sqrt{n}$) and a term for the spread of the x's because increasing either of these *decreases* the slope's standard error.

The b_1's vary from sample to sample. As you'd expect, their sampling distribution model is centered at β_1, the slope of the idealized regression line with standard deviation estimated by $SE(b_1)$. What about its shape? When we standardize the b_1's we get a Student's t model, this time with n - 2 degrees of freedom:

$$\frac{b_1 - \beta_1}{SE(b_1)} \sim t_{n-2}$$

What About the Intercept?

The same reasoning applies for the intercept. We can write

$$\frac{b_0 - \beta_0}{SE(b_0)} \sim t_{n-2},$$

but we rarely use this fact for inferences. Most hypothesis tests and confidence intervals for regression are about the slope. (We've included the formula for the standard error of the intercept in the appendix at the back of the book.)

Regression Inference

Now that we have the standard error of the slope, we test hypotheses about it. The usual null hypothesis about the slope is that it's equal to 0, so the test statistic is

$$t = \frac{b_1 - 0}{SE(b_1)}$$

and the test uses a Student's t model with $n - 2$ degrees of freedom. This looks an awful lot like the one-sample t-test for the mean.

Why is the natural null hypothesis that the slope is zero? A slope of zero would say that y doesn't change at all when x changes — in other words, that there is no association between the two variables. If the slope were zero, then the regression equation would be reduced to

$$\hat{y} = b_0$$

In this model, y has the same value for all x's, so the null hypothesis of a zero slope questions the entire claim of a linear relationship between the two variables – and often that's just what we want to know.

We build a confidence interval in the usual way, as an estimate ± a margin of error. As always, the margin of error is just a multiple of the standard error, so a 95% confidence interval for β_1, the slope of the population regression line is

$$b_1 \pm t^*_{n-2} SE(b_1).$$

The Regression Table

Regressions are almost always found with a computer or calculator. The calculations are too long to do conveniently by hand for data sets of any reasonable size. No matter how the regression is computed, the results are usually presented in a table that has a standard form. Here is a portion of a typical regression results table along with annotations showing where the numbers come from:

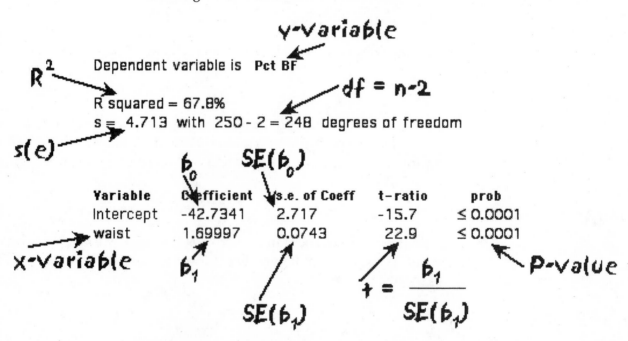

The regression table gives the coefficients (once you find them in the middle of all this other information), so we can see that the regression equation is

$$\hat{\%BF} = -42.7 + 1.7\,waist$$

and that the R^2 for the regression is 67.8%. (Is accounting for 68% of the variation in % body fat good enough to be useful? Health professionals would not be satisfied with this. We'll soon see how useful it may be.)

The column of *t*-ratios gives the test statistics for the respective null hypotheses that the true values of the coefficients are zero. The corresponding P-values are also usually reported.

Another Example

Every spring, Nenana, Alaska hosts a contest in which participants try to guess the exact minute that a wooden tripod placed on the frozen Tenana river will fall through the breaking ice. The contest started as a diversion for railroad engineers with a pot of $800 in 1917. It has grown into an event in which hundreds of thousands of entrants enter their guesses on the internet[2] and vie for more than $300,000.

Because so much money and interest depends on the time of breakup, it has been recorded to the nearest minute with great accuracy ever since 1917. And because a standard measure of breakup has been used throughout this time, the data are consistent. An article in *Science* [3] used the data to investigate global warming – whether greenhouse gasses and other human actions have been making the planet warmer. But others might just want to make a good prediction of next year's breakup time. We can use regression for both of these tasks.

Who: Years
What: *Year* and *Day and hour* of ice breakup
Unit: Years since 1900. Day and hour as days and fraction of days after midnight Jan 1 of the year. Unit is "days".
When: 1917 – present
Where: Nenana, Alaska
Why: Wagering, but proposed to look at global warming.

Here are some of the data:

Years (since 1900)	Days since Jan1
17	119.4792
18	130.3979
19	122.6063
20	131.4479
21	130.2792
22	131.5556
23	128.0833
24	131.6319
25	126.7722
26	115.6688
27	131.2375
28	126.6840

[2] http://www.ptialaska.net/~tripod/.

[3] "Climate Change in Nontraditional Data Sets" *Science* 294, 26 October 2001, p. 811

29	124.6535
30	127.7938
31	129.3910
32	121.4271
33	127.8125
34	119.5882
35	134.5639
36	120.5403
37	131.8361
38	125.8431
39	118.5597
40	110.6437
41	122.0764

A Regression Slope *t*-Test, Step-by-Step

Do these data provide any evidence for global warming? This is the question the scientists who examined the data asked in their article. If the breakup date has become earlier, it might argue for global warming. The slope of the regression gives the change in breakup date per year. Let's test the hypothesis.

Think

Hypotheses

State what we want to know.

Hypotheses on the intercept are not particularly interesting for these data.

Plan: State the **Null Model**.

a) Check the **conditions**

We wonder whether the time of ice breakup has become earlier.

H_0: There is no change in the date of ice breakup $\beta_1 = 0$

H_A: Yes, there is: $\beta_1 \neq 0$

- **Straight Enough Condition:** There is no obvious bend in the scatterplot.

- **Independence Assumption:** These data are a time series, which raises our suspicions that they may not be independent. Check the residuals plot:

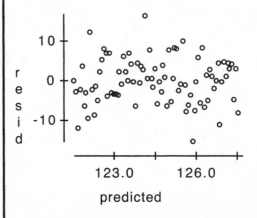

There is no clear evidence of dependence in the data, above,

DRAFT: Do not distribute or copy

although there may be some hint that the date oscillates up and down over time. They are not a random sample.

- **Does the Plot Thicken? Condition:** The residuals plot shows no obvious trends in the spread.

- **Nearly Normal Condition:** A histogram of the residuals is unimodal and symmetric

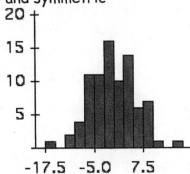

b) State the sampling distribution.

Under these conditions the sampling distribution of the regression slope can be modeled by a Student's t model with $(n - 2) = 82$ degrees of freedom.

We will use a **regression slope t-test**.

c) Choose your method.

Computer output for this regression looks in part like this:

Show

Mechanics:

The regression equation can be found from the formulas we saw in Chapter 10, but regressions are almost always found from a computer program or calculator.

The P-values given in the regression output table are from the Student's t distribution on $(n-2) = 82$ degrees of freedom. They are appropriate for two-sided alternatives.

Dependent variable is: breakupday

R squared = 8.6%
s = 5.747 with 84 - 2 = 82 degrees of freedom

Variable	Coefficient	s.e. of Coeff	t-ratio	prob
Constant	128.753	1.638	78.6	≤ 0.000
year	-0.071961	0.0259	-2.78	0.0067

The estimated regression equation is

$$\widehat{Breakupday} = 128.8 - 0.07\, year$$

Tell

Conclusion:

The P-value of 0.067 means that the

State the conclusion.

association we see in the data is unlikely to have occurred by chance. We reject the null hypothesis, and conclude that there is strong evidence that on average the ice breakup is occurring earlier each year. But the oscillation pattern in the residuals requires further investigation.

Show More

Create a confidence interval for the true slope:

A 95% confidence interval for β_1 is:

$$b_1 \pm t_{82}^* SE(b_1) = -.072 \pm (1.99)(.0259)$$

or (-0.12, -0.02) days.

Tell More

Interpret the interval:

Simply rejecting the standard null hypothesis doesn't guarantee that the size of the effect is large enough to be important. Whether we want to know the breakup time to the nearest minute or are interested in global warming, a change measured in hours each year is big enough to be interesting.

We are 95% confident that the ice has been breaking up on average between 0.02 days (about a half hour) and 0.12 days (about 3 hours) earlier each year since 1900.

Predicted Values

Once we have a useful regression model, how can we indulge our natural tendency to predict without being irresponsible? We can use our regression model to predict a value of y for any given value of x. To compute the predicted value of the ice breakup time, for example, we would multiply the x-value by the slope, -0.07 and add the intercept, 128.8. This predicted value would be our best estimate, but it's still just an informed guess. How confident are we in our prediction? Maybe a confidence interval could fudge the result in the right way, honestly reporting our uncertainty.

From our model of body fat and waist size, we might want to use waist size to get a reasonable estimate of body fat. A confidence interval can tell us how precise that prediction will be. But the precision depends on the question we ask, and there are two questions. Do we want to know the mean %body fat for *all* men with a waist size of, say 38 inches? Or do we want to estimate the %body fat for a particular man with a 38-inch waist without making him climb onto the x-ray table?

DRAFT: Do not distribute or copy

What's the difference between the two questions? The predicted %body fat is the same, but which one is less certain. We can predict the *mean* %body fat for all men whose waist size is, say, 38 inches with a lot more precision than we can predict the %body fat of a particular individual whose waist size happens to be 38 inches, but both are interesting questions.

For either question, we start with the same prediction. We predict the value for a new individual, one that was not part of the original data set. To emphasize this, we'll call his x-value "x sub new" and write it x_v.[4] So, here, x_v is 38 inches. The regression model predicts %body fat as $\hat{y}_v = b_0 + b_1 x_v$. From our model, $\hat{y}_v = -42.7 + 1.7 \times 38 = 21.9\%$.

We construct both intervals around this same predicted value. Both take the form

$$\hat{y}_v \pm t^*_{n-2} SE .$$

The difference between the two intervals is all in the standard error. The t^* value is the same for both. It's the critical value (from a t-table or computer program) for $n - 2$ degrees of freedom and the specified confidence level. But the standard error differs depending on which interval we want.

The standard errors depend on several things: the variance of our slope estimate, the spread around the line, the sample size and, a new factor, the distance of x_v from the center of the x values. The first three factors we've seen before. If there is more spread around the line, we'll be less certain when we try to predict the response. If we're less certain of the slope, we'll be less certain of our prediction. If we have more data, our estimate will be more precise. The last factor is new, but makes intuitive sense. It's a lot easier to predict a data point near the middle of the data set than to extrapolate.

Each of these factors contributes uncertainty – that is, variability – to the estimate. And since they are independent we can add variances to find the total variability. Note that the resulting formula for standard error explicitly takes into account each of the factors:

$$SE(\hat{\mu}_v) = \sqrt{s^2(b_1) \times (x_v - \bar{x})^2 + \frac{s^2(e)}{n}} .$$

Need a picture with Confidence and prediction intervals about here.

---

[4] Yes, this is a multi-lingual pun. The Greek letter v is called "nu". Don't blame me; my co-author suggested this.

Because individual values vary more than means, the standard error for a single predicted value has to be larger than the standard error for the mean. In fact, the standard error of the single predicted value has an *extra* source of variability: the variation of individuals around the mean. That appears as the extra variance term under the square root:

$$SE(\hat{y}_v) = \sqrt{s^2(b_1) \times (x_v - \bar{x})^2 + \frac{s^2(e)}{n} + s^2(e)}.$$

Remember to keep this distinction between the two kinds of intervals when looking at computer output. The smaller interval is a **confidence interval for a mean prediction**, and the wider interval is a **prediction interval for an individual**.[5]

Finding Intervals

What would our analysis predict as the mean percent body fat for men with 38 inch waists? The regression output table provides most of the numbers we need:

$s(e) = 5.747$

$n = 84$

$s(b_1) = 0.0259$, and from the data, we need to know that

$\bar{x} = 36.3$

The regression model gives a predicted value of %body fat of

$$\hat{y}_v = \text{-}42.7 + 1.7 \times 38 = 21.9\%.$$

Let's find the 95% *confidence interval for the mean* %body fat for all men with 38-inch waists. We find the standard error from the formula:

$$SE(\hat{\mu}_v) = \sqrt{0.074^2 \times (38 - 36.3)^2 + \frac{5.747^2}{84}} = 0.64.$$

The t^* value that excludes 2.5% in either tail with 84 - 2 = 82 df is (according to the tables) 1.989.

Putting it all together, we find the margin of error as

$$ME = 1.989 * 0.64 = 1.27$$

So, we are 95% confident that the mean %body fat for a man with a 38 inch waist is

$$21.9\% \pm 1.27\%.$$

---

[5] Both of these standard error expressions are often written in other equivalent ways, but the forms we give here offer the clearest understanding and use only values that appear in computer output tables for regression.

DRAFT: Do not distribute or copy

Suppose, instead, we want to predict the %body fat for an *individual* with a 38-inch waist. We need the larger standard error:

$$SE(\hat{y}_\nu) = \sqrt{0.074^2 \times (38-36.3)^2 + \frac{5.75^2}{84} + 5.75^2} = 5.79\%.$$

The corresponding margin of error is

ME= 1.989 *5.79=11.52,

so the prediction interval is:

21.9% ± 11.52%.

We can think of this interval as having a 95% chance of capturing the true %body fat of a randomly selected man whose waist is 38 inches.[6] Notice how much wider this interval is than the previous one. As we've known since Chapter 18, the mean is much less variable than a randomly selected individual value.

What can go wrong?

By now we hope you understand confidence intervals enough to know that a "significant" test may not be meaningful. But beware of others who haven't learned those lessons. Regression analyses appear to offer both predictions and "confidence." Some people who set policy and make business decisions may not know enough to be skeptical.

Regression inference is particularly sensitive to failures of the assumptions. We can usefully fit a least squares regression to a scatterplot even when the formal assumptions are not quite met, and the resulting description may be useful and interesting. But when the assumptions fail, our confidence intervals, prediction intervals, and tests can become misleading.

The linearity assumption is the most fundamental. When it fails we can't even check the conditions for the other assumptions.

Repairing Broken Conditions

We can often modify data so that it more nearly satisfies three of the four regression conditions by re-expressing the values. We have already seen that re-expression can make a curved relationship more nearly linear, that re-expression can make the spread of different groups more similar, and that re-expression can make a distribution more nearly Normal. Remarkably, a well-chosen re-expression of the *y*- variable can often accomplish all three of these results at once for a regression.

---

[6] Technically, it's a little more complicated, but it's very close to this.

Copyright © 2001, Dick De Veaux and Paul Velleman

If the scatterplot of the data is not straight, but still grows or declines consistently, you should always try to re-express the data to improve linearity. Without a linear relationship, you can't do regression at all. But in straightening the relationship you will often find that you've made the spread of the residuals around the line more consistent and their distribution more symmetric.

Fitting other Shapes

There are methods for fitting quadratic, exponential, and other forms of relationship to data on two variables. Although they are often fit by the least squares criterion, these methods lack many of the simple interpretations of linear regressions. If re-expressing the data can make the relationship linear, that is usually the better path. If by re-expressing, you improve both linearity and one or more of the other conditions, then you should certainly choose to work with the re-expressed data.

Extrapolation

We saw back in chapter 11 that extrapolation beyond the range of the x

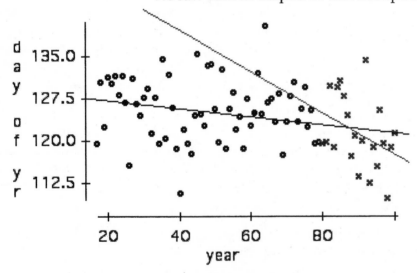

values can be very dangerous. This, of course, is especially true when the extrapolation tries to peer into the future. We can see an example in the ice breakup times data. The researchers who published these data were concerned with evidence of global warming. But is there any reason to think that global warming has been constant across the 20th century? The graph shows a regression line fit to the data since 1980 compared to the regression for the entire dataset. It shows a much steeper slope. Did global warming increase in the last two decades of the century?

We know you would never gamble, but if you *were* to place a bet on next year's breakup time, which of these two regressions would you choose as the basis for your guess? But wait! Before you make a decision, consider just the years since 1992:

DRAFT: Do not distribute or copy

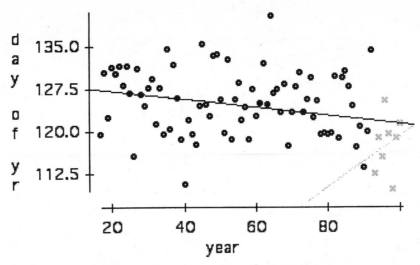

These points give a strongly *positive* slope! As you can see, any prediction can depend heavily on choices about the data and model. The danger of extrapolation is that it magnifies the effects of these choices. The farther out we extrapolate, the more our initial choices determine the predicted values and the less reliable those values become.

Connections

We would never consider a regression analysis without first making a scatterplot. And the aspects of scatterplots that we always look for relate directly to regression. We can't use regression methods unless the form of the relationship is linear. The direction of the relationship gives the sign of the regression slope. The scatter in the plot is measured by the standard deviation of the residuals—which plays a central role in the inference calculations. It is also reflected in the R^2 statistic, which gives the fraction of the variability of y accounted for by the regression model and is the square of the correlation.

Regression inference is connected to just about every inference method we have seen for measured data. The assumption that the spread of data about the line is constant is essentially the same as the assumption of equal variances required for the pooled-t methods. And our use of all the residuals together to estimate their standard deviation is a form of pooling.

Inference for regression is closely related to inference for means, so your understanding of means transfers pretty directly to your understanding for regression. Here's a table that displays the similarities:

	Means	Regression Slope
Parameter	μ	$\beta 1$
Statistic	$\bar{y}$	$b1$
Population spread estimate	$s(y) = \sqrt{\dfrac{\sum(y - \bar{y})^2}{n-1}}$	$s(e) = \sqrt{\dfrac{\sum(e - 0)^2}{n-2}}$
Standard error of the statistic	$SE(\bar{y}) = \dfrac{s(y)}{\sqrt{n}}$	$SE(b_1) = \dfrac{s(e)}{s(x)\sqrt{n-1}}$
Test statistic	$\dfrac{\bar{y} - \mu_0}{SE(\bar{y})} \sim t_{n-1}$	$\dfrac{b_1 - 0}{SE(b_1)} \sim t_{n-2}$
Margin of error	$ME = t^*_{n-1} SE(\bar{y})$	$ME = t^*_{n-2} SE(b_1)$

Regression Analysis and the Computer

All statistics packages make a table of results for a regression. These tables differ slightly from one package to another, but all are essentially the same. We've seen two examples of such tables already.

All packages offer analyses of the residuals. With some, you must request plots of the residuals as you request the regression. Others let you find the regression first and then analyze the residuals afterwards. Either way, your analysis is not complete if you don't check the residuals with a histogram or normal probability plot and a scatterplot against x or the predicted values.

Although you should, of course, always look at the scatterplot of your two variables (make a picture, make a picture,…) before computing a regression analysis, it can be useful to find the regression directly. In Chapter 8 we showed the path by way of scatterplots to regression for each package, but some of those regressions gave only the regression equation and not the t-statistics or P-values.

Here we show the direct path to a full regression table for each package.

Can we trust you to still look at the scatterplot?

DRAFT: Do not distribute or copy

Package	Commands & Location	Comments
Data Desk	To compute a linear regression in Data Desk • Select Y and X variable icons. • From the Calc menu, choose Regression. • Data Desk displays the regression table. • Select plots of residuals from the Regression table's HyperView menu.	You can change the regression by dragging the icon of another variable over either the Y or X variable name in the table and dropping it there. The regression will re-compute automatically.
Excel	To compute a linear regression using Excel's Data Analysis Add-in: • From the tools menu, select Data Analysis. • Select Regression from the Analysis Tools list. • Click the OK button. • Enter the data range holding the Y-variable in the box labeled "Y-range". • Enter the range of cells holding the X-variable in the box labeled "X-range". • Select the New Worksheet Ply option. Select Residuals options. Click the OK button.	The Y and X ranges do not need to be in the same rows of the spreadsheet, although they must cover the same number of cells. But it is a good idea to arrange your data in parallel columns as in a data table. Although the dialog offers a normal probability plot of the residuals, the data analysis add-in does not make a correct probability plot, so don't use this option.
JMP	To compute a linear regression in JMP • From the Analyze menu select Fit y by x. • Select variables: a y-Response variable and an x-Factor variable. Both must be continuous (quantitative). • JMP makes a scatterplot. • Click on the red triangle besides the heading labeled Bivariate Fit... and choose Fit Line. JMP draws the least squares regression line on the scatterplot and displays the results of the regression in tables below the plot. • The portion of the table labeled "Parameter Estimates" gives the coefficients, their standard errors, t Ratios and P-values.	JMP chooses a regression analysis when both variables are "Continuous". If you get a different analysis, check the variable types. The Parameter table does not include the residual standard deviation $s(e)$. You can find that as the square root of the Mean Square Error in the Analysis of Variance panel of the output.
Minitab	To compute a multiple regression in MINITAB, • Choose Regression from the Stat menu. • Choose Regression... from the Regression submenu. • In the Regression dialog, assign the Y variable to the Response box and assign the X variable to the Predictors box. • Click the Graphs button. • In the Regression - Graphs dialog, select "Standardized residuals", and check "Normal plot of residuals" and "Residuals versus fits". • Click the OK button to return to the Regression dialog. • Click the OK button to compute the regression.	You can also start by choosing a Fitted Line plot from the Regression submenu to see the scatterplot first—usually good practice.

SPSS	To compute a linear regression in SPSS • Choose Regression from the Analyze menu. • Choose Linear from the Regression submenu. • In the Linear Regression dialog appears, select the Y variable and move it to the dependent target. Then move the X-variable to the independent target. • Click the Plots button. • In the Linear Regression Plots dialog, choose to plot the *SRESIDs against the *ZPRED values. • Click the Continue button to return to the Linear Regression dialog. • Click the OK button to compute the regression.	
TI-83	Under STAT TESTS choose 2-Samp Tint or 2-Samp Ttest	The TI-83 expects the data in two separate lists, one for each group.

Key Concepts

Conditions for Inference in Regression (and checks for some of them).	• Linearity. (Check that the scatterplot of y against x has linear form and that the scatterplot of residuals against predicted values has no obvious pattern). • Independent residuals. (Think about the nature of the data. Check a residuals plot.) • Constant variance. (Check that the scatterplot shows consistent spread across the range of the x-variable, and that the residuals plot has constant variance too. A common problem is *increasing* spread with increasing predicted values – the *plot thickens!*) • Normality of the residuals. (Check a histogram of the residuals.)
t-ratio for the slope	The t-ratio for the slope coefficient tests the null hypothesis that the true value of the slope is zero against the alternative that it is not. A zero slope would indicate a complete lack of linear relationship between y and x.

DRAFT: Do not distribute or copy

Skills

Upon completing this Lesson you should:

Think

- Understand that the "true" regression line does not fit the population data perfectly, but rather is an idealized summary of that data.

- Know how to examine your data and the scatterplot for violations of assumptions that would make inference for regression unwise or invalid.

- Know how to examine the residuals from a regression to double-check that the conditions required for regression have been met.

Show

- Know how to test the standard hypothesis that the true regression slope is zero. Be able to state the null and alternative hypotheses. Know where to find the relevant numbers in standard computer regression output.

- Be able to find a confidence interval for the mean of the predicted *y*-values and a prediction interval for a particular *y*-value based on the summary statistics for *x* and the values reported in a standard regression output table. Know how to interpret these intervals in terms of the regression.

Tell

- Be able to summarize a regression in words. In particular, be able to state the meaning of the true regression slope, and interpret the P-value of the t-statistic for the slope.

- Be able to interpret a prediction interval for a predicted *y*-value for a given *x*-value and a confidence interval for the mean of *y*-values for a given *x*-value.

- Be able to interpret a regression when one or both variables have been re-expressed.

- Be able to explain why you omitted an outlying or influential data value and to interpret the regression on the remaining data values.

Exercises

1. **Ms. President?** In chapter 7 we saw data collected by the Gallup organization (www.gallup.com). They have, over six decades, periodically asked the question:

   If your party nominated a generally well-qualified person for president who happened to be a woman, would you vote for that person?

   Here is a scatterplot of the percentage answering "yes" *vs* the year of the decade (37 = 1937)

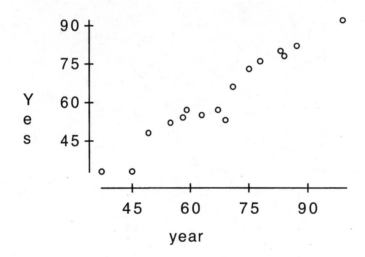

   In chapter 7 we could only describe the relationship in general terms. Now we can learn more.

   Here is the regression analysis:

   Dependent variable is: Yes
   R squared = 94.2% R squared (adjusted) = 93.8%
   s = 4.274 with 16 - 2 = 14 degrees of freedom

Variable	Coefficient	s.e. of Coeff	t-ratio	prob
Constant	-5.58269	4.582	-1.22	0.2432
year	0.999373	0.0661	15.1	≤ 0.0001

   a) Explain in words and numbers what the regression says.
   b) State the standard null and alternative hypotheses for the slope (both numerically and in words) that refer to how voters' thoughts have changed about voting for a woman.
   c) Perform the hypothesis test at the 5% level and state your conclusion. Be sure to state it in terms of voters' opinions.
   d) Explain what the R-squared in this regression means.

DRAFT: Do not distribute or copy

2. **No Opinion** Here is a regression of the percentage of respondents whose response to the question about voting for a woman President was "no opinion." Is there evidence that the percentage of the public who have no opinion on this issue has changed over the years?

Dependent variable is: No Opinion
R squared = 9.5% R squared (adjusted) = 3.0%
s = 2.280 with 16 - 2 = 14 degrees of freedom

Variable	Coefficient	s.e. of Coeff	t-ratio	prob
Constant	7.69262	2.445	3.15	0.0071
Year	-0.042708	0.0353	-1.21	0.2458

a) State the appropriate hypotheses for the slope.

b) Test your hypotheses and state your conclusion in the proper context.

Here is the scatterplot corresponding to the regression for No Opinion:

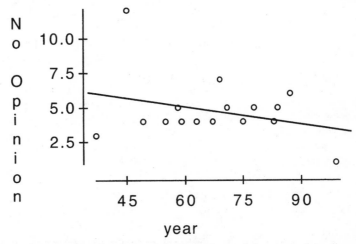

c) How does the scatterplot change your opinion of the trend in "no opinion" responses? Do you think the true slope is negative? Does this change the conclusion of your hypothesis test of the previous question? Explain.

3. **Drug Use** The *European School Study Project on Alcohol and Other Drugs*, published in 1995, investigated the use of marijuana and other drugs. Data from 11 countries are summarized in the scatterplot and regression analysis below. They show the association between the percentage of a country's ninth graders who report having smoked marijuana and who have used other drugs such as LSD, amphetamines, and cocaine. Is there a strong association, and do these results indicate that marijuana use leads to the use of harder drugs?

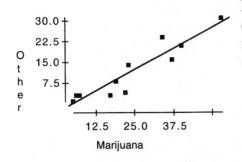

Dependent variable is: Other

R squared = 87.3%

s = 3.853 with 11 - 2 = 9 degrees of freedom

Variable	Coefficient	s.e. of Coeff	t-ratio	prob
Constant	-3.06780	2.204	-1.39	0.1974
Marijuana	0.615003	0.0784	7.85	0.0001

4. **Cholesterol** Does a person's cholesterol level tend to increase with age? Data collected in Framingham, MA from 294 adults aged 45 to 62 produced the regression analysis shown. Describe the association between age and cholesterol level.

Dependent variable is:	Chol			
Variable	Coefficient	s.e. of Coeff	t-ratio	prob
Constant	196.619	33.21	5.92	≤ 0.0001
Age	0.745779	0.6075	1.23	0.2206

5. **Marriage Age** The scatterplot suggests a decrease in the difference in ages at first marriage for men and women since 1975. Is this decrease significant?

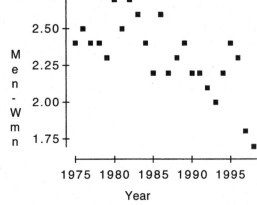

Dependent variable is Men-Wmn

cases selected according to   post75

R squared = 46.3%

s = 0.1866 with 24 - 2 = 22 degrees of freedom

Variable	Coefficient	s.e. of Coeff	t-ratio	prob
Constant	49.9021	10.93	4.56	0.0002
Year	-0.023957	0.0055	-4.35	0.0003

Examine the regression.

a. Write appropriate hypotheses.

b. Here are the residuals plot and a histogram of the residuals. Do you think the conditions for inference are satisfied? Explain.

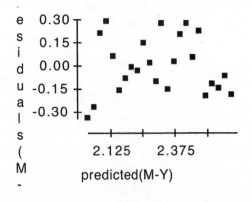

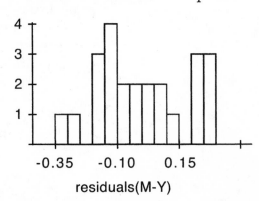

c. State your conclusion.

DRAFT: Do not distribute or copy

Give a 95% confidence interval for the rate at which the age gap is closing. Clearly explain what your confidence interval means.

6. **Fuel Economy** A consumer organization has reported test data for 50 car models. We will examine the association between the weight of the car (in thousands of pounds) and the fuel economy (in miles per gallon). Shown below are the summary statistics, scatterplot, and regression analysis:

Variable Count Mean StdDev
MPG 50 25.0200 4.83394
wt/1000 50 2.88780 0.511656

Dependent variable is: MPG
R squared = 75.6
s = 2.413 with 50 - 2 = 48 df

Variable	Coefficient	s.e. of Coeff	t-ratio	prob
Constant	48.7393	1.976	24.7	≤ 0.0001
wt/1000	-8.21362	0.6738	-12.2	≤ 0.0001

a. Is there strong evidence of an association between the weight of a car and its gas mileage? Write appropriate hypotheses.
b. Are the assumptions for regression satisfied?

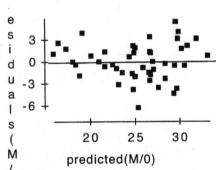
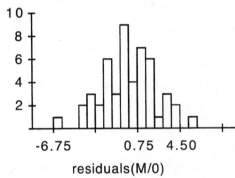

c. State your conclusion.
d. Create a 95% confidence interval for the slope of the regression line.
e. Explain in this context what your confidence interval means.
f. Create a 95% confidence interval for the average fuel economy among cars weighing 2500 pounds, and explain what your interval means.
g. Create a 95% prediction interval for the gas mileage you might get driving your new 3450 –pound SUV, and explain what that interval means.

7. **SAT Scores** How strong is the association between student scores on the Math and Verbal sections of the SAT? Here are summaries and plots of the scores for a recent graduating class at Ithaca High School.

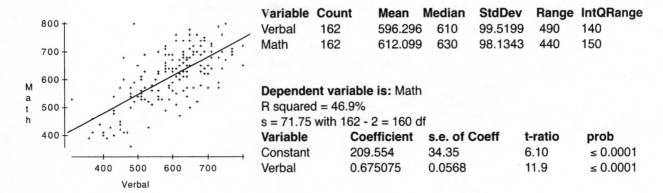

Variable	Count	Mean	Median	StdDev	Range	IntQRange
Verbal	162	596.296	610	99.5199	490	140
Math	162	612.099	630	98.1343	440	150

Dependent variable is: Math
R squared = 46.9%
s = 71.75 with 162 - 2 = 160 df

Variable	Coefficient	s.e. of Coeff	t-ratio	prob
Constant	209.554	34.35	6.10	≤ 0.0001
Verbal	0.675075	0.0568	11.9	≤ 0.0001

a. Is there evidence of an association between scores? Test an appropriate hypothesis, using the plots below to examine the assumptions. State an appropriate conclusion.

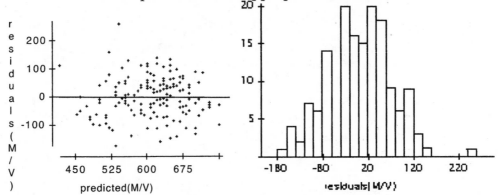

b. Find a 90% confidence interval for the slope of the line of regression, and explain in this context what it means.
c. Find a 90% confidence interval for the mean SAT-Math score for all students with an SAT-Verbal score of 500.
d. Find a 90% prediction interval for the Math score of the senior class president, if you know she scored 710 on the Verbal section.

8. **Used Cars** Classified ads in the Ithaca Journal offered several used Toyota Corollas for sale. Listed below are the ages of the cars and the advertised prices.

Age (years)	Prices advertised
1	12995, 10950
2	10495
3	10995, 10995
4	6995, 7990

5	8700, 6995
6	5990, 4995
9	3200, 2250, 3995
11	2900, 2995
13	1750

a) Make a scatterplot for these data.
b) Do you think a linear model is appropriate?
c) Find the equation of the regression line.
d) Check the residuals to see if the conditions for inference are met.
e) Create a 95% confidence interval for the slope of the regression line.
f) Explain what your confidence interval means.

9. **Body Fat** Do these data indicate an association between waist size and body fat index?
   a. Check that the conditions for regression inference are met.
   b. Test an appropriate hypothesis about the association and state your conclusion.
   c. Give a 95% confidence interval for the mean percent body fat found in people with 40″ waists.

10. **Body Fat, Again** Do these data indicate an association between weight and body fat index?
    a. Check that the conditions for regression inference are met.
    b. Find a 90% confidence interval for the slope of the line of regression of Body Fat on Weight.
    c. Interpret your interval in context.
    d. Give a 95% prediction interval for the body fat index of an individual who weighs 165 pounds.

Waist (inches)	Weight (pounds)	Body Fat (%)
32	175	6
36	181	21
38	200	15
33	159	6
39	196	22
40	192	31
41	205	32
35	173	21
38	187	25
38	188	30
33	188	10
40	240	20
36	175	22
32	168	9
44	246	38
33	160	10
41	215	27
34	159	12
34	146	10
44	219	28

11. **Strike Two** Remember the Little League instructional video? Ads claimed that the techniques would improve the performances of Little League pitchers. To test this claim 20 Little Leaguers threw 50 pitches each, and we recorded the number of strikes. After the players participated in the training program we repeated the test. The table shows the number of strikes each player threw before and after the training. A test of paired differences failed to show that this training was effective in improving a player's ability to throw strikes. Is there any evidence that the effectiveness of the video depends upon the player's initial ability to throw strikes? Test an appropriate hypothesis and state your conclusion.

Copyright © 2001, Dick De Veaux and Paul Velleman

Number of strikes (out of 50)	
Before	After
28	35
29	36
30	32
32	28
32	30
32	31
32	32
32	34
32	35
33	36
33	33
33	35
34	32
34	30
34	33
35	34
36	37
36	33
37	35
37	32

12. **Sales and Profits** A business analyst was interested in the relationship between a company's sales and its profits. She collected data (in millions of dollars) from a random sample of Fortune 500 companies, and created the regression analysis and summary statistics shown. The assumptions for regression inference appeared to be satisfied.

Summary of	**Profits**	**Sales**		Dependent variable is:	**Profits**	
Count	79	79		R squared = 66.2%		s = 466.2
Mean	209.839	4178.29		**Variable**	**Coefficient**	**s.e. of Coeff**
Variance	635172	49163000		Constant	-176.644	61.16
StdDev	796.977	7011.63		Sales	0.092498	0.0075

a. Is there a significant association between sales and profits? Test an appropriate hypothesis and state your conclusion in context.

b. Explain, in context, the meaning of R-squared.

c. Find a 95% confidence interval for the slope of the regression line. Interpret your interval in context.

d. Last year the drug manufacturer Eli Lilly, Inc. reported gross sales of $9 billion (that's 9000 million). Create a 95% prediction interval for the company's profits, and interpret your interval in context.

13. **Ozone** The Environmental Protection Agency is examining the relationship between the ozone level (in parts per million) and the population (in millions) of US cities. Part of the regression analysis is shown.

Dependent variable is Ozone		
R squared = 84.4%		
s = 5.454	with 16 - 2 = 14 df	
Variable	**Coeff**	**s.e. of Coeff**
Constant	18.892	2.395
pop	6.650	1.910

a. We suspect that the greater the population of a city the higher its ozone level. Is the relationship significant? Assuming the conditions for inference are satisfied, test an appropriate hypothesis and state your conclusion in context.

b. Give a 90% confidence interval for the approximate increase in ozone level associated with each additional million city inhabitants.

c. For the cities studied the mean population was 1.7 million people. The population of Boston is approximately 0.6 million people. Predict the mean ozone level for cities of that size with an interval in which you have 90% confidence.

14. **Property Assessments** The software outputs below provide information about the size (in square feet) of 18 homes in Ithaca, NY, and the city's assessed valuation of those homes.

Variable	Count	Mean	Median	StdDev	Range
SqFt	18	2003.39	2020	264.727	890
Asse$$	18	60946.7	61027.5	5527.62	19710

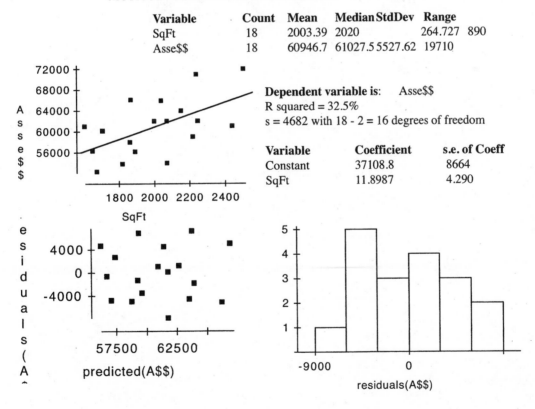

Dependent variable is:	Asse$$	
R squared = 32.5%		
s = 4682 with 18 - 2 = 16 degrees of freedom		
Variable	**Coefficient**	**s.e. of Coeff**
Constant	37108.8	8664
SqFt	11.8987	4.290

a. Explain why inference for linear regression is appropriate with these data.
b. Is there a significant association between the size of a home and its assessed value? Test an appropriate hypothesis and state your conclusion.
c. What percentage of the variability in assessments is explained by this model?
d. Give a 90% confidence interval for the slope of the true regression line, and explain its meaning in the proper context.
e. The owner of a home measuring 2100 square feet files an appeal, claiming that the $70,200 assessed value is too high. Do you agree? Explain your reasoning.